About the author

Allyn J. Waterman (Ph.D., Harvard University) is Scientist Administrator of the Center for Population Research, National Institute for Child Health and Human Development.

About the collaborating authors

B. E. Frye is a Professor of Zoology at The University of Michigan.

Arnold G. Kluge is Curator of the Museum of Zoology at The University of Michigan.

Kjell Johansen is a Professor of Zoology at the University of Washington.

Ingrith D. Olsen is a Professor of Zoology at the University of Washington.

Melvin L. Moss is Dean of the School of Dental and Oral Surgery at Columbia University.

Charles R. Noback is a Professor of Anatomy at Columbia University's College of Physicians and Surgeons.

George R. Zug is Assistant Curator of the Division of Reptiles and Amphibians at the Smithsonian Institution.

Chordate structure
and function

Chordate

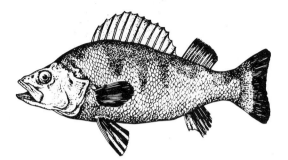

structure and function

Allyn J. Waterman National Institutes of Health

in collaboration with
B. E. Frye University of Michigan
Kjell Johansen University of Washington
Arnold G. Kluge University of Michigan
Melvin L. Moss Columbia University
Charles R. Noback Columbia University
Ingrith D. Olsen University of Washington
George R. Zug Smithsonian Institution

The Macmillan Company New York
Collier-Macmillan Limited London

Preface

Chordate Structure and Function is designed to serve in those undergraduate courses most often entitled "Comparative Vertebrate Anatomy," "Evolutionary Morphology of Chordates," or "Patterns of Vertebrate Evolution." A cursory examination of the book reveals that it differs in many ways from the textbooks traditionally used in these courses. In integrating the synthesist and reductionist approaches to biological research we have, first, provided an objective procedure for ordering and synthesizing biological facts (Chapters 1 and 2) and, second, emphasized the interrelationship of structure and function (Chapters 3-13). When used separately the two approaches allow a unique understanding of certain aspects of life, but higher-order generalizations are most expeditiously and most profitably achieved by integrating them into a meaningful whole.

The first goal follows simply from the synthesist's thesis that, before one can generalize, one must first synthesize objectively. In presenting the interrelationship between structure and function we have followed the reductionist's or empiricist's approach and have attempted to give readers a feeling for detailed description and for the elegance of experimental design; in the last chapter we have integrated the two approaches into a working whole. We believe that by separating our two goals through Chapters 1-13, and then demonstrating the integrating approach in the last chapter, we will find our greatest educational success among beginning biology students. Chapter 14 is a working model of the integrating approach; it may be followed throughout by more advanced students.

Space limitations have forced us to sacrifice many details of the structure and function of chordate animals, and we have been able to present only one method of synthesizing biological data. We have attempted only to provide the reader with a useful textbook and an appreciation of the comparative method as it relates to the synthetic and empirical approaches practiced in biology.

We wish to express our gratitude to many biologists for their pointed comments, helpful suggestions, and new insights. Among those who offered their suggestions were Dr. Daniel A. Guthrie of The Claremont Colleges, Dr. Albert E. Feldman of Dutchess Community College, Dr. Reinhard Harkema of North Carolina State University, Dr. Ellis A. Hicks of Iowa State University, Dr. Richard C. Snyder of the University of Washington, Dr. John S. Stephens, Jr., of Occidental College, and Dr. Keith S. Thomson of Yale University. We incorporated many of the changes they suggested; any errors are our own.

Miss Rosalind DeMatteis also deserves our thanks for cheerfully typing and retyping the more difficult parts of the manuscript.

Short contents

Contents

Introduction

This book was written with a very definite purpose in mind: to enhance your knowledge and appreciation of animal life. The specific subject of the book is the anatomy of vertebrate animals. We have, however, written *Chordate Structure and Function* in the hope that while you read it you will discover much more than a passive increase in your knowledge of anatomical details. The living vertebrates about which we write are active and complex organisms that have made successful adaptations to the wide range of conditions on earth. There is no aspect of biology more fascinating than vertebrate evolutionary history viewed in the light of developmental patterns and the functioning of systems of organs. A careful study of their structures is an excellent approach to a real understanding of these animals.

Perhaps an analogy will explain why we have written this book. Imagine that you are an archeologist and that you have discovered a stone tool made by a human being who lived long ago. What will you do with your discovery? You might merely label it with the date and place where you found it, and then store it away in a museum. On the other hand you might use it as a key to understand prehistoric man. If you would use the key, you must observe the structure of the tool with great care. The place where you found it may reveal something about its age; its shape, as compared with other known tools, may suggest ideas about its historical background or evolution. In part, the form of the tool depends on the material from which it was made. Because stone, depending on its nature (hard or soft, crystalline or amorphous, and so forth) may be chipped or flaked in patterns, the steps in the manufacture of the tool—its developmental pattern—must have played a part in determining its final contour. Now take the tool in your hand. Does it fit against your palm smoothly with space for your fingers to grasp it? Or does it seem more natural to hold the tool lightly between thumb and forefinger? Could you use it in a scraping motion, as if to clean the inside of an animal's hide? Or drive its point through the hide to make a hole for a thong? Would you use it for cutting tree branches or for stripping bark from a twig? However you answer these questions, you are using the structure of the tool to reveal its function. Looking at it from all these points of view will not only enrich your knowledge about the tool but will also stimulate your imagination. Perhaps it will help you recreate the man who made the tool, and the ancient people who originated the pattern after which it was fashioned.

We have, then, written *Chordate Structure and Function* to give you a broader understanding of vertebrate animals. We have stressed function both in relation to structure and in the comparison of functionally similar

structures among the range of living vertebrates. Each approach—
evolutionary, developmental, functional, and the comparative study
of structures—is equally necessary for a real understanding of the living
animal.

   We knew at the outset that space limitations would force us to omit much
that we ourselves find interesting and important. Because we had to concentrate on relatively few aspects of vertebrate structure, we stressed the
functional approach most heavily; it happens to be a major interest of us
all. We realize that you, the reader, may find that other approaches are
more appealing to you, and for this reason we have given, at the end of
each chapter, lists of books that present other points of view on vertebrate
anatomy. Perhaps you will decide to read further, not only to learn other
approaches, but also to enrich your understanding of the function of specific
structures in the overall pattern of vertebrate life.

For Further
Reading   The following books are general anatomical and physiological references.

Bolk, L., E. Göppert, E. Kallius, and W. Lubosch, *Handbuch der Vergleichende
   Anatomie der Wirbeltiere*. Berlin: Urban and Schwarzenberg, 1936.
   Reprinted 1967 by A. Asher and Company, Amsterdam.
Fawcett, D. W., *An Atlas of Fine Structure*. Philadelphia: W. B. Saunders,
   1966.
Florey, E., *General and Comparative Animal Physiology*. Philadelphia: W. B.
   Saunders, 1966.
Gordon, M. S., G. A. Bartholomew, A. D. Grinnell, C. Barker-Jørgensen, and
   F. N. White, *Animal Function: Principles and Adaptations*, New York:
   The Macmillan Company, 1968.
Grassé, P. P. (ed.), *Traité de Zoologie, Anatomie Systématique, Biologie*.
   Paris: Masson et Cie., 1948-present.
Hoar, W. S., *General and Comparative Physiology*. Englewood Cliffs, New
   Jersey: Prentice-Hall, 1966.
Jollie, M., *Chordate Morphology*. New York: Rheinhold Publishing Co.,
   1962.
Porter, K. R., and M. A. Bonneville, *Fine Structure of Cells and Tissue*. Phila-
   delphia: Lea and Febiger, 3rd ed., 1968.
Prosser, C. L., and F. A. Brown, *Comparative Animal Physiology*. Philadelphia:
   W. B. Saunders, 1961.
Romer, A. S., *The Vertebrate Body*. Philadelphia: W. B. Saunders, 3rd ed.,
   1962.
Schmidt-Nielsen, K., *Animal Physiology*. Englewood Cliffs, New Jersey:
   Prentice-Hall, 2nd ed., 1965.
Young, J. Z., *The Life of Vertebrates*. New York and London: Oxford Univ.
   Press, 2nd ed., 1962.

Part one: the pervasive concepts and factual background

1

Concepts and principles of morphologic and functional studies

Introduction The purpose of this book is to present the history of morphologic systems, their functions, and the whole organisms of which they are a part. The underlying theme of the book is organic evolution; comparative morphology and related functions of chordate animals is the medium by which that theme is presented. Whatever the reason for pursuing this explanation, whether general intellectual curiosity or specific knowledge for some tangible end, inquiry must follow the scientific method.

Although it may sound formal and possibly suggest an elaborate formula, the scientific method of inquiry can be reduced to a simple procedure and to a set of rules. To practice the method in its most elementary form one need only ask sensible questions and pursue sensible answers. The more sophisticated practice of the method, however, entails (1) formulating the problem, (2) proposing the hypothesis that best explains the specified phenomena of that problem, and (3) testing the premises and conclusions of that hypothesis.

The formulation of the problem requires first an awareness that the problem exists, and then its description. The greater the detail in which the problem is described, the more precise are the questions that can be asked as well as the resulting answers. A hypothesis is a provisional explanatory statement that proposes a possible relationship of an unsolved problem to other, already tested and accepted, statements. In order to be scientific, the statement must be tested, either directly or indirectly, by observation. The rejection of authority, that is, the refusal to accept a statement simply because someone says it is so, should be a matter of routine in science. In testing a hypothesis, one is seeking exceptions to the premises embodied in the proposition. This is accomplished by means of the logical induction of conclusions derived from the premises of the hypothesis. If exceptions to the premises are found, then either the observations or the hypothesis itself is incorrect. If the observations are repeatable, then the hypothesis is incorrect, and must be either discarded or modified. The hypothesis that has met extended tests and is the most probable explanation is more appropriately called a theory or principle. A good theory is one that continues to draw together previously unrelated facts and in this way exemplifies and clarifies our understanding of natural phenomena. Observation of a particular object or occurrence is the fact from which all science stems and to which all scientific theories must return for verification.

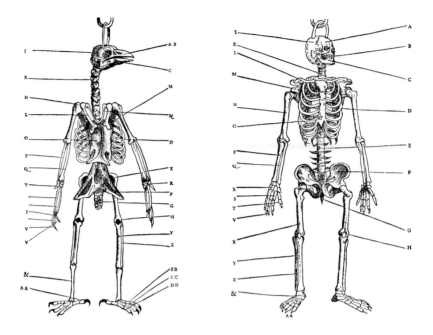

Figure 1-1. The skeletons of a man and a bird were compared in 1555 by Pierre Belon du Mans [1]; a plate from his book is reproduced here. His study is believed to be the first detailed work on the equivalence between numerous parts of different organisms.

History of Evolutionary Morphology

The study of the evolution of structure and function, the central theme of this book, is the product of at least a thousand years of endeavor by both scientists and nonscientists, and, like most sciences, it has proceeded through a definite sequence of levels of study. The sequence first began with the description of separate phenomena; next came comparative studies of groups of phenomena, then generalizations as to relationships among phenomena, and finally the explanation of those generalized relationships. It should be noted that this trend closely follows the sequence described for the scientific method of inquiry. As in that method, the earlier levels of investigation are still pursued today, and rightfully so, because they will always be a necessary preliminary to a better understanding of the final product.

In 1555 the French anatomist Pierre Belon du Mans [1] (1517-1564) published a detailed comparison of the skeleton of a human and of a bird (Figure 1-1). This research, generally acknowledged as the first demonstration of the importance of comparative studies, marks the departure from purely descriptive anatomy. From Belon's work, which clearly suggests the equivalence between parts of different organisms, stems the most important generalization of anatomy, the *principle of homology*. From its relatively unassuming origin in sixteenth-century anatomy, the principle of homology has become one of the most important concepts of comparative and evolutionary biological studies.

From 1555 to 1859 the main tenet of the study of morphology was that the equivalences between different organisms constituted an idea (Plato's meaning of the word), or a basic plan or pattern (Aristotle's use). In either case, "idea" or "plan" are mental constructs without reality. The Kantian transcendental method of philosophy, which dominated much of this period of history, is clearly responsible for maintaining for so long the explanatory theory embodied in that tenet. The leaders of this idealistic morphologic or typologic school of thought were Johann Wolfgang von Goethe (1749-1832), Lorenz Oken (1779-1851), and Richard Owen (1804-1892). Their influence was uninterrupted until 1859 when Charles Darwin published his first edition of *On the Origin of Species by Means of Natural Selection.* Owen, who formed generalizations about the relationships of equivalent or similar structures, in his later works recognized three kinds of homology. (1) General homology, which was the correspondence between the structure of an actual organism and an ancestral archetype. (2) Special homology corresponded more or less to homology as defined and used in this book, but without the explanatory criterion of common ancestry. (3) Serial homology corresponded to the anatomical relationship among repetitive structures within a single organism, such as vertebrae or ribs. The historian Francis J. Cole [2] succinctly described the meaning of the break with the pre-Darwinian school of thought: "Until an evolutionary *principle* was demonstrated, further random research could but swell the accumulation of data which awaited integration into a science. In this inchoate state anatomy remained until it was quickened by the publication of the *Origin of Species*, which forthwith raised this uneventful record of factual competence to the dignity of a learned discipline."

In the *Origin of Species*, Darwin devoted an entire chapter to morphology and embryology, in which he stressed the importance of evolutionary interpretation for understanding the data derived from these subjects. He also, of course, examined these areas for the derived data that would provide strong evidence for his general theory of evolution. He considered homologous structures, the equivalences between different organisms, to be those derived through inheritance from a common ancestry. As the result of Darwin's definition of homology and the definitions of related phenomena within the context of evolutionary theory, the final phase of the historical sequence leading to evolutionary morphology was entered. This phase is the explanation of generalized relationships.

Major Tenets of Evolutionary Theory

Many students begin the study of morphology, as it is treated here, with little or no understanding of organic evolution. Obviously, as a result of this deficiency, they may complete their investigation without realizing that one of the important uses of the data derived from anatomical and functional subject matter is in the understanding of organic evolution. For this reason alone the following paragraphs will briefly summarize the basic processes of evolution and speciation in sexually reproducing diploid organisms, with particular emphasis on those aspects that are essential to a better understanding of this course of study.†

Broadly defined, evolution simply means change, and broadly applied, all matter, animate and inanimate, undergoes this process. The details and the consequences of the evolution of living and nonliving matter are, however,

†Chordate animals reproduce sexually and possess a diploid set of chromosomes; among the protochordates asexual methods are also present.

totally different. In this study only organic evolution pertains, and it may be defined formally as a change in the genetic composition of a population of organisms from generation to generation. The fossil record provides overwhelming evidence that the *phenotype* of former life was different from that of the present day, and both laboratory and field studies clearly demonstrate the details of changes in gene frequency from one generation to another.

The Raw Material   In order for organic evolution to occur there must be available a permanent source of changeable, hereditable matter, capable of being transferred from one generation to the next. The chromosomes and their genes possessed by all organisms are the changeable matter, and they constitute a pool of hereditable information in the interbreeding population. The relevant initial changes occur in the gonadal germinal tissue of the individual organism as a result of the intrinsic mutability of gene and chromosomal materials. During gametogenesis, the paired chromosomes and genes are sorted independently into haploid sex cells, the sperm and eggs. With fertilization these genotypically highly varied haploid gametes are randomly recombined into a wide variety of diploid products. In summary, the initial changes are *mutation*, which in turn is greatly amplified in the interbreeding population as a whole by the process of genetic *recombination*. Also greatly increasing the variability of the gene pool of a population is the addition of immigrant individuals with different genotypes. Here again recombination is operative in the manner just described.

Recent biochemical-genetic studies indicate that more similar *genotypes* usually produce more similar phenotypes. In accordance with this causal relationship, at least theoretically by adherence to the explanatory part of the Darwinian definition of homology, the student of evolutionary morphology and function is concerned with genotypic homology. Extrapolating still further, he is concerned with the interaction between the replicative capacity of the genetic system and natural selection—that interaction which determined genotypic homology. It is important to note that if replication were perfect, evolution almost certainly would not occur. Therefore, homology of genotype and phenotype is a concept that has meaning only when one considers attributes that are similar but not identical. In almost all morphologic and functional studies, genetic similarity, which is inferred from phenetic similarity, is used as indirect evidence of common descent.

It is very important to recognize in the application of the concept of homology that the same genotype may produce different phenotypes under different environmental conditions. An extreme environment may bring out developmental potencies that are not expressed under usual conditions; such an environment permits genetic factors that do not usually reach the threshold of phenotypic expression to manifest themselves. The researcher in evolutionary morphology and function must constantly remain aware of this problem.

The Agent: Although mutation and recombination are the sources of variability, it is
Natural Selection   *natural selection* that determines the direction of change. All parts of the environment, biotic and abiotic, are potentially capable of directing the course of change. Natural selection may be defined as the sum of the envi-

ronmental factors that determine the relative success of different genotypes. The environment is like a filter; it preserves individuals that are better adapted to it and eliminates by means of differential reproduction those less well adapted. No thinking or planning is involved. The filtering operation is based solely upon natural and physical laws.

The Criterion of
Success:
Adaptation

Adaptation may be defined as the hereditary adjustment of an organism to its environment by means of natural selection. Although adaptation may be viewed as the total fit of the phenotype to its environment, it is clear that each organism is a complex of more specific adaptions that enable it to perform its numerous life functions. The environment to which an organism is adapted is a varied series of many factors, e.g., physical, social, biotic, and so on. The adaptation produced by selection for one aspect of the total environment need not necessarily be useful, and may even be detrimental in relation to other environmental parameters. Moreover, selection is opportunistic in that it produces adaptations to existing environmental conditions; such adaptations may or may not be beneficial to descendents in future environments. The collective forces of natural selection that promote diverse kinds of adaptations do not guarantee evolutionary success in the constantly changing environment.

Evolution is opportunistic and experimental. Natural selection operates only upon organisms extant during a period of environmental change. Although there is no evidence of anticipating future need, *viz*., the operation appears to be totally mechanistic, the sequence of organism succession lends itself readily to the idea of a "Master Planner" and the existance of a "Divine Design." Perhaps the most concise statement of this thesis is that of George Gaylord Simpson [15], one of the most outstanding present-day students of evolutionary morphology: "Adaptation is real, and it is achieved by a progressive and directed process. This process achieves the aspect of purpose without the intervention of a purposer, and it has produced a vast plan, without the concurrent action of a planner. It may be that the initiation of the process and the physical laws under which it functions had a Purposer and that this mechanistic way of achieving a plan is the instrument of a Planner—of this still deeper problem the scientist, as scientist, cannot speak."

The Product:
Speciation

Strictly speaking, the formation of new species, *speciation*, is not evolution, but may be considered a very frequent adjunct to it. Evolution is simply hereditable change through time from generation to generation, and in space (that is, geographically) at one horizontal plane in time. With the interruption of the continuity of the common gene pool of an interbreeding population and the maintenance of the discontinuity, almost invariably by geographical isolation, the resultant populations often gradually shift to different genotypic modes. The differences in the derived populations are the result of inescapable mutation and recombination and, most important, of the different forces of selection imposed upon the populations by their different environments. The genotypic differences are at first subtle. They gradually accumulate, however, and may eventually manifest themselves, singly or collectively, in some mechanism (structural, behavioral, ecological, physiological, and so on) that prevents the divergent populations from inter-breeding should they come into contact when the geographical barrier disappears. Such derived populations are *species* (Figure 1-2). In summary, a biological species may be defined as groups of actually or potentially interbreeding natural populations that share in a common gene pool and that are reproductively isolated from other such groups.

When divergent evolution occurs, as just described, the ancestral population does not remain static but continues to evolve in response to the constantly changing environment. For example, it is highly probable that reptiles were derived from primitive amphibians, but it is fruitless to look for the reptilian ancestor among modern amphibians. Both groups have had equal time to diverge from their common ancestral population.

With a knowledge of evolutionary theory as now generally accepted, it is easy to visualize how all attributes, morphological or functional, have originated and have been modified through time. Jean Baptiste de Lamarck (1744-1829) was the first biologist to maintain clearly and consistently that all species have arisen by evolution and form a continuum—that is, they

Figure 1-2. Major physical and spatial events in speciation. A = single population.

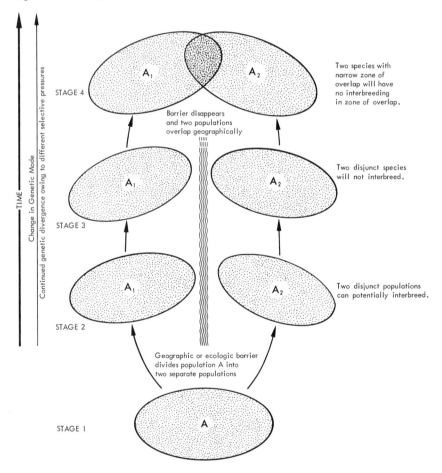

exhibit *phylogeny*. The process of evolution tends to produce groups of organisms, however, because of different rates of change and because some of the divergent lineages become extinct. In spite of this clumping, the most fundamental criterion for relating two or more individual organisms or two or more groups of organisms is still the same: to use Darwin's phrase [3], their propinquity of descent. The similarities and differences between organisms are interpreted as evidence of phylogenetic affinities and are ranked and evaluated in accordance with their possible bearing on propinquity of descent.

The very nature of an evolutionary continuum appears to have contributed to at least one major misconception. This is the irreversibility of evolution, which is most often referred to as Dollo's Law (after Louis Dollo, a famous Belgian paleontologist, 1857-1931). It is now generally recognized that there is no genetic or evolutionary phenomenon which of itself absolutely prohibits reversal. Certainly, back mutations occur, and even the usual genetic variation that is carried in a population is distributed on either side of the mode so that at least potential reversal by the process of selection can occur. Another likely source of reversal, although not yet studied adequately in a wide variety of organisms, is the reconstitution of a recombinate that has been lost. It is generally agreed that populations that exhibit greater genetic variability produce more successful descendent lineages than those gene pools with little or no variability. In the usual condition, then, *heterozygosity* is a probable condition in derived phyletic lines, and the greater the length of time the heterozygosity persists, the greater chance there will be for alternative phenotypes to be produced by segregation within the descendent gene pools. When such a process occurs, the genotypes responsible for the phenotypes will be homologous, but the phenotype may appear independently [17]. In short, completely homologous genotypes can occur independently in species derived from species that did not show the phenotype because the genotype for the characteristic was potentially within their common gene pool.

In spite of all the possible ways in which evolutionary reversals can be realized, the actual phenomenon appears to be extremely rare because of the statistical probability that a complete or nearly complete reversal to a previous condition, particularly a remote one, must be very small for most structures and functions. This probability is derived from three factors: the length of time necessary for a change, such as a reverse mutation, to occur; genes usually have the capacity to affect several different aspects of the total phenotype (*pleiotropy*); and virtually all structures and functions appear to have at least a moderately broad genetic foundation (*polygenic*).

Morphologic and Functional Data and Their Interpretation

The relationship between structure and function in organisms, to which most of the references in the later chapters of this book are made, resembles the relationship between a well-designed instrument or machine and its action. This relationship is a product of evolution, but as even a casual reading of any one of the following chapters indicates, most of the relationships described have no obvious bearing on *mortality* and *natality*, the demographic parameters usually referred to in discussions of natural selection. How, then, is the relationship between structure and function involved in the process of natural selection? Most of the relationships that will be described can be thought of as affecting in some way the amount of energy that an organism utilizes in its metabolism. The genotype that has a relatively smaller energy consumption for a given set of conditions will be more likely to increase the number of offspring produced and consequently will be favored by selection. This point of view explains adaptations in terms of small savings of energy.

In the study of the relationship between structure and function one must consider the interaction between different functions of a single structure, that is, all the implications of a single aspect of design. Equally important is that the evolution of a structure very often results in modification of other structures which serve very different functions. An obvious example is the change in the size of the eye in the course of bony fish evolution, which in turn resulted in changes in the shape of the skull, jaw muscles, and suspensorium, and even in the brain [10]. A structure can take on a new function, or functions, in the course of its evolution, and may even lose its original function altogether. New designs can evolve only by modification of existing designs. The evolution of structures with new functions depends on the opportunities offered by existing structures.

A natural extension of the use of data derived from evolutionary studies is in the discipline of *taxonomy*. This is in accord with the generalizations as to relationships among phenomena that so characterize this level of study. The term taxonomy may be defined as the study of those theoretical bases, principles, and procedures that are necessary to an understanding of the relationships of organisms. Modern taxonomy is evolutionary. Its basis involves phylogeny, not directly observed and often inferred only from *neontologic* data lacking the important dimension of time.

A further natural extension of the use of data derived from evolutionary morphology is *classification,* a product of taxonomy. Classification is the formal arrangement of kinds of organisms into various groups (taxa) and the application of *nomenclature* to the groups that are recognized. Thus classification is an application of taxonomy, and both classification and taxonomy are parts of the more inclusive *systematics*, which is in its broadest context, the study of the evolutionary relationships of organisms. Taxonomy consistently has been criticized for its method of inferring evolutionary relationship from phenetic similarity, particularly in the absence of a relevant fossil record. This inference justified by the hypothesis of phenetic similarity corresponding to propinquity of descent, is a "tendency" statement and not intended as categorical. Where numerous fossils and/or unequivocal cytological data are known, phenetic similarity has been demonstrated, a posteriori, to be a good indicator of phyletic relationships in those groups. This does not mean that exceptions have not been recorded, but they are so few that the inductive inferences made in reconstructing the phyletic history may still be regarded as highly probable. Remember that all scientists' statements of "proof" are probabilistically based evaluations of observed phenomena [6].

Morphologic characters have long been used as the objective evidence for deducing phylogeny and classification. It has been only recently that biochemistry, cellular and systemic physiology, developmental dynamics, ecology, behavior, and so on, have been considered as evidence. These newer areas of investigation in no way supersede the morphologic studies; their use in modern systematics reflects the current advances in instrumentation and methodology in these areas and supports the generally accepted thesis that some large part of the biology of organisms should be analyzed within the framework of evolutionary theory if a definitive conclusion is to be approached.

Propinquity of descent, which is crucial in recognizing related individuals or groups of individuals, is judged on similarities among, as well as differences between, the individuals or groups. This judgment is made on attributes of many different kinds. The taxonomist compares organisms in terms of the presence, absence, or degree of expression of specific attributes of their phenotypes. Homologous attributes in different organisms are termed *character states*; a set of homologous attributes is said to be a *character*, which is thus only an abstraction. For example, the variable number of teeth on the mandible of adult mammals is a character, and the real numbers of mandibular teeth exhibited by different mammals are the states of that character. Character as it is used in this context is defined as any independently variable structure, substance, or action of an organism which is the product of the interaction of the underlying genome and the environment. Even the habitat of the organism may be considered indirectly a character. There are two basic classes of characters: those that are continuously variable, such as *morphometric* and color and color pattern characters, and those that are discontinuously variable, that is, *meristic* characters. Typically, characters are also considered either as quantitative or qualitative. Characters may vary ontogenetically in the individual and within and between taxonomic groups of organisms. In addition, they may vary both geographically and from generation to generation.

Not only characters in common but also sequences of varying characters within taxonomic groups are used in phylogenetic studies. Here the main problem is to distinguish the *primitive* from the *advanced* state of a character; that is, to relate the different expressions of a character in different individuals or taxonomic groups to the propinquity of the common ancestry. The following discussion evaluates both the theoretical background of morphologic and functional characters and their use in phylogenetic studies.

Criteria
Derived from
Similarity

The concept of homology. The meaning of homology, as defined by Darwin, is contained in that part which indicates that the similarities of two structures were derived through inheritance from a common ancestor. The significance of the explanatory clause can be readily appreciated when compared with Owen's redefinition of the term homologue (special): "the same organ in different animals under every variety of form and function." [12] From Darwin's definition it is obvious that the evidence of gene identity is the most conclusive possible estimate of phenotypic homology. It is important to recall that in most cases the similarities are the consequence of a similar replicative capacity of the genetic system and natural selection. If the criterion of gene identity is adhered to in the determination of homology, then nearly all those phenotypic expressions which are considered homologous would be without proof, certainly all those of fossil organisms. To be sure, very little genetic information is available at present for most living animals, and it seems highly improbable that such information will ever be available for many of them. Even in the more easily manipulated and long studied research organisms of geneticists, the fruit fly *Drosophila* for example, the underlying genic background has not yet been discerned fully for many structural similarities in any two closely related species. Successful hybridization which appears to correspond to a degree of chromosomal and genic resemblance, may be used as a second-order approximation of phenotypic homology in the absence of more direct knowledge of the relevant genetic constitution. Aside from the only slight impracticability of this approach, such evidence is almost completely confined to the species and infraspecies levels where homologies are rarely questioned. Here again fossils cannot be studied in an experimental manner.

Although the definitions of homology and related phenomena are theoretical, or at least have a low incidence of applicability, they still provide the necessary framework for a more useful operational approach to the study of similarity. The following classification of kinds of similarities† is much enlarged over Darwin's, the definitions here, however, are strongly rooted in his system. As the classification indicates, it is extremely important to distinguish between the various kinds of similarities, structural and functional, and particularly between those not inherited from a common ancestry. Unlike the definitions attempted by the idealistic morphologists, they involve both inferred causes and the evolutionary significance of the similarities in question.

I. Structural similarity of two or more attributes.
   A. *Homology* is structural similarity in different organisms, resulting from a common ancestral inheritance. The commonness of embryonic origin (*viz.*, from the same anlage) of two or more structures is very often used as explicit evidence of homology. The similar attributes involved, hereafter referred to as character states, are *homologous*. (The noun for them is *homologues*). Homologues exhibit a narrow-to-broad spectrum of degree of similarity which is generally considered proportional to the amount of evolutionary change involved.
   B. *Homoplasy* is structural similarity in organisms *not* due directly to the inheritance from a common ancestry or development from a common anlage. The similar attributes involved are *homoplastic*; there is no current noun for them.
      1. *Parallelism* is homoplasy involving the separate evolution of similar attributes in organisms having lineages of common ancestry. The similarity is not a direct result of that ancestry, although it may be channeled by it. The similar attributes are *parallel*; there is no noun for them.
      2. *Convergence* is homoplasy involving the separate evolution of similar attributes in organisms *not* having lineages of common ancestry. The similarity results from adaptation to environments that have identical or similar selective forces. The similar attributes are *convergent*; there is no common noun for them.
      3. *Mimicry* is homoplasy involving the evolution of similar attributes

†Modified after G. G. Simpson, *Principles of Animal Taxonomy*. New York: Columbia University Press, 1962.

in organisms that may or may not have lineages of common ancestry. Where the lineages have common ancestry, the similarity is not a direct result of that ancestry, although it may be channeled by it. The similarity of the *mimic* is selected when it is adaptively advantageous in the *model*.

4. *Chance Similarity* is homoplasy involving the separate evolution of similar attributes in organisms *not* having lineages of common ancestry. The similarity results from independent causes and is without causal relationships involving the similarity as such.

II. Functional similarity of two or more attributes.

A. *Analogy* is functional similarity in different organisms which results from homology of the structures involved. From this it does not necessarily follow that all homologous structures have similar functions. The similar functional characters are *analogous*, and the noun for them is *analogues*. The restricted definition of analogy has been used because of the phylogenetic context in which it is used here.

B. *Anaplasy* is functional similarity in organisms as a result of the homoplasy of the structures involved. The similar characters are *anaplastic*; there is no noun for them.

The term *serial homology*, as defined by Owen, is still in use. It must be recognized however, that the concept has a different connotation from that of homology between different organisms; therefore the term is not directly relevant to taxonomic studies. The *homonomous series* as a whole, such as the vertebral column, may be homologous among different organisms, but a specific vertebra of the series need not be homologous with a similarly positioned element in the sequence of the other organism. As a case in point, with few exceptions the nearly constant number of cervical vertebrae of mammals are considered homologues, both individually and as a series within the taxonomic group of vertebrates. On the other hand, the homology of mammalian cervical vertebrae to those of amphibians and reptiles, which usually have very different numbers of cervicals, applies only to the series as a whole, or the embryonic field producing it, and not to the individual vertebrae.

The operational basis of homology. A statement that two or more structures are homologous is the result of a decision about their degree of resemblance. It is important to repeat that the concept of homology involves structures that are similar but not absolutely identical. How then are two or more structures compared with each other to establish the degree of resemblance between them, and what minimal degree of resemblance is considered sufficient to justify the relationship termed homology? Operationally, for almost all studies, the decision of homology and its degree obtains only after a two-stage sequence of comparisons has been carried out. As a scientist, one cannot accept, either philosophically or operationally, the often-used rationale that "Two structures are homologous when in the opinion of a competent comparative anatomist they are considered so."

The first stage in estimating homology is to maximize the overall similarity (minimize the overall difference) of the two or more whole organisms being compared. Since all whole organisms are to some degree phenotypically different, it follows that different degrees of overall similarity will be derived. These different estimates of the degree of similarity between different sets of organisms provide a relative estimate of the likelihood of a statement of homology being correct. This obtains from the fact that if the homologies have been correctly assessed, the resulting estimate of overall similarity between organisms will be greater (i.e., their difference will be less) than if errors of homology have been made [8]. In addition, the first stage of comparison has an important second function which must precede the second stage. From the actual process of maximizing the overall similarity of two organisms, the features that are to be hypothesized as homologues in the second stage have a greater chance of being matched correctly. In a way this logically may be considered a tentative recognition of homologues. The second stage in the operation of estimating homology requires the detailed comparison of what one has tentatively hypothesized as homologues from the first stage of one-to-one matching. Within this final level a structure of one organism is compared to a structure of a different organism; the two structures are considered homologues to some degree if they have similar shapes and occur in similar positions relative to other structures [7]. Similar embryonic origin and pattern of development would also apply here; however, like genotypic homology, the difficulties inherent in obtaining this information reduce the operational value of the concept for most structures to the point where it can be used only rarely.

The other structures with which the first are compared lie in a definite corresponding spatial relationship, frequently show a similarity of shape, and are related in some degree of homology from the matching operation of stage one. It seems safe to generalize that for all studies a relatively objective statement of homology involves a sequence of comparisons in the second stage, using as yet uncompared sets of structures as reference points. From this generalization it follows that the validity of using these subsidiary structures as reference points is justified only when they in turn are compared with other sets of structures. In theory then, but rarely in practice unfortunately, the sequence of comparisons will be carried back to the original structures that were compared. In summary, the comparisons are made sequentially and involve the entire organism; the whole process is one of reciprocal illumination. Theoretically, the advantage of the system is that by the very nature of the circularity of the chain of comparison it is possible to make some general distinction between most homologous and homoplastic structures and between analogous and anaplastic functions. As will be demonstrated later, this is an estimation that must be made if the explanation of the relationships between two or more attributes is to be used to establish a preliminary objective phylogeny.

Because of the complexity of the form and spatial relationships of almost all structures it is extremely difficult, if not impossible, to make an exact statement about the degree of resemblance at any of the levels of comparison in the sequence. Each step can only be prefaced by some estimate, in the form of a probability value, which reflects the investigator's judgment about the relative form and anatomical position of the structures compared. The kinds of organisms and structures involved and the time available for study are usually proportional to the precision of estimation. Although the procedure is intrinsically not as quantitatively precise as one would like, such chains of probable inferences are inherent in any discussion of universals.

The method may seem more satisfactory when one realizes that a chain of probable inferences is usually stronger than its weakest link and may even be stronger than its strongest link.

The following example demonstrates the details of the actual operation of the sequential series of comparisons in the second stage and its value in distinguishing between homologous and homoplastic structures. The original reason for studying a particular structure is immaterial to this discussion; suffice it to say that an investigator is interested and that he has selected a set of structures for comparison, for example, a and a′ of hypothetical organisms 1 and 2, respectively (Figure 1-3). A working hypothesis of homology is erected with respect to these structures: a and a′ are homologous. This hypothesis results from maximizing the overall similarity of the whole animals (stage 1). The first step of stage 2 is to compare structure a with a′; they are identical. When these structures are in turn compared with other structures in the same relative position, A and A′, they too are identical. These in turn are compared with others, B and B′, and so on. For the two hypothetical organisms shown in Figure 1-3, all the structures can be compared easily, and the chain of comparison can be completed. Because the nature of the two organisms is identical, and the sequence can be completed, the probability that structures a and a′ are homologues carries a value of 1. Obviously it is impractical, if not impossible, to compare the seemingly infinite number of structures of organisms and thus realize the complete sequence that involves the whole animal. Moreover, no two structures of living organisms are ever identical (probably not even in identical twins). In actual practice then, one must be satisfied with a probability value of less than 1 and a long but incomplete chain of comparisons for the hypothesis of homology.

A similar sequence of comparisons between organism 1 (and/or 2) and 3 (Figure 1-3), suggests that a and a″ are not homologous because of the dissimilarity of form and spatial relationship of many of the structures (a low probability value) and because of the impossibility of completing the circle; from this it follows that a and a″ are homoplastic structures. A universally

Figure 1-3. Three hypothetical organisms. Organisms 1 and 2 are identical. [Modified after W. G. Inglis, "The Observational Basis of Homology." *Systematic Zoology,* **15,** No. 3 (1966), pp. 219-222.]

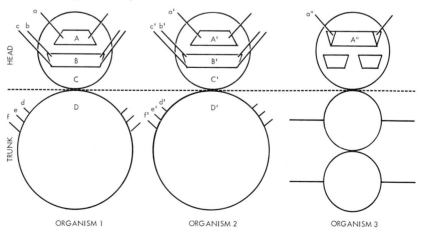

applicable probability value and number of links in the chain of comparisons cannot be prescribed as the basis for the distinction between homology and homoplasy. The investigator must be satisfied with a probability value that is less than that for other structures estimated to be homologous and with a shorter chain of comparisons. Analogy and anaplasy follow the decision of homology and homoplasy, respectively. One must remember that a hypothesis is never proven or disproven by a probability value of less than one, or by the number of links in the chain of comparisons; the results of a test are merely evaluated by the investigator as acceptable or unacceptable with respect to the hypothesis. Inexact as this operational method is, it is most important that the investigator's reasoning, both the kind and degree of discrimination he applies, be clearly understood if his study is to be evaluated and utilized by other workers.

Criteria
Derived from
Evolutionary
Trends

Chronoclines.   As stated earlier, much of the evolution that is viewed as simple phenotypic change has the perspective of linearity and of orientation. The linearity and orientation are perceived from the way in which the changes in a character, or characters, are sequentially ordered in time. Defined on these two bases, a *chronocline* may be considered a sustained, prevailing tendency of modification in one or more characters through geologic time. Almost all stratigraphic sequences of fossils that are long enough to be called sustained exhibit linearity and prevailing tendencies in certain characters, or character complexes, and it is to these that the term chronocline is specifically applied. It is obvious that the detailed explanation of the "how and why" of such trends is in itself a fertile field of study, and it is one that should be kept in mind throughout the later chapters of this book.

A cursory review of the paleontological literature reveals that chronoclines are extremely common and well documented. Such a review also indicates that trends can involve any part of the organism that remains, and that the descendant lines of common, or near common, ancestry often exhibit similar trends, some of which probably involve parallelism. Less often observed than parallelism are the superficially similar trends found in very distantly related lineages. These are termed convergence. In convergence, unlike parallelism, the contemporaneity and ancestry of the lineages of the organisms have had nothing to do with the similarity observed; the similarity is the result of adaptation to environments that have identical or similar selective forces.

It is unusual for a trend to involve only a single characteristic; it usually consists of a complex of characters. Although our knowledge is not based entirely on evidence derived from fossils, two specific kinds of trends involve character complexes. First, it has been demonstrated frequently that when a group of numerous and similar morphologic parts tends to be reduced in number, the remaining parts become more differentiated from each other. Second, when a series of relatively few similar morphologic parts tends to increase in number, the differences between the parts tend to become less. Both of these trends, in all the many organisms that exhibit them, involve a complex of characters that have a broad functional interrelationship. As a corollary to the foregoing statement, it can be said that a given function may be performed by a series of similar morphologic parts acting as a whole, or the function may be performed by one or more different parts acting as separate units or limited sets of units.

A chronocline, as just defined, proceeds through time and may consist of either a single character (although only rarely) or numerous characters, many of which are complementary owing to their common or related functions, or even whole organisms if as such they are preserved as fossils. The modifications, that is, character states, that constitute a single character cline are homologues, being very similar in form and spatial relationship and suggesting a high probability of descent.

This probability value is often incorrectly said to be more reliable when the successive manner in which the fossils are laid down is taken into consideration. In this context it is important to point out that the successive manner in which fossils are laid down does not obviate the need to operationalize the concept of homology, nor is it correct to think that the time dimension accompanying paleontologic study provides an essential, or even important, parameter in operationalizing that concept. The operation is identical regardless of whether the material compared is fossil or recent.

In Figure 1-4 a chronocline in a single character is shown as it progresses through time.† In this example the trend is made up of five character states a, A, A*, A**, and A***. The example depicts five fossilized right hindlimbs which were collected in successive geologic strata. The character states are those stages of modification, here the loss of entire toes, that were coincidentally fossilized and collected. The character state A*** may be considered that of a living species.

All chronoclines, as exemplified by Figure 1-4, exhibit *polarity*; that is, one character state is evolved sequentially from another. The derived character state is said to be advanced relative to the character state from which it was derived, whereas the character state that gives rise to a derived state is primitive relative to that state. Of the character states expressed in the cline in Figure 1-4, state a is the most primitive and A*** the most advanced. The relative terms *specialized* and *generalized* have been reserved for other phenomena, and they should not be considered synonyms of *advanced* and *primitive* respectively. Again referring to Figure 1-4, it should be noted that theoretically between primitive state a and the derived extreme A*** a much larger number of intermediate states exist than the three shown (A, A*, and A**). These might be said to correspond to the different stages in reduction and the ultimate loss of the individual phalangeal elements of each toe. The actual number of intermediate states in a cline depends upon the duration of the trend and the number of relevant mutations and recombinations that occurred. The completeness of the collection of material from the continuum and the degree of refinement of the investigator's observation are also involved. From one operational standpoint only three character states are required for the investigator to be able to recognize a chronocline and to determine its direction, whereas theoretically only two states are required to determine the polarity of a cline. Two states are sufficient in theory, but

---

† Diagrammatic representation of concepts of chronoclines and morphoclines modified after T. Paul Maslin, "Morphological Criteria of Phyletic Relationships." *Systemic Zoology,* Vol. 1, No. 2, 1952, pp. 49-70.

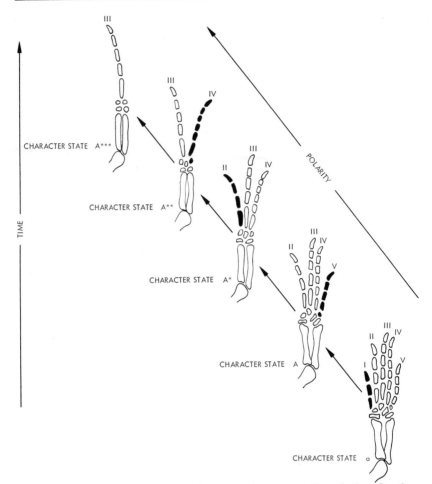

Figure 1-4. A chronocline in a single character as it progresses through time. See the text for further explanation.

obviously not in practice because each character state of a trend must precede the derived extreme.

When a character state of any chronocline is similar to an extreme of another trend, then the first cline is primitive and that character state which forms an extreme of the second trend is its primitive extreme. This criterion can be visualized in Figure 1-5 where the chronoclines are interlocking or precurrent. Here the primitive and derived states can be determined because two of the clines are successively dependent on character states of the preceding cline for their origin. The chronoclines in this example might be the successive loss of unmodified toes, a, A, A*, A**, and A***, the origin and distribution of terminal T-shaped phalangeal elements, A, A′*, A′**, and A′***, and the bifurcation of the terminal T-shaped bones, A′**, A″***, and A″****.

Morphoclines. When a temporally successive series of populations, each exhibiting a character state of the ancestral chronocline, diverges and at the same time stays in the same field and intensity of selection for that characteristic, then at any level in time, *viz.* horizontally or contemporaneously, a sequence of character modifications will exist. In Figure 1-6 this series of modifications is identical to the character states of the ancestral chronocline. Such a contemporaneous sequence of stages of modification is called a *morphocline* and, like the chronocline, exhibits polarity. This example is in accord with the generalization that most evolution is divergent. The degree of resemblance between a morphocline and its corresponding chronocline depends upon the amount and direction of evolution in the divergent lineages. Also affecting the correspondence between the two is the fact that some of the divergent lineages become extinct at different levels in time.

A major operational problem in using morphoclines in the elucidation of phylogeny is the determination of their polarity. This of course is a diffi-

Figure 1-5. An example of precurrent chronoclines. The trends are the loss of simple toes (a-A-A*-A**-A***), the origin and distribution of terminal T-shaped phalangeal elements (A-A′*-A′**-A′***), and the bifurcation of the T-shaped elements (A′**-A″***-A″****). See the text for further explanation.

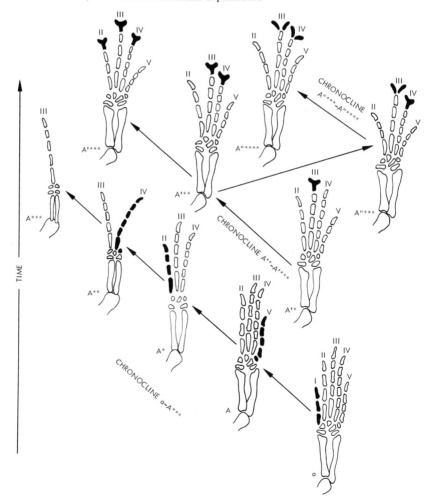

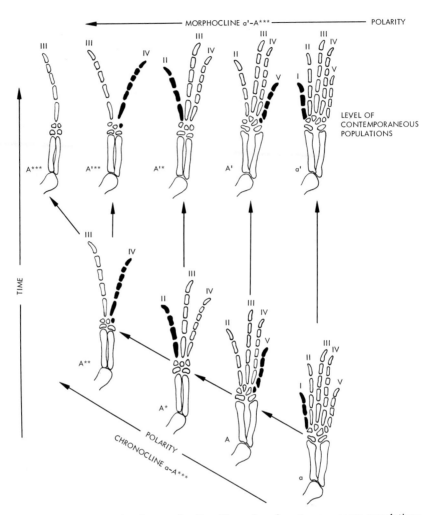

Figure 1-6. An example of a morphocline. The series of contemporaneous populations that form the morphocline exhibit the identical character states of their ancestral chronocline. No change in the character state has occurred in each divergent line. See the text for further explanation.

culty most often encountered by the neontologist where reference to a chronocline cannot be made. In Figure 1-6 if character state a′ resembles A′ but a′ occurs in an organism that on the basis of other character similarities and dissimilarities must be referred to a different but related group of organisms, then A′ is probably the derived state. Since character state A represents most closely state A′ before the latter diverged, A should therefore resemble state a found in the chronocline of a contemporary organism or group of organisms closely related to it. In more general terms it may be stated that if one extreme of a morphocline resembles a condition found in the less modified member of a related group(s), then that extreme is primitive. As a logical extension of this criterion, it may be stated that when two or more different morphoclines appear in different groups of organisms, except for an extreme of each morphocline which occurs in the same related group of organisms, then these extremes are very likely the most primitive. Furthermore, it is obvious that when the two extremes of two clines are identical and are found in the same group of organisms, the identical extremes are primitive and the dissimilar extremes are advanced. This statement is expressed in the example given in Figure 1-7. A possible alternative interpretation to this, however, is shown in Figure 1-8. Here the problem of distinguishing between homologous and homoplastic characteristics is encountered. A method of resolving this problem will now be discussed.

It is often observed that one member of a group of related organisms is conspicuously different from others of its group in one or more characters. This degree of difference in a character results from the absence of organisms exhibiting intermediate character states. The intermediate organisms were present in the chronocline, but the divergent populations (other chronoclines) did not materialize, or if they did they became extinct before reaching the level of time in which the morphocline in question occurs. The number of "absentees" determines the degree of continuity of the morphocline. A relatively discontinuous morphocline is difficult to

Figure 1-7. An example of two different morphoclines involving the shape of the interclavicle (cross-hatched) of lizards where the primitive extreme of each occurs in a related group of organisms. a and b, and a' and b' are identical states. See the text for further explanation.

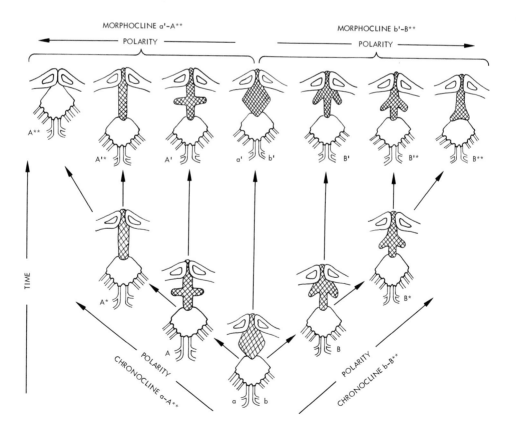

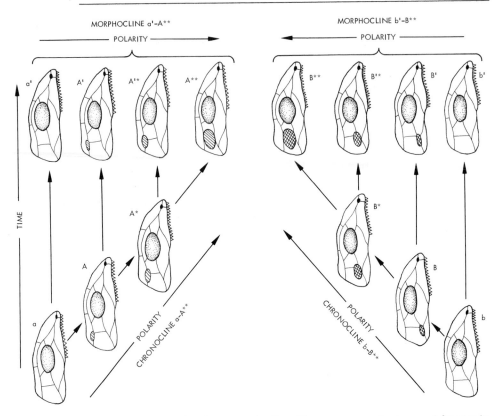

Figure 1-8. An example of two morphoclines (the appearance of a temporal fenestra in the skull of reptiles) where their opposing polarities have produced homoplastic character states in a related group of organisms. See the text for further explanation.

recognize as the product of a single evolutionary trend because too few of the intermediate character states persist.

This problem is further exemplified in the two ways shown in Figures 1-9 and 1-10. In Figure 1-9 the isolated character state A*** is the most highly modified or advanced while in Figure 1-10 the isolated character state a′ is the most primitive. Operationally the polarity of such discontinuous clines may be determined as follows. When an isolated character state occurs in one member of a group of related organisms and also in the primitive member of closely related groups, then the character state in question is primitive. If, however, an isolated character state is unique or appears only sporadically in the derived forms of related groups of organisms, then the character state in question is advanced. These examples are given because they depict the usual circumstance where, for biologic or completely fortuitous reasons, intermediate character states are lacking and the continuity of the morphocline is poorly represented. The same problem of discontinuity is also observed in chronoclines, where it is probably more common. The discontinuities in chronoclines are in large part abrupt and are probably a result of the fortuitous nature of the process of fossilization and the more difficult collection of fossil material. It has been observed in a number of combined paleontological-neontological studies of a related group of organisms that character discontinuities may exist in both the morphocline and the chronocline of a particular character. These same studies also show that considerable reciprocal evidence for the actual presence of absentees in a character trend can be obtained by using both the living organisms and the relevant fossil record.

Before proceeding to the actual study of phylogeny, this important question should be posed again: how does an investigator recognize the morphocline that represents two or more parallel or convergent chronoclines as exemplified in Figure 1-8? In addition, how does he recognize a situation in which the most advanced character state of one chronocline approximates a possible but unknown advanced condition of a second chronocline and morphocline (Figure 1-11)? Certainly for almost all neontologic studies, and only slightly less for paleontologic investigations, the a priori delimitation of at least most homoplastic characters involves the simultaneous study of many evolutionary trends. In almost all the preceding discussion of evolutionary

Figure 1-9. A discontinuous morphocline where the isolated character state A*** is the most highly modified or advanced. See the text for further explanation.

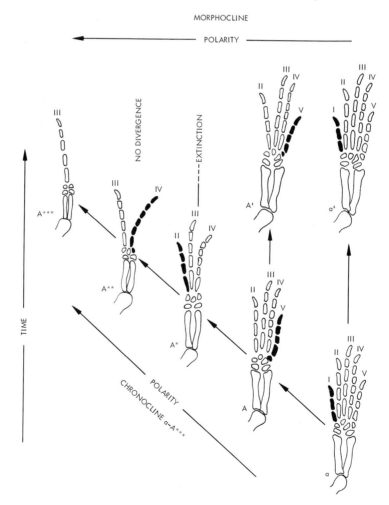

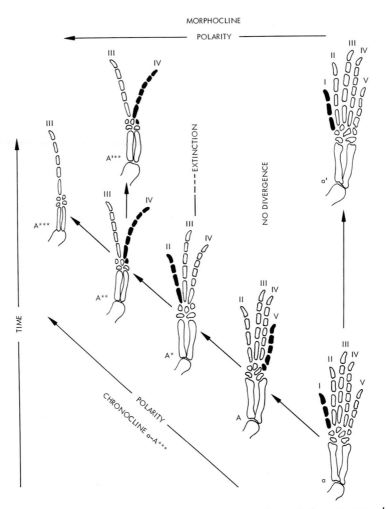

Figure 1-10. A discontinuous morphocline where the isolated character state a′ is the most primitive or least modified. See the text for further explanation.

trends examples have been given that involve only a single character. This has been done only for the sake of simplicity and clarity. In practice, however, the simultaneous study of more than two clines is very often possible, and it is highly desirable in delimiting homoplastic characters. Adaptive evolution usually involves the simultaneous modification of a number of characters. In this context it is important to emphasize again that evolutionary trends are complementary and that it is populations of whole integrated individual organisms that are evolving. In spite of the fact that some characters are modified more rapidly than others and that the divergence of phyletic lines segregate, and even initiate new evolutionary trends, the total effect of evolution is composite change, the parts of which often have a similar polarity. On the basis of this generalization, it seems reasonable to postulate that if an unknown and a known cline exhibit the same direction of change in the same organisms, the polarity in the unknown cline is very likely the same as that of the known one. In addition, if two or more clines occur in groups of related organisms, that group which has the largest number of primitive extremes is the most primitive. The a posteriori recognition of conditions of homoplasy will be considered later.

Parsimonious reasoning is fundamental to the study of similarity and chronoclines and morphoclines and to the use of the criteria derived from them for the construction of phylogenetic trees. The *rule of parsimony* was first promulgated by the scholastic William of Ockham in 1347 in response to the unnecessary and irrelevant hypotheses given in explanation of phenomena. This old rule of logic and science states that of several possible explanations the one that is the simplest, that is, has the fewest assumptions and is the most consistent with the data at hand, is the most probable one.

Postulates for the Estimation of Polarity

A synthesis of the criteria of similarity and chronoclines and morphoclines, coupled with parsimonious reasoning, has led to the formulation of the following probabilistically based postulates which can be readily used to estimate which of two or more character states of a cline is primitive. The postulates are listed in order of predictive reliability (1-4).

1. A character state is primitive when it is identical or very similar to one occurring in temporally antecedent organisms presumed to be directly

Figure 1-11. An example of a condition (the formation of a foramen in the pelvic girdle) where the most advanced character state of one chronocline (B***) approximates a possible but unknown advanced condition of a second chronocline and morphocline (a-A**). See the text for further explanation.

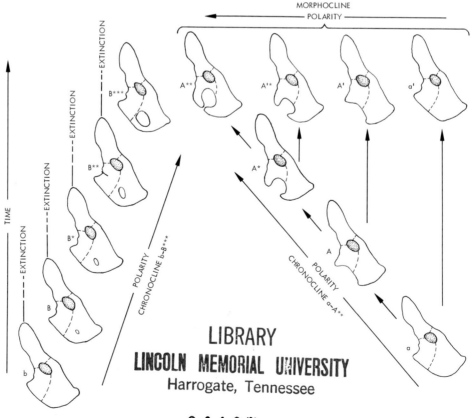

ancestral, or at least closely related, to the ancestors of the more modern group being studied.

2. A character state is primitive when it is identical or very similar to one that is universally or frequently exhibited by contemporaneous groups of organisms presumed to be related to the group being studied. The more widely an identical or very similar character state occurs among related organisms, the more probable that it results from an identical or very similar genetic origin.

3. A character state that is restricted to the group of organisms being studied is primitive when it is universally or frequently exhibited by the individuals in that group. The probability that a character state is primitive increases very rapidly with the increase in the number of individuals in the group that exhibits that state.

4. A character state that is restricted to the group of organisms being studied although only infrequently exhibited, is primitive when it occurs in those individuals that have the greatest number of primitive states as determined by postulates 1, 2 and/or 3. The probability that a character state is primitive increases very rapidly with the increase in the number of primitive characters with which it is positively correlated.

In the application of criteria 1, 2, and 3, the "related groups" can be determined prior to detailed analysis of the group under study through estimates of overall similarity that make no assumptions about primitive conditions. In criteria 2 and 3, "occurring widely" means more than just the number of taxa exhibiting a particular state. A character state is said to be widespread when it occurs in many taxa, at least several of which are relatively dissimilar.

Phylogeny: A Summation of Data and Hypotheses

Phylogeny is the amount of evolution (the totality of changes), direction of the change of characters, character complexes, whole organisms, populations, and the sequence of the different directions of change. For many years taxonomists have attempted to express these parameters graphically in the form of a family tree or *dendrogram* (Figure 1-12). The shape of the tree, the number of branches or divergent lineages, and the length of the interval between the branches with few exceptions are, however, not determined objectively. The tree is only the visual product of the feeling or *gestalt* of the investigator. Such an expression of the taxonomist's understanding of the phylogeny of a group of organisms does not embody much, if any, meaningful information (Figure 1-12) and, more important, the methods and reasoning of the worker cannot be followed and tested by other investigators. Principally because of newly formulated evolutionary hypotheses and the development of certain quantitative methods the reconstruction of phylogeny is no longer considered an intuitive, and therefore nonscientific, endeavor of interest only to classical taxonomists.

A phylogeny is logically the final and most encompassing summation of all data gathered in a comparative study. Even prior to this stage the different kinds of research that necessarily precede the reconstruction of a phylogeny provide numerous avenues of feedback, or counterchecks and balances, on the investigator's experimental technique and his working premises. Furthermore, an objectively constructed phylogeny provides a final framework from which new hypotheses may be realized more readily and against which previously formulated hypotheses may be tested more rigorously. Above all else the predictive powers of phylogenies reconstructed by the newer quantitative methods have been found to be so great that comparative biologists can no longer fail to take advantage of them in their research and teaching, regardless of whether they compare and contrast sets of related phenomena or whole organisms or populations.

There can be no question that any set of organisms has had but a single evolutionary history and that certain biological criteria and mathematical formulae lead to a most probable estimate of that unique phylogeny. Like any scientific hypothesis, the predictive power of the reconstructed phylogeny provides the most meaningful test of its own reality.

To reconstruct phylogeny objectively the following parameters must be assessed in some quantitative form: (1) degree of relationship between populations, (2) relative position of divergent lineages, and (3) direction of evolutionary change. A fourth dimension, absolute time, can be derived only from the fossil record and is not necessary to the reconstruction of phylogeny. The third parameter has already been treated in detail; parameters 1 and 2 will be discussed, and one of the most readily used objective methods for reconstructing phylogeny is outlined following that discussion. It is hoped that the beginning student will learn to use this powerful tool in his study of the morphology and function of chordate animals.

A Rationale for Estimating Evolutionary Relationship
The evolution of one population from another involves a change in some character, more often a complex of characters, which results from a change in gene frequency. The phyletic line that connects the ancestral and derived populations is usually characterized by phenotypic change, and the amount of evolution that has occurred between these two populations may be estimated by how much they differ phenotypically. Thus, degree of evolu-

Figure 1-12. An example of a subjectively reconstructed phylogeny which purports to indicate the relationships of four contemporaneous populations. The question marks have been included to point out some of the major areas of subjectivity.

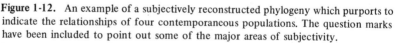
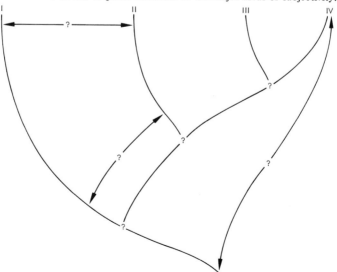

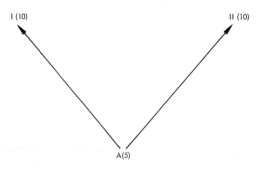

Figure 1-13. An example of two divergent phyletic lines (A-I, and A-II) which are connected to each other by a common ancestor (A). The three populations, A, I, and II, are described in terms of phenotypic values (numbers in parentheses).

tionary relationship is calculated as the sum of the character state differences of all of the characters used to describe the two populations.

Phyletic lines, even short ones, diverge from other phyletic lines. Recognizing this divergent aspect of evolution, can we directly compare the phenotypes of any two populations and realize a meaningful estimate of the amount of evolution that has occurred between them? The answer is no. For example, in Figure 1-13, populations I (described by a phenotypic value of ten) and II (value of ten) have evolved from a common ancestor, A (value of five). Direct comparison of populations I and II in terms of the difference of their phenotypic values gives an estimate of zero difference. This nonlinear comparison does not take into account the branching nature of evolution, that is, the amount of change that has occurred between ancestor and derived population. To estimate the true evolutionary relationship of populations I and II in Figure 1-13 the linear sum of their phenotypic differences is calculated [(I to A = 5) + (A to II = 5) = 10]. This simple model demonstrates that although evolutionary relationship is estimated by phenotypic difference, it is the sum of the differences between two populations and their common ancestor that is calculated. With this distinction clearly in mind note that the amount of homoplasy between two populations can be calculated as the difference between the linear and nonlinear comparisons. In the example just given the amount of homoplasy between populations I and II is ten.

A Method of Estimating Evolutionary Relationship

The best approximation of the phylogeny of a group of populations is their arrangement in the form of the dendrogram that has the greatest chance of being true on the basis of the data employed. It has been suggested [9] that the phyletic tree with the shortest total length produces the most likely set of relationships of the populations compared regardless of the time that has passed during their evolution. The total length of the tree is easily measured by simply calculating the sum of the character state differences of the populations involved. Minimizing this difference in the actual reconstruction of a phylogeny is accomplished by the parsimony procedure described as follows.

Coding characters.   How many and what kinds of characters are used as data in the reconstruction of phylogeny? The question is answered easily. Use all available evidence; the more characters employed, the greater the likelihood that the phyletic product will be correct. With the following two exceptions, no limitation is placed on the kind of characters employed. Data from many different biological systems ensure that the investigator has assessed the evolution of the whole organisms and the populations of which they are a part. To use the parsimony procedure correctly, he must code the characters so that they have equal average change per unit of time and are independent in evolution. Therefore, each character must be rescaled in units of its intra-population standard deviation (e.g., the character state divided by the standard deviation) and those characters that are correlated statistically with one another removed from consideration. For convenience, in the remainder of this chapter we will assume that these requirements have been met.

The actual coding of the characters that have been studied is the first step in the parsimony procedure. The simplest coding method and the most meaningful one visually involves the use of letter symbols for the characters and their recognized character states (See Figures 1-4–1-11). The characters may be given different symbols arbitrarily, and the states of each ranked according to their polarity, that is, their position in the chronocline or morphocline of which they are a part. The following list of five characters exemplifies the method of coding and the variety of characters that can and should be employed.

Character a-A*: Condition of the hyoid arch
  a hyoid cornua large, hypohyal-ceratohyal union not tenuous (primitive)
  A hyoid cornua small, hypohyal-ceratohyal union tenuous (advanced)
  A* hyoid cornua absent, hypohyal-ceratohyal union broken (more advanced than state A)
Character b-B: Development of the premaxillary bone
  b from two centers of ossification (primitive)
  B from one center of ossification (advanced)
Character c-C: Number of eggs laid
  c two (primitive)
  C one (advanced)
Character d-D*: Q_{10} values for oxygen consumption at 10-15°C
  d 1.40 (primitive)
  D 1.75 (advanced)
  D* 2.50 (more advanced than D)
Character e-E*: Mean pulse rate (per second) of mating call at 10°C
  e 24.0 (primitive)
  E 80.5 (advanced)
  E* 119.8 (more advanced than state E)

For further exemplification of methods it will be useful to consider these characters and the conclusions concerning the relative primitiveness of the character states as derived from a study of *operational taxonomic units.* OTU may be defined as a related group of organisms (even an individual) that is separated from others by character discontinuities. By using the general term OTU the researcher is not committed to an a priori (that is, before the phylogeny has been reconstructed) taxonomic and nomenclatural decision. The five characters coded above as a-A*, b-B, c-C, d-D*, and e-E* can be reduced now to a simple tabular form with respect to the distribution of their states among five OTUs (I-V). The tabular arrangement of character states and OTUs as shown in Table 1-1 is termed a data matrix. A completely primitive hypothetical OTU (designated H) can also be determined for all the characters considered, and it too should be added to the data matrix.

The characterization or definition of each OTU is readily obtained from the data matrix when it is read horizontally. Also, the concordance in the clines, if any, can be visualized readily by reading up or down the columns.

For further analysis of these data in an empirical form the letter symbols of the original data matrix must be translated into a numerical form. For example, using characters a-A* and b-B, the following conversion of the character states of each character is prescribed. In an actual study, the numerical state would be divided by the standard deviation of the character state in the population.

Letter symbols used in Table 1-1: $a \rightarrow A \rightarrow A^*$ $b \rightarrow B$
Numerical equivalent of Table 1-2: $0 \rightarrow 1 \rightarrow 2$ $0 \rightarrow 1$

By this conversion, Table 1-1 is reconstituted into the entirely numerical form shown in Table 1-2. The origin of the hypothetical OTUs (VI-VIII) that have been added to the matrix will become apparent as the study of this example develops.

Table 1-1. Data matrix.

OTU		Characters				
		a-A*	b-B	c-C	d-D*	e-E*
Hypothetical	H	a	b	c	d	e
Real	I	A	B	c	D*	e
	II	A*	b	C	d	e
	III	A*	B	c	d	e
	IV	a	b	c	D*	E*
	V	a	b	C	D*	E

Table 1-2. Data matrix.

OTU		Characters				
		a-A*	b-B	c-C	d-D*	e-E*
		0-2	0-1	0-1	0-2	0-2
Hypothetical	H	0	0	0	0	0
Real	I	1	1	0	2	0
	II	2	0	1	0	0
	III	2	1	0	0	0
	IV	0	0	0	2	2
	V	0	0	1	2	1
Hypothetical	VI	2	0	0	0	0
	VII	1	0	0	0	0
	VIII	1	0	0	2	0
	IX	0	0	0	2	2

Reconstruction of phylogeny. In reconstructing the most probable phylogeny by the parsimony procedure to be described, each OTU is successively attached to a specific part of the tree. The order and place of attachment is carried out to minimize the total length of the network of lines that link the OTUs together in the form of a set of relationships. The line that links two OTUs is called an interval, and it is calculated as the sum of all the character state differences between two OTUs. The order in which OTUs are placed on the tree is determined by their degree of similarity to the completely primitive hypothetical OTU. The most similar OTU is added first, and to some point along the interval from which it differs the least. It may be linked to the OTU that forms either the beginning or the end of that interval, or to a hypothetical OTU within that interval. A hypothetical OTU may be placed within any previously existing interval in order to minimize the unplaced OTUs linkage to that interval. Again, degree of similarity determines to which of the three OTUs of the interval the unplaced OTU will be attached. When an OTU is added to the tree, it is attached to a previously placed OTU by a straight line proportional to their similarity, that is, the sum of all the character state differences that separate them. No known biological meaning can be referred to the angles that the lines form. It is important to keep in mind that the parsimony procedure gives the shortest tree, but other equally short trees may exist. There are some sets of data for which there is no unique solution—the trees are equally probable.

In the process of forming the most parsimonious tree, two different kinds of data matrixes are often referred to for information on the order and place of attachment of an unplaced OTU. The methods used to form the two matrixes as well as a hypothetical OTU will be described before the steps in the procedure are listed. This will greatly facilitate the description and subsequent use of the procedure.

In the process of carrying out the parsimony procedure, OTUs are compared frequently in terms of their similarity; therefore an OTU X OTU similarity matrix should be constituted before the procedure is even initiated (see Table 1-3). To form a similarity matrix all the OTUs are compared to each other in terms of the sum of all of their character state differences. When any two OTUs are compared, each of their character state values will

Table 1-3. OTU X OTU similarity matrix.[†]

	H	I	II	III	IV	V	VI	VII	VIII	IX
H	0	4	3	3	4	4	2	1	3	3
I	4	0	5	3	4	4	4	3	1	3
II	3	5	0	2	7	5	1	2	4	6
III	3	3	2	0	7	7	1	2	4	6
IV	4	4	7	7	0	2	6	5	3	1
V	4	4	5	7	2	0	6	5	3	1
VI	2	4	1	1	6	6	0	1	3	5
VII	1	3	2	2	5	5	1	0	2	4
VIII	3	1	4	4	3	3	3	2	0	2
IX	3	3	6	6	1	1	5	4	2	0

† Derived from the data matrix in Table 1-2

be the same or different. If the values are the same, then there is zero difference between them in that character. When their character state values are different, then the smallest number is subtracted from the largest and the result is an expression of how much they differ in that character. The sum of these differences for all characters is the overall difference between two OTUs. This difference is used as the estimate of their relative similarity.

Another kind of OTU × OTU similarity matrix is formed whenever a comparison of an unplaced OTU with its most similar interval is carried out. This temporary matrix consists of a comparison of the unplaced OTU with only the three OTUs that define that interval: the OTU that forms the beginning of the interval, the one that terminates it, and the hypothetical intermediate OTU among the three of them. When the unplaced OTU is linked to the hypothetical OTU, then the hypothetical, owing to its greater similarity, may be added to the permanent similarity matrix.

In contrast to the OTU × OTU matrix, the second basic similarity matrix is completely recomputed with the placement of each OTU on the tree. It consists of similarity values that result from comparing the unplaced OTU with both the initiating and terminating OTUs of all intervals that are already on the tree. The values upon which the unplaced OTU × interval similarity matrix are calculated may be taken directly from the OTU × OTU similarity matrix. Each unplaced OTU × interval similarity value is computed as follows: Determine the similarity value of the unplaced OTU to the beginning and to the terminating OTUs of an interval and add the two values together. Next, find the similarity value between the beginning and the terminating OTUs themselves and subtract this result from the former. Last, divide this result by two.

To reconstruct the most parsimonious tree for most sets of data a large number of hypothetical OTUs must be used. They usually equal the number of real OTUs placed on the tree. As stated before, a hypothetical OTU may be placed within any previously existing interval in order to minimize the unplaced OTUs' linkage to that interval. The hypothetical OTU is formed from the median character state value of each character of the initiating and terminating OTUs of the interval and the unplaced OTU that is to be linked to it.

The basic procedure for forming most parsimonious trees consists of six steps, the last five of which form a sequence that is repeated until all of the real OTUs have been placed.

Step 1. Compute the OTU × OTU similarity matrix. Find the OTU that is the most similar to the ancestor (H) and link them together to form the first interval.

Step 2. Of the remaining unplaced OTUs find the one that is the most similar to the ancestor.

Step 3. Compute an unplaced OTU × interval similarity matrix using the unplaced OTU found in step 2. Find the interval from which that unplaced OTU differs the least.

Step 4. Reconstruct a hypothetical intermediate OTU from the initiating and terminating OTUs of that interval and the unplaced OTU.

Step 5. Connect the unplaced OTU to the OTU of the interval length from which it differs the least. If the hypothetical OTU is the most similar one, add it to the OTU X OTU similarity matrix.

Step 6.   Go back to step 2 until all of the real OTUs have been placed on the tree.

The following rules ensure that the most parsimonious tree will be formed.

Rule 1.   When two or more intervals are equally similar to an unplaced OTU, select the interval that produces the shortest attachment between the unplaced OTU and the tree. When the attachment is the same, choose that interval that is closest to the ancestor.

Rule 2.   When a hypothetical OTU is connected to an identical real, or hypothetical OTU, retain only one of the two.

The data and OTU X OTU similarity matrixes shown in Tables 1-2 and 1-3 respectively are used to illustrate the simplicity of the procedure. The exemplification gives only the placement of OTUs I, II, and III and the reader should complete the tree by correctly attaching IV and V. The necessary actions in the procedure of placing OTUs I, II, and III are described in the following steps.

Step 1.   The OTU X OTU similarity matrix is computed (see Table 1-3). OTUs II and III are equally similar to the ancestor (H). OTU II is selected arbitrarily and is connected to the ancestor [Figure 1-14(a)]. The length of the interval between them is proportional to the sum of their character state differences.

Step 2.   Of the remaining unplaced OTUs, III is the most similar to the ancestor.

Step 3.   OTU III is compared to the only existing interval, H,II.

Step 4.   Within the interval H,II, hypothetical OTU VI is reconstructed with the character states 20000.

Step 5.   OTU III is more similar to OTU VI than it is to either H or II. Therefore, OTU III is linked to VI [Figure 14(b)]. OTU VI is added to the OTU X OTU similarity matrix.

Step 6.   OTUs I, IV, and V have not been placed on the tree. Go back to step 2.

Step 2.   OTUs I, IV, and V are equally similar to the ancestor (H). OTU I is selected arbitrarily.

Step 3.   OTU I is compared to the intervals H,VI and VI,III and VI,II. OTU I differs the least and by an equally small value from both intervals H,VI and VI,III. Rule 1 dictates that OTU I be linked to interval H,VI.

Step 4.   Within the interval H,VI, hypothetical VII is reconstructed with the character states 10000.

Step 5.   OTU I is more similar to OTU VII than it is to either H or VI. Therefore, OTU I is linked to VII [Figure 1-14(c)]. OTU VII is added to the OTU X OTU similarity matrix.

Step 6.   OTUs IV and V have not been placed on the tree. Go back to step 2.

The completed most parsimonious tree based on the five OTUs and five characters shown in Tables 1-1 and 1-2 has a total length of eleven [Figure 1-15(a)]. The total length is computed by successively summing the character state differences that describe the lengths of all the intervals of the tree. In the completed tree the homoplastic states are underlined, the evolutionary reversal is indicated by a subscript x, and the sum of the character state differences between two OTUs is circled.

As mentioned earlier, there may be other trees that are equally parsimonious for the same set of data, that is, they exhibit the same total length. For example, as can be seen from a comparison of Figures 1-15(a) and (b), two eleven-step trees, one with a reversal and two homoplasious states, and the other with no reversals and three homoplasious states, can be derived from the same data and must be considered equally probable. At present there seems to be no realistic guideline for deciding between two trees of equal length when homoplasy is present in one but not in the other. Certainly, one way of obtaining a unique solution in all cases is to carry out further research and to employ additional characters.

In summary, the merits of the parsimony procedure are numerous. The phylogeny produced clearly describes the relative degree of relationship between OTUs, and the direction of the evolution of individual characters, complexes of characters, whole organisms, and populations. The tree

Figure 1-14. The results of the placement of OTUs: (a) II; (b) III; and (c) I by the parsimony procedure described in the text. The OTUs are referenced by the states of the five characters that describe them (in parentheses).

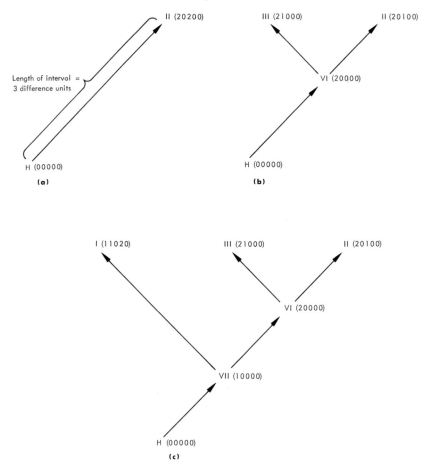

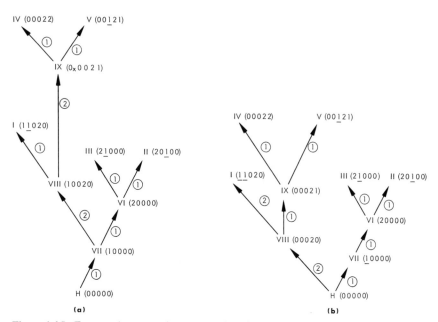

Figure 1-15. Two maximum parsimony trees based on the same set of data (Tables 1-1 and 1-2). The tree shown in Figure 1-15(a) was generated by the parsimony procedure described in the text.

provides a recheck of presumed homoplasious states and even recognition of previously unnoticed ones. Moreover, it permits the investigator to postulate hypothetical OTUs. But perhaps the most important value of the procedure is that it causes the scientist to lay bare his methodology and reasoning at all levels of investigation and provides an objective framework against which other hypotheses can be rigorously tested. It should be quite obvious by now that the product of this procedure embodies a greater amount of more readily available information for other investigators to use than does the intuitively formed phylogeny shown in Figure 1-12. With the masses of data that already exist in original research papers and textbooks on chordate structure and function, and the data which even the beginning student can research for himself in his laboratory, the parsimony procedure provides the tool with which to challenge objectively the classically constructed phylogenies that are now almost universally accepted as fact.

Character Weighting
In the objective reconstruction of the phylogeny of any group of organisms one should always try to obtain as accurate an estimate of the degree of relationship of the OTUs as possible. The first and most important question that must be asked is "Are all characters the same weight?" At least intuitively, the answer should be no. The usual objective method of character weighting, as used here in its simplest form, requires only a knowledge of the relative variability of the individual characters. The method is rooted in the concept of conservatism whereby some characters are more important to the survival of organisms than are others. The French botanist A. P. DeCandolle (1778-1841) was the first to discuss and use differential weighting relative to the survival value of characters. It is now generally agreed that a

conservative character is one that exhibits little or no variability, and the restricted variability is a result of strong selective forces [5]. It follows that a character that is highly variable is either undergoing rapid evolution or is of little adaptive value to the organisms in the adaptive field open to them at that time. Because conservative characters are those that have changed more slowly during phylogeny than nonconservative ones, it is important to reiterate a point that was made earlier: patterns of relationship are easier to trace in the less variable characters because more rapidly changing ones tend to produce greater gaps in the chronoclines and resulting morphoclines.

In accordance with the concept of conservatism, the relative variability of the individual characters can be used to change differentially the lengths of the intervals of a phylogeny. And it seems that the use of some variance-related statistic, such as the standard deviation, is the most realistic way to accomplish the weighting. One method requires only that the difference between two OTUs in each character be divided by the standard deviation of that character, after which the sum of the differences between the two OTUs in all characters is computed.

In addition to the a priori differential character weighting just described, it is possible to apply a second kind of weighting, but only after a phylogeny has been constructed. This a posteriori form of weighting is related to the fact that the variability of characters may be increased as the result of the actual reconstruction of the most parsimonious arrangement of the OTUs. Remember, some cases of evolutionary reversal and homoplasy are realized only after the tree has been formed. To accomplish this a posteriori weighting, simply count the number of evolutionary steps for each character in the entire tree. For example, in Figure 1-15(a) character a-A* exhibits an increase in its variability because it reverses its evolutionary direction at OTU IX. Another example of increased variability is demonstrated by character b-B. In this case, however, the increase results from the homoplasy of state B between OTUs I and III. Here again, the difference between two OTUs in each character may be multiplied by its newly computed standard deviation, after which the sum of the differences between the two OTUs in all characters is found and the length of the interval that separates them is corrected accordingly.

Last, there is a third category of weighting that should be considered before the degree of similarity between OTUs can be considered final. Occasionally an investigator can obtain evidence, either directly or indirectly, about the relative difficulty of the observed state changes that are made within a character. For example, in character a-A* of the previous example, it may be known that the change a to A is a very difficult step (e.g., an organized two-step sequence of biochemical events resulting from multiple allelic differences), whereas A to A* is an easy change (e.g., a single biochemical event). Therefore, some additional differential weighting is required so that the relative degree of this difficulty can be reflected in the length of the interval between those OTUs that exhibit a to A and those that involve A to A*. A method similar to that applied to the a posteriori discerned levels of variability can also be used here.

Classification: A Product of Phylogeny

Why Classify Organisms?

The classification of organisms and the application of scientific nomenclature to the units of classification are extremely important to all biologists. A classification provides the necessary framework for the mental storage of vast amounts of information into a condensed and readily retrievable form. The nomenclature associated with the classification also provides a standardized terminology that can be used to communicate objectively with others about the information embodied in the classification. In addition to these practical aspects, a classification may in itself provide the stimulus for further conceptualization. The percept of the way in which the information is ordered in a classification may lead to new, and probably otherwise unidentifiable, meaningful concepts. Both the original information that is used to construct the classification and the other data that are later superimposed on it can contribute to, and be a part of, the new concepts.

To be of value a classification system must be both practical and meaningful. In the field of biology, where knowledge continues to increase very rapidly, much of the practicability of the system must rest on its ability to incorporate changing data and ideas with facility and yet maintain some overall stability. Since organic evolution pervades all fields of biology and related disciplines, it is generally agreed that the most meaningful classificatory system is one that at least in part is based on this common theme. The Linnaean binomial hierarchical system of classification uses phylogeny as its interpretative basis and appears to be moderately practical. Moreover, the system is widely accepted by both evolutionary and nonevolutionary biologists.

What Is a Phylogenetic Classification?

A phylogenetic classification is a hierarchical arrangement of the way and degree to which OTUs are linked together in phylogeny; therefore evolution is its interpretative basis. The taxonomic units of a phylogenetic classification are equivalent to organisms that have common descent. A more inclusive classificatory unit appears in terms of a phyletic equivalent or stage only in retrospect after the less inclusive lines of affinity have been delimited.

Rule of monophyly. The only scientific rule that must be followed in translating a phylogeny into a classification is that the taxonomic units be *monophyletic*. A monophyletic taxon is one that consists of one or more phyletic lines that have evolved from a single immediately ancestral taxon. The operational criterion of assessing monophyly of a group of organisms rests on their contiguity as estimated by the way they are linked together in phylogeny.

The taxonomic category of species, as defined earlier on the basis of other criteria, is on occasion exceptional to the thesis of monophyly. For example, a species may be a hybrid, that is, a product resulting from interbreeding between two related or unrelated species when their usual isolating mechanisms have temporarily and locally broken down. The phenomenon, which appears to be extremely rare in animals, is known to be very common in plants. The strict application of the rule of monophyly to the category of species that are not hybrid products and to all lower taxonomic units ensures that the propinquity of descent delimited by the phylogeny is translated into the classification.

Classificatory units. In spite of the many advances that have been made in taxonomic theory and procedure in the last century, the general form of classification has changed very little from the pre-Darwinian hierarchial binominal system of nomenclature used by Carl von Linné in 1758 in his tenth edition of *Systema Naturae Regnum Animale.* In this edition Linné used only five units, species, genus, order, class, and kingdom, to classify all the animals known to him. With the correlation of the many species that have been recognized since 1758 and the attempt to relate classification to

Table 1-4. Classificatory categories.

Kingdom	Animalia	Animalia
Phylum	Chordata	Chordata
Subphylum	Vertebrata	Vertebrata
Class	Mammalia	Mammalia
Order	Carnivora	Primates
Family	Felidae	Hominidae
Genus	*Felis*	*Homo*
Species	*domestica*	*sapiens*
Familiar name	domestic cat	man

Table 1-5. Estimation of relative degrees of evolutionary divergence.

Monophyletic Clusters of OTUs	Maximum Difference
IV or V-IX-VIII-VII-VI-II or III	7
I-VIII-IX-IV or V	4
II-VI-III	2
IV-IX-V	2

Table 1-6. A relationship between degrees of evolutionary divergence and classificatory categories.

Form A	Form B
Rank 4 (7)	Order
Rank 3 (4)	Family
Rank 2 (2)	Genus
Rank 1, species I	Species
Rank 2 (2)	Genus
Rank 1, species IV	Species
Rank 1, species V	Species
Rank 3 (4)	Family
Rank 2 (2)	Genus
Rank 1, species II	Species
Rank 1, species III	Species

phylogeny, and with ever increasing fineness of discrimination, the number of classificatory units has been expanded to approximately twenty-one levels. Only those categories most frequently used today are listed in Table 1-4 in order of their taxonomic inclusiveness (from bottom to top). In this example of the system, the nomenclature of the domestic cat, *Felis domestica*, and man, *Homo sapiens*, are compared relative to these categories.

Deriving an
Evolutionary
Classification

In keeping with the practical and theoretical goals of the optimum biological classification stated before, equal degrees of diversity must be equated and then ranked accordingly in a hierarchical scheme. This can be accomplished objectively by using the phylogeny reconstructed by the parsimony procedure. As we have seen, it is the branching aspect of the phylogeny that provides the information necessary to apply the rule of monophyly objectively. Some form of the similarity, that is, the length of the interval between the OTUs within a monophyletic group, can be used as an index to the equivalence of evolutionary divergence. The most realistic form of evolutionary divergence for this use seems to be the maximum difference of any two OTUs within a monophyletic group [4]. The maximum evolutionary difference is the only divergence index minimizing the instability in classification that results primarily from including previously unstudied OTUs within the monophyletic groups of the phylogeny.

The following hypothetical example illustrates the actual steps involved in the translation of a maximum parsimony phylogeny into an evolutionary classification. Again, the phylogeny given in Figure 1-15(a) can be used as an example in which there are only four possible monophyletic categories. These are listed in Table 1-5 opposite the maximum summed character state differences of any two OTUs within the monophyletic group. Using these values as relative degrees of evolutionary divergence and assuming that the real OTUs, I, II, III, IV, and V, are species, then the classification given in Table 1-6, form A, results. Species are given the hierarchic rank of 1, and the remaining ranks 2, 3, and 4 correspond to the maximum differences 2, 4, and 7, respectively. These ranks have been translated in turn into the more familiar Linnean categories of genus, family, and order, respectively (Table 1-6, form B). According to other rules and usages, previously published names are selected that are applicable to the recognized classification; for example, the generic name of the common house cat is *Felis*, the species name is *domestica*. If no previously published name is applicable, then a new one is coined by the researcher.

Other than the category of species, which may be designated as rank 1, the relationships between the other different equivalent degrees of evolutionary divergence and the kinds of classificatory categories used are flexible within certain limits. This flexibility is demonstrated in Figure 1-16 above the hypothetical phylogeny where either a coarse or a fine discrimination of the same tree can be used. Both products are consistent with the degree of evolutionary divergence and the rule of monophyly. Usually the more rigorously objective the assessment of the phylogeny of a group of taxa and the more divergent their phylogenetic history, the finer is the classificatory discrimination to be employed. New discoveries, and often only restudy, will continue to fill in gaps at classificatory levels in studies of both extant and

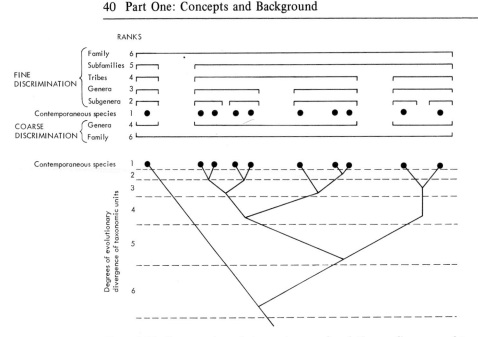

Figure 1-16. Correspondence between degrees of evolutionary divergence of taxonomic units. The degrees of evolutionary divergence below are translated into Linnean taxonomic categories above. The brackets at each taxonomic level indicate the species that are included. (Modified after G. G. Simpson, *Principles of Animal Taxonomy.* New York: Columbia Univ. Press, 1962.)

extinct organisms. It must be remembered that evolution is a continuum, and the large gaps are only convenient results of the processes of extinction and/or fossilization. As a corollary, it may be stated that the continuum of evolution causes difficulty in classification, and that continued difficulty is logical evidence of evolution.

References for Chapter 1

[1] Belon du Mans, Pierre, *L'Histoire de la Nature des Oyseaux.* Paris: 1555.

[2] Cole, F. J., *A History of Comparative Anatomy from Aristotle to the Eighteenth Century.* London: Macmillan Company, 1944, p. 471. This book is a detailed treatment of the origin and evolution of concepts pertaining to comparative anatomy.

[3] Darwin, Charles, *On the Origin of Species by Means of Natural Selection, or the Preservation of Favoured Races in the Struggle for Life.* London: John Murray, 1859. (Cited from a reprint of the sixth edition, with all additions and corrections. A. L. Burt Company, New York.)

[4] Farris, J. S., "Categorical Ranks and Evolutionary Taxa in Numerical Taxonomy." *Syst. Zool.,* **17,** No. 2 (1968), 151-159. A concise method of deriving an evolutionary classification from a phylogeny that has been derived quantitatively.

[5] ——, "Estimation of Conservatism of Characters by Constancy within Biological Populations," *Evol.* **20,** No. 4 (1966), 587-591. A recent account of objective methods for weighting characters by the concept of conservatism.

[6] Hull, David L., "Certainty and Circularity in Evolutionary Taxonomy," *Evol.,* **20**, No. 1 (1967), 174-189.

[7] Inglis, W. G., "The Observational Basis of Homology." *Syst. Zool.,* **15**, No. 3 (1966), 219-228.

[8] Key, K. L. H., "Operational Homology," *Syst. Zool.,* **16**, No. 3 (1967), 275-276.

[9] Kluge, Arnold G., and James S. Farris, "Quantitative Phyletics and the Evolution of Anurans," *Syst. Zool.,* **18**, No. 1 (1969), 1-32.

[10] McNeill, A. R., Functional Design in Fishes, Hutchinson University Library, 1967. McNeill's short essay on aspects of fish design is presented and interpreted in the context of natural selection. For this reason, the book will very likely serve as a model for further research into form and function.

[11] Maslin, T. Paul, "Morphological Criteria of Phyletic Relationships." *Syst. Zool.,* **1**, No. 2 (1952), 49-70. Maslin's paper provides an introduction to the concepts and methodologies of delimiting chronoclines and morphoclines and their polarity.

[12] Owen, R., *Lectures on the Comparative Anatomy and Physiology of Invertebrate Animals.* London: Longman, Brown, Green and Longmans, 1843.

[13] Simpson, G. G., *Principles of Animal Taxonomy.* New York: Columbia University Press, 1962.

[14] ——, "Anatomy and Morphology: Classification and Evolution: 1859 and 1959." *Proc. Amer. Phil. Soc.,* **103**, No. 2 (1959), pp. 286-306. Simpson examines the relationship between anatomical observations and evolutionary theory.

[15] ——, *The Meaning of Evolution.* Yale University Press, 1949.

[16] Stebbins, G. L., *Processes of Organic Evolution.* Englewood Cliffs, New Jersey: Prentice-Hall, 1966. This is a short paperback book that will serve adequately as a concise overview of organic evolution.

[17] Throckmorton, L. H., "Similarity versus Relationship in Drosophila." *Syst. Zool.,* **14**, No. 3 (1965), 221-236.

[18] ——, "Concordance and Discordance of Taxonomic Characters in Drosophila Classification." *Syst. Zool.,* **17**, No. 4 (1968), 355-387. Throckmorton's arguments (pp. 358-359) for a logical separation between the methods of comparative anatomy and those of taxonomy will be of considerable interest to the readers of this book.

2

A framework for the further study
of chordate animals

Introduction It will be valuable at this point to review briefly some observations and hypotheses. This will give the reader a preliminary perspective that will increase his understanding of the more detailed discussions of individual morphologic parts and even of the whole systems and related functions that are to follow. The perspective depends upon a general mental image of the taxa considered. For example, when a particular function of a holostean fish is described and compared with that of a chondrostean fish, the student must be able to relate automatically the information to (1) the organism's general body form and its major kinds of variability, (2) the characters that diagnose it taxonomically as an adapted kind of animal, (3) its phylogenetic position, that is, its usually accepted intertaxonomic and intrataxonomic relationships, and (4) aspects of its general biology such as environments occupied, feeding and reproductive habits, and so on. The following descriptions of the major kinds of chordate taxa attempt to provide this necessary perspective.

In an effort to further the student's understanding of the more isolated and as yet unrelated subject matters, the generally accepted and largely intuitively constructed phylogeny of chordates is given in Figure 2-1. This readily permits data to be tested for fit in the more objective phyletic form described earlier. In addition, the usually accepted classification of chordates is presented as another kind of framework against which to test objectively estimated relationships of information involved (Table 2-1). Similarly, the tabularized summary of the major features of biotic and abiotic evolution through geologic history (Table 2-2) gives a rigid framework upon which conclusions can be displayed relative to absolute time. The table also draws attention to the correspondence between major changes in animal and plant life, long-term climatic conditions, and major geologic events. In many ways these correspondences permit the reader to determine more accurately cause and effect and to consider probabilistically phyletically based conclusions.

What Are Chordates? Chordates are those animals that at some time during their life history possess the following conditions: (1) a pharyngeal wall containing bilaterally symmetrical openings, gill pouches, and associated slits; (2) a mid-dorsal hollow cylinder of nervous tissue, the central nerve cord; (3) a single mid-dorsal axial supportive structure, the notochord, located below the nerve cord; (4) a discrete subpharyngeal gland that can bind iodine and synthesize thyroxine and related substances; (5) a body segmented throughout or in part; (6) an early stage of embryogenesis in which the organism consists of three well-defined germ layers; ectoderm, chordamesoderm, and endoderm; (7) an embryonic blastopore that may become the anus of the adult, (8) coelomic (body) cavities lined with tissue of mesodermal origin; (9) a postanally located muscularized tail at some stage in the life history of the organism; (10) structural bilateral symmetry; (11) cephalization; and (12) an internal skeleton derived from mesoderm. Characters 1-4 are restricted to the chordates, whereas the remaining conditions are shared with a variety of ver-

Table 2-1. An intuitively constructed classification of chordate-like animals.

Phylum Hemichordata	†Order Palaeonisciformes	†Subclass Euryapsida
Class Pterobranchia	Order Polypteriformes	†Subclass Ichthyopterygia
Class Enteropneusta	Order Acipenseriformes	†Subclass Synapsida
Class Planctosphaeroidea	Infraclass Holostei	*Class Aves*
	Order Semionotiformes	†Subclass Archaeornithes
Phylum Chordata	†Order Pycnodontiformes	Subclass Neornithes
Subphylum Tunicata	Order Amiiformes	*Class Mammalia*
Class Ascidiacea	†Order Aspidorhynchiformes	Subclass Prototheria
Class Thaliacea	†Order Pholidophoriformes	Order Monotremata
Class Larvacea	Infraclass Teleostei	†Subclass Allotheria
Subphylum Cephalochordata	Subclass Sarcopterygii	Subclass Theria
Subphylum Vertebrata††	Order Crossopterygii	†Infraclass Trituberculata
Class Agnatha	†Suborder Rhipidistia	Infraclass Metatheria
Subclass Monorhina	Suborder Coelacanthini	Order Marsupialia
†Order Osteostraci	Order Dipnoi	Infraclass Eutheria
†Order Anaspida	*Class Amphibia*	Order Insectivora
Order Cyclostomata	†Subclass Labyrinthodontia	†Order Tillodontia
Suborder Petromyzontoidei	†Subclass Lepospondyli	†Order Taeniodontia
Suborder Myxinoidei	Subclass Lissamphibia	Order Chiroptera
†Subclass Diplorhina	Superorder Salientia	Order Primates
Order Heterostraci	Order Anura	†Order Creodonta
?Order Coelolepida	Superorder Caudata	Order Carnivora
†Class Placodermi	Order Urodela	†Order Condylarthra
Order Petalichthyida	Order Apoda	†Order Amblypoda
Order Rhenanida	*Class Reptilia*	Order Proboscidea
Order Arthrodira	Subclass Anapsida	Order Sirenia
Order Phyllolepida	†Order Cotylosauria	†Order Desmostylia
Order Ptyctodontida	†Order Mesosauria	Order Hyracoidea
Order Antiarchi	Order Chelonia	†Order Embrithopoda
Class Chondrichthyes	Subclass Lepidosauria	†Order Notoungulata
Subclass Elasmobranchii	†Order Eosuchia	†Order Astrapotheria
†Order Cladoselachii	Order Squamata	†Order Litopterna
†Order Pleuracanthodii	Suborder Lacertilia	Order Perissodactyla
Order Selachii	Suborder Ophidia	Order Artiodactyla
Order Batoidea	Order Rhynchocephalia	Order Edentata
Subclass Holocephali	Subclass Archosauria	Order Pholidota
Order Chimaeriformes	†Order Thecodontia	Order Tubulidentata
Class Osteichthyes	Order Crocodilia	Order Cetacea
†?Subclass Acanthodii	†Order Pterosauria	Order Rodentia
Subclass Actinopterygii	†Order Saurischia	Order Lagomorpha
Infraclass Chondrostei	†Order Ornithischia	

†The dagger indicates extinct taxa; all other taxa have living representatives.

††This classification of the vertebrates is modified after A. S. Romer, *Vertebrate Paleontology*, 3rd ed., 1966.

tebrates. As whole animals, chordates vary in size from microscopic larval forms to quadruped and fish-like mammals that reach lengths of over 100 feet and weights of over 150 tons. The diversity of size and shape corresponds relatively closely to the kinds of physical environments they inhabit, namely acquatic, both fresh-water and marine, and aerial, both strictly land-dwelling and flying.

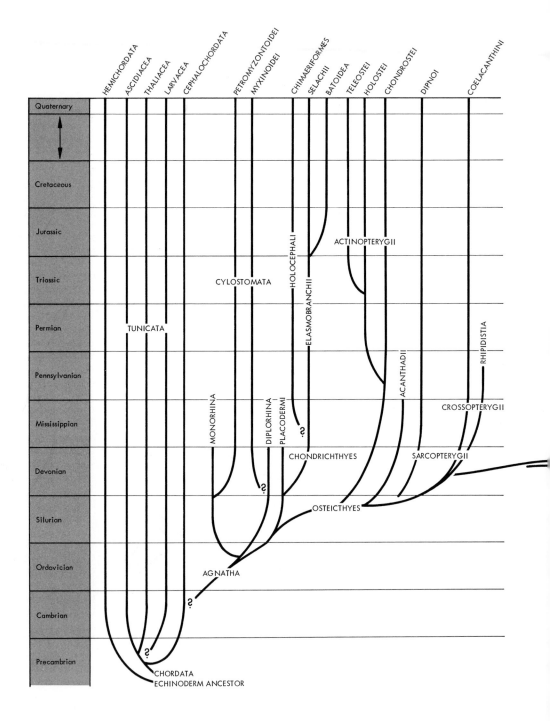

Vertebrate
Ancestors

The phylum Chordata, as usually delimited taxonomically, consists of three major categories at the rank of subphylum: Tunicata, Cephalochordata, and Vertebrata. The Hemichordata are now rarely considered a subphylum within the Chordata, but are related to them. Vertebrate animals—cyclostomes, fish, amphibians, reptiles, birds, and mammals—are familiar to nearly everyone,

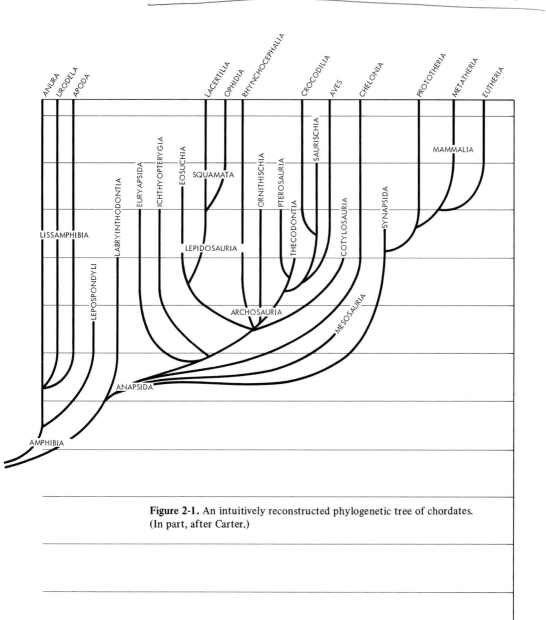

Figure 2-1. An intuitively reconstructed phylogenetic tree of chordates. (In part, after Carter.)

but the other chordate subphyla, on the contrary, are not well known. Both have relatively few species and superficially appear to exhibit little intraphylum diversity of general body form and function. Closer inspection of the Tunicata, however, reveals that they are a very heterogeneous group. The kind and degree of the differences between the Tunicata and Cephalochordata suggest that they are survivors of lineages that have had a long and divergent evolutionary history. Relative to the Chordata as a whole, and in particular to the major group therein, the Vertebrata, these two subphyla contain the only available evidence of invertebrate ancestry and the early stages of chordate phylogeny. The Hemichordata will be treated in some

Table 2-2. The major features of biotic and abiotic evolution through geologic time.

Eras (major vertebrate radiations and duration)	**Precambrian**		**Paleozoic** ——————▶ *(Age of Fish; 340,000,000 years)*	
Periods			*Cambrian*	*Ordovician*
Epochs				
Duration (years)			70,000,000	50,000,000
Beginning (years ago)	3,000,000,000		570,000,000	500,000,000
Animal life	First known fossils— primitive marine invertebrates, nonsegmental and segmental worms, and algae and fungi.		Most modern phyla established; abundance of marine invertebrates, particularly trilobites and brachiopods.	Jawless fish evolve, probably in fresh water.
Plant life		Great Revolution (considerable destruction of fossils)	Marine algae become diversified, especially blue-green algae and probably green algae.	Marine algae abundant; early stages of terrestrial plant evolution.
Climate and climatic conditions			Rapid rise in temperatures from conditions much like today.	Warming trend increases and is uniform over most of earth.
Geologic and physical events			Lands low; formation of major geosynclines and adjacent archipelagos.	Extensive submergence of land; continents remained low with shallow seaways; one of greatest marine inundations of all time.

detail, even though they are not considered a true chordate because they exhibit invertebrate as well as a few chordate characters.

Hemichordata   The Hemichordata are solitary or colonial vermiform animals with bodies conspicuously divided into three parts; proboscis (protosome), collar (mesosome), and trunk (metasome).† Directly corresponding to this subdivision are the major internal body cavities which also exhibit three divisions. In hemichordates these coelomic cavities develop by the process of

†Unknown for the Planctosphaeroidea.

Paleozoic

Silurian	*Devonian*	*Mississippian (Carboniferous)*	*Pennsylvanian (Carboniferous)*
50,000,000 *450,000,000*	*60,000,000* *400,000,000*	*30,000,000* *340,000,000*	*30,000,000* *310,000,000*
Jawed placoderm fish evolve; eurypterid arthropods at their peak of radiation; arthropods invade land.	Amphibians evolve; lung-fish, sharks abundant; beginning of radiation of bony fish; first winged insects appear.	Radiation of sharks and primitive amphibians; insects evolve wings.	Considerable specialization in amphibians; origin of reptiles; gigantic terrestrial arthropods abundant.
Radiation of terrestrial plants, psilophytes, club and spike "mosses," horsetails, sphenopsids and ferns.	Terrestrial plants exhibit considerable diversity; forests appear; primitive seed plants, gymnosperms evolve; liverworts evolve.	Club and spike "mosses" horsetails, and sphenopsids dominant; gymnosperms increasingly widespread; extensive lowland forests.	Extensive coal swamp forests; primitive tropical fern and seed fern forests present; true mosses evolve.
Peak of warming trend reached.	Cooler at beginning of period, then warmer; trend toward increasing aridity.	Warm and humid at first of period, cooler later with local dry conditions	Warm and very humid.
Continents relatively flat; inland seas still widespread; land slowly uplifted.	Smaller inland seas; land higher; glacial mountain building; filling in some of geosynclines; inter-mountain fresh-water basins; extensive inland seas.	Widespread inland seas; mountain building; beginning of great coal measures.	Filling in of great geosynclines; formation of coal in swamps; shallow inland seas; some glaciation in southern hemisphere; great coal measures.

enterocoely, i.e., they are evaginations from the embryonic gastrocoel. The body is covered by cilia, and a cuticle-like covering appears to be absent. The nervous system of the group is epidermal in embryonic origin and remains largely within the integument in adults. Both large open spaces and relatively small discrete vessels along with a contractile sac comprise the circulatory system. The excretory system includes a number of nephridium-like structures. A projection at the anterior end of the digestive tract (the supposed notochord) is usually referred to as the buccal diverticulum. The sexes are separate. Fertilization and development are external and the bilaterally symmetrical larva is encircled by an irregularly placed band of cilia.

Table 2-2 (continued).

Paleozoic	Mesozoic ⟶ (Age of Reptiles; about 167,000,000 years)		
Permian	*Triassic*	*Jurassic*	*Cretaceous*
50,000,000 280,000,000	50,000,000 230,000,000	50,000,000 180,000,000	67,000,000 130,000,000
Reptiles radiate, which initiates displacement of amphibians as dominant group; modern insect orders established; first mammal-like reptiles appear.	Origin of mammals; dominance of mammal-like reptiles; appearance of dinosaurs, turtles, ichthyosaurs, and plesiosaurs; extinction of primitive amphibians.	Origin of birds; peaks of reptile evolution on land, in sea and air.	Extinction of large land and marine reptiles at end of period; appearance of a few modern orders and families of mammals; archaic mammals common; modern groups of insects present; primitive birds become extinct.
Decline of club and spike mosses, horsetails, and sphenopsids; extensive development of glossopteris forests.	Gymnosperms, cycads, ginkgos, and conifers dominant; angiosperms evolve; extinction of seed ferns.	Increase in dicotyledon angiosperms; cycads and ginkgos common; appearance of modern genera of conifers.	Dominance of angiosperm plants commences; flowering plants; monocotyledons appear; first oak and maple forests; gymnosperms decline.
Extreme drop in temperature at beginning of period, followed by high temperatures; trend of increasing aridity.	Rising temperatures; with arid and semi-arid environments.	Uniformly high temperatures with aridity.	Warm at beginning of period, cool at its close.
Widespread glaciation; elevation of continents; elimination of geosynclines.	Continents exposed; widespread deserts.	Continents with only moderate elevations; shallow seas restricted over some parts of northern hemisphere.	Mountain building toward close of period; last extensive spread of oceanic waters over the continents; swamps common.

(Appalachian Revolution (some destruction of fossils))

Hemichordates are exclusively marine, occurring throughout a wide range of depths and in numerous different habitats. With few exceptions they are rarely encountered in large numbers.

The Hemichordata are divided into three taxonomic groups; the Class Enteropneusta, Class Pterobranchia, and the Class Planctosphaeroidea. The enteropneusts, more commonly referred to as acorn worms, are those worm-like hemichordates with numerous gill slits, a straight digestive tract, and a terminal anus. They lack tentaculated arms (Figure 2-2), are solitary, reproduce sexually, and the adults grow from moderate to great lengths (2 centimeters to 2.5 meters). They are found buried in the mud, under rocks, or in masses

Cenozoic ⟶
(Age of Mammals; about 63,000,000 years)

Tertiary ⟶

Paleocene	*Eocene*	*Oligocene*	*Miocene*
7,000,000 *63,000,000*	*22,000,000* *56,000,000*	*9,000,000* *34,000,000*	*13,000,000* *25,000,000*
Primitive mammals dominant; modern groups of birds and many new groups of marine invertebrates evolve.	Rise of many modern orders and suborders of mammals; some primitive mammals still present.	Origin of more modern families of mammals; extinction of primitive mammals.	Radiation of anthropoid apes; appearance of modern subfamilies of mammals; rise and rapid evolution of grazing mammals.
Trending toward subtropical plants.	Subtropical forests dominant.	Plants evolving toward temperate kinds; maximum spread of forests; rise of monocotyledons, flowering plants.	Evolution of grasslands; temperate kinds of plants dominant; retreat of polar flora.
Cool at beginning of period, becoming warmer; relatively dry.	Warmer—heavy rainfall, little or no frost.	Warm and humid to cooler and drier.	Cooler; moderate seasonal climates.
Culmination of late Cretaceous mountain building; trend toward transgression of marine waters into epicontinental embayments.	Mountains eroded; no continental seas.	Holarctic land connection; some mountain building; restriction of inland embayments; lands lower.	Development of plains and steppe grasslands; invasion of marine water into epicontinental embayments; continental erosion.

Rocky Mountain Revolution (little destruction of fossils)

of vegetation. Locomotion is sluggish and much like that of earthworms. Food is obtained by filtering nutriment out of the water and mud as it is ingested and passed out through the gill slits or on through the digestive tract.

The pterobranchs are small to minute moss-like animals (Figure 2-3). They have a U-shaped digestive tract, may or may not possess gill slits, and exhibit one to nine pairs of ciliated tentaculated arms or lophophores. Pterobranchs are colonial, living within a common or individually-secreted encasement, the coenecium. Some colonies are made up of a closely compacted mass of separate individuals and encasements; others include within a common

Table 2-2 (continued).

Cenozoic

| Pliocene | Quaternary ⟶ | |
	Pleistocene	Recent
Pliocene	*Pleistocene*	*Recent*
10,500,000	*1,500,000*	*10,000*
12,000,000	*1,500,000*	*10,000*
Man evolving; appearance of many modern genera of mammals.	Most modern species evolve; decline of large mammals; evolution of human social life.	Rise of man through stone, bronze, and iron ages.
Decline of forests, spread of grasslands.	Extensive extinction of species.	Decline of woody plants; rise of herbaceous ones.
Semiarid—dryer and cooler.	Fluctuating, cold and mild.	Warmer.
Continued rise of continental elevations; retreat of inland marine embayments; volcanic activity.	Repeated widespread glaciation; four major glacials; high relief of continents.	End of last ice age; extensive continents.

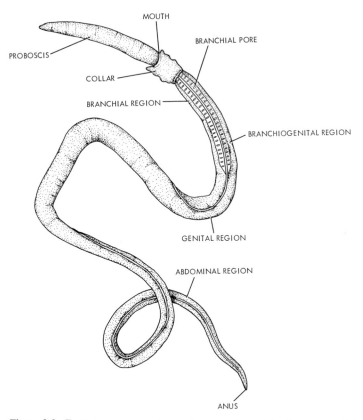

Figure 2-2. External anatomy of an enteropneust hemichordate (genus *Balanoglossus*). (Modified after Crouch.)

encasement numerous individuals joined by a continuous organic tube, the stolon. Asexual budding appears to be the rule among pterobranchs. The colonies are usually found on the surfaces of dead parts of corals, rocks, shells, and so on; and unlike many hemichordates do not occur below the substrate. They feed by trapping small organisms in the mucus of their tentacles, and passing the food-ladened mucus in deep ciliated grooves along the ventral surfaces of the arms to the mouth where ingestion takes place.

The Planctosphaeroidea is known only from a few transparent, spherical larvae. In some respects these resemble the larvae of the other two classes, but their numerous differences suggest a very different adult form and accordingly they are placed in a different class.

Together the two classes Enteropneusta and Pterobranchia are characterized as exhibiting three of the unique characters of chordates: (1) pharyngeal gill slits and pouches, (2) a notochord, and (3) a hollow dorsal nerve cord. However the homology of the latter two characteristics with those of chordates may be questioned. For example, in the hemichordates there are both large dorsal and ventral solid nerve cords that are connected to each other by a ring of nervous tissue at the junction of the collar and trunk (Figure 2-4). It is only within the collar that the dorsal cord continues

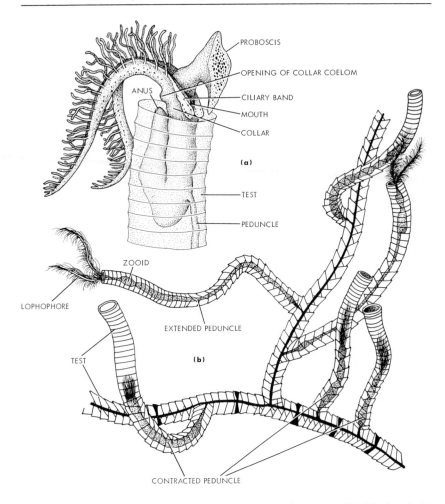

PROBOSCIS

OPENING OF COLLAR COELOM

CILIARY BAND

MOUTH

COLLAR

ANUS

(a)

TEST

PEDUNCLE

ZOOID

LOPHOPHORE

EXTENDED PEDUNCLE

TEST

(b)

CONTRACTED PEDUNCLE

Figure 2-3. External anatomy of a pterobranch hemichordate (genus *Rhabdopleura*): (a) an individual extending from the aperture of the test; (b) part of a colony. (Modified after Dawydoff.)

anteriorly and may have a central cavity or cavities that approximate the usual chordate state of "hollow dorsal nerve cord." Moreover, this area of the nervous system does not appear to integrate nervous stimuli as does the supposedly equivalent central nervous system of vertebrates. It seems difficult if not impossible to justify the often-described equivalence of the spinal nerves of typical chordates and that condition found in the collar of hemichordates. Second, it seems highly questionable whether the supportive structure in the collar of the hemichordates (buccal diverticulum or stomochord) is homologous with the notochord of vertebrates. They differ in gross and microscopic appearance, pattern of development, and apparently in embryologic origin. A similarity of function is also difficult to accept.

Even from this brief discussion it seems reasonable to assume that the relationships of hemichordates to chordates is very tenuous and distant in time; the only character that relates them conclusively is the detailed similarity of the gill slits and pouches. If confirmed by additional study, the homology of the proboscis pore of hemichordates and the adenohypophysis of vertebrates may add further support to that thesis. Other evidence that hemichordates are only distantly related to chordates obtains from the following characters: (1) a postanal tail is absent in most larvae; (2) the direction of the flow of blood is annelid-like, *viz.*, anteriorly in the dorsal vessel and posteriorly in the ventral vessel, and (3) segmentation of the major functional systems, such as muscular, nervous, circulatory, and excretory, is absent.

The relatively close relationship of hemichordates to echinoderms is easily demonstrable. It involves the considerable similarity of their tornarian and bipennarian larvae, the details of development of the coelom, the madreporic vesicle and heart vesicle, muscle chemistry and blood proteins, and probably the axial gland and glomerulus in the respective groups. It is generally agreed that the hemichordates are more closely related to echinoderms than they are to chordates. And, it also seems likely that the hemichordates have retained more characters that are primitive than have the echinoderms. It is for these reasons that the hemichordates seem best treated as a separate phylum, phyletically between chordates and echinoderms, but closer to the latter.

That the pterobranchs are more primitive than the enteropneusts is generally acknowledged, and the argument for this supposition rests largely on the degree of continuity of the collar portion of the nervous system with the epidermis in the pterobranchs. On this basis it follows that enteropneusts have lost the tentaculated arms that are characteristic of pterobranchs and primitive echinoderms, and the postanal tail seen in some juvenile entero-pneusts is probably homologous with the stalk of pterobranchs and primitive echinoderms. The general similarity of the arms of pterobranchs and the tentaculated projections of lophophorate invertebrates, namely, phoronid worms, the moss-like ectoprocts and the lampshells or brachiopods, may indicate the phyletic origin of hemichordates.

Figure 2-4. The anterior end of an enteropneust hemichordate (sagittal section). The proboscis is highly contracted in this view. (Modified after Dawydoff.)

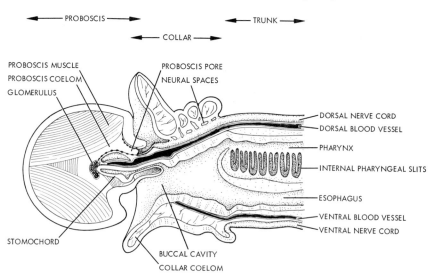

Tunicata   The Tunicata are soft-bodied solitary or colonial, relatively inactive animals that as a group of filter feeders exhibit a wide variety of sizes, shapes, colonial structure, and life histories (Figure 2-5). They range from solitary sessile or free-floating individuals that are microscopic or large to forms connected by stolons or encased within a common outer covering or tunic. Some species are larviform, and they may be either pelagic or nectonic when reproductively mature. As sessile adults other species are sac-like in appearance. Despite a general diversity of form, they have a large number of characters in common that appear to relate them relatively closely and suggest that they are a monophyletic group. As either free-swimming larvae or sessile adults, tunicates almost uniformly possess the following attributes: (1) absence of coelomic cavities, unlike other chordates the tail muscles and body mesenchyme develop directly from bands of mesoderm without passing through the usual embryonic stage of coelom formation; (2) bilateral symmetry; (3) a thin secreted mantle forming an outer acellular fibrous covering or tunic containing a cellulose-like substance called tunicin; (4) incurrent (branchial pore or mouth) and excurrent (atrial pore) siphons that together with the cilia control the circulation of water into the much enlarged pharynx and through its ciliated apertures or stigmata into the atrial cavity; (5) large atrium surrounding the pharynx, that funnels this water to the exterior via the excurrent siphon; (6) thyroid gland homologue, the endostyle, located in the wall of the pharynx; (7) in the adult a large solid neural ganglion connected to nerve fibers that appear to control the muscular activity associated with the siphons as well as the lateral body musculature; and (8) a conspicuous neural gland closely associated with the neural ganglion, the function of which is now in dispute. Formerly the gland was widely thought to be a primitive state of the pituitary gland (hypophysis) of vertebrates and of Hatschek's pit, which is its homologue in cephalochordates. Tunicates are marine exclusively, ranging in distribution from the Arctic to Antarctic seas and from tidepools to great depths in most oceans.

The commonly encountered sessile adult stage of the life history of tunicates exhibits little or no resemblance to vertebrates, e.g., *Molgula manhattensis* found along the Atlantic Coast. On the other hand, the tadpole-like form possesses numerous similarities with vertebrates. This developmental stage (Figure 2-6) exhibits (1) a muscularized tail, but with unsegmented muscles (this view may be in error); (2) a hollow dorsal nerve cord in the tail, which is widened into a brain-like vesicle in the body portion of the organism; and (3) a notochord located completely within the tail and composed of large vacuolated cells encased within a thin fibrous sheath. In addition to these vertebrate characteristics it possesses a relatively large pharynx perforated by ciliated stigmata and also rather well-developed equilibrium and photosensory structures. When the tail is free from the tunic

Figure 2-5. (next two pages). Representatives of the three major classes of tunicates. (a) A solitary ascidiacean—left and right lateral views. (b)-(c) A colonial ascidiacian—(b) is an individual removed from the colony shown in (c). (d) A pelagic thaliacean. (e) A pelagic larvacean.

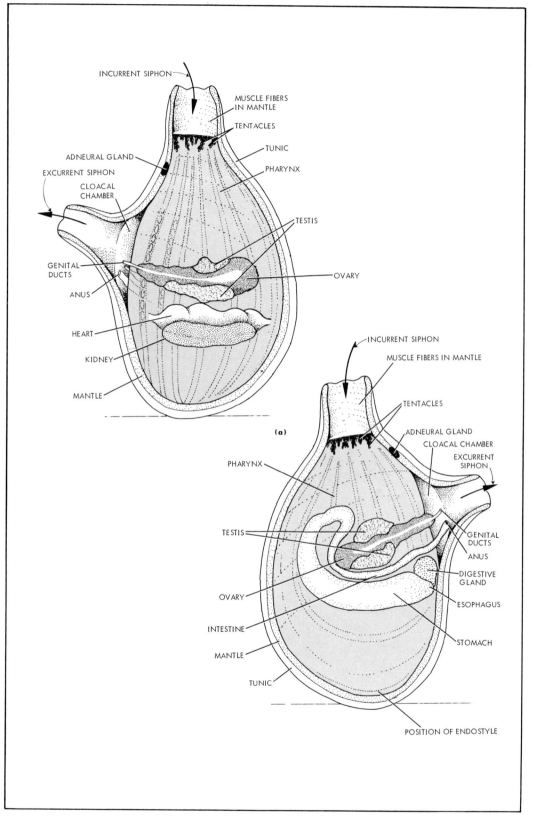

INCURRENT SIPHON

MUSCLE FIBERS
IN MANTLE

TENTACLES

ADNEURAL GLAND

TUNIC

EXCURRENT SIPHON

PHARYNX

CLOACAL
CHAMBER

TESTIS

GENITAL
DUCTS

OVARY

ANUS

HEART

KIDNEY

MANTLE

(a)

INCURRENT SIPHON

MUSCLE FIBERS IN MANTLE

TENTACLES

ADNEURAL GLAND

CLOACAL CHAMBER

EXCURRENT
SIPHON

PHARYNX

GENITAL
DUCTS

TESTIS

ANUS

DIGESTIVE
GLAND

OVARY

ESOPHAGUS

INTESTINE

STOMACH

MANTLE

TUNIC

POSITION OF ENDOSTYLE

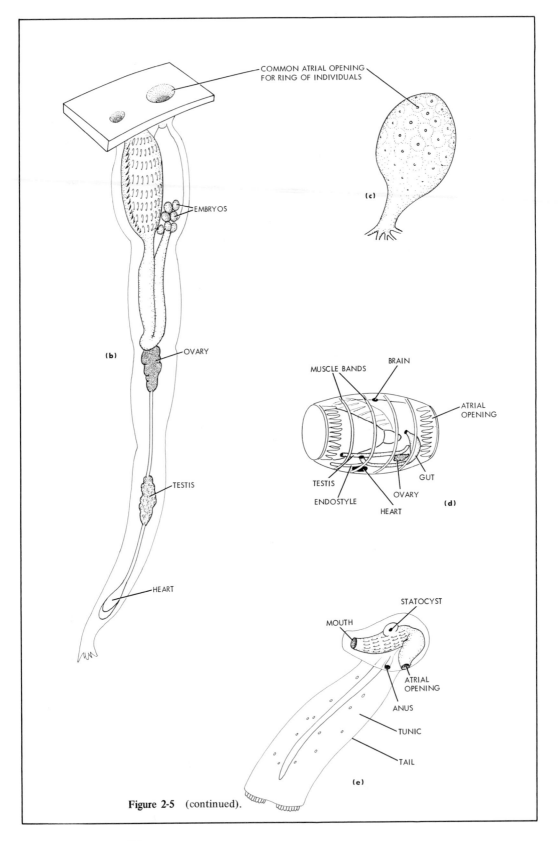

Figure 2-5 (continued).

56

encasement it may be used as a propulsive organ and thereby aids in larval dispersal. If there is an adult sessile stage in the life history, the larva swims for a few hours before settling and attaching to a suitable object by means of small cephalic adhesive projections. Following attachment the larva rapidly undergoes a very dramatic metamorphosis during which the tail, which houses the vertebrate characteristics of nerve cord and notochord, decreases and is absorbed into the body. In addition, the brain vesicle, located between the larval incurrent and excurrent siphons, becomes reduced to the neural ganglion of the adult, and the associated sensory structures of a larva appear to be lost entirely. In those species with a sessile adult stage the larva does not feed. It is in the larva-sessile adult type of life history that the pharynx, upon metamorphosis, becomes greatly enlarged. In the sessile stage, feeding involves this complex pharyngeal structure associated with a ciliary-mucoid feeding action. The sessile adults may be hermaphroditic or they may produce offspring by simple budding. Only those individuals that result from the union of sperm and egg go through a larval stage.

Within the Tunicata three distinct lineages are usually recognized: the classes Ascidiacea, Thaliacea, and Larvacea (Figure 2-5). The ascidiaceans, or sea squirts as they are commonly referred to, exhibit the greatest degree of divergence; about 2,000 living species are now recognized. The ascidiacean life history includes a motile larva and a sessile adult. About one hundred living species make up the Thaliacea. In this group the adults are usually barrel-shaped and nectonic. Larvae may or may not be present. The remaining class, called the Larvacea or Appendicularia, consists of about seventy-five living species. Larvaceans are readily distinguished from the other tunicates by the presence of a free-swimming adult which differs little from its larval stage.

The body of a solitary sea squirt is ovoid and covered by an opaque leath-

Figure 2-6. A summary of the internal anatomy of a larval ascidiacean (genus *Clavelina*). (Modified after Jollie.)

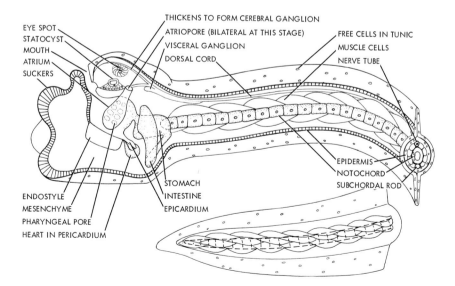

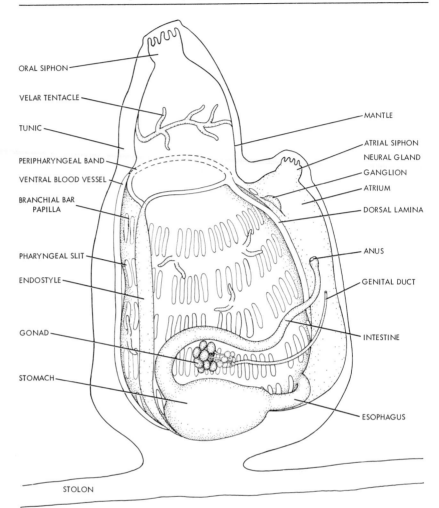

ORAL SIPHON

VELAR TENTACLE

TUNIC

PERIPHARYNGEAL BAND

VENTRAL BLOOD VESSEL

BRANCHIAL BAR
PAPILLA

PHARYNGEAL SLIT

ENDOSTYLE

GONAD

STOMACH

MANTLE

ATRIAL SIPHON
NEURAL GLAND

GANGLION

ATRIUM

DORSAL LAMINA

ANUS

GENITAL DUCT

INTESTINE

ESOPHAGUS

STOLON

Figure 2-7. A summary of the internal anatomy of an adult ascidiacean (genus *Per-ophora* shown in lateral view. This form is colonial. (Modified after Crouch.)

ery-textured tunic. In some species the animal is fastened to the substrate directly, in others it is fixed at the end of a long stalk. The shape of the individuals of a colonial form (Figure 2-7), whether joined by stolons or massed within a common tunic, is largely influenced by the kind and degree of contact between the individuals. In any case, the siphons are directed upward, opposite the point of attachment, and the pharynx is extremely large and perforated by numerous ciliated stigmata. As would be expected, food is filtered out of the incurrent flow of water at the level of the stigmata. Coelomic cavities are absent. A few large vessels or haemoeoels conduct the blood, containing variously structured and pigmented cells, from the heart which alternately pumps it into and out of the same vessel. The blood of ascidians has many interesting features and differs markedly from that of vertebrates; notably in salt content and cell types. Reproduction in most ascideans occurs either sexually or by budding. Without exception they are hermaphroditic but apparently because of the different temporal activity patterns of the male and female gonads in the same individual only cross-fertilization occurs.

Thaliaceans (Figure 2-5) with the following major exceptions are similar to sea squirts: (1) they are nearly transparent, (2) they are barrel-shaped and the incurrent and excurrent siphons are located at opposite ends of the longitudinal body axis; (3) the body wall encases six to ten bands of muscle that contract and thereby jet-propel the organism through the water; and (4) reproduction is usually asexual. Some sexual reproduction may exist, however, in which case the animals are hermaphroditic. Probably the most distinctive feature of the thaliaceans is a complicated life cycle. For example, some species are dimorphic; that is, one morph is solitary, has no gonads, and produces a chain of individuals asexually, whereas the other morph reproduces sexually and gives rise to the asexual morph.

The Larvacea (Figure 2-5) possess all the usual chordate characters both as larvae and as sexually mature adults. They are minute and free-swimming, and with few exceptions possess a short endostyle and a single pair of stigmata. The larval animal may shed its thaliacean-like tunic and then secrete another. When encased in a tunic the larva does not utilize its elongate tail for propulsion; it is nectonic.

Two very different points of view are held on the evolutionary relationship between the three classes of tunicates. These views are based on morphology and the nature of reproduction. The first and oldest interpretation is that the larvaceans are primitive and that the ascidiaceans and thaliaceans are derived from such primitive forms. In accordance with this point of view, both the sessile and pelagic non-larviform sexually mature adult stages of the two classes must be considered advanced conditions acquired within the radiation of the Tunicata. The second interpretation holds that the Larvacea are derived either from an ascidiacean or thaliacean ancestor by neoteny. Neoteny is that process by which sexual maturity becomes fixed evolutionarily in progressively earlier stages of the life history until the usual adult form is lost. If the gonads were removed from a larvacean adult, all the essentials of an ascidacean tadpole would remain.

Cephalochordata

All adult cephalochordates are small (five to one hundred millimeters), compressed and elongated fish-like marine organisms (Figure 2-8). They possess all the obvious attributes diagnostic of the Phylum Chordata (see under the previous heading), and similarities to the vertebrates are most obvious in this group. However, cephalochordates are conspicuously exceptional in the developmental asymmetry found in many systems, some of which remain in the adult. Although the group consists of a very homogeneous assemblage of approximately twenty-five living species distributed among three closely related families, it almost certainly had diverged by the Precambrian Period from the line leading to vertebrates. Probably the best known species biologically is *Branchiostoma lanceolatum*, often referred to by the common name Amphioxus.

Most cephalochordate species are found in shallow marine waters in many regions of the world, and in some they are very abundant. Poor fin development makes most species relatively ineffective swimmers; they spend their time buried in the substrate with only the anterior ends exposed. No true

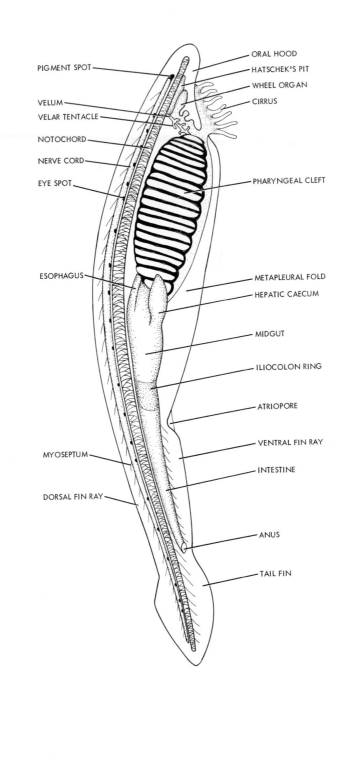

PIGMENT SPOT

VELUM
VELAR TENTACLE

NOTOCHORD

NERVE CORD

EYE SPOT

ESOPHAGUS

MYOSEPTUM

DORSAL FIN RAY

ORAL HOOD
HATSCHEK'S PIT
WHEEL ORGAN
CIRRUS

PHARYNGEAL CLEFT

METAPLEURAL FOLD
HEPATIC CAECUM

MIDGUT

ILIOCOLON RING

ATRIOPORE

VENTRAL FIN RAY

INTESTINE

ANUS

TAIL FIN

paired fins are present; cartilage-like material supports the dorsal fin, and the end of the animal terminates in a single caudal fin resembling superficially that of many fish. Cephalochordates are covered with an acellular cuticle secreted by the underlying epidermis which is only one cell layer in thickness. Beneath this lies gelatinous mesodermal tissue. The endoskeleton of the adult consists of a notochord extending the entire length of the animal, U-shaped cartilage-like rods in the tissue surrounding the gill slits, jointed chitin-like rods inside the oral projections or cirri, and fin rays, each within a fluid-filled cavity, in the single dorsal and paired ventrolateral folds of skin (metapleural folds) that are distributed along most of the length of the body (Figure 2-9). The coelom is much reduced, with spaces persisting along the dorsal wall of the pharynx and in the metapleural folds. These cavities which develop from mesoderm are typically enterocoelic in their mode of development. Dorsal to the notochord is a hollow nerve cord, enlarged anteriorly into a brain-like vesicle, and with paired dorsal and ventral nerves arranged segmentally along its length. Dorsal and ventral root ganglia are absent. Sense organs corresponding to the olfactory and lateral line systems of vertebrates appear to be lacking, as is also a trace of any type of eye-like structure. Photosensory cells are present in the lateral walls of the hollow nerve cord.

The body musculature consists of a segmentally arranged series of ⟨-shaped blocks or myomeres with the apex of each directed anteriorly. An alternate contraction of the myomeres produces the undulatory swimming motion. The digestive tract is a simple type. Within the oral funnel is a mouth opening almost completely surrounded by stiffened cirri which in turn are covered with sensory papillae. Posterior to the straight elongated pharynx the gut is a simple tube with little division into chambers. The diverticulum from the anterior portion was once considered a homologue of the vertebrate liver. A ciliated fossa called Hatschek's pit within the roof of the oral funnel to the right of the midline as well as some ciliated "wheel" organs direct a current of water into the mouth. From the pharynx the water passes outward through the fifty or more pairs of ciliated gill slits into the atrium. From there, the water is directed to the exterior of the animal through the single atriopore located near the junction of the metapleural folds with the ventral fin. Each gill slit is divided by nearly horizontal bands of tissue into numerous smaller openings. Through these very small apertures the water is propelled by ciliary action and food particles are filtered out. In contrast to most aquatic vertebrates, respiration occurs generally through the skin rather than at the level of the pharyngeal bars. Within the pharynx is a longitudinal midventral groove, the endostyle, wherein mucus is secreted. As ciliary movement carries the mucus upward past the gills to the epibranchial groove filtered food particles are entrapped. Within the epibranchial groove food-ladened mucus is transported backward into the stomach.

The large blood vessels exhibit a plan similar to that of the vertebrates; the direction of flow is posterior in the dorsal vessel (dorsal aorta) which is paired in the pharyngeal region and a single tube in the body and tail; and

Figure 2-8 (opposite). A summary of the internal and external anatomy of a cephalochordate (genus *Branchiostoma*) shown in sagittal section. (Modified after Crouch.)

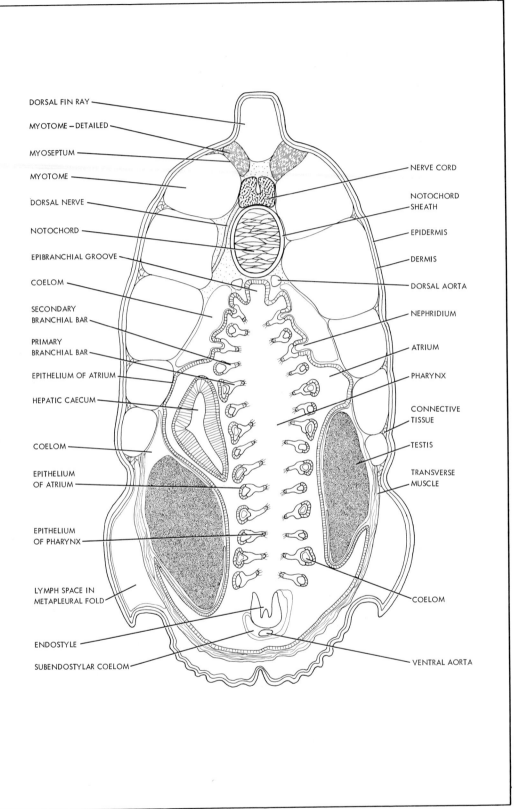

DORSAL FIN RAY

MYOTOME – DETAILED

MYOSEPTUM

MYOTOME

DORSAL NERVE

NOTOCHORD

EPIBRANCHIAL GROOVE

COELOM

SECONDARY
BRANCHIAL BAR

PRIMARY
BRANCHIAL BAR

EPITHELIUM OF ATRIUM

HEPATIC CAECUM

COELOM

EPITHELIUM
OF ATRIUM

EPITHELIUM
OF PHARYNX

LYMPH SPACE IN
METAPLEURAL FOLD

ENDOSTYLE

SUBENDOSTYLAR COELOM

NERVE CORD

NOTOCHORD
SHEATH

EPIDERMIS

DERMIS

DORSAL AORTA

NEPHRIDIUM

ATRIUM

PHARYNX

CONNECTIVE
TISSUE

TESTIS

TRANSVERSE
MUSCLE

COELOM

VENTRAL AORTA

the flow is anterior in the ventral vessel (ventral aorta). Unlike a majority of vertebrates, however, cephalochordates do not appear to have any capillaries, blood cells, or pigment. The blood is moved by the pumping action of a large series of muscularized bodies located along the major arteries of the pharyngeal region rather than by a single heart located along the ventral aorta.

The sexes are separate and the numerous gonads, mesodermal in embryonic origin, are segmentally arranged along the ventro-lateral margins of the body. These features appear to be exceptional in chordates. At sexual maturity the gonads project into the atrium. The gametes are shed directly into the atrium and then carried to the outside via the atriopore. Of all the organ systems in the Cephalochordata, the excretory system shows the most divergence. Ectodermal in origin, it consists of a series of segmentally arranged vesicles into which project a large number of flagellated cells or solenocytes draining into the atrium (Figure 2-10). The similarity of morphology and function of this system to that of annelid worms, with which it has most frequently been compared, is almost certainly not the result of a common ancestry but rather of convergence.

Observing the numerous similarities, few investigators deny that the cephalochordate and vertebrate lineages are very closely related. However, there is still some disagreement as to the relative evolutionary position of the two lines. The majority opinion holds that the vertebrate line was derived from an ancestor similar to cephalochordates and a minority believe that cephalochordates are "degenerate" vertebrates. The latter point of view is predicated on the morphological and behavioral similarity of adult cephalochordates and the ammocoete larva of lampreys. This minority reasons that the larval stage of a primitive vertebrate became sexually mature (neoteny) and the typical adult stage disappeared to give rise to the Cephalochordata. The arguments against this interpretation almost always rest on the presence of the atrium and on numerous differences in the excretory, circulatory, and reproductive systems. Here it is argued that if cephalochordates were "degenerate" vertebrates one would find typical vertebrate conditions rather than divergent morphology.

Ancestry and Evolution of Chordates

The three most prominent theories concerning the evolutionary origin of chordate animals are based on annelids, spider and scorpion-like arthropods (Arachnida), or echinoderms as ancestors. Annelids have been considered because they are similar to vertebrates in bilateral symmetry, segmentation, and the presence of an enlarged "brain-like" structure at the anterior end of the dorsal longitudinal nerve cord. However, the following points have been used most effectively to remove annelids from further consideration as a vertebrate ancestor: (1) their segmentation is complete; (2) the large longitudinal nerve cord is ventral in position; and (3) the mesoderm formation is schizocoelous. These same arguments, both for and against, are also used to support the theory that chordates evolved from arachnids.

Figure 2-9 (opposite). A summary of the internal and external anatomy of a cephalochordate (genus *Branchiostoma*) shown in cross-section through the pharyngeal region. (Modified after Crouch.)

Today the most widely accepted interpretation of chordate ancestry appears to be their evolution from echinoderms. This relationship is inferred from the similarity of tunicates to hemichordates and, in turn, of hemichordates to echinoderms. The similarity of the larvae of hemichordates and echinoderms and the detailed similarity of the development of certain of their systems seem to document this interpretation adequately. Fundamental to this argument is the recognition that primitive echinoderms are sessile forms, some of which are firmly anchored to the substrate. It is precisely this kind of echinoderm that possesses the series of ciliated tentacles (lophophore) that surround the mouth and that also characterize the pterobranch hemichordates. This thesis necessarily requires that we accept chordate ancestors as being sedentary, ciliary-tentacle feeding forms, from which evolved sedentary species with a gill-filter feeding system; these first chordates in

Figure 2-10. The nephridium and associated structures in a cephalochordate (genus *Branchiostoma*): (a) general view of the nephridium; (b) a detailed view of solenocytes projecting through the nephridial wall. (Modified after Dawydoff.)

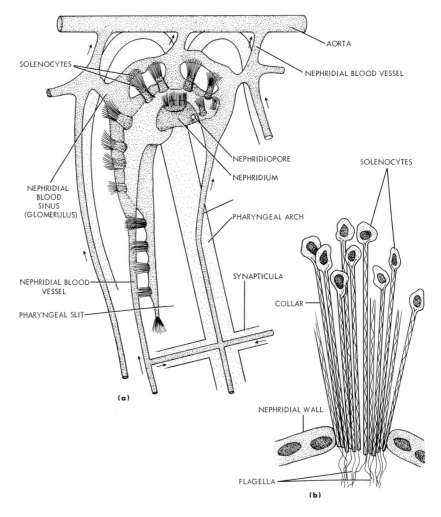

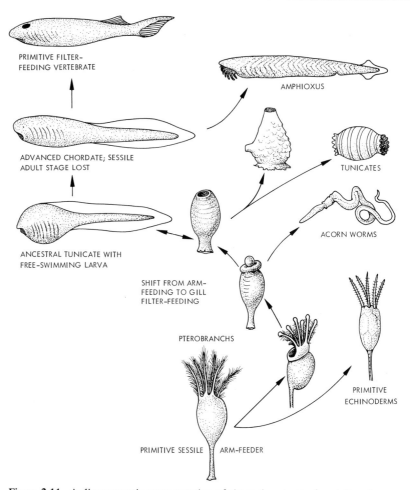

Figure 2-11. A diagrammatic representation of the major stages of evolution from echinoderms to vertebrates. (Modified after Romer.)

turn gave rise to mobile organisms that actively sought their food. The process of neoteny has been evoked (Figure 2-11) to explain the sedentary nature of the reproductively mature adult vertebrate ancestor. It is helpful to know that there is direct evidence of the occurrence of neoteny in the amphioxides type of cephalochordate and in the tunicates as well.

From the Cambrian to Devonian period a little known group existed, the class Stylophora, whose close relationship to echinoderms, hemichordates and chordates is reasonably certain. At least one recent publication [1] suggests that the stylophores be included in the Chordata as the subphylum Calcichordata, rather than in its customary position in the Echinodermata. The stylophores are characterized by an external skeleton of calcite plates, a body (theca), and a strongly flexed tail (stem) (Figure 2-12). A large mouth is located at the anterior end of the theca, and branchial slits and an anus are also present; all exhibit some degree of asymmetry. The theca includes a buccal cavity, a pharynx, and coelomic cavities. Superficially the stem of

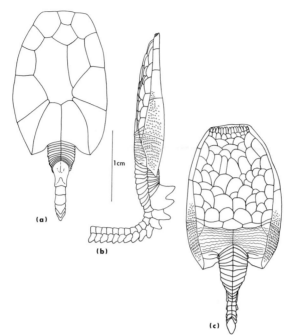

1cm

(a)

(b)

(c)

Figure 2-12. A summary of the external anatomy of a calcichordate (genus *Mitrocystella):* (a) dorsal view; (b) lateral view; (c) ventral view. (Modified after Jeffries.)

stylophores is similar to the stock of crinoid echinoderms and in detail it is believed to include primitive states of the chordate notochord, dorsal nerve cord, and segmented blocks of muscle and nerves with paired segmental ganglia. It seems that stylophores generally lay on the bottom, although a "swimming" mode of locomotion has been postulated. They are believed to have filtered food out of suspension or directly from the substrate. These few generalizations suggest numerous intermediate conditions between typical echinoderms and chordates, emphasizing the need for further study of this group.

Stem Vertebrates (Agnatha)

The lampreys, suborder Petromyzontoidei, and the hagfish, suborder Myxinoidei, are the only living species of the class Agnatha (Figure 2-13). In addition to these two, there are at least four extinct orders of jawless fish, collectively called ostracoderms, which clearly document an extensive and

Figure 2-13. A lateral view of representatives of the two major groups of living cyclostomes: (a) *Bdellostoma,* a myxinoid; (b) *Petromyzon,* a lamprey. (Modified after Romer.)

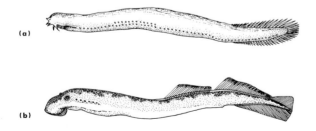

(a)

(b)

diverse adaptive radiation of early vertebrates. Both the living and fossil agnathans, as the name implies, lack jaws. Moreover, all living species and most fossil forms lack paired appendages.

The ostracoderms are geologically the oldest (Ordovician-Devonian) and structurally the most primitive vertebrates known. Superficially ostracoderms are unlike lampreys and hagfish (Figure 2-14), but the similarity of some of the more detailed features of their morphology indicates that they are almost certainly ancestral to them and therefore nearer the stem of vertebrate phylogeny. Ostracoderms were relatively small fish, less than one foot long usually, and were restricted largely, if not exclusively, to fresh-water habitats such as streams and ponds. Most of the species had a single nostril located high up on the head, and most lacked paired appendages; paired spines or flap-like appendages extending from the enlarged head region were present in others. Apparently ostracoderms were not predators. Their large gill chamber suggests a filter-feeding mode of life. Some with flattened heads and body regions and compressed tails were almost certainly bottom dwellers. Others were compressed throughout their length and were probably active swimmers. All ostracoderms were covered with a dermal bony armor which varied from large plates to small scales, and in some the endoskeleton was bony as well. It has been hypothesized by some researchers that large predaceous aquatic arthropods were the selective force responsible for the evolution of heavy armor so early in the history of vertebrates.

The ostracoderms are usually divided into two groups, the Monorhina and Diplorhina. The latter subclass is distinguished from the former by the following characteristics: (1) the paired eyes are farther apart and located on the side of the head; (2) the pineal organ often fails to pierce the top of the head; (3) there is no opening for a dorsal nostril, although evidence now suggests the presence of paired nasal sacs at the tip of the snout or on its ventral surface; (4) the median fins, other than the tail, are absent, although spines protruding from the armor may be analogous; and (5) an internal bony skeleton is absent (apparently only cartilaginous).

The petromyzontoids are small to moderately large eel-like organisms. They are soft bodied and scaleless and the skeleton consists only of cartilage. Adult lampreys, which are actively predaceous on other fish, are primarily marine. Some lampreys spawn in fresh water, others are landlocked. The funnel-shaped mouth is lined with circlets and rows of cornified teeth; the tongue is also covered with horny denticles. The buccal funnel forms a cup by which the lamprey attaches to its prey, and the rasping tongue is used to penetrate the host's skin. Lampreys possess a single nostril, more appropriately called a nasohypophyseal duct, which does not extend completely through to the pharyngeal region. Behind the small eyes is located a series of seven gill openings. They are small and nearly circular and each possesses a leaf-like valve.

The slimy hagfish are exclusively marine. They differ from lampreys in the following principal ways: (1) they are scavengers; with their horny tongues they burrow into the flesh of dead or dying fish; (2) the single nasohypophyseal opening is at the tip of the snout and connects with the pharynx; (3) the mouth is not funnel-shaped nor lined with horny teeth; (4) three pairs of tentacles surround the mouth and nasohypophyseal opening; (5) the eyes

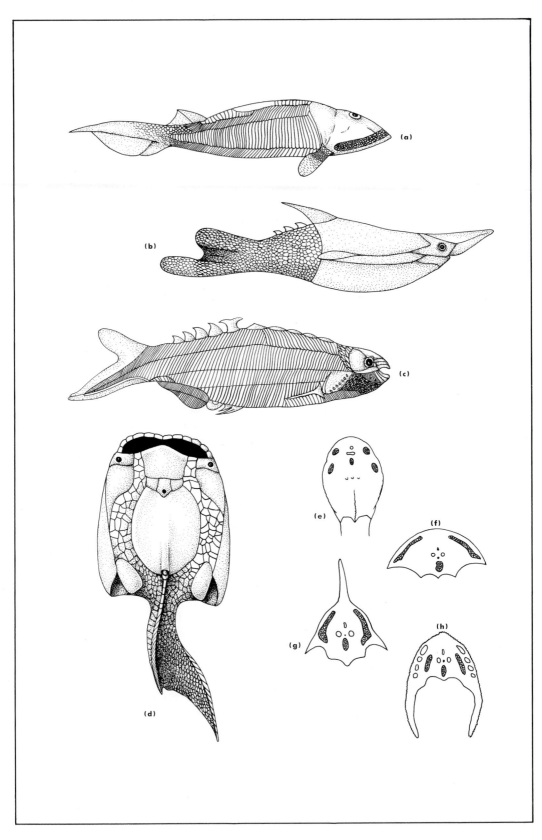

may not be distinct; (6) there are five to fifteen pairs of gills which may be united by a common duct to the outside; and (7) there are numerous slime glands in a ventrolateral row along each side of the body. Furthermore, hagfish eggs are laid at sea and the young develop directly unlike some lampreys which have a distinct fresh-water larval stage and a marked metamorphosis. Lampreys typically spawn in streams and the larvae that develop, often referred to as ammocoetes, remain in the mud and gravel of the stream bed for several years. During this period they are filter feeders; in this and other respects they are similar to cephalochordates.

The absence of fossil hagfish and only a single species of lamprey from the Pennsylvanian makes it very difficult to resolve their relationships to ostracoderms. It is now agreed generally that cyclostomes are derived from ostracoderm ancestors, and most researchers also agree that lampreys were derived from monorhine ostracoderms. The origin of hagfish, however, is still being argued. One school of thought holds that the cyclostomes are a monophyletic group and another thinks that hagfish evolved from diplorhine ostracoderms. If the latter view is substantiated, then the use of the order Cyclostomata to include both lampreys and hagfish would be in violation of the concept of monophyly. In any event it appears that the absence of a bony skeleton in lampreys and hagfish, the only living representatives of the jawless class of vertebrates, is a derived character state, as are the predaceous and scavenging habits and all related adaptations.

A question of considerable interest in connection with the phylogeny of the cyclostomes and ostracoderms is whether vertebrates originated in a freshwater or marine environment. It seems certain that the ancestors of vertebrates were marine because the main groups of invertebrates are marine, as are the Hemichordata and the primitive Chordata, the enteropneusts, pterobranchs, tunicates, and cephalochordates. Of interest then, is the question of whether primitive vertebrates too were marine. The study of the kinds of deposits in which the earliest known fossils have been found coupled with the structure and physiology of the excretory system of the living groups has led some to the conclusion that the origin was in fresh water and others to believe that it was in a marine environment. The issue may be resolved in favor of brackish water as the original habitat of the earliest vertebrates.

The Evolution of Jaws (Placodermi)

Placoderms are a highly varied group of fish that appeared at the end of the Silurian period during the peak of ostracoderm radiation, and became extinct in the Mississippian. The early portion of placoderm evolution appears to have taken place in fresh water, with a derived radiation in the marine environment in the Devonian. Adult placoderms varied in size from a few inches to over thirty feet in total length. Some, which seem to have been highly mobile predators, were shark-like in general body form; others were flattened bottom-dwelling species that may have eaten molluscs and bottom vegetation (Figure 2-15).

Figure 2-14 (opposite). Representative ostracoderms: (a)-(c) lateral views of three distinct forms; (d) a dorsal view of another; (e)-(h) outline drawings of the cephalothoracic region of other species. (Modified after Romer.)

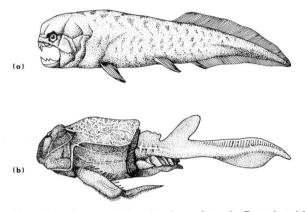

(a)

(b)

Figure 2-15. Representative placoderms from the Devonian: (a) a large arthrodire, genus *Dinichthys*; (b) an antiarch, genus *Bothriolepis*. (Modified after Romer.)

Unlike the ostracoderms from which they evolved, placoderms possessed primitive upper and lower jaws. It was only with the appearance of jaws that a truly predatory vertebrate could be realized—for the first time food of more than microscopic size was readily ingested. One of the anterior-most pharyngeal bars (the mandibular arch) is believed to have been modified into the jaws while the other bars remained relatively unmodified as typical gill-supporting structures. It should be emphasized, however, that the sequence of morphological steps that led to fully formed jaws is not characterized explicitly by known placoderms, apparently because of the incomplete nature of the fossil record. Most of the steps have been inferred from the morphology and development of living species of fish. It seems that at least part of the upper jaw was fused to the skull and that some species possessed true teeth on the jaws. Immediately behind the jaws of most placoderms was a large gill slit, unlike chondrichthyian and osteichthyian fish where this slit is reduced to a small aperture (spiracle) or is absent altogether.

All placoderms are believed to have possessed paired appendages. Some of the fins consisted of a large spine followed by a fleshy web of skin; other types included jointed solid spines without a connecting web, hollow spines fixed to the thoracic armor, or fleshy fins without a leading spine. The large number of paired fins found in some placoderms and even more dramatically expressed in primitive bony fish has been inferred to be the remnants of the breakup of an ancestral continuous lateroventral fold of skin similar to that seen in the metapleural folds of the Cephalochordata. Like ostracoderms the head and thoracic region of most placoderms were covered with large heavy armor plates; only a few were encased with small diamond-shaped bony scales. Also worth emphasizing is the fact that true lungs are known to have been present in at least some placoderms.

That placoderms evolved from an ostracoderm ancestor is no longer questioned. However, the absence of intermediates between the two groups makes their precise linkage very difficult to describe. Some researchers have suggested that placoderms are not a monophyletic cluster of species, that is, two or more groups were derived from different ostracoderm ancestors.

Similarly,, the relationship between placoderms and chondrichthyian and osteichthyian fish is difficult to interpret. Not only is the placoderm ancestor for the two groups still being debated but mounting evidence indicates it was not a single stock.

A Major Evolutionary Side Branch (Chondrichthyes)

In the Middle Devonian fossil record appeared what has become a highly differentiated lineage of fish, the Chondrichthyes. Many representatives of the group still exist today; in the past, however, they were far more numerous, with their greatest radiation centered in the Carboniferous and Permian. Bone is unknown in all living and most fossil species. The presence of only a cartilaginous endoskeleton is the most striking characteristic of the group and the one from which the assemblage takes its name. Certain cartilaginous parts of the endoskeleton become calcified when calcium salts infiltrate the cartilage matrix and these parts may resemble bone in terms of firmness. Calcified cartilage still lacks the developmental history and microanatomical form of true bone.

Almost all chondrichthyians possess a heterocercal tail (Figure 2-16); the dorsal flange is larger than the ventral and includes the tip of the upturned vertebral column. Tooth-like denticles, placoid scales, present in the skin along with the spines that form the leading edge of the dorsal fins of some species are believed to be remnants of the armor that encased their predecessors. Most chondrichthyians possess ventral subterminal mouths, in front of which are paired nostrils on the underside of the snout. The upper ramus of the well-developed jaws exhibits varying degrees of attachment to the skull. Part of this attachment at least is by means of the articulation of the hyomandibular portion of the hyoid pharyngeal bar with the brain case together with the point of articulation between the upper and lower jaws. In accordance with the position of the hyomandibular element, the gill slit that precedes it is reduced to a very small dorsally located aperture, the spiracle. Typical gill slits are located posterior to the spiracle, and lungs and swimbladders are absent. In the male the well-developed paired fins, characteristic of the group, possess claspers. These modified inner portions of the pelvic fins are intromittant organs which accomplish the act of internal fertilization that typifies the assemblage.

Within the class Chondrichthyes are two evolutionary lineages that have living representatives readily distinguished from each other: the subclass Elasmobranchii, the sharks, skates and rays, and the subclass Holocephali, the chimaeras or rat-fish (Figure 2-16). In the latter subclass the external gill slits are covered by a fleshy operculum. Sharks first appeared in the latter part of the Devonian. Most sharks are predaceous and with a few tropical exceptions are marine. The upper jaws are not attached directly to the skull and typically there are five to seven pairs of gill slits in addition to the spiracle. Some species lay large heavily yolked eggs enclosed in a leathery egg case; other species bear living young.

During the Mesozoic skates and rays evolved from the more primitive sharks. Unlike the sharks, the gill slits, other than the spiracle located behind the eye, are on the ventral surface. Typically, the tail, pelvic and dorsal fins are reduced in size and locomotion occurs by the undulating movement of the greatly enlarged pectoral fins. Skates and rays developed a bottom-dwelling existence and a diet of molluscs.

The chimaeras are a special group of marine cartilaginous fish and almost all are inhabitants of the deep sea. As their teeth are modified into large plates, it is not surprising that they too are mainly mollusc feeders. The upper jaw is solidly fused to the brain case, the well developed notochord persists into adult life as the main axial body support, the vertebrae are poorly developed, and few placoid scales are present in the adult skin. There is some evidence that chimaeras had their origin among the predecessors of modern sharks.

The exact derivation of chondrichthyians from the placoderms is still disputed; however, that they are derived from that group of bony fish is no longer questioned. From this relationship it must follow that the absence of bone in cartilaginous forms is a result of the reduction from the primitive bony state of placoderms; it does not represent an evolutionary stage leading to the placoderm condition as once was thought. Although the fossil record of chondrichthyians is poor because of their reduction of bone, it now seems

Figure 2-16. Representative chondrichthyian fish: (a) an extinct elasmobranch, genus *Cladoselache*; (b) a living selachian, genus *Mustelus*; (c) a living batoid, genus *Dasybatus*; (d) a living chimaera, genus *Chimaera*. (Modified after Romer.)

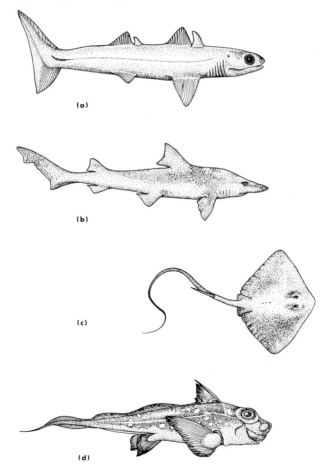

certain that they diverged earlier than did the osteichthyians and that the chondrichthyian line, in the sense that it did not give rise to a subsequent major adaptive radiation, was a dead end.

Diversity of
Form and Function
in the Aquatic
Environment
(Osteichthyes)

The fish included in the class Osteichthyes first appeared in fresh-water deposits of late Silurian age. Since their origin bony fish have continued to radiate in both fresh-water and marine environments, with the major expansion taking place during the Cretaceous. The marine environment does not appear to have been invaded until the Mesozoic. The more primitive osteichthyians and most of the derived forms have a bony endoskeleton. Typically the operculum is bony and covers a gill chamber of not more than five gill slits. The operculum is supported by a series of bones which in turn form a hinge with the cranium. Lungs appear to have been present in all primitive members of the class. In at least one major phyletic line lungs have become highly modified in structure and function as a hydrostatic organ, the swim bladder. It is now generally recognized that the greatest selective advantage for lungs was realized in fresh water where considerable seasonal drought occurred. Historically the selective advantage of a swim bladder materialized in the marine environment where the problem of buoyancy was greater.

Even the broadest outlines of bony fish phylogeny cannot be agreed upon by a majority of fish evolutionists. In the present text an early phyletic divergence in the Silurian is recognized by the reference to the Acanthodii (Figure 2-17) and in the Devonian by the reference to the subclasses Actinopterygii and Sarcopterygii (often termed Choanichthyes). The actinopterygians, or ray-fins as they are commonly called, are not on the main phyletic branch that led to tetrapods. They are believed to have evolved from either placoderms or an ancient sarcopterygian ancestor. The ray fins became the dominant group in the Carboniferous and have remained dominant ever since; there are an estimated 30,000 living species. The group is typified by the absence of internal nostrils, and with few exceptions its members do not possess fleshy, lobed paired fins. Both characteristics distinguish them from the Sarcopterygii. The fins of actinopterygians are almost always membranous and are supported by horny or bony rays that may be jointed and branching and originate at the point from which the fin itself rises from the body. Three grades or levels of evolution are delimited within the ray-fin line: the superorders Chondrostei (Figure 2-18), Holostei (Figure 2-19), and Teleostei (Figure 2-20). The chondrosteans are the most primitive; they were the abundant ray-finned fish from the Devonian to the near end of the Mesozoic. The holostean line evolved from the chondrosteans and became dominant in the middle of the Mesozoic. The teleosts had

Figure 2-17. A primitive acanthodian, genus *Climatius*, from the Devonian. The Acanthodii are questionably placed in the Class Osteichthyes. (Modified after Romer.)

their origins in the holosteans during the Triassic and since the late Mesozoic have remained the dominant group. The following list describes the general evolutionary trends that typify the successive stages of actinopterygian evolution.

Chondrostei	Holostei	Teleostei
Relatively little bone, particularly in more recent species	Moderate amount of bone, internal skeleton partly cartilaginous	Almost all species have completely ossified skeletons
Spiracle present in most species	Spiracle present in only a few species	Spiracle absent
Most species have strongly developed heterocercal tail	Tend to lose upturned shark-like tail	Symmetrical tail in almost all species, at least superficially
At least primitively, scales thick and rhombic, covered with an enamel-like layer called ganoin	Scales tend to lose their ganoin covering and become thinner; most are rhombic in shape	Scales thin, round in shape; ganoin layer lost
Maxilla attached to cheek	Maxilla not attached to cheek; jaws become shortened	Maxilla free, functions in protruding mouth; as a result, cheek region becomes open
Pelvic fins usually located posteriorly	Pelvic fins usually located posteriorly	Pelvic fins often located relatively far from craniad
Lungs present in most species; swim bladder in only a few species	Lungs absent; swim bladder present	Lungs absent; swim bladder present
Fresh water	Primitively fresh water, extensive marine radiation in Mesozoic; only fresh-water survivors	Numerous fresh-water forms; however, marine radiation more extensive
Only sturgeons, paddle-fish, and bichir and related forms extant (Figure 2-18)	Only bowfins and gars extant (Figure 2-19)	Dominant group of living fish. (Figure 2-20)

One of the extant chondrosteans of Africa, the bichir *(Polypterus),* is of particular significance because of its fleshy lobed, paired fins, a well ossified internal skeleton, typical lungs, and primitive ganoid scales. These features strongly suggest that the bichir is the most primitive living descendent of the ancient actinopterygians.

The progenitors of the subclass Sarcopterygii were almost certainly placoderms. A knowledge of the constitution of this phyletic line is critical to the understanding of vertebrate phylogeny because the ancestors of the first land dwellers are found there. Sarcopterygians are typified (with few exceptions) by internal nostrils, fleshy lobed, paired fins, and heavy scales that consist of a bony base covered by a thick layer of cosmine (a dentine-like substance) and spongy bone. The sarcopterygians are almost always divided into two taxa, the orders Crossopterygii and Dipnoi, both of which

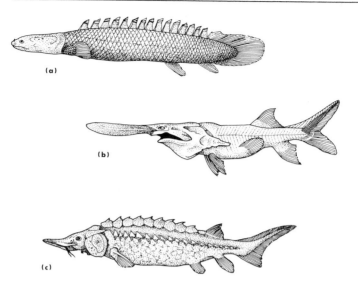

Figure 2-18. Representatives of the three major groups of living chondrosteans: (a) the African bichir, genus *Polypterus;* (b) the North American paddlefish, genus *Polyodon;* (c) the North American sturgeon, genus *Scaphyrhynchus*. (Modified after Romer.)

appeared as fossils in the late Silurian-lower Devonian (Figure 2-21).

Most dipnoans, or lungfish as they are commonly referred to, differ from the crossopterygians in these ways: absence of a spiracle, reduced ossification of the skeleton, symmetry of the appendicular skeleton consisting of a central series of elements in each appendage from which radiate, both anteriorly and posteriorly, smaller bones, and teeth modified into large plates for eating plant material. Among the living dipnoans the nares appear to be used primarily for olfaction rather than respiration. Most crossopterygians possess a spiracle; the skeleton is largely, or completely ossified; the internal skeleton of the paired limbs is asymmetrical; they are predaceous; and the enamel of the individual teeth is folded in labyrinthine patterns.

The dipnoans resemble the amphibians, the most primitive terrestrial vertebrates, in several respects: the lung is supplied by a branch of the

Figure 2-19. Representative living holosteans: (a) the gar, genus *Lepidosteus*; (b) the bowfin, genus *Amia*. (Modified after Romer.)

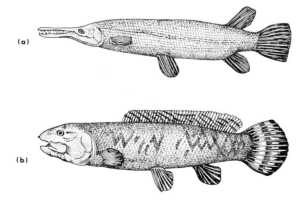

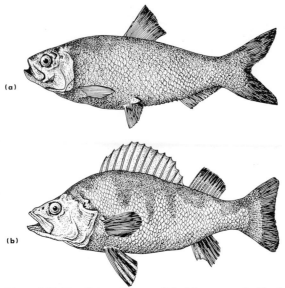

Figure 2-20. Two living teleostean fish: (a) a more primitive herring, genus *Clupea;* (b) a more derived perch, genus *Perca.* (Modified after Romer.)

sixth aortic arch, the atrium of the heart is partially divided into two chambers, the mode of development is comparable, and external gills are present in their larvae. These few similarities caused early evolutionists to propose that lungfish were ancestral to terrestrial vertebrates. The similarities between crossopterygians and amphibians, more specifically such forms as the rhipidistian crossopterygians *Eusthenopteron* (Figure 2-22) and *Osteolepis*, are now believed to be so numerous and so detailed that few can argue

Figure 2-21. Representative choanichthyan fish: (a) the only living genus of crossopterygian, *Latimeria*; (b) a living dipnoan from Australia, genus *Epiceratodus*. (Modified after Romer.)

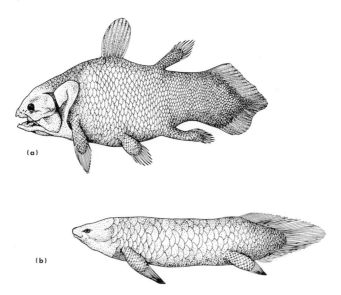

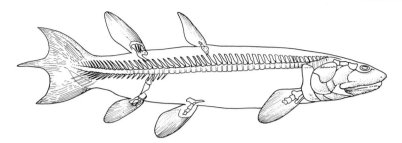

Figure 2-22. A reconstruction of the skeleton of the Upper Devonian rhipidistian cross-opterygian, genus *Eusthenopteron*. (Modified after Gregory and Raven.)

against their relatively close relationship. The rhipidistians, which were primarily fresh-water species, became extinct in the early part of the Permian, but not before they gave rise to a terrestrial lineage. Today cross-opterygians are represented only by a single living marine species, the coelocanth, *Latimeria chalumnae* (Figure 2-21). The coelocanth phyletic line was thought to have become extinct by the end of the Cretaceous, but in 1939 the first specimen of *Latimeria* was dredged up from the depths of the sea off the east coast of South Africa.

Invasion of the
Land (Amphibia)

Much of the evolution of the anatomical and functional features necessary for a terrestrial vertebrate, and one completely free of the aquatic environment, was realized fully by the class Amphibia. Because it opened up new adaptive horizons the invasion of land by amphibians has been likened to the evolution of jaws by placoderms. The two most obvious challenges that amphibians met successfully were to respire by means of lungs, the gills not being an efficient mechanism for gaseous exchange in an aerial environment, and to develop appendages that would lift the body off the ground and permit a walking gait rather than a fish-like undulatory movement. The limbs of those crossopterygians that gave rise to amphibians were already well suited to a semiwalking gait and posture. And, of course, lungs had been secondary respiratory organs since the time of placoderms. The limbs of crossopterygians were very effective for moving over the debris of a swamp environment, certainly much more so than the ray fins of actinopterygians, which are relatively easily torn.

The end of the Devonian was a period of great seasonal droughts, and it is assumed that the lungs of crossopterygians allowed them to move from one pool to another as each dried up; their fleshy lobed, paired fins aided them in their movement on land. Furthermore, the earliest amphibians were little more than fish in that they too encountered dry land only in their journeys between pools. In the search for those selective forces responsible for the evolution of terrestrialism, the then unexploited terrestrial food supply of insects should not be overlooked. It is important to emphasize that amphibians today are still not completely free of the aquatic environment. Most species have retained the thin slimy fish-like character of skin and must return to the water to reproduce. In that regard it is believed that amphibians have necessarily been restricted from "some higher evolutionary achievements."

The Amphibia differ from their crossopterygian ancestors in the reduction and loss of many of the opercular bones. They differ from their reptilian derivatives in not possessing epidermal scales, amnionic and chorionic membranes around the embryo, true claws, and generally a corneal layer in the epidermis. In addition, almost all species have single cervical and sacral vertebrae, and most adult amphibians lack external gills and gill slits. The extant species, at least, have a highly glandular skin and are incapable of involuntarily regulating their body temperature within narrow limits. Certain aquatic forms retain a lateral line system very much like their crossopterygian forebears. Almost all extant amphibians require an aquatic, or at least moist, habitat during some part of their life history. This primitive environmental constraint is most often realized during the courting season and the period of egg laying as there are no extra-embryonic living protective membranes to prevent dessication of the developing embryo. Most extant amphibians have a free-living stage, either typically larviform or tadpole-like, and both types respire by means of external integumentary gills. The tadpole differs from a larva in that its metamorphic changes to a subadult are considerably more drastic. The larva resembles the adult of the species in general body form and proportions and possesses typical adult appendages and true teeth on both jaws. It is not unusual for the larva to become sexually mature. The tadpole on the other hand is dramatically unlike the adult in that the head and body are not distinct; it possesses a long tail (often with a median fin), a horny beak, and rows of cornified denticles. At the time of metamorphosis the gills disappear and lungs develop, the tail is reabsorbed, and the legs appear.

Three major assemblages of amphibians are usually recognized: the subclasses Labyrinthodontia, Lepospondyli, and Lissamphibia (Figures 2-23–2-26). Only the latter group possesses living species which occur in each of three orders, Anura, Urodela, and Apoda. The labyrinthodonts were dominant during the late Paleozoic and early Mesozoic periods. The labyrinthodont radiation had died out by the end of the Triassic, but not before it gave rise to the class Reptilia in the Carboniferous. Labyrinthodonts were large as adults differing from their immediate crossopterygian ancestors in only a few attributes: their median fins were greatly reduced or absent and they possessed short sturdy legs, large heads, and long tails. Labyrinthodonts, at least primitively, possessed arch-like vertebrae very similar to those of crossopterygians. The ichthyostegid group of labryinthodonts, the most primitive of amphibians (Figure 2-23), made their appearance in the middle Devonian. Although they possessed fish-like tails with fin rays and the external nostril was located far down on each side of the head near the margin of the upper jaw very much like their crossopterygian progenitors, they had five-toed appendages, the hyomandibular bone had become the

Figure 2-23. A reconstruction of the skeleton of a Devonian amphibian, genus *Ichthyostega.* (Modified after Jarvik.)

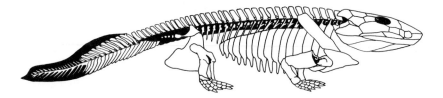

Figure 2-24. An anuran amphibian. (Modified after Noble.)

innermost middle ear ossicle, and a distinct otic notch was present in the posterior portion of the skull that accommodated the tympanic membrane. Both the ear ossicle and the tympanic membrane were almost certainly used in the reception of sound and its subsequent transmission to the central nervous system. The lepospondyls appear to have evolved from the labyrinthodonts. Typically, they were of smaller adult size and differed most conspicuously in their spool-shaped vertebral centra.

Anurans, the frogs and toads (Figure 2-24), occupy a wide variety of habitats from deserts to fresh water. Their greatest diversity occurs in the tropics, although they extend well into the temperate regions of both hemispheres. They exhibit a tadpole type of life history and as adults most of their morphological and functional characteristics relate to their saltatory (jumping) mode of locomotion. The evolution of saltation has resulted in a shorter trunk with a reduction in the number of vertebrae (as few as five are known), lack of definition of the neck region, reduction of the skull and ribs, lengthening of the hindlimbs—an extra joint at the level of the ankle and absence of a tail; the posterior vertebrae are fused into a single spike-like bone, the urostyle, located between the two rami or ilia of the pelvic girdle. The hind feet of anurans may be fully webbed, functioning in the aquatic environment as major propulsive organs. Most species produce sounds by passing air over vocal cords; they receive airborne sounds through the tympanic membrane.

The Urodela, or salamanders as they are most often referred to (Figure 2-25), are almost always found in moist habitats. They are widely distributed

Figure 2-25. A North American salamander, genus *Dicamptodon*. (Modified after Noble.)

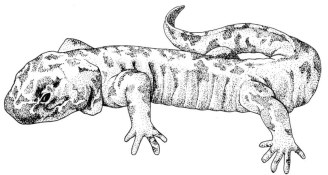

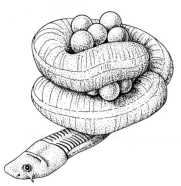

Figure 2-26. An apodan amphibian shown encircling a clutch of eggs. (Modified after Smith.)

in the northern temperate regions and throughout the New World tropics. In general appearance they are most like primitive tetrapods. Median fins are usually absent, the fore- and hindlimbs are nearly equal in length, the tail is well developed, and the head, neck and trunk regions are well differentiated. There is considerable reduction of dermal bone (a general trend towards retention of embryonic cartilage) in the skull and in particular in the pectoral girdle. Vocal cords and tympanic membranes are absent, salamanders being incapable of detecting airborne sounds. In the major group of lungless salamanders integumentary respiration is their primary method of gaseous exchange.

The Apodans, or caecilians, are believed to be more closely related to salamanders than to anurans (Figure 2-26). They are worm-like burrowers; however, a few species are completely aquatic. Both limbs and girdles have been lost, the tail has been greatly reduced, the anus is almost terminal, vocal cords are absent, and the eyes are usually greatly reduced in size. Caecilians have retained typical fish-like dermal scales embedded in the skin. As adults they may reach a maximum total length of about two feet. They are circumtropical in geographic distribution.

The Amniote Egg (Reptilia)
The first group of vertebrates to become completely free of the aquatic environment were the reptiles. The class Reptilia originated from labyrinthodont amphibians in the early Pennsylvanian and by the Mesozoic they had become the dominant vertebrate. Considering both extinct and extant species the diversity of reptiles has been greater than any other group in tropical environments and at least equivalent to that of the more recent and better known radiation of mammals. During some period in their long phylogenetic history reptiles have come to occupy all possible environments. There are typical terrestrial quadrupeds, bipeds, limbless species, burrowing forms, as well as those that invaded the aerial and both the marine and fresh-water habitats. The aquatic invasion certainly is convergent in the different reptile lineages and is not the primitive state. Reptiles are characterized by epidermal scales, dry skins owing to the absence of mucous glands, true claws, and the inability to regulate involuntarily their body temperature within narrow limits. A few species of reptiles give birth to living young, but

the majority lay heavily-yolked, terrestrial eggs enclosed within protective layers of albumin, shell membranes and shell. The yolk serves as a large endogenous food supply. Very early in development the yolk becomes enclosed within a cellular sac, the yolk sac, and the embryo itself is surrounded by several embryonic membranes, amnion, chorion and allantois, which are discarded at hatching when the young reptile escapes from the shell. These membranes present in the embryonic stages of birds and mammals are first found among the reptiles. Albumin is also consumed during incubation. Unlike most amphibians, reptiles have no metamorphosis and even during very early stages of development the young do not breathe by means of gills.

Laying an egg on land requires certain basic conditions, all of which appear to have been met by the so-called amniote egg. The leathery or lime-impregnated shell provides protection from physical and chemical shock and dessication, and is sufficiently porous to allow exchange of the gases oxygen and carbon dioxide. Internal fertilization is necessary since the laid egg is enclosed by a shell. The amnion surrounds the developing young, enclosing it in a fluid-filled cavity, and the amniotic fluid secreted mainly by cells of the amnion prevents dessication. The allantois is a sac-like development from the embryo's hind gut. It increases in size with the growth of the embryo, comes into contact with the chorion and with it serves both as a repository for nitrogenous metabolic wastes and as a respiratory mechanism. The extra-embryonic layer from which the amnion is formed gives rise to the chorion (Chap. 3). This thin cellular membrane encloses the whole complex: embryo, amnion, yolk sac, albumin and allantois. When did terrestrial egg-laying originate and what were the selective pressures responsible for its evolution? These are two very important questions which have not yet been answered satisfactorily.

At present there are recognized six subclasses and about sixteen orders of reptiles and of the latter taxonomic level only four include living species (Figure 2-27). The number of fenestrae (openings) in the temporal region of the skull and the specific bones that border them are the sets of characters most commonly used to distinguish the subclasses. The subclass Anapsida does not possess a temporal fenestra; this group consists of only two orders, the Cotylosauria or stem reptiles and Chelonia. Of all known reptiles the cotylosaurs are the most primitive assemblage and are considered to have evolved directly from Carboniferous labyrinthodonts. These short-legged animals with their massive skulls appear to have been terrestrial and therefore one can only assume that the aquatic to terrestrial transition period preceded their appearance. Before they became extinct in the late Triassic, cotylosaurs gave rise to most of the subsequent radiations, such as turtles, pelycosaurs, eosuchians, mammal-like reptiles, and thecodonts, within the Reptilia. The chelonians, or turtles as they are usually called, first appear in Triassic deposits, and look very much like modern forms. The group is characterized by a protective shell of enlarged dermal bony plates and overlying horny epidermal scales, constituting the dorsal carapace and ventral plastron. With the evolution of the shell came the loss of many of the muscles of the body wall, and in most species the ribs and trunk vertebrae are solidly fused to the carapace. Except for the most primitive forms, all of which are extinct, turtles lack teeth. All species lay eggs, and the males possess a single median copulatory organ; the anal opening is often a longitudinal slit. There are terrestrial, semi-aquatic, and fully aquatic marine and fresh-water forms. Many of the aquatic species come on land only to lay their eggs. Particularly in the marine group, the forelimbs are modified into large oar-shaped flippers. There is relatively little diversity of form within the Chelonia, the greatest difference being size.

The subclass Synapsida is characterized by a single lateral temporal opening, bounded above by the postorbital and squamosal bones. Three extinct orders, Pelycosauria, Therapsida, and Mesosauria are included in this subclass. The therapsids are the advanced fossil reptiles that gave rise to mammals. They were quadrupedal, the limbs had evolved to positions nearer to the median line of the body, the teeth became differentiated into differ-

Figure 2-27. A suggested phylogenetic history of the major groups of reptiles. (Modified after Romer.)

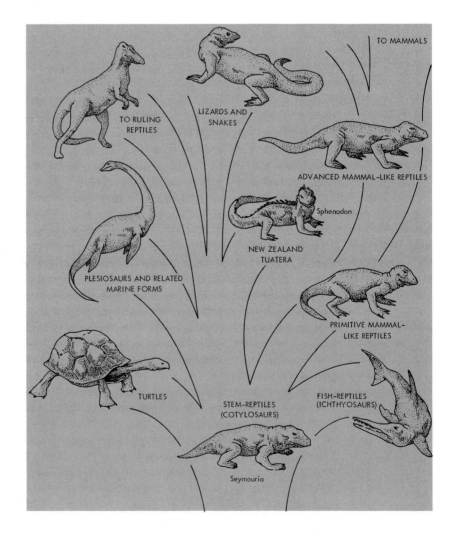

ent types (molars, canines, and incisors), and they possessed the beginning of the secondary palate. The subclass Parapsida consisting of a single extinct order, the Ichthyosauria, is characterized by a single superior temporal opening bounded below by the postfrontal and supratemporal bones. Ichthyosaurs were similar to porpoises in their habits, size, and form, but differed from them in the lateral compression of the tail. They lacked a distinct neck region; had short paddle-formed appendages and the terminal caudal vertebrae projected downwards into the ventral tail fin. The group was marine and almost certainly viviparous owing to their completely aquatic nature.

The subclass Euryapsida includes two marine orders, Protosauria and Sauropterygia. The subclass is characterized by a single superior temporal opening bounded below by the postorbital and squamosal bones. Euryapsids had a long neck, a long snout, or both; the body was short, broad, and relatively flat; the limbs were large, oar-like paddles. Their gross morphology suggests that they were restricted to aquatic environments, or that they moved minimally on land as the seal does today.

The subclasses Archosauria and Lepidosauria are typified by two temporal openings separated by the postorbital and squamosal bones. The Archosauria includes five orders: Thecodontia—the "ruling reptiles" of the Mesozoic; Crocodilia—the alligators, crocodiles, and relatives; Pterosauria—the "flying reptiles"; Saurishia—the reptile-like dinosaurs; and Ornithischia—the bird-like dinosaurs. Thecodonts were mostly small, slender, predaceous, and largely bipedal in their posture. It was the thecodont stock that very likely gave rise directly and independently to all the other archosaurian orders. The Crocodilia are characterized by very large cornified epidermal scales, those on the dorsal side covering plates of dermal bone. They have a single median copulatory organ, a bony (hard) palate separating the mouth from the nasal passages, and a longitudinally oriented anal slit. It appears that at least some of the modern crocodilians possess a completely divided ventricle in the heart. Crocodilians are predatory, equipped with large teeth set in sockets, and are all semi-aquatic. There are only a few living species, all of which are relatively similar in general body shape. The Pterodactyls probably glided and soared, but it seems unlikely that they actually flew. The largest had wing spreads of over twenty-five feet. They left no descendants. It is recognized that they did not give rise to either birds or bats as was once commonly thought. The pterodactyl wing was a leathery web stretched between an elongated finger, the bones of the forelimb and the body wall. The bones were light and compact, some species were toothless, and all appeared to have had small, poorly developed feet. Saurischian dinosaurs possessed a typical reptilian pelvis, in contrast to the ornithischian dinosaurs, with a bird-like pelvis. The Saurischia included both primitive bipedal and quadrupedal species, as well as primitive bipedal carnivores and herbivores. The largest of all terrestrial carnivores, *Tyrannosaurus* belongs to this taxon, as does the largest terrestrial animal known, *Brachiosaurus*. *Brachiosaurus* and related large species probably spent most of their lives grazing in shallow lakes. This supposition is based on the fact that only water could buoy up the tremendous weight. The ornithischians also encompassed both bipedal and quadrupedal species, all of which were herbivorous. Why did dinosaurs become extinct so abruptly near the end of the Cretaceous? This again is a major question that still remains to be answered satisfactorily; suggestions have included the drying up of swamps and the exposure of the animals to sunlight.

The Lepidosauria includes the primitive extinct order Eosuchia, and the orders Squamata and Rhynchocephalia both of which have living representatives. The rhynchocephalians had an extensive radiation that existed as far back as the Permian. Today the order is represented by only a single species *Sphenodon* that is restricted to New Zealand. The modern form looks like a lizard, although unlike that group it lacks a copulatory organ and the teeth are fused to the margins of the jaws. Its anal opening is a transverse slit, and the well developed pineal eye contains both a lens and a retina. The Squamata, which evolved in the early Mesozoic from an eosuchian progenitor, radiated in the Cenozoic. The group is characterized by paired copulatory organs (hemipenes) in males and a transversely oriented anal slit. Squamates are the most numerous of living reptiles. Like their reptilian forebears their greatest diversity is in the tropics. The suborders Lacertilia (lizards) and Ophidia (snakes) are the most familiar groups. Typically, lizards have legs, eyelids, ear openings, and a relatively immovable quadrate; the halves of the lower jaw are firmly united together, the teeth are not set in sockets, and a single temporal arch is present. Snakes on the other hand lack legs, eyelids and ear openings; the quadrate is highly movable, the lower jaws are loosely united by a ligament that permits the swallowing of very large prey, and temporal arches are absent. Most of the differences between the two suborders reflect an early ophidian evolutionary history of burrowing. As evidenced by the vestiges of the hindlimbs and pelvic girdles found in some species the Ophidia almost certainly evolved from a quadruped, probably a primitive lacertilian.

Feathers and Sustained Flight (Aves)

It now seems reasonably certain that the class Aves evolved from an archosaurian ancestor. While it also seems certain that the archosaurian pterosaurs were capable of soaring and gliding short distances, as do some squamates and a few modern frogs, birds appear to have been the first animals to evolve self-sustained flight. Birds are characterized most obviously in terms of their feathers and wings which are highly modified pectoral appendages. The wing and tail feathers greatly increase the surface area of the animal, adding relatively little weight, and thus offer a great deal of resistance to the air when the animal is in flight. Birds have light-weight bones, many of which are hollow and contain air sacs projecting from the enlarged lungs. Birds are necessarily bipedal owing to their pectoral appendage modifications for flight, and the enlarged sternum provides increased surface area for pectoral muscle attachment. They usually have large well-developed eyes, horny scales on legs and feet, and only a left ovary and oviduct. Their body temperature is high, and their ability to regulate it involuntarily within narrow limits, together with the modifications of the circulatory system, aid the high metabolic rate necessary to supply the energy for sustained flight. As a rule soaring birds have wings with a large surface area; fast-flying birds have small, short, rapidly beating wings; and in flightless birds the wings are absent or greatly reduced in structure and size. Since they are capable of sustained flight, many birds can migrate great distances annually and many species have the ability to home, that is, to find their way back to their home area over short to very long distances. Birds are peculiar in their possession of a relatively short intestine and the absence of a urinary bladder. Teeth are absent in modern forms; their function has been replaced by a horny derivative of the skin which forms the beak or bill and which has been modified in numerous ways for different food habits. Birds usually exhibit a very elaborate social behavior. Eggs which are laid on the ground or in a nest must be incubated by the parent. Not all birds are small; the adult of at least one species on Madagascar (now extinct) was ten feet tall and weighed eight hundred pounds. As a group, birds are relatively invariant compared with other classes of vertebrates. There are numerous orders, most of which differ in relatively few characteristics.

Usually birds are divided into two subclasses, Archaeornithes and Neornithes. The former subclass is known only from two species (about four individuals) from the late Jurassic. These species were about the size of a crow (Figure 2-28). Their teeth, set in sockets, were present in both jaws; the wings had three-clawed fingers; the tail was very long and had typical feathers projecting outward along the margins; and abdominal ribs (gastralia) were present. The fact that the sternum was very small in these primitive forms strongly suggests that sustained flight had not yet evolved. Like modern birds the feathered wing had at least parts of three digits, and the hindfeet had four toes. Neornithean birds in contrast to their archaeornithean ancestor possess a short tail, of thirteen or fewer compressed vertebrae, from which the tail feathers radiate. The wing bones are reduced in number and with very few exceptions there are no clawed digits on the wings. This subclass encompasses all modern birds, with about 8500 species recognized currently, and a primitive group of toothed forms which are known from marine Cretaceous deposits of North America. Teeth appear to have been lost in all neornithean phyletic lines by the Mesozoic.

The Evolution of Higher Levels of Integration in the Central Nervous System (Mammalia)

The class Mammalia evolved from a therapsid reptile stock in the Triassic, radiated widely in the Cenozoic, and today mammals are the dominant terrestrial vertebrates. All mammals have at least some hair and suckle the young; these two features are unique to them. A few species have retained the reptilian epidermal scale in certain hairless areas on the body and appendages. All mammals above the egg-laying monotremes have an intra-uterine parent-embryo connection of some type called a placenta, which serves to nourish the young and to remove its waste products before birth. Although the placenta is a highly variable structure interspecifically, it can be characterized for the entire class as a functional intermediary between the blood vascular system of the young and that of the mother. The paired sets of mammary glands are modified skin glands, which furnish nourishment until the young can fend for themselves. When first born, mammals are relatively helpless compared with other vertebrate offspring, and the offspring requires the parent for nutrition, protection, and some education. Mammals can be characterized further, with few exceptions, as having (1) a four-chambered heart; (2) a single aorta (the left fourth); (3) three small bones (the malleus,

Figure 2-28. A skeleton with impressions of feathers of the earliest bird known, genus *Archaeopteryx*. (Modified after Colbert.)

incus, and stapes) in the middle ear cavity that transmit the airborne sounds by mechanical vibration to the nervous system; (4) a temporal cranial element that represents a fused series of reptilian skull bones; (5) in the lower jaw a single bone, the dentary, on each side of the mandibular symphysis; (6) a muscular diaphragm separating the thoracic and abdominal cavities; (7) sweat glands; (8) urogenital and intestinal systems that open to the outside separately rather than empty their products into a common cavity; (9) heterodont dentition; (10) two successive sets of teeth, the "milk" teeth being replaced by a permanent set; (11) marrow cavities in the long bones; (12) circular, biconcave, and enucleate red blood cells; (13) a well-developed sound collecting lobe, the pinna, accessory to the outer ear cavity; (14) a larynx that produces a wide range of sound; (15) an extensive development of the cerebral cortex; (16) a double occipital condyle similar to amphibians and their most immediate ancestors, the synapsid reptiles; and (17) the physiological capability of involuntarily regulating their body temperature within narrow limits, that is, they are homeothermic. Homeothermism has been responsible almost certainly for their ability to invade successfully those regions where the climate is very extreme and fluctuating. Mammals are a diverse group, particularly in their patterns of locomotion and their teeth. Both sets of characters are often used to exemplify adaptive radiation. About thirty-two orders of mammals are recognized, fourteen of which are extinct; they are divided among three subclasses. Only two of the three subclasses, Prototheria and Theria, include living species.

   The order Monotremata are the living prototherians. More specifically, the extant species are the duck-bill platypus and spiny anteater, all of which are restricted to the Australian region today (Figure 2-29). Monotremes are truly exceptional mammals in that they lay large reptile-like eggs which are incubated in a nest or in a temporary abdominal pouch. The mammary glands are poorly developed, there are no nipples and the milk simply accumulates on tufts of hair. Monotremes have a number of features which

Figure 2-29. A suggested phylogenetic history of the major groups of mammals. (Modified after Romer.)

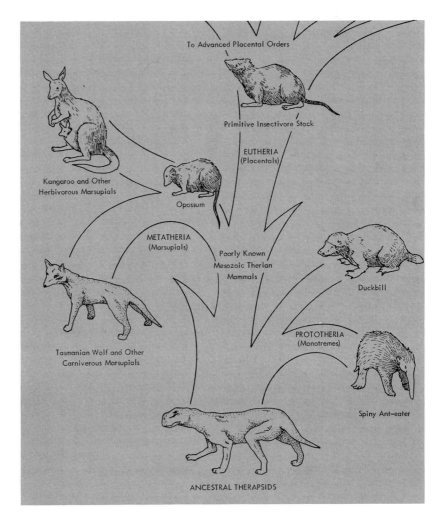

are obviously primitive: (1) a cloaca is present and receives both digestive and reproductive products; (2) the pectoral girdle includes bones that are lacking in other mammals; (3) a ventral mesentery is present that extends the length of the abdominal cavity; (4) a functional abdominal vein has been identified; (5) the testes are abdominal; (6) the pinna is very small or absent; (7) the malleus and incus are very large and resemble the articular and quadrate bones of reptiles from which they were modified; (8) the fiber tract that connects the two cerebral hemispheres in higher mammals, the corpus callosum, is absent; and (9) they exhibit little ability to maintain a constant body temperature. On the other hand, certain characteristics of monotremes, such as the absence or reduction of their teeth, are obviously derived features. It has been re-emphasized recently that monotremes may have evolved from a therapsid stock very different from the one that gave rise to the therians. Early fossils are only now being discovered in Australia and the question of the phyletic relationships of monotremes seems certain to be solved.

The subclass Theria, in contrast to the Prototheria, do not lay eggs, they bear living young, and their mammary glands are supplied with well-formed nipples. The Marsupialia is the only order in the therian infraclass Metatheria with living representatives (Figure 2-29). Fossil marsupials are known as far back as the middle Cretaceous, and it is certain that the group was once widespread throughout the world. Today marsupials are restricted to the Australian region, with the exception of two genera in the New World. A well developed abdominal pouch, or marsupium, is present in all species, with a few exceptions where it seems to have been lost. The marsupium opens either anteriorly or posteriorly, and its walls are supported by two slender bones (termed epipubics) which are attached to the pelvic girdle. The newborn marsupial is poorly developed and it undergoes a second period of maturation in the parent's pouch. Once the young animal has made its way inside the marsupium it becomes firmly attached to one of the nipples located there, and it completes its development. The female marsupial produces eggs with very little yolk. Following fertilization the young embryo comes into contact with the parent's uterine wall to form a poorly developed placenta of the "yolk-sac" type. Marsupials are convergent with many kinds of eutherian mammals in many different ways. There are, or at least were, large grazers, wolf- and cat-like carnivores, fossorial mole-like species, rabbit and bear forms, as well as one group that glided from tree to tree and looked much like a "flying" squirrel. The marsupial radiation is believed to have declined as a result of competition with eutherian mammals.

The infraclass Eutheria, or so-called "true" or placental mammals, encompasses about sixteen orders (Figure 2-30). The earliest known members of living orders can be traced back to the Eocene or Paleocene, with the exception of the insectivores and primates that are known from the Cretaceous. In contrast to the marsupials, eutherians possess a well-developed placenta, most often referred to as the chorioallantoic type; the yolk sac is vestiged and does not contact the wall of the uterus. Of course, eutherians

Figure 2-30 (opposite). A suggested phylogenetic history of the major orders of eutherian mammals. (Modified after Romer.)

Mouse Group

CARNIVORES

Toothed Whales

Guinea Pig Group

Whalebone Whales

CETACEANS

Squirrel Group

PERISSODACTYLES

PRIMITIVE RODENTS

ARTIODACTYLS

LAGOMORPHS

HYRAX

PRIMATES

SUBUNGULATES

PRIMITIVE UNGULATES

BATS

ELEPHANTS

INSECTIVORE STOCK

PANGOLIN

SIRENIANS

EDENTATES

AARDVARK

also differ in the absence of a marsupium and epipubic bones. In the Eutheria, the young are relatively well developed when born; however, there is still considerable post-parturition care in many species. Unfortunately, many of the primitive orders of eutherians are now extinct but the living members of the order Insectivora, however, do provide some clues to the ancient relationships between marsupials and eutherians. Insectivores have a shallow cloaca, flat feet, five toes, smooth cerebral hemispheres, small sharp pointed teeth, and some have permanent abdominal testes. Of a number of general evolutionary trends seen in eutherians, the following appear to be the most significant: (1) increase in tooth size; (2) reduction in tooth number, (3) reduction of toes, and (4) an increase in the size of the forebrain and complexity of the cerebral cortex. Much of the eutherian diversity is believed to be associated with the adaptability of their dentition and limbs and feet. It is also assumed that the increase in number and complexity of the integrative pathways and centers in the central nervous system, particularly the cerebral cortex, has been responsible for their success.

References for Chapter 2

[1] Barrington, E. J. W., *The Biology of Hemichordata and Protochordata.* San Francisco: W. H. Freeman and Company, 1965. A concise review of the biology and evolutionary relationships of hemichordates and primitive chordates.

[2] Carter, G. S., *Structure and Habit in Vertebrate Evolution.* Seattle: University of Washington Press, 1967. Carter's work is intended to be a full textbook of vertebrate zoology. Its phylogenetic framework is based on slightly outdated information; however the facts of organismal biology are still very useful.

[3] Jefferies, R. P. S., "The Subphylum Calcichordata (Jefferies 1967), Primitive Fossil Chordates with Echinoderm Affinities," Bull. Brit. Mus. (Nat. Hist.), *Geol.,* **16**, No. 6 (1968), 243-339. The first comprehensive review of the relationships of the extinct calcichordates.

[4] Romer, A. S., *Vertebrate Paleontology.* Chicago: University of Chicago Press, 3rd edition, 1966. This is an accurate summary of our knowledge of the fossil history of vertebrates.

[5] Young. J. Z., *The Life of Vertebrates.* Oxford: Clarendon Press, 2nd edition, 1962. A lengthy account of structure and function in vertebrates.

3
Changing patterns of organization during early development

Introduction   A discussion of the early development of vertebrate embryos is included in order to lay a foundation for the analysis of the adult vertebrate structural patterns which constitute the subject matter of this book. The brief survey will be concerned with the changing patterns that spring initially from organization within the unfertilized egg as well as from certain of the mechanisms involved later when masses of cells move to new locations during gastrulation and primordia begin to appear at the succeeding neurula stage. During this latter stage of embryonic development the fundamental structural pattern of the adult organism becomes visible, a pattern which will undergo subsequent modification only with the progress of growth and differentiation in structure and function of the various components. The pathways of differentiation and growth will be followed as far as necessary to clarify base lines of changing structure. The ontogeny of organs and organ-systems will be taken up where relevant in the chapters that follow. Animals chosen for this introduction are specimens that have found wide usage among investigators interested in development, largely because of their availability, hardiness, reproductive behavior, and manipulative suitability. A number of current references dealing with various aspects of vertebrate embryology are listed in the bibliography following this chapter.

At any stage of embryonic development there is a correlated though transitional organization between what precedes and what follows, and this becomes increasingly complex with age as the genotype progressively sends forth its coded messages. This process may be seen in the organization of the early embryo during cleavage and in its gradual replacement by the organization of the embryonic germ layers. The pattern then changes as cellular movements and inductions occur during gastrulation. Tissue and organ primordia subsequently arise from these germ layers, individually or in association, and in turn develop into the organ systems that constitute the body of a mature organism. A knowledge of embryology gives meaning to structure just as a study of evolution contributes to knowledge of the basis of vertebrate variability, and reference should be made to the facts of development in order to interpret the presence of modified or different structures and to show the origins of others. The study of comparative anatomy has always relied upon the story of development.

In its broadest perspective development may be viewed as covering the whole life span of the organism from fertilization to old age and death

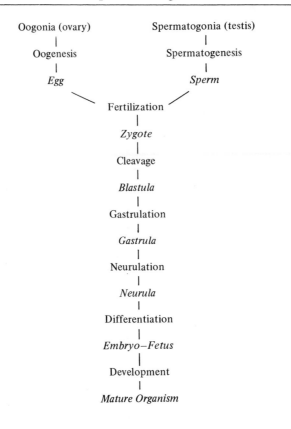

Table 3-1. Course of progressive development of an organism to maturity.

(Table 3-1). Although both progressive and regressive aspects may thus be included and the term is synonymous with change, it is commonly and more restrictively applied to the following: continuously progressive phenomena seen in the embryo, fetus, and/or the growing organism; replacement or regenerative phenomena in wound healing, limb regeneration, and replacement of blood cells or germ cells; growth and differentiation of blood vessels, kidneys, skin, and so on. The term has even been applied to the degenerative or regressive processes in aging organs as in the case of the progressive disappearance of optic nerve fibers, neurons, islets of Langerhans, renal glomeruli, and skin elasticity along with other phenomena characteristic of aging. Development takes into account the whole gamut of physiological processes: replication, substitution, growth, interaction, conversion, degeneration, regeneration, differentiation, and aging. There are critical stages in the early development of the organism when gross structural patterns may be determined, namely during the meiotic and fertilization processes, gastrulation, and neurulation, as well as during metamorphosis (amphibia) when striking change normally occurs in body structure as an organism adjusts to a new environment and way of life. Disturbance in developmental processes at any time may result in abnormalities or even early death.

Structure and Composition of Gametes

Spermatozoa

Both the egg and spermatozoan of any organism are precisely structured (Figure 3-1). The morphology and metabolism of sperm are specialized to transmit the male hereditary units into the egg. Sperm are characterized by a capacity for a short period of sustained activity, absence of much reserve food material, and structural and enzymic mechanisms for quick penetration of the egg with its investing membranes. The primary groundwork of this architectural pattern is laid down during the course of spermatogenesis, or sperm development, which takes place within the testicular cysts (amphibia) or in the walls of the seminiferous tubules (amniotes), and subsequently elaborated as cell-like nonmotile spermatids containing the haploid (half) number of chromosomes characteristic of the species (Figure 3-2). Chromosome reduction is accomplished by a sequence of two cell divisions during which the chromosomes replicate only once. In turn the spermatid metamorphoses, or transforms into the functionally motile spermatozoan composed of head, middle piece, and flagellum. After liberation from the testis and preceding its functional role, the sperm acquires the ability (capacitation or maturation) to react to egg hormones and enter into fertilization reactions with the egg. This final phase of the metamorphic process may take place in water or some portion of the reproductive duct system depending upon the vertebrate organism. Interest in the development, structure, and aging of sperm and the capacitation factor, as well as in the accompanying detectable changes within the sperm associated with these processes, is shown by current research.

Morphology of a selected spermatozoan is illustrated in Figure 3-2. Sperm of different species exhibit great variability in shape and size, particularly of

Figure 3-1. Spermatozoa of the bull. (Courtesy General Biological Supply Co.)

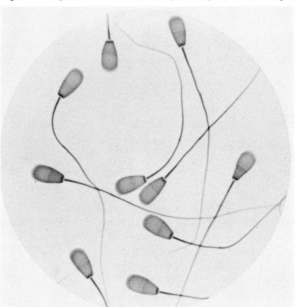

the head. Certain types may possess accessory structures such as the vibratile membrane on the flagellum of *Amphiuma* sperm (an amphibian). Length varies from around twenty microns in the crocodile to as much as two millimeters in *Balanoglossus* (a hemichordate). Throughout the chordates, sperm are of the flagellated (tadpole-like) type.

Within the sperm head is the nucleus, homogeneous and electrondense, which stains intensely with basic dyes and absorbs strongly in the ultraviolet. Capping the nucleus is the acrosome, which plays a conspicuous role in the fertilization reaction . Certain *enzymes* are also present, apparently in the acrosome, some of which are involved in the fertilization reaction, e.g., *antifertilizin* and *egg membrane lysine* (proteases). These break down the *vitelline* membrane around the egg to effect sperm entrance, neutralize fertilizin (an egg enzyme), and then possibly explode the egg cortical granules which in turn contribute to the *fertilization* and *hyaline plasma* membranes enclosing the fertilized egg. Also present in some mammalian sperm is an enzyme, hyaluronidase. When spermatozoa are vitally stained

Figure 3-2. Transformation of the spermatid into a spermatozoan: i.e., parts (a) to (g) show the transition; part (g) is the last stage. The acrosome with its enzymes aid in penetration of the egg membranes and cytoplasm, the nucleus contains the genetic contribution from the male parent, while the midpiece and flagellum function as the power plant and motile organ respectively.

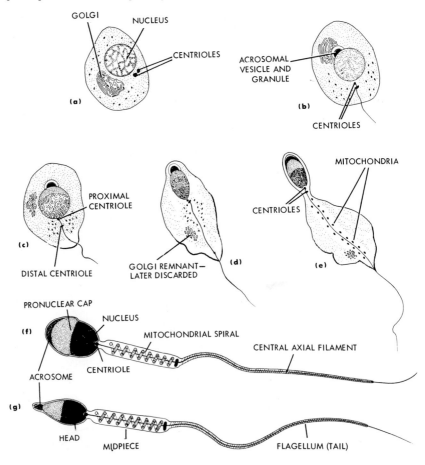

with acridine orange and photographed by fluorescent microscopy, the nuclear material is colored green; the acrosomes, containing some of the same enzymes as the *lysosomes,* are orange. On the proximal side of the nucleus lie several *centrosomes,* two within the so-called neck of the sperm, the proximal and ring-shaped distal centrosomes. Within this region may also be found the origins of the principal filaments of the middle-piece and flagellum that are considered to play a role in sperm movement. *Mitochondria* occupy much of the midpiece as aggregates or spiral bands external to these filaments, which in turn have the typical flagellar-like arrangement of two central and nine double peripheral *fibrils.* Mammalian sperm possess an additional ring of nine outer filaments lying just under the mitochrondria of the midpiece. In some manner all these filaments are involved in movement. The fibrous sheath of the flagellum is sometimes ribbed.

Current methods of selective staining, *pulse labeling,* differential centrifugation, electron microscopy, and immunological and biochemical analyses are contributing rapidly to our knowledge of sperm morphology and physiology. Sperm may be refrigerated in suitable media or be frozen for a period of time without diminishing their capacity for fertilization. Artificial insemination is now widely practiced in domestic animals and man. As a result of the human population explosion, there is an interest in current research into the processes of the biology of reproduction.

Ova   Study of the changing structural patterns during animal development might profitably begin with the unfertilized egg when it attains a fertilizable condition near the time of ovulation. Depending upon the species, oogenesis (or egg-cell maturation) may have been initiated (mammal) or completed by this time; certain egg enzymes are present, including fertilizin and antifertilizin; and cytoplasmic organization has attained a structured state that will later change following activation at fertilization. Eggs of any organism are complex specialized cells which in the mature and fertilizable condition have advanced considerably at the subcellular level of organization and have attained a state of unstable equilibrium that requires only some kind of stimulus to cause development to be resumed. Such a stimulus starts the potential organism on its long and progressively complicated pathway of development. A specialized cell, with all the potentialities for producing an organism contained in its nucleus and cytoplasmic organelles with their boundary membranes, is suddenly brought to a halt. Early maturity or aging of some type has been attained, and the cell will die unless activation occurs soon. The effective fertilizable period of the human ovum following ovulation is less than thirty-six hours, and in the rabbit around six hours. Fertilization of aged eggs may produce developmental abnormalities in any species.

Chordate eggs are illustrated in Figures 3-3 and 3-4. All types are intimately enclosed by a living plasma membrane and by an external vitelline or primary membrane (zona pellucida in placental mammals). As eggs of various species are passed down the oviduct following ovulation, a secretory acquisition is made to the primary membrane. In amphibians and rabbits this consists of a jelly-like protein-polysaccharide material; a chitinous chorion is added to fish eggs. Cleidoic (enclosed) eggs become surrounded by an inner nutrient bacteriostatic albumen and external to this by an inorganic fibrous shell membrane plus either parchment-like or *calcareous shells* (reptiles, birds, and monotreme mammals). Throughout the chordates the eggs vary greatly in their content of nutritive yolk, and this yolk is also important in the cleavage pattern. The term telolecithal has been applied to eggs containing large amounts of this inert material which is more or less concentrated in the lower hemisphere.

For convenience telolecithal eggs may be classified into two groups: (1) macrolecithal eggs in which the large amount of yolk does not divide and the embryo forms on one side of this yolk that later is enclosed in a cellular yolk sac (as in many elasmobranchs, most teleost fish, reptiles, and birds); (2) microlecithal (mesolecithal) eggs in which there is relatively less yolk that divides into cells (amphibians). Since this type is widespread among lower vertebrates, it has been suggested that it may have been characteristic of the ancestral forms (Romer); (3) *isolecithal* (oligolecithal) eggs of protochordates and marsupial and placental mammals (Figure 3-4), the smallest of the three types, contain little food material. These either develop rapidly to a feeding larval stage (protochordate species) or the early embryo (mammal) soon acquires a nutritive connection with the mother via the *placenta*. Although in most respects mammalian development is distinctive, it has long been recognized that mammals have probably descended from reptilian-like ancestors that possessed heavily yolked eggs. One reason for this belief is that the early human embryo, lacking any yolk, possesses for a time a vestigial yolk sac.

When chordate eggs are mature and ready for fertilization, they are at some stage of the meiotic cycle, generally at a metaphase stage of the second of the two divisions (Figure 3-5). The first polar body has been given off

Figure 3-3. Unfertilized eggs of frog and hen, showing the primary and secondary membranes associated with each one of these microlecithal and macrolecithal eggs. (From Saunders' *Animal Morphogenesis.* New York: Macmillan, 1966.)

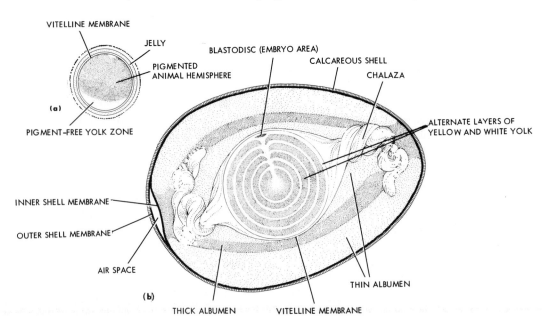

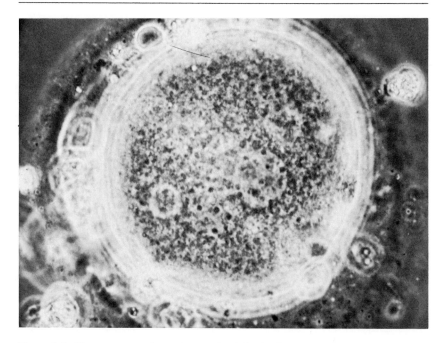

Figure 3-4. Phase contrast photomicrograph of the fertilized human ovum at the pronuclear stage. The zona pellucida membrane encloses the egg. (Courtesy of Stanley R. Glasser, Vanderbilt Medical School. Photographed by the Vanderbilt Medical Center. The specimen was discovered by T. H. Clewe, M.D.)

and division for the second has been initiated in the secondary oocyte. At this time the structural organization shows a cell rich in *RNA*, as demonstrated by numerous cytochemical studies. Eggs stain deeply basophilic with basic dyes. (e.g., egg of the placental mammal) and the stainable material

Figure 3-5. Oviductal egg of the mouse, showing first polar body, metaphase stage of the second maturation spindle, and the zona pellucida. Fertilization of placental mammal eggs takes place at this stage of ovum development.

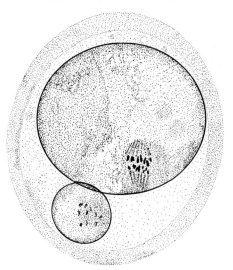

may be removed with the enzyme *ribonoclease*. The several RNAs differ relatively in eggs of different species, with ribosomal RNA particularly abundant in amphibian eggs. Little is known about the origin or pattern of aggregation of this material or its distribution within the cell. Cytoplasmic *DNA* has been reported. Yolk is present as granules of lipid, protein, lipo-protein and fat.

Within the egg cytoplasm are most of the organelles found in any somatic cell (Figure 3-6) except for the temporary absence of a nucleolus. Ribo-somes, lysosomes, pigment granules, endoplasmic reticulum, mitochondria, and a Golgi appartus may be identified. In contrast to that of somatic cells, the scattered endoplasmic reticulum is poorly formed with varying numbers of ribosomes lying free or attached to it. Granules in the outer cortical cytoplasm of the egg beneath the plasma membrane contain the same enzymes, with similar staining reactions, as are found in lysosomes. These granules have been described as submicroscopic, sac-like organelles about one-quarter micron in diameter and contain enzymes that break down carbo-hydrates, proteins, and fats. All this organization has been effected during

Figure 3-6. Diagrammatic drawing of a secretory-type body cell of the adult organism showing the several types of organelles found in somatic cells. A number of the organelles may be found in the germ cells.

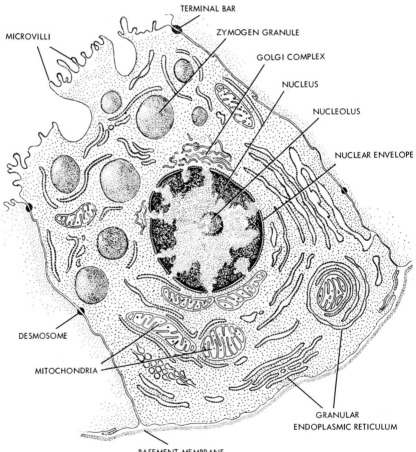

the ovarian growth of the egg in its development from an oogonium of germinal epithelial origin.

The concentration of yolk in the lower hemisphere of telolecithal eggs points to a visible polar organization; the relatively yolk-free upper cytoplasmic region is called the animal hemisphere in contrast to the yolk-laden lower vegetal hemisphere. An imaginary line drawn between the center of these hemispheres delineates the central axis of the cell. Internal organization relates to this axis; it may be radially symmetrical like the spokes of a wheel from the hub as in the frog's egg or bilateral to either side of it, as in the hen's egg. Symmetry may change on fertilization. Other evidence of structural polarity is seen in the location of the nucleus toward the animal pole, formation of polar bodies in that region, and in the fact that a spermatozoan enters the egg generally in the animal hemisphere. In heavily yolked eggs cleavage begins in this region.

Within the cortical cytoplasm of an egg there is some type of cytoplasmic structural organization of invisible formative or ground substances; an organization that will change first as a result of fertilization and later in response to progressive *morphogenetic movements* and *inductive actions*. This cytoplasmic pattern will be affected later by the genes from male and female parents as embryonic *differentiation* progresses. Patterns of these regionally different areas, established genetically during ovarian growth, vary somewhat in different eggs. Certain areas may be marked by the presence of pigments (amphibians) of several colors (protochordates) which may change position following sperm penetration. However, pigments themselves bear no functional relation to the formative materials that characterize different presumptive areas. There is wide variation in the size of eggs, from the fertilized isolecithal mouse egg (0.07-0.08 millimeter) and human egg approximately 0.14 millimeter in diameter, or just within the range of visibility of the human eye, to the telolecithal egg of the ostrich with its large content of nutrient yolk.

The Beginnings of Development

Fertilization

Development begins with the union of germ cells in fertilization when the egg is jarred out of its state of unstable equilibrium and resumes development. The genetic structure of the new individual is established at this time; shifts of protoplasmic areas may take place (grey crescent in the frog's egg, pigment crescents in the egg of *Styela*, a tunicate), interaction between chromosomes and cytoplasm may be initiated, and chromosomal sex is determined. Barring accidental disturbance, disease, adverse environment, and unusual genetic factors, the basis of future structural organization becomes established. After a sperm enters the egg the second polar body is extruded as the second meiotic division is completed, and the *ootid* (zygote) is prepared for the first cleavage division. The zygote possesses everything essential for development although the unfertilized egg alone contains sufficient essential material to form a complete organism even without the contribution from a male parent, as is shown by parthenogenetic development.

Sperm entrance may be likened to any stimulating agent that triggers the basic mechanisms in the egg. This stimulus may be furnished under appropriate conditions by means other than sperm entrance, e.g., by artificial means, either chemical or physical. One artificial parthenogenetic technique, employed successfully with amphibian eggs, consists of spreading blood over eggs which have been newly shed as a result of hormonal stimulation from transplanted pituitary glands; then each egg is pricked with a fine needle in the *animal hemisphere*. When this pricking introduces a blood cell into the egg's interior, the latter acts as a center around which the first cleavage division proceeds. Fish eggs have also been activated artificially by a variety of techniques, and *parthenogenesis* has been reported in the chicken and turkey.

Meiosis is also a critical process, contributing to the formation of the total genotype of the fertilized egg as chromosomes are segregated in a random manner between polar bodies and ovum. In addition to these two critical periods in development we may add the later process of gastrulation with its accompanying phenomena of cell movement and inductive organizer action. Although much study in past decades has been devoted to these three periods, it is surprising to find that little significant information exists about any one of them.

Pattern Change at
Fertilization

The earliest of the visible morphological changes to take place during and after contact of the fertilizing sperm with the egg's vitelline membrane (or *zona pellucida* of placental mammals) and its entrance into the egg is the breakdown of the cortical granules or vacuoles. This liberates the vacuolar material containing sulfonated glycoprotein, which is added to both the vitelline and hyaline plasma membranes. Subsequent elevation of the combined vitelline-secretion membrane to form the fertilization membrane leaves the fluid-filled *perivitelline space* between it and the hyaline-plasma membrane. The elevation of the fertilization cone from the egg cortex to meet the sperm then takes place. As the sperm penetrates the fertilization membrane, the sperm acrosomal and membrane materials unite with the fertilization cone and nuclear and other spermatic substances pass into the cone. This is followed by withdrawal of the cone into the egg and completion of the second meiotic division. The sperm and egg nuclear materials form two haploid pronuclei which may unite or come to lie in close proximity, constituting the *zygote* (diploid) nucleus for the first cleavage mitotic division. Streaming movements within the cytoplasm cause extensive redistribution of *ooplasmic* substances, including pigments (fish, frog), and the reorientation of internal symmetries which are indicative of structural change. Biochemical phenomena such as the activation of protein synthesis by ribosomes, formation of a nucleolus in some cases, and various physiological reactions (increase in oxygen consumption and carbon dioxide production) are beyond the scope of this chapter. Heavily yolked eggs tend to be polyspermic, and several sperm enter the egg although only one completes the fertilization reaction with the egg haploid pronucleus. Much has been written about the cortical components of the gametes and their roles in fertilization, the enzymatic fertilizin-antifertilizin aspects of the fertilization reaction, the role of lysins in sperm penetration, sperm acrosome reactions with the egg surface, and membrane fusion in relation to sperm-egg association. Research in these areas continues to be active, as an examination of current scientific literature will show. All these factors reflect the evolving morphological pattern of a specialized cell progressing to the next stage of its development.

Numerous examples of eggs can be found that exhibit conspicuous changes during and following sperm entrance. The egg of *Styela* is particularly good in this respect as several differently colored areas in the form of crescents subsequently appear as a result of cortical movements. Such areas have been traced during development to the *presumptive materials* of the *primary germ layers* (ectoderm, endoderm, and chorda-mesoderm). The term "presumptive" as applied here refers to the state or condition of a material characterized by marked lability and considerable prospective potency that shows little evidence as yet of its future developmental role. In the frog's egg there occurs a partial withdrawal of *melanin* pigment from a crescentic area in the marginal zone almost opposite the point of sperm entrance. Gastrulation will later be initiated in this gray crescent area with formation of the dorsal lip of the blastopore; moreover the gray crescent marks a change from radial to bilateral symmetry in the arrangement of the internal formative materials. These and other examples discussed in textbooks of embryology indicate that following egg activation marked changes have taken place in the internal arrangement of future building materials. In certain heavily yolked eggs, massive cytoplasmic movements take place, as in the egg of the killifish, *Fundulus,* where cytoplasm flowing toward the animal pole actually produces the blastodisc on the surface of the yolk mass from which the embryo will develop.

Cleavage Patterns   Following entrance of the spermatozoan the zygote divides wholly (isolecithal and microlecithal eggs) or in part (macrolecithal eggs) by repeated synchronous mitotic divisions into progressively smaller-sized cells known as blastomeres; this period of development terminates at the *blastula* stage. Although a late stage of cleavage may eventually contain as many as 1000 cells, the total volume of the embryo has increased very little over that of the fertilized egg during this period. Cleavage cell multiplication occurs so rapidly that the daughter cells show little or no growth between successive mitotic divisions and hence the cells become smaller (Figure 3-7). In this respect cleavage differs from somatic cell division in which the cells grow in size between successive divisions. Cleavage, however, represents more than mere cellular multiplication, as evidenced by the arrangement of the blastomeres with respect to each other to form the different cellular patterns (radial, bilateral) characteristic of the species. It must be assumed that there is a coordinating mechanism that determines timing and orientation of each mitotic division to produce such patterns. Furthermore, cleavage converts the presumptive areas of the fertilized egg into a cellular structure facilitating the later migration of cells during gastrulation. Cell patterns may be experimentally deranged in many types of animals without disturbing development, a fact that confirms the labile character of the early structural arrangements. A great deal of evidence from the nuclear transplants into activated enucleated amphibian eggs, separation of blastomeres in eggs with *holoblastic* divisions, constriction or pressure of the zygote that results in irregular nuclear distribution (amphibians), and destruction of nuclei [3]—all point to the genetic equivalence of the nuclei (gynomes) of the blastomeres during this period and to their lack of appreciable change (maturation). There is no change in the original cytoplasmic structure pattern during this type of division.

Cleavage patterns appear to be correlated not only with the determined developmental patterns of the larvae, but also with the amount and distribution of yolk that influence the rate and method by which the protoplasm is divided. Isolecithal eggs are characterized by total (holoblastic) and practically equal cell division that results in only slight difference in blastomere size between animal and vegetal hemispheres (rat, man). Among placental mammals the cleavage rate and arrangement of the cells with respect to each other are irregular from the beginning (Figure 3-8), and cleavage occurs as the young embryo is moved down the oviduct. At the time of entrance into the uterus, about four days after fertilization, the embryo is in the *morula* (solid mass) stage. In Amphioxus, whose development is well known, bilateral symmetry is established before fertilization. The first cleavage, which passes through the center of this egg, produces two cells destined to become the left and right sides of the embryo. The second cleavage occurs at right angles to the first, and the third cuts the embryo at right angles to the first two slightly above the equator. This mass of eight cells which encloses

Figure 3-7. Cleavage stages and blastula of the frog. Cleavage is holoblastic but unequal, and the blastula is an unequal coeloblastula. The fertilization and jelly membranes are not shown. Gastrulation will be initiated within the gray crescent area. This type of cleavage is also found in the sturgeon. (From Waddington's *Principles of Development and Differentiation.* New York: Macmillan, 1966.)

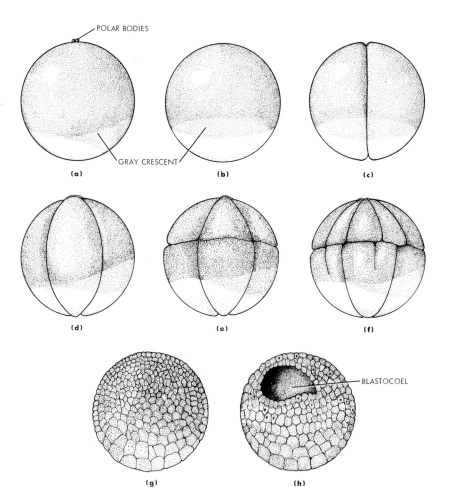

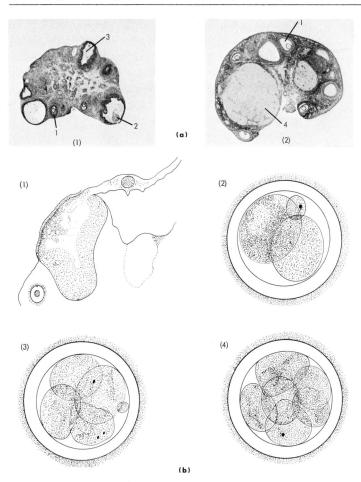

Figure 3-8. (a) Sections of the ovary of the rat showing (1) developing Graafian follicles with ova; (2) egg enclosed by corona radiata cells and separated from the follicular stratum granulosum, previous to rupture of the follicle during the process of ovulation; (3) early stage in the transition of the ruptured Graafian follicle to a corpus luteum; (4) corpus luteum of pregnancy. (Courtesy of Dr. Richard Blandau, University of Washington School of Medicine.)

  (b) (1) Portion of a section of the ovary of the golden hamster, *Cricetus auratus,* at 1 a.m. of day 2 of the estrous cycle, showing ovulation of an egg from a Graafian follicle. (After M. C. Ward, 1946.) (2)-(4) Cleavage in a hanging drop culture of a two-cell stage of the rhesus monkey recovered about thirty hours after ovulation. (After W. H. Lewis and C. G. Hartman.)

a small central cavity, the segmentation cavity, shows an upper quartet of cells somewhat smaller in size than the lower quartet where the yolk is present. Cleavage continues in this geometric progression: the next division is in the vertical plane of each blastomere and results in sixteen cells arranged in two tiers of eight cells each. This is followed by a horizontal division with the formation of four rows of eight cells each; after the sixty-four-cell stage cleavage becomes increasingly irregular.

  By contrast, in microlecithal eggs of amphibians (some fish) the heavily yolk-laden cells of the vegetal hemisphere are larger and fewer than the essentially yolk-free cells in the animal hemisphere (Figure 3-7). At any particular cleavage stage their slower division rate is correlated with the larger volume of yolk in this region, the relatively inert yolk tending to retard the rate of cell division. This is total (holoblastic) but unequal cleavage. The cleavage pattern at first is quite regular in the frog or urodele egg. A late cleavage stage is characterized by a wall several cells thick with a cavity displaced into the animal hemisphere.

In macrolecithal eggs cleavage is confined to the relatively yolk-free cytoplasmic disc on one side of the yolk (most fish, reptiles, birds, monotreme mammals) that remains undivided (Figure 3-9). This cleavage pattern is termed meroblastic (superficial) and is discoidal. First and second cleavages, which are vertical and at right angles to each other, pass only through the protoplasmic disc. With subsequent cleavages the eight- and sixteen-cell stages may be recognized, but cleavage soon becomes irregular in pattern. With the appearance of horizontal cleavages a cellular sheet results that is for the most part separated by a cavity from the undivided mass of yolk beneath it. Later the yolk becomes enclosed within a cellular yolk sac attached to the ventral body wall of the embryo and serves as a food reservoir until hatching takes place.

As pointed out before, organization of the presumptive cytoplasmic materials is less rigidly specified in eggs of some species at the onset of cleavage than in others. In such instances the eggs and early cleavage stages are capable of considerable self-regulation (repair) to compensate for any loss of egg substance or later of blastomeres. This has been demonstrated by a variety of experiments which include separation or fusion of blastomeres, vital staining (with vital dyes such as neutral red, bismarck brown, janus green B, Nile blue sulfate), centrifugation to disturb the location of certain cytoplasmic contents, and deletion (removal) of a portion of the cytoplasm [3]. If each of the first two blastomeres or a later bilateral division of the amphibian early cleavage embryo contains a portion of the gray crescent, (gastrulation area) then a complete embryo will be formed. These and other studies point to a more developmentally labile or undetermined type of organizational pattern of the cytoplasmic structure in such "regulative" eggs, and cleavage is said to be indeterminate.

A special instance of the lability of mammalian blastomeres during early cleavage has been demonstrated by Dr. Beatrice Mintz and Dr. K. Silvers [12], who in their research on immunological tolerance (Figure 3-10) studied "multimice" produced from pairs of conjoined undifferentiated cleavage-stage embryos of different histocompatible genotypes. These individuals of multi-embryonic origin are permanently tolerant of cells of both original parents, but they display a normal and specific immune response to the introduction of a foreign antigen. The animals are formed by first assembling all the blastomeres from two (or more) genetically distinctive embryos into one composite group *in vitro*; later this group is transferred surgically to the uterus of a pseudopregnant female. Here regulation from double to single embryos occurs during implantation. Normal development to birth frequently follows, and Mintz and Silvers have obtained healthy

Figure 3-9 (opposite). Cleavage in the macrolecithal egg of the hen, surface and cross-sectional views of the blastoderm. (After Patterson, 1910.)

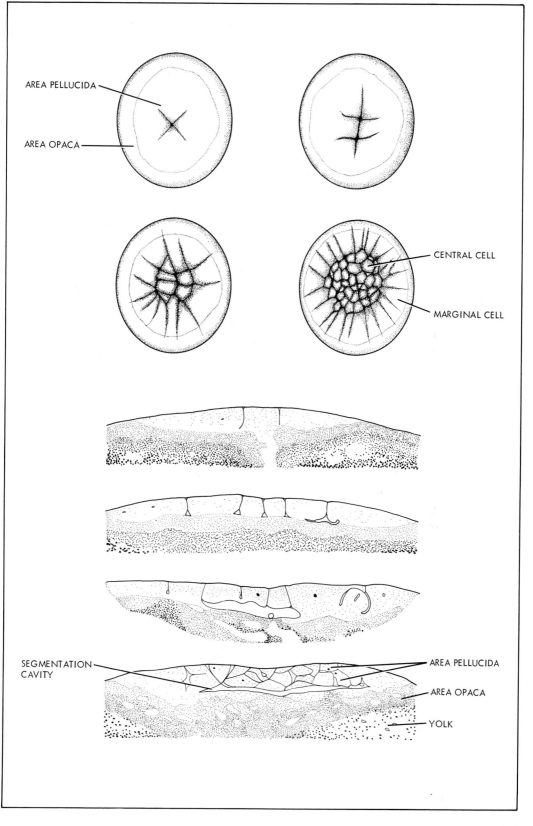

AREA PELLUCIDA

AREA OPACA

CENTRAL CELL

MARGINAL CELL

SEGMENTATION
CAVITY

AREA PELLUCIDA

AREA OPACA

YOLK

105

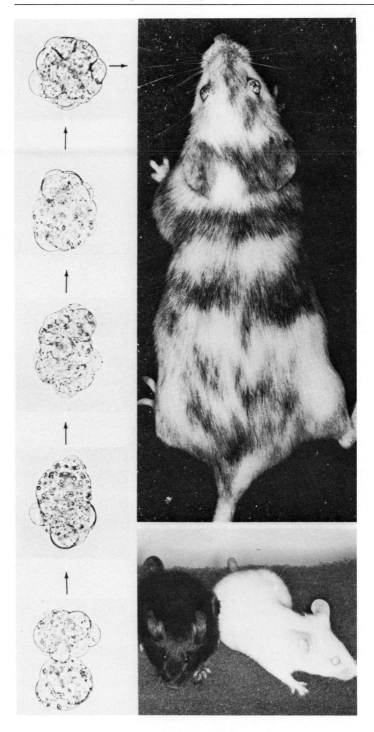

Figure 3-10. Following removal of the fertilization membrane the cleavage stages of different ova may be combined to form a single embryo, a "multi" or allophenic mouse. When transplanted to the uterus of a stimulated female mouse such cell combinations have given rise to viable young, demonstrating the organizational lability of mammalian cleavage stages. (Courtesy of Dr. Beatrice Mintz.)

adults comprising many pairs of genotypes. The name "allophenic" has been applied to such animals because of the orderly coexistence of cells with different phenotypes ascribable to known allelic genotypic differences. An embryo may have had four or more parents. It would be interesting to know more about the immunologic properties as they appear during vertebrate development, and studies of this and related areas are being actively pursued at this time.

In other species ooplasmic segregation of formative materials is more rigidly determined and the removal of parts of eggs, or later of blastomeres during cleavage, may bring about developmental deficiencies in the embryo, the type and severity of which are correlated with the area or amount of material removed. Eggs and early developmental stages of this character have been studied particularly in relation to gene activation and determination. The eggs of tunicates and of Amphioxus, which are unable to compensate for even a small loss of material, are good examples of this more rigid structural pattern, and the term "determinative" has been applied to them [Figure 3-11 (a)]. There are all degrees between strictly determinate and indeterminate types. Various physical and chemical factors may influence both morphological and physiological patterns in any type of egg, and hence modify the course of cleavage, e.g., temperature that affects the rate of enzyme action, X-rays, drugs, and so on.

Control of cleavage probably operates at the cortical level of egg organization. Changes in the cortex are believed to initiate furrow formation and cell division, with subcortical synthesis of new cortical material taking place before a cleavage furrow forms. Much of this work has been carried out on amphibian eggs [3]. Research has determined that the cortex has the properties of an elastic solid, the egg does not behave like a liquid sphere; the cortex transmits a surface change at fertilization, and there occurs a passive behavior at the cleavage furrow where the cortex appears to buckle inward. These findings have dispelled a number of earlier theories as to the mechanism of cleavage, e.g., the "surface tension theory" of Spek. Attempts to slow down cleavage with mitotic inhibitors have not been enlightening.

In summary, cleavage is more than mere cellular multiplication: (1) Cells ultimately have a definite and predetermined pattern in relation to each other and the embryonic parts to which they will contribute their progeny. According to this, cleavage and the onset of differentiation (cell specialization) occur concurrently and interrelatedly. (2) There is little or no increase in the total cell mass during the period of cleavage. (3) Synthesis of nuclear material, correlated with the number of cells present in the early embryo and with no growth in the size of daughter cells between successive cleavage division, takes place at a rapid rate. (4) The fundamental basis of cell heredity is manifested because cleavage patterns are genetically determined. Patterns of cleavage may be modified and the rate changed by certain extrinsic forces without interfering with the normalcy of the embryo. (5) The amount and distribution of yolk is correlated with the several cleavage patterns. (6) During cleavage the *organ-forming areas* become separated from each other more distinctly and also are broken up into cell units. This emphasizes the precocious segregation of cytoplasmic materials. (7) Cellular architecture of the embryo is initiated, to be subsequently acted upon by

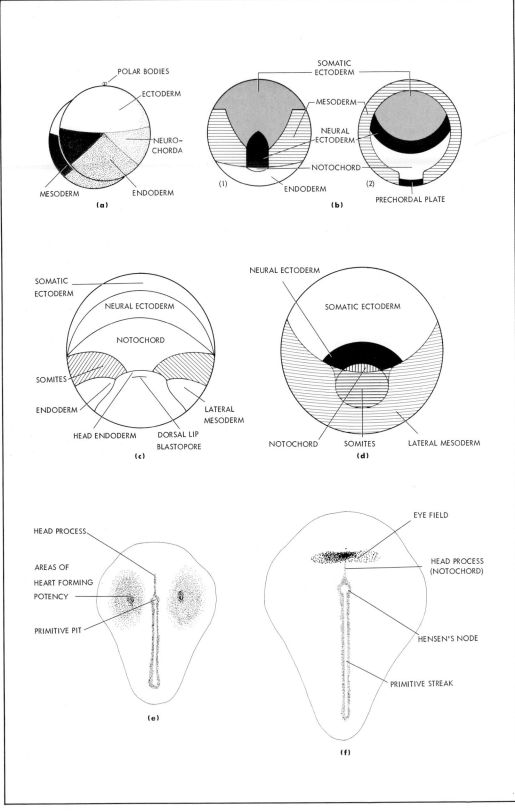

POLAR BODIES

ECTODERM

NEURO-
CHORDA

MESODERM ENDODERM

(a)

SOMATIC
ECTODERM

MESODERM

NEURAL
ECTODERM

NOTOCHORD

(1) ENDODERM

(2) PRECHORDAL PLATE

(b)

SOMATIC
ECTODERM

NEURAL ECTODERM

NOTOCHORD

SOMITES

ENDODERM

HEAD ENDODERM DORSAL LIP
BLASTOPORE

LATERAL
MESODERM

(c)

NEURAL ECTODERM

SOMATIC ECTODERM

NOTOCHORD SOMITES LATERAL MESODERM

(d)

HEAD PROCESS

AREAS OF
HEART FORMING
POTENCY

PRIMITIVE PIT

(e)

EYE FIELD

HEAD PROCESS
(NOTOCHORD)

HENSEN'S NODE

PRIMITIVE STREAK

(f)

108

the processes of gastrulation. (8) Synthetic mechanisms are chiefly those related to mitotic activity. As cleavage progresses the segmentation cavity appears among the cells in many animal eggs, and soon afterward the embryo attains the blastula stage of development.

Blastula Stage of Development

The blastula stage marks the end phase of the period of cleavage. In most chordates the embryo at this stage consists of either a single- or multi-cell layer in the form of a hollow sphere or of a flat sheet upon the surface of a mass of undivided yolk. Differences in the size of cells, pigmentation, and amount of yolk in different parts of blastulae continue to emphasize the specific areas destined to form the various embryonic germ layers from which the tissues and organs of the adult organism will develop. The blastula stage is reached at two days following fertilization in the frog; late during the first day in the incubated hen's egg; and by three to four days in placental mammals when the embryo is entering the uterine cavity. The blastula of an isolecithal egg, like that of Amphioxus, is a hollow sphere with a wall one-cell thick which is still enclosed by the fertilization membrane. Polarity continues to be indicated by the presence of smaller-sized cells, the micromeres, in the animal hemisphere and larger cells, macromeres, in the vegetal hemisphere. "Fate" maps of the distribution of presumptive formative materials of blastulae and gastrulae, illustrated in Figures 3-11 and 3-16, show the distribution of the materials destined to form the embryonic germ layers of presumptive ectoderm, chorda-mesoderm, and endoderm. The basic structural organization has not changed from that of the fertilized egg except the presumptive areas have broken into many cells. Blastulae of Amphioxus, which are coeloblastulae of the equal type. enclose the blastocoel, a large central cavity filled with a chemically complex fluid of cellular derivation.

Unequal coeloblastulae characterize organisms with holoblastic but unequal cleavage in which the wall may be multilayered and the blastocoel displaced toward the animal pole. Among chordates the blastulae of amphibians are of this type (Figure 3-7) and show a clear-cut distinction between pigmented animal and vegetal hemispheres. In certain respects this type resembles that of Amphioxus, but there is a greater size difference between cells in the animal and vegetal hemispheres. The blastocoel is relatively small. Analyses have shown that the fluid within the blastocoel possesses certain distinguishing characteristics from that of environmental fluids, including chemical content and a pH which is more basic than that of the enclosing cells. With

Figure 3-11 (opposite). "Fate" maps of the presumptive organ-forming areas in the early stages of chordate embryos. (a) Presumptive areas of the embryonic tissues in the two-cell stage of the tunicate, *Styela*. (b) Fate maps of teleost blastoderms: (1) *Fundulus*, (2) trout. The undivided yolk of these macrolecithal eggs is not shown. (After Oppenheimer, 1947, and Pasteels, 1936.) (c) Presumptive areas in the surface of the early frog gastrula. The dorsal lip of the blastopore (future posterior end of the embryo) is used as the point of reference. (d) Blastoderm of the bird previous to the appearance of the primitive streak. (After Waddington.) (e) Bilateral location of the heart-forming areas in the blastoderm of the chick embryo at the head process stage. (After Rawles, 1943.) (f) Eye-forming area of the chick blastoderm at the head process stage. (After Willier and Rawles, 1935.)

the development of cilia on the surface cells of the amphibian blastula, the embryo begins a slow rotary movement within the perivitelline space.

The only perceptible organization of the amphibian blastula at this time is reflected in the rapid multiplication of the small cells in the region of the gray crescent, and the initiation of cell growth in the margin of the pigmented region along with its downward movement over the yolk-laden cells of the vegetal hemisphere (*process of epiboly*). This region of over-growth, the germ ring, will continue to spread downward until all the yolk-laden cells eventually are enclosed internally by pigmented cells. However, indirect evidence of the structural organization existing in the blastulae of different species of amphibians has been obtained by staining the surface cells and following their subsequent movements during gastrulation. These along with deletion and transplantation studies have demonstrated a definite arrangement of organ-forming materials in areas in the wall, including the gray crescent area, which mirrors the structural pattern of the fertilized egg (Figure 3-11). Although such fate maps may differ somewhat in pattern between different genera of amphibians, the basic arrangements are compar-able. Some of the cellular areas, as the presumptive mesoderm and noto-chord, will later move to the interior during gastrulation; others, like the presumptive neural ectoderm, will spread over the dorsal surface of the embryo. It should be re-emphasized that although these areas will definitely appear in certain embryonic tissues in normal development, they are far from being irreversibly destined at this stage as to the types of tissue into which they will differentiate. Although the neural ectoderm will normally end up in the nervous system, at this stage its fate is labile or loosely determined and it can easily be channeled into other types of tissues through appropriate inductor (evocator or releasing) influences. Primordial germ-cell material has been located among the yolk-laden cells in the floor of the amphibian blastula. Actually this generative material has been reported earlier in development from the vegetal region of the fertilized amphibian egg.

Macrolecithal eggs show cell division restricted to a small blastodermic cap on the surface of a large inert mass of yolk. In the bird, for example, the blastoderm shows two zones: (1) a central lighter-colored *area pellucida*, beneath which is the cavity of the blastocoel, and (2) a darker peripheral band, the *periblast* or *area opaca*, where the cells are in close association with the underlying yolk. The embryo forms in the area pellucida while a subsequent outward extension of the blastoderm over the yolk continues by growth within the zones of the area opaca.

Another type of blastula, of which there are several variations, is found among placental mammals (Figure 3-20). For example, at five to six days after mating the blastocyst of the rabbit, like that of the human, has attained considerable size and can no longer be flushed from the uterine tube. Rabbit blastocysts of this age can, however, be obtained easily by gently tearing open the uterine tube from one end to the other while the tube lies immersed in mammalian physiologic solution. Implantation into the uterine wall has not yet been initiated; at this stage each blastocyst has the form of a hollow sphere whose wall, the *trophoblast*, is one-cell thick. This wall encloses a blastocoel cavity. A small inner cell mass attached to the inner surface of the spherical trophoblast [Figure 3-20(a)] contains the precursors of the embryo, the vestigial yolk sac, and part of the extra-embryonic membrane complex. Although not directly demonstrated, there is reason to suspect that the pattern organization of presumptive materials within the inner cell mass at this time is bilateral and hence more or less comparable to that described for the earliest blastoderm of the chick embryo. One to two days later *deciduation* (disappearance of the old zona pellucida) has taken place and uterine implantation is being initiated at a time when the definitive primitive streak stage of development has been reached and there is a small vestigial yolk sac. Implantation of the human embryo takes place at about the same time after fertilization and at a similar developmental stage. Descriptions of other types of mammalian blastulae may be found among the references at the end of this chapter.

Thus far in the survey of structural patterns during development we have noted the types present in the fertilized egg as well as the ways in which they are related to the respective axes and symmetries of the egg. During cleavage the specific components are broken up without much change into a cellular organization. Even at the blastula stage these original structural patterns remain relatively the same. The next period of development will see striking alterations within the areas of formative materials as well as in the location, shape, and neighbors of each area as gastrulation progresses. Toward the end of this phase the earliest signs of the basic characteristic structure of the adult organism will begin to emerge from the germ layers in the form of primordia of future tissues and organs. Additional primordia will continue to appear and undergo differentiation in structure and function as the body of the embryo, developing in an orderly fashion, takes shape. There will be no subsequent relocation of the structural units.

Gastrulation:
The Beginning of
Differentiation

Gastrulation is a critical developmental period which is characterized by profound morphogenetic cell movements accompanied by tissue interactions of a determinative (restrictive) or specializing nature, The three embryonic germ layers make their appearance: ectoderm, chorda-mesoderm, and endoderm. In the late blastula stage the surfaces of cells in the presumptive areas of these embryonic tissues begin to exhibit intense activity both individually and in relation to each other. This activity, which continues in individual cells or cells in association as they move to other locations, is not clearly understood. Surface cells are thereby brought into the interior of the embryo, whereas others become spread out in layers and occupy the areas just vacated. The order and character of these formative movements executed in response to the genetic *gynome* are correlated with the amount and distribution of yolk. The mechanics appear essentially similar, but the patterns differ in the several types of blastulae.

During this early phase of differentiation cells take the first step in the long series of events leading to the appearance of definitive tissues and eventually of the association of tissues in organs and organ systems. It was noted previously that within any formative area of the blastula the cells were developmentally multipotential and lacked precise determination. For example, presumptive muscle cell mesoderm in the amphibian embryo could be experimentally provoked to join cells of the future neural tube through the action of the *evocator* effect of the chorda-mesodermal roof of the *archenteron* (primitive gut). Their fate now becomes fixed, and cells of a developing tissue will give rise only to cells characteristic of that particular tissue. In other words, the developmental potentiality of a cell within the new location of a presumptive area gradually becomes restricted by new environmental influences until it attains a nonmodifiable condition. Not all presumptive areas become restricted during the period of gastrulation. Other evidences of inductive action may be seen later in development, as in the case of the determination of the lens of the eye from body ectoderm through inductive action of the optic cup, or of the cornea of the eyeball through influences from the combined optic cup and lens. Few organs in the body have been found to complete their differentiation in structure and function without the involvement of the inductor (organizer) phenomenon in the course of their early history.

Gastrulation and later developmental phenomena will now be discussed briefly for eggs containing large amounts of yolk and for the special egg of the placental mammal. For other types of eggs, reference should be made to current texts on embryology.

Amphibian Embryo — An initial step in gastrulation in the moderately telolecithal frog's egg is the formation of the dorsal blastoporal lip within the gray crescent area about twenty-nine hours after fertilization. It will be recalled that the crescent originally appeared opposite the sperm entrance point during fertilization of the ovum. Cells of the presumptive notochord (chorda) and somatic mesoderm converge toward the dorsal midline and, in association with yolk-endoderm cells, move (involute) into the internal blastocoel (Figure 3-12). Factors responsible for the activity at this particular place have not been precisely identified. The new cavity taking form in this manner is the gastrocoel, or primitive gut, and its opening to the exterior is the beginning of the blastopore. Elsewhere the superficial pigmented layer of presumptive mesoderm and ectoderm, showing intensive mitotic activity, continues its downward movement over the yolk-endoderm toward the vegetal pole (process of epiboly). When other presumptive mesoderm cells reach the blastoporal region, they involute at the lateral blastoporal lips. The last ones to involute are those approaching the blastoporal region from the ventral side. In this manner a circular blastopore is soon formed with its opening plugged by a mass of yolk-endoderm, termed the yolk plug (Figure 3-12). The dorsal side of the embryo is occupied now by the presumptive neural plate cells which have moved into the area vacated by the departing chorda-mesoderm.

Figure 3-12 shows a median sagittal section of the yolk-plug stage. The original blastocoel has become almost obliterated by the involuted cells which also enclose the new cavity of the archenteron. Yolk-endoderm material forms the walls and floor of the archenteron, and the roof is a layer

Figure 3-12 (opposite). The course of gastrulation in the embryo of the frog shown in whole mounts and cross-sections. The structural pattern changes markedly as areas of presumptive organ-forming materials move to other positions either on the surface or to the interior of the embryo. The first of the cellular interactions, known as inductions, have been identified during this phase of development. (From Saunders' *Animal Morphogenesis*. New York: Macmillan, 1966.)

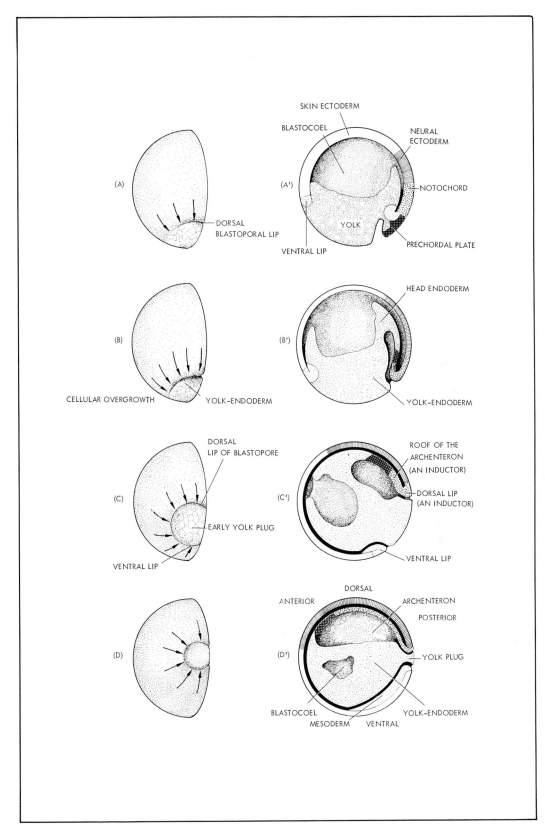

of inner endoderm cells separated from the dorsal neural plate area above it by the involuted chorda-mesoderm. Soon the dorsal endoderm becomes distinct and the chorda-mesoderm differentiates into the median notochord bounded by lateral strips of somatic mesoderm. Elsewhere around the embryo a layer of somatic mesoderm lies beneath the body ectoderm and separates it from the large yolk-endoderm mass.

In the salamander a slight difference occurs in the origin of the dorsal endodermal roof of the archenteron. In this form the endoderm above the dorsal lip is the first to involute and gives rise to the anterior wall of the gut. The endoderm is followed by the chorda-mesoderm, which soon forms into distinct notochord and somatic mesoderm as the temporary roof of the archenteron. Shortly thereafter the side endodermal walls of the archenteron extend toward the median line beneath the chorda-mesoderm and unite to form the endodermal roof.

Many years ago Spemann and his students showed that the dorsal blastoporal lip and dorsal archenteric roof are causative factors in the differentiation of the neural ectoderm from its presumptive competent predecessor, and they gave the term "primary inductor" (organizer) to this material. When transplanted beneath indifferent ectoderm of another embryo of similar age, either material induced and organized a secondary embryonic axis containing elements that originated from the competent ectoderm as well as those differentiating from the transplant itself. As chorda-mesoderm cells pass through the lip during the course of normal development, they become endowed with organizing capacity. The chorda-mesodermal layer becomes the inductor of the central neural tube from the presumptive neural ectoderm above it, and thus determines the fate of this tissue. Actually, it was demonstrated that the chorda-mesodermal roof possesses regional evocating capacities; transplantation of the anterior part induces brain and head structures, whereas the posterior part initiates trunk and tail structures.

By the end of the gastrulation period in amphibian development the major cellular shifts in position have been completed. Also, instead of being able to differentiate into a variety of structures under suitable stimulation, some originally presumptive materials have become irrevocably determined along special lines. For example, as shown above, after gastrulation the presumptive neural plate will form only nervous system. The influence of this particular determination has been traced by a variety of experimental techniques to the underlying chorda-mesodermal layer. What are the source and nature of the stimulus that passes from the chorda-mesoderm to influence the prospective fate of the neural plate cells? The search for an explanation has reached the molecular level with the most sophisticated methodologies but after decades of intensive research the question still remains unanswered [9].

Neurulation   About the time the blastopore finally closes and the yolk plug becomes covered, two longitudinal neural folds, separated by a groove and connected by an anterior transverse fold, appear in the neural plate ectoderm. These folds proceed to arch dorsally and unite, in this manner cutting off an internal neural tube that shows initial division into future brain and spinal cord regions. Three parts of the embryonic brain soon become distinguishable: fore-, mid-, and hindbrain regions, designated respectively as the *pros-*

encephalon, *mesencephalon*, and *rhombencephalon*. Some of the main derivatives of these regions are briefly summarized in Table 3-2. The nervous system will be discussed in Chapter 11.

Mention should be made of the neural crest cords that arise from the neural plate as the neural folds close. Fate of the neural crest cells has been traced by deletion, transplantation, and staining methods. If these cords are experimentally removed the organism will lack the medulla of the adrenal gland, ganglion cells of spinal and certain cranial nerves, the autonomic system, pigment cells or *melanocytes*, cells ensheathing nerve fibers, visceral cartilage, parts of tooth germs, meninges of cord and brain, and so on.

Other structures make their appearance during neurulation as seen in Figure 3-13 and 3-14, as the embryo undergoes a change in shape with the appearance of the head and early tail bud. The notochord becomes distinct from the mesoderm as a median cylindrical rod. It is now bordered on each side by somites, forming in the somatic mesoderm, from which muscle cells, dermis of the skin, and units of the vertebral column will later develop. Ventral to the somite band on each side of the body is a narrow strip of somatic mesoderm, the *nephrotome*, from which will develop the elements of the kidneys and their ducts. Below the nephrotomal strip the lateral mesoderm consists of two cellular layers, outer somatic and inner sphanchnic, with the primordium of the body (coelomic) cavities between them. The two hypophyseal primordia are visible: *Rathke's pouch*, an ingrowth of the body ectoderm ventral to the brain, and the infundibular evagination of the prosencephalon. The paired rudiments of the heart are taking shape beneath the foregut. Fore-, mid-, and hindgut portions of the digestive tube are distinguishable. At this time, subordinate derivatives of the gut have been located as primordia: liver, bile duct, thyroid gland; others have been traced experimentally by vital staining and other methods.

Table 3-2.

Prosencephalon	Telencephalon	Cerebral hemispheres, corpus striatum Lateral ventricles (1 and 2) Olfactory lobes
	Diencephalon	Optic cups, thalamus (epi- and hypo-) Third ventricle, anterior tela choroidea Neurohypophysis and stalk, pineal body
Mesencephalon–Mesencephalon		Optic lobes Portion of the aqueduct of Sylvius (iter)
Rhombencephalon	Metencephalon	Cerebellum Portion of the aqueduct
	Myelencephalon	Medulla oblongata Fourth ventricle Motor components of certain cranial nerves (nerves 5-12)

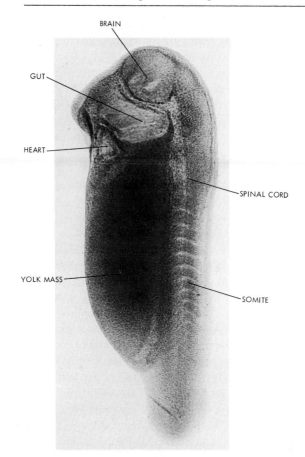

BRAIN

GUT

HEART

SPINAL CORD

YOLK MASS

SOMITE

Figure 3-13. Photomicrograph of a sagittal section of the 3-mm frog embryo at the tail-bud stage. The developing brain and spinal cord, bordered by somites, are visible in the dorsal part of the body. Ventral to these are gut and darkly stained yolk mass. Anteriorly, the heart and foregut lie ventral to the brain. At this and earlier stages numerous other body structures are present only as "fields" or undifferentiated areas. (Courtesy General Biological Supply Co.)

Figure 3-14. Cross-section through the trunk region of the three-millimeter frog embryo shown in Figure 3-13.

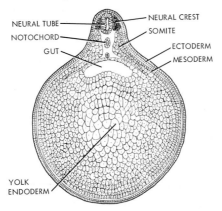

NEURAL TUBE
NOTOCHORD
GUT

NEURAL CREST
SOMITE
ECTODERM
MESODERM

YOLK
ENDODERM

The early embryo is a mosaic of structural areas or "fields" of determination, each of which will subsequently proceed to differentiate according to its presumptive fate. When any one of these fields is isolated and transplanted to the flank of another embryo of comparable age or stage of development, or cultured *in vitro* in a suitable medium, it will differentiate according to its degree of pattern determination. This is the usual method for testing such developmental capacity. Tests of this type also give evidence of the nature and degree of determination that has taken place. In this new environment a field will not be subjected to additional inductive influences and hence will differentiate independently of other structures on the basis of its inherent organization. It is said to show a capacity for independent self-differentiation which will become more complete with age.

Not all structures of the organism are determined at this time, nor are fields capable of differentiating into all parts peculiar to the mature organ. Determination of some organs occurs later, and even that within a field may occur slowly. An early field may give rise to an organ that is deficient or deformed. With advancing age a field progressively differentiates a more normal structure. The field concept of organization is easily applied to the embryos of fish and chick although these organisms are not so easily obtainable and the techniques of transplantation are more difficult. Little is known about reptilian and mammalian embryos of comparable stages of development, but there is reason to believe that a similar type or organization is present.

A number of facts have been ascertained about fields, as illustrated by the ear and limb fields. (1) Any field is larger in area than that portion which will later become incorporated into the organ, and any major part of an ear field will differentiate an internal ear. Several internal ears may be obtained from one ear field, which indicates the labile nature of the field at this time. A transplant from the center of the field gives a more complete ear than one from the peripheral; there must be then, an existing gradient of internal organization. The gradient concept previously has been referred to in connection with the fertilized egg, cleavage, and blastula stages of development. (2) As early stages of any field may show some overlapping with neighboring fields, transplants from peripheral regions usually contain more than one organ. (3) Transplants combining two similar fields may form one giant organ; this result demonstrates a capacity for regulation on the part of the fields. Another type of regulative ability during morphogenesis is seen in the capacity of a deficient or partial field to form a complete internal ear. These examples of regulative ability to compensate for loss of a part of itself or to combine two fields forming one ear are reminiscent of a similar capacity exhibited by fertilized egg or cleavage stages of certain indeterminate embryonic types. (4) Gradually the cells lose their lability and for a time may form different subparts of a field as progressive differentiation takes place. Even the major axes of an organ, such as the limb, become fixed in a characteristic order. The anterior-posterior axis becomes fixed first as shown by transplantation of a rotated field, followed shortly thereafter by the dorso-ventral axis. The last to be determined is the medial-lateral axis. Within amphibian limbs determination may never become absolutely fixed, as shown by the regenerative capacity of the limbs of the frog tadpole or of the aquatic newt following amputation.

Tail-bud   By the following tail-bud stage (Figures 3-13 and 3-14) the organization of
Stage   primordia of some organs of the amphibian embryo have reached a stage of
differentiation where their further development can no longer be modified
experimentally. Now the embryo is becoming structurally organized in the
pattern of the tadpole larva. The segmental arrangement of structures is seen
in the somites, primitive kidney tubules, neural crest derivatives, and vascular
system. The tail-bud itself is a mass of undifferentiated chorda-mesodermal
material which was the last to involute at the dorsal lip of the blastopore
during gastrulation. The heart develops at the tail-bud stage from lateral
mesoderm beneath the pharyngeal region. Blood islands and the first blood
cells have appeared in the vicinity of the liver and at the base of the tail.

Numerous and radical changes will take place later during the course of
metamorphosis when certain structures will disappear and others become
modified for the new life of the land-dwelling animal. Discussion of these
cannot be taken up here; for further details reference should be made to a
textbook of vertebrate embryology.

Chick   Two steps mark the course of gastrulation in the chick embryo. During the
Embryo   first, which is initiated before the egg is laid, the primitive endodermal layer
forms by a splitting or proliferation (*delamination*) of cells into the blastocoel from the thickened posterior portion of the area pellucida. As these
cells accumulate they spread outward with other contributions from the
blastoderm to form an inner cell layer beneath the blastoderm. This new
layer includes the endodermal material called the *hypoblast*, whereas the
original layer, now referred to as the epiblast, contains the chorda-mesoderm
and ectoderm. Long ago C. H. Waddington showed that this endodermal
sheet is the inductor of the primitive streak within the epiblast dorsal to it.
The epiblast continues to contribute cells to the hypoblast for some time. In
placental mammals the endoderm originates in the same manner, i.e., by
delamination of cells from the inner cell mass.

In the second step of chick gastrulation the cells in the epiblast (i.e., those
containing presumptive material of the mesodermal somites, heart, and
lateral and extra-embryonic mesoderm) migrate posteriorly and toward the
anterio-posterior midline of the epiblast. Here they accumulate and invaginate to form a structure known as the primitive streak (Figures 3-11 and
3-15). These cells spread laterally toward the area opaca as the middle
mesoderm layer between epiblast and hypoblast. Of the numerous methods
used to show that invagination of cells through the streak actually occurs,
the latest has been to trace the migration of radioactive-labeled cells as they
are added to the underlying layers. At the same time, presumptive noto-
chordal material moves into the anterior end of the streak at Hensen's node
from where it extends in the midline anterior to the streak between the
presumptive neural ectoderm and hypoblast in the form of the head process
(precursor of the notochord). Gradually the notochord elongates as the
streak recedes in a posterior direction. The three-layered embryo now
consists of upper epiblast, middle chorda-mesoderm, and lower hypoblast
layers. Cells that do not invaginate through the primitive streak and notochord remain in the epiblast as the ectoderm. In rabbit and man the streak is

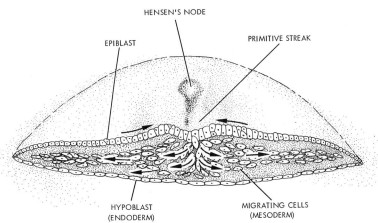

Figure 3-15. Diagrammatic cross-section of the primitive streak to illustrate movement of epiblast cells into the streak and their passage outward to contribute to the meso-dermal and endodermal layers. (From Waddington's *Principles of Development and Differentiation*. New York: Macmillan, 1966.)

believed to form in a manner comparable to that of the chick; there is no contrary evidence.

Fate maps showing the locations of presumptive organ-forming materials at the maximum (definitive) primitive streak stage are shown in Figures 3-11 and 3-16.

Culture *in vitro* is a technique widely used by investigators. The course of cellular movement during gastrulation has also been followed by sprinkling finely divided carbon on blastoderms cultured on the surface of plasma clots or on artificial culture media, both media containing embryo extract as a food source. Marking cells with vital dyes has been employed successfully with both living blastoderms *in situ* and transplants to the chorioallantoic membrane as well as to the embryonic coelomic cavity to determine the locations, extent, and organization of the presumptive organ-forming areas.

The developmental capacity of early mammalian embryos cultured *in vitro* has long been of interest. It is known that the inner cell mass of the rabbit will grow for a time on the surface of chicken plasma clots containing rabbit embryo extract as a food source, or on food-enriched artificial media. Recently the growth of blastocysts has been reported to take place in both artificial media and serum. Mammalian eggs have been fertilized *in vitro*, and the resulting development likewise followed in the culture medium to the blastocyst stage. When transplanted to the uterus of a hormone activated female, such blastocysts have become implanted. Transplants have been made to the anterior chamber of the adult eye in chicken, rat, and rabbit. In placental mammals, transplants also have been made to the omental bursa and beneath the capsule of the kidney where the foreign material becomes incorporated and vascularized as a graft.

The primitive streak of the chick embryo has been likened to the blasto-poral lips of the amphibian gastrula. Both possess inductor capacity. Cellular migrations toward the midline occur in both forms, and similar presumptive materials invaginate (Figures 3-12 and 3-15). Furthermore, in both chick and

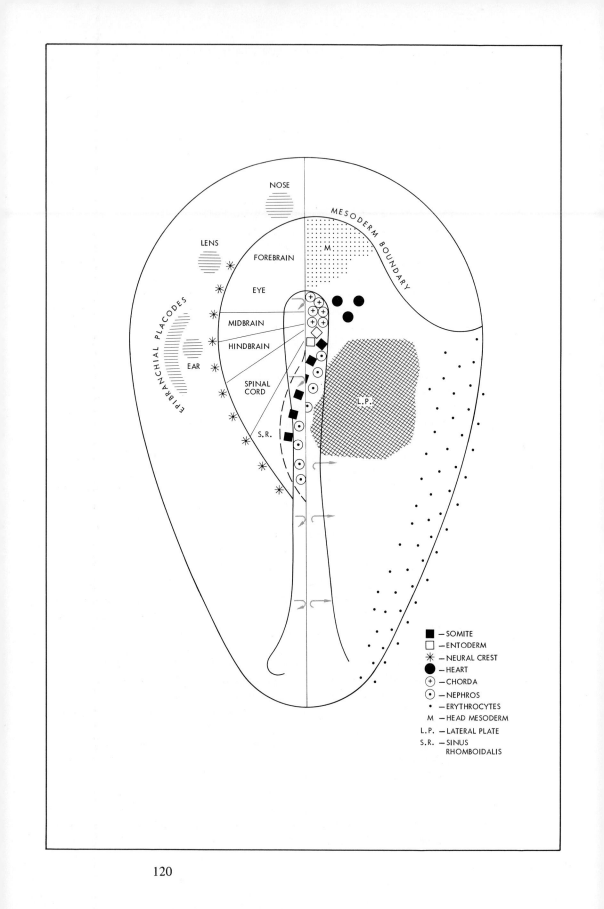

NOSE

MESODERM BOUNDARY

LENS

FOREBRAIN

M

EYE

MIDBRAIN

HINDBRAIN

EPIBRANCHIAL PLACODES

EAR

SPINAL
CORD

L.P.

S.R.

■ — SOMITE
□ — ENTODERM
✳ — NEURAL CREST
● — HEART
⊕ — CHORDA
⊙ — NEPHROS
• — ERYTHROCYTES
M — HEAD MESODERM
L.P. — LATERAL PLATE
S.R. — SINUS
RHOMBOIDALIS

120

amphibians the presumptive areas have greater potency than their presumptive values and are still labile at this time. If the chick blastoderm is cut transversely into equal anterior and posterior halves, each will form a complete embryo. This could be one of the methods of the origin of monozygotic twins; another may involve the separation of cells during some stage of cleavage. Transplants of the anterior part of the chick primitive streak will induce neural tubes in indifferent ectoderm as well as differentiate certain organ structures such as the heart and kidney. This is another example of the interaction of tissues in induction.

As the area pellucida of the chick embryo elongates, the zone of cell invagination (streak) appears to recede posteriorly. This involves an initial displacement followed by a progressive shortening of the streak itself as the last of the invaginating epiblast cells destined to change positions pass through it and the embryo begins to take form anteriorly (Figure 3-17). These cells are also added to the internal layer of mesoderm and notochord. Structures of the embryonic axis have begun to make their appearance in an antero-posterior order. Stages of early development of the chick embryo are shown in Figure 3-18. At the thirty-three-hour stage some remnant of the primitive streak may still be found at the extreme posterior end of the embryo, showing that the process of gastrulation in this form overlaps early structural development (Figures 3-17 and 3-18).

Within seventy-two hours of incubation the beginnings of many adult organs have made their initial appearance from the germ layers [Figure 3-18(c)]. From the neural ectoderm have arisen the primordia of the spinal cord and five-part brain following the fusion of lateral folds in the neural plate, the neural crest cords from which many diversified structures will later differentiate, the eyes, and certain cranial ganglia. The body ectoderm has formed the lens and the beginning of the cornea of the eye as a result of induction by the optic cup and lens itself, the otic vesicle (otocyst, primordium of the internal ear) by inductive action of the hindbrain, and the beginning of the mouth and cloacal cavities. Cephalic, caudal, and lateral body folds have given shape to the embryo and formed the foregut and hindgut from the endodermal sheet. Derivatives of the foregut include the primordia of the visceral pouches, thyroid gland, lungs, trachea, thymus and parathyroid glands, liver, pancreas, esophagus, and stomach-intestine. The allantois is an outgrowth of the hindgut. Derivatives of the mesoderm at this stage are heart, early pro- and mesonephric tubules, somites, and certain arteries and veins with their connections. Mesoderm in the form of mesenchyme has been induced to aggregate around certain primordial structures such as optic cup, otocyst, neural tube, and others. In addition to subordinate parts already initiated, many other structures will subsequently take form. At this stage the primordia of the organs just mentioned have all attained a state of development in which they are capable of independent self-differentiation when transplanted to a suitable site or cultured *in vitro*.

At this developmental stage the chick embryo is enclosed by inner

Figure 3-16 (opposite). Prospective organ-forming areas in the definitive primitive streak stage of the chick. Superficial areas are shown in the left side, invaginated material in the right. (After Rudnick.)

amniotic and outer chorionic membranes, which have had their origins in the fusion of folds of the somatopleure, or extra-embryonic ectoderm-mesoderm layer (Figure 3-19). The extra-embryonic splanchnopleure or meso-endo-dermal layer now partially encloses the yolk in a yolk sac, and the chorion extends over the somatopleure. As an evagination of the hindgut, the allan-toic sac is a small projection into the extra-embryonic coelom between the chorion and yolk sac wall. There is active circulation of blood at this time; actually the heart has been beating since the twenty-eight-hour stage. Food continues to be obtained from the yolk and albumin by way of the vitelline circulation; nitrogenous wastes of metabolism will be collected by the

Figure 3-17. Structure of an early chick embryo with four pairs of somites. The embryo begins to form in front of the primitive streak, with more posterior parts taking shape as the streak recedes and shortens. Neural folds are in the process of fusing about the level of the future hind brain to form the neural tube from which will arise the brain, spinal cord, and motor components of cerebral and spinal nerves. Somite material gives rise to the dermis of the skin, dorsal body muscles, and vertebrae. (From Wadding-ton's *Principles of Development and Differentiation.* New York: Macmillan, 1966.)

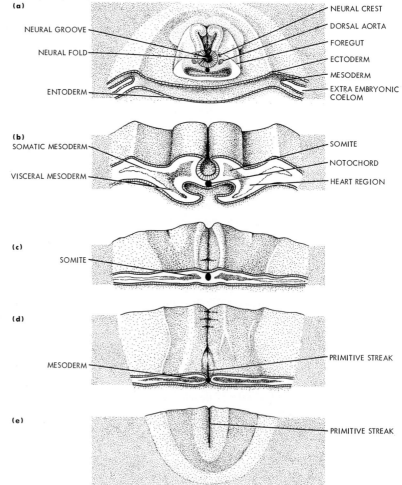

kidneys to be stored as insoluble uric acid in the *allantois*. Exchange of oxygen and carbon dioxide is taking place between the blood and the external air through the fused chorio-allantoic membrane via the allantoic circulation.

The Mammalian Embryo   The development of a placental mammalian embryo, e.g., rabbit or man, follows the same general pattern described for the chick. The exceptional features include the various ways in which the extra-embryonic membranes form, the additional role of the allantois and/or its blood vessels in excretion with nutrition and gaseous exchange via the placenta, and the relationship of the chorion and uterine endometrium in the placenta. The isolecithal mammalian egg, which contains little food material, must secure it from external sources. During cleavage and development of the blastocyst stage

Figure 3-18. Stages in the development of the chick embryo. Numbers indicate development stages in the Hamburger-Hamilton series. EB, end bud; FB, forebrain; H, heart; HB, hindbrain; LB, leg bud; MB, midbrain; NF, neural fold; PS, primitive streak; S, somite; SP, segmental plate; TB, tail bud. (From Saunders' *Animal Morphogenesis*. New York: Macmillan, 1966.)

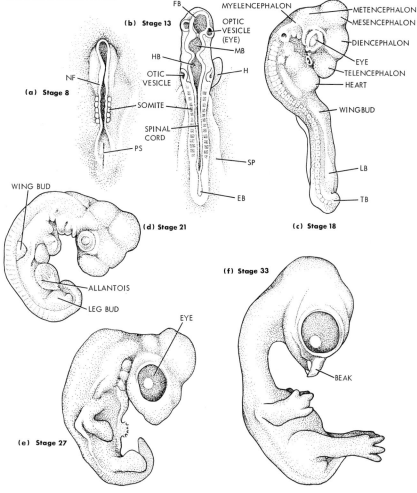

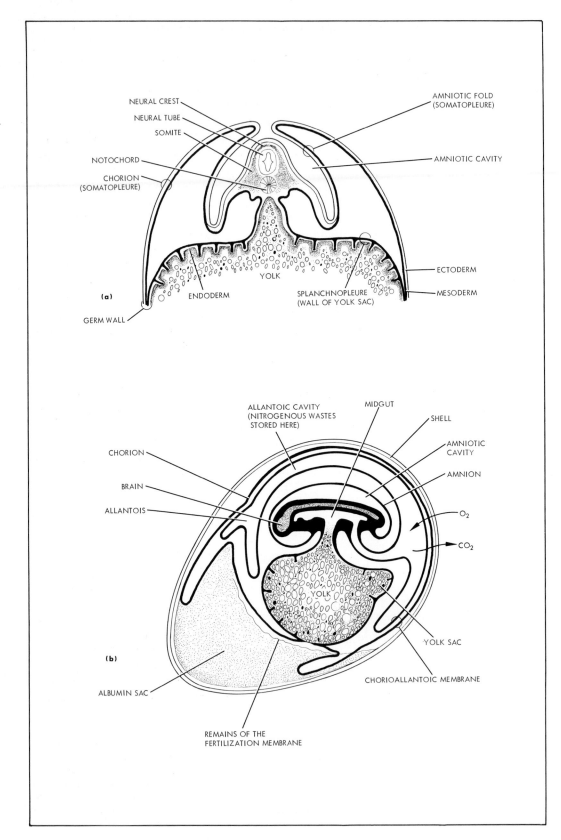

the luminal fluids of oviduct and uterus probably constitute the earliest food sources; however, seven or eight days following fertilization the blastocyst undergoes nidation and initiates invasion of the uterine wall. For a time the debris resulting from this implantation process may be engulfed by cellular (trophoblastic) phagocytic action, but the invading embryo soon establishes a functional relationship with the mother's blood via chorionic villi which contain branches of the embryonic allantoic blood vessels. From this period throughout the subsequent course of gestation the needs of the embryo-fetus are met by the passage of materials between the two vascular tissues. In the human, few layers of cells eventually separate the blood streams of fetus and mother, whereas in the contact type of placenta found in the pig, little or no erosion of maternal tissues has occurred and the two blood systems are separated by all the cellular layers characterizing both chorionic and uterine endometrial structures. In any case the blood of the embryo is at all times in equilibrium with the maternal blood, a phenomenon which is regulated by the permeability of cell membranes and other factors. The placenta has additional functions; e.g., it becomes an endocrine gland in the human, secreting those corpora luteal-like hormones that maintain pregnancy. Many substances pass more or less freely across the placenta, whereas others are stopped by this screening barrier.

Human
Development
Fertilization of the human egg occurs in the upper portion of the oviduct following ovulation. During its passage down the oviduct (*Fallopian tube*) cleavage takes place, and when the embryo reaches the uterus three days later it has attained the late morula stage of development. During the following four days changes occur that convert the young embryo from a more or less compact group of cells to a structure known as the blastocyst. Fluid accumulates within the cellular mass, and by the one-hundred-cell stage the embryo consists of a fluid-filled vesicle with a wall or trophoblast one-cell thick; a small mass of cells, the inner cell mass, is attached to the inner surface of the trophoblast (Figure 3-20).

Near the end of this free uterine period the inner cell mass has been divided into an upper ectodermal portion, the ectoderm layer of the amnion, and a lower embryonic disc from which the embryo will develop. Separating the two is a fluid-filled space, the progenitor of the amniotic cavity. Endoderm is proliferating from the posterior lower surface of the embryonic disc; chorda-mesoderm is invaginating through the primitive streak in a manner comparable to the chick embryo (Figure 3-20); and the mesoderm has split peripherally with one layer (somatic) growing over the amniotic ectoderm and the other over the endoderm to form the vestigial yolk sac and primitive gut. Meanwhile additional mesoderm has formed over the inner surface of

Figure 3-19 (opposite). Formation of the extra-embryonic membranes (amnion and chorion) and appendages (allantois and yolk sac) of the chick embryo. Oxygen and carbon dioxide are exchanged with the outside air via the circulation in the wall of the allantois. Nitrogenous waste products of metabolism in the form of insoluble uric acid is stored in the allantois, an evagination of the hind gut; the amnion and chorion arise as folds of the embryonic somatopleure and serve a protective function; the wall of the yolk sac is an extension of the splanchnopleure. (After Kent's *Comparative Anatomy of the Vertebrates*. The C. V. Mosby Company, 1965.)

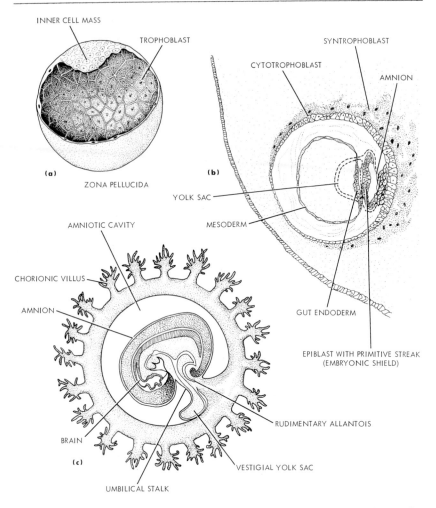

Figure 3-20. Early stages of human development: (a) the blastocyst, comprising trophoblast and inner cell mass; (b) differentiation of the trophoblast into syntrophoblast and cytotrophoblast during implanation; formation of the embryonic shield, amnion, and yolk sac; (c) the embryo floats in amniotic fluid and is attached by the umbilical stalk to the developing placenta; within the stalk are the vestigial allantois and yolkless yolk sac. (From Saunders' *Animal Morphogenesis.* New York: Macmillan, 1966.)

the trophoblast. Once attached to the uterine endometrium the trophoblast cells undergo rapid multiplication and in the first stages of implantation (Figure 3-21) invade the uterine endometrium. By the ninth day the embryo is completely embedded in the endometrium, cavities are appearing in the mass of trophoblast cells in the initial stages of placentation, and embryonic structures are beginning to form in front of the primitive streak. The amnion has expanded to enclose the embryo in a sea of amniotic fluid (Figure 3-22), and the whole is enclosed within the mesectodermal trophoblast. Space does not permit further description of human origins, but additional information may be found in the following references.

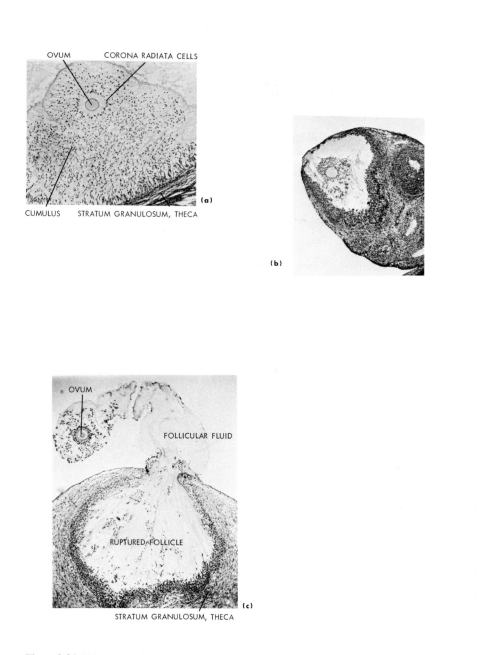

Figure 3-21 (this page and next page). Photomicrographs of the first stages of mammalian development: (a) portion of an ovarian follicle of the rat, showing ovum enclosed by corona radiata cells, cumulus, stratum granulosum, and theca; (b) early stage of ovulation, with the ovum and its enclosing cells separated from the stratum granulosum and lying free in the follicular fluid; (c) escape of ovum and follicular fluid; (d) living blastocyst of the guinea pig, enclosed by the zona pellucida; (e) section of the blastocyst of the guinea pig, six days following fertilization; (f) six-day blastocyst of the guinea pig beginning implantation into the wall of the uterus; the superficial uterine epithelium has been eroded. (Courtesy of Dr. Richard Blandau, University of Washington School of Medicine.)

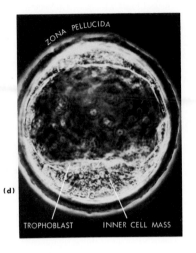

(d)

ZONA PELLUCIDA

TROPHOBLAST   INNER CELL MASS

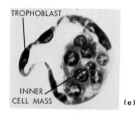

TROPHOBLAST

INNER
CELL MASS

(e)

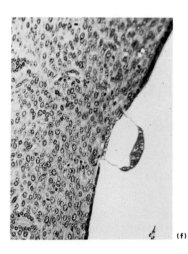

(f)

Figure 3-21 (continued).

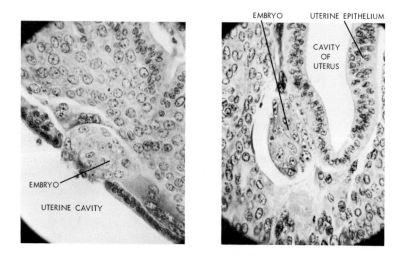

Figure 3-22. Photomicrographs of two stages in early implantation of the guinea pig embryo into the wall of the uterus: (a) six-day embryo almost implanted; (b) early seven-day embryo with implantation completed. The embryo and trophoblast lie completely embedded in the uterine endometrium, and the epithelium is reconstituted above these embryonic tissues. (Courtesy of Dr. Richard Blandau, University of Washington Medical School.)

References for Chapter 3

[1] Arey, L. B., *Developmental Anatomy.* Philadelphia: W. B. Saunders, 7th ed., 1965. A textbook and laboratory manual of human embryology, including teratologies, reproductive cycles, formation and function of the placenta.

[2] Austin, C. R., *Fertilization.* Englewood Cliffs, New Jersey: Prentice-Hall, 1965. (Extensive bibliography.) For students and research workers who seek a general knowledge of fertilization in its comparative aspects, as well as of the various cytological, physiological, and behavioral mechanisms concerned with the union of the gametes.

[3] Balinsky, B. I., *An Introduction to Embryology.* Philadelphia: W. B. Saunders, 2nd ed., 1965. (Good bibliography.) Embryology is presented as a single science in which the descriptive morphological and experimental physiological approaches are integrated. The subject is interpreted in a broadly comparative sense, as the science dealing with ontogenetic development of animals. Included are such topics as postembryonic development, regeneration, metamorphosis, sexual reproduction, and gene control.

[4] Barth, L. G., *Embryology.* New York: Holt, Rinehart and Winston, 1953. Combines a clear, uncomplicated discussion of the basic principles of embryology with a survey of the anatomy of selected embryos. Lucid, readable discussion.

[5] Bell, Eugene, *Molecular and Cellular Aspects of Development.* New York: Harper and Row, 1965. Focuses on some problems of developmental biology through the presentation of key papers in fourteen different but closely allied areas: serial transplants of

embryonic nuclei, differentiation of cells *in vitro,* reconstruction of tissues by dissociated cells, directed movements and selective adhesion of cells, embryonic potency of embryoid bodies, chromosomes and cytodifferentiation.

[6] Deuchar, E. M., *Biochemical Aspects of Amphibian Development.* London: Methuen and Co., Ltd., 1966. A chemical approach to the understanding of the problems of amphibian development. Recommended for the more advanced student.

[7] Ebert, J. E., *Interacting Systems in Development.* New York: Holt, Rinehart and Winston, 1965. Discusses the interactions that occur between cells at several critical periods of development, e.g., fertilization and gastrulation. Later developmental phenomena are also discussed.

[8] Gurdon, J. B., "Transplanted Nuclei and Cell Differentiation." *Sci. Am.* **219** (1968), 24-35. The nucleus of a cell from a frog's intestine is transplanted into a frog's egg and gives rise to a normal frog. Such experiments aid the study of how genes are controlled during embryonic development and the interaction of nucleus and cytoplasm in the development of structure.

[9] Jacobson, A. G., "Inductive Processes in Embryonic Development." *Sci.* **152** (1966), 25-34. Most organs form as a result of gradual cumulative effects of interactions between embryonic tissues. The mechanisms of cell differentiation present some of the most provocative problems of biology; in animal embryos one such mechanism is embryonic induction.

[10] Mascona, A. A., and A. Monroy (eds.), *Current Topics in Developmental Biology.* New York: Academic Press, 1966. A series of thought provoking papers dealing with current topics in developmental biology.

[11] Metz, C. B., and A. Monroy (eds.), *Fertilization, Comparative Morphology, Biochemistry and Immunology.* New York: Academic Press, 1967. An excellent account of the process of fertilization based on data from several disciplines.

[12] Mintz, B., and W. K. Silvers, "Intrinsic Immunological Tolerance in Allophenic Mice." *Sci.* **158** (1967), 1484-1487. An illustration of the lability of mammalian cleavage cells; mice of multiembryonic origin and the problem of immunity.

[13] Nelsen, Olin E., *Comparative Embryology of the Vertebrates.* New York: Blakiston., 1953. A broad, comprehensive and descriptive presentation of the morphology of vertebrate development in a wide variety of species. Profusely illustrated; references at the ends of the chapters.

[14] Saunders, J. W., Jr., *Animal Morphogenesis.* New York: The Macmillan Co., 1966. Deals with the way form and function of the organism develop from the fertilized egg. For beginning students.

[15] Spratt, N. T., Jr., *Introduction to Cell Differentiation.* New York: Reinhold Publishing Corp., 1964. Provides information for beginning students on the principles of the differentiation of cells that occur during the development of an individual. A presentation of a point of view.

[16] Waddington, C. H., *Principles of Development and Differentiation.*
New York: The Macmillan Co., 1966. Mainly concerned with
principles; contains little discussion of the changes in anatomy that
go on within various types of embryos. For the beginning student.

[17] Wessels, N. K., and W. J. Rutter, "Phases of Cell Differentiation." *Sci.
Am.* **220** (1969), 36-44. By cultivating embryonic tissue in the
laboratory the specialization of cells can be studied in the mammalian
pancreas. Three regulatory phases seem to occur, each of which leads
to a new stage of organizational differentiation.

and united in different combinations, has been an effective mechanism for the study of the principles of morphogenesis and physiology. The manner in which genes determine skin and hair color, the functional importance of differences arising between epidermis from the different regions of the body, the role of the dermis, regeneration, aging phenomena, the ability of the skin to withstand certain treatments such as temperature changes and stress, evaluation of tissue viability, and others have been studied by transplantation techniques. Grafts are of many types: isolated nuclei, single cells, disorganized masses of cells, solid tissues, combinations of tissues, whole and even nonviable integumentary tissues. The incompatibility of homografts has been analyzed by this technique, as well as the means to combat it. In certain analytical studies culture *in vitro* has been productive, but this method is more complicated than grafting. Laboratory-grown cell suspensions have yielded interesting results. Biochemical methods are contributing data on metabolic pathways within the skin along with the enzymes involved, melanogenesis, vitamin D synthesis, and keratinization. Physical studies are yielding information on the flow of blood through the dermal blood vessels under different conditions.

Man, in his efforts to meet the many problems that afflict the skin, has utilized the techniques of various scientific disciplines. The intense direct heat of the laser light rays is just beginning to find biological application. Formerly untreatable birth marks, formed by purplish blood vessels adjacent to the skin and extending into the dermis, are now being erased by these rays. They are also reported to remove warts, moles, and tattoo marks. Both warts and cancer are examples of uncontrolled growth. Warts have been shown to be nonmalignant tumors caused by a virus, and although the viral etiology of certain kinds of human cancer has not been demonstrated it is suspected from studies on lower animals. The continuing function of skin transplants between individuals depends on the development of some "tolerance" between the graft and the recipient, along with the use of immuno-suppressive therapy to encourage adaptability. When major incompatibility is present, the graft is rigorously rejected. This area of study has received much attention in recent years, and will receive increasingly more as we seek to replace lost or diseased parts of the body in animals that have lost all powers of regeneration except wound healing. Along with methods of matching graft and recipient, massive steroid therapy has been employed. Another skin problem, hyperplasia, is provoked by mite bites and X-rays.

Functions of the Skin   At any level of animal organization, from protozoa to man, organisms are dependent upon the properties of this uni- or multilayered, never-stationary, covering- membrane that constitutes an unbroken continuous barrier for the body. In one way or another any derivatives, if present, are also vitally involved. The skin furnishes protection against physical and chemical attacks from the environment; it is pliable, yet resistant of fracture. Any loss of water in both aquatic and terrestrial organisms, or too great an influx of water in fresh-water forms, is largely controlled. Although skin resists organismic invasion, some parasites (hookworm) have little difficulty in penetrating the thickest of skins. Metallic nickel, the oleoresins of poison ivy, and secretions of the poison oak and sumac enter the skin easily. The surface of the skin is slightly on the acid side of neutrality. Communication with the external environment occurs by way of the skin—within it are located the major sense organs as well as the lesser sensory receptors of pain, temperature, and pressure, which alert the organism (Figure 4-2).

Through the reaction of pigment cells and changes in corneal thickness the skin offers protection against injurious amounts of light. This organ, along with hair, feathers, or thick scales, insulates the body against sudden loss or gain of heat. It is a nonconducting retainer that includes elements assisting in body temperature regulation. The skin also functions to control blood pressure and to direct blood flow. Through moist skin membranes or glandular structures it has an active physiological part in absorption or elimination of materials. Elements for sex distinction (pheromones) and sexual attraction through coloration are also present. Coloration is a conspicuous property of

Figure 4-2. Cutaneous encapsulated sensory receptors: (a) Meissner's corpuscle from the dermal papilla; (b) Pacinian corpuscle; (c) end bulb of Krause; (d) Meissner's corpuscle.

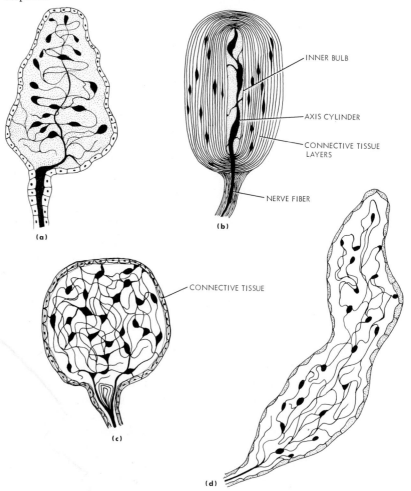

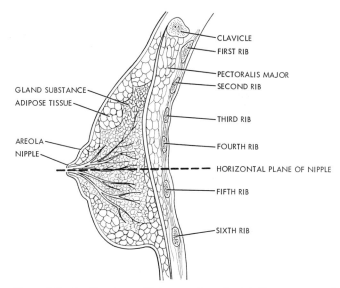

CLAVICLE

FIRST RIB

PECTORALIS MAJOR

SECOND RIB

GLAND SUBSTANCE

ADIPOSE TISSUE

THIRD RIB

AREOLA

NIPPLE

FOURTH RIB

HORIZONTAL PLANE OF NIPPLE

FIFTH RIB

SIXTH RIB

Figure 4-3. Another type of integumentary gland is the mammary gland. Diagrammatic section of the structure of the human mammary gland.

the skin and its derivatives. Through matching or contrasting color patterns animals may blend with their backgrounds or stand out prominently (skunk). The human skin follows a characteristic life cycle from fetal to old age; epidermal proliferation shows an endogenous or circadian rhythm of cell activity.

Along with underlying muscles and bone structure, the skin, aided by fat distribution, is responsible for shaping the face and body contours. Human organisms have long been identified by the pattern of ridges and sulci on the finger pads. No two sets of whorls and loops are similar, except possibly those of monozygotic twins, and females have distinctly different patterns from males. Such patterns are established during the third and fourth fetal months.

A dynamic organ that continually undergoes growth, differentiation, and replacement in its reaction to external stimuli, the skin reflects the physiologic state of the body's internal environment. Wound healing, and in lower organisms total regeneration of certain parts, may take place. Man loses cells from the surface of the skin, and lower organisms can molt whole sheets of skin. Food in the form of fat or blubber (whales) is stored in the deeper subcutaneous layer where it takes the form of pads or cushions of adipose tissue.

Skin produces numerous and different end products, e.g., secretions and bony or horny structures. Irritating and even poisonous substances serve many animals as a defense against predators. Most of the complex biological syntheses occurring in the skin are involved in the production of secretions, e.g., sweat, sebum, milk (Figure 4-3), and proteinaceous keratin. The epidermis is also an effective barrier against the penetration of a wide variety of substances, the absorption of which depends upon their physical and chemical properties as well as upon the normal and abnormal state of the skin. Studies of cutaneous permeability, unlike transport investigations in other cell systems and biological membranes, are only beginning to yield useful information.

No other organ of the vertebrate body has so large a total mass nor so much free surface as does the skin. For example, in an average-size man thirty-three years old, the weight of the skin with subcutaneous fat removed has been estimated to be between ten and eleven pounds and that of a female between seven and eight pounds with an area of approximately five square feet. In rabbits the weight of the skin may constitute 13 to 17 percent of the total body weight, with some variation existing between sexes, among species, and during different seasons of the year. This percentage is reported to be even greater among reptiles. The organ, which forms about 5 percent of the body weight in the smallest cat fetuses, increases rapidly at first and then more slowly until a maximum of a little over 20 percent is attained at birth. A postnatal decrease is shown by the newborn cat, and the adult ratio is about 13 percent.

The skin supports a large population of micro-organisms and hence may be considered a peculiar ecosystem with diverse ecological niches. This environment and the populations that live in it constitute a discrete world whose living and nonliving components, all interacting with one another, exist in equilibrium [15].

The Skin of Man

The Epidermis

Human skin, like that of all vertebrates, has a dual origin. The epidermis arises from the surface layer of cells in the embryo, known as the nonnervous ectoderm. At first it is only a single layer of cells and constitutes the early periderm. This primary "skin" is characterized by the swollen appearance of the cells and their peculiar staining qualities which indicate particular chemical properties. Shortly thereafter mitotic activity accelerates and the dermis begins gradually to differentiate from the underlying mesoderm. By the third month of fetal life the epidermis shows approximately five layers of cells, one of which is a basal layer covered on its free surface with the single-layered epitrichium. At five months hairs make their appearance and the fetus is soon almost completely covered with these epidermal derivatives. At this time the epitrichium, except for the palms and soles, is shed from the body and the epidermis and dermis continue to show mitotic activity and structural differentiation. Meanwhile a subcutaneous fatty layer, also of mesodermal origin, has made an appearance between the dermis and the underlying fascia of the muscles.

The human adult epidermis (Figure 4-1) includes a number of regions. Essentially cellular in character with little intercellular material and no vascularization, it has (1) a single-cell, basal, germinative layer from which successive generations of epidermal cells are produced; (2) a thick, living Malpighian layer; and (3) an outer specialized, transparent, corneal layer of variable thickness. This stratum corneum of dead, flattened, keratinized cellular remains is largely responsible for the impermeability of the skin. Following its removal or chemical alteration the remainder of the skin becomes freely permeable to water and dissolved substances.

Cells produced by mitosis in the germinative layer are pushed through the spinosum and granulosum zones of the Malpighian layer by successive genera-

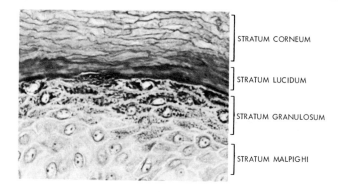

Figure 4-4. Section of the epidermis from the sole at higher magnification. As the cells of the stratum Malpighii are pushed toward the surface of the skin, they become progressively larger and stainable granules appear in the cytoplasm; such cells constitute the stratum granulosum. The cells also become markedly flattened. The photograph emphasizes the characteristics of the cellular constituents of the several strata. Although nonliving in the stratum corneum, the cell remnants in "pressure areas" of the epidermis retain some cellular appearance, are firmly cemented together, and are not easily sloughed. (Courtesy of Dr. William Montagna, Oregon Regional Primate Research Center, and Academic Press, New York.)

tions of new cells toward the free surface of the epidermis. Each new generation is discarded from the surface of the overlying corneal stratum in flattened, scale-like "squames" of dead cells. During this journey the cells become progressively modified in shape and composition. When they reach the corneal region, all nuclei are lost and the cytoplasm is replaced by horny keratin (Figure 4-4). The process of keratinization, which has intrigued biologists for many years, is still not clearly understood. A point of interest has been why some of the progenitors of the epidermal cells retain mitotic capacity and remain in the germinative layer to give rise to future generations of epidermal cells and why others lose this capacity and undergo these processes of irreversible differentiation (keratinization).

The human skin continues to develop throughout life, as is obvious when we contrast the skin of a young child with that of an adult or aged person. It is thinnest over the eyeball, where it is also transparent, and thickest even in the early fetus on the palms and soles. Dorsal and extensor surfaces of the body have thicker skin than ventral and flexor surfaces; skin is also thicker in men than in women. Corns, callouses, and other local thickenings form in response to excessive friction or pressure, and freckles are a reaction to sunlight. With the onset of old age the skin becomes discolored and increasingly wrinkled and chemical and structural changes occur throughout its several regions. Wrinkles formed by smiling or knitting the brow and the weathered skin of the aged result from the pull of muscles together with the loss of both elasticity and subcutaneous fat. The capacity of the skin to be stretched depends on its thickness, the presence of folds, elasticity and the composition of the dermis, firmness of attachment, and age. The greatest capacity is in skin from the abdomen.

The surface of the human epidermis is both smooth and heavily marked with ridges and furrows. It is characterized by the exit point of hairs, pores of sebaceous and sweat glands, and by wrinkles. Some areas (palms, soles) are hairless, others are not. The thickness and surface of the corneum, together with the amount and nature of the cutaneous secretions, makes the epidermis rough or smooth, dry or moist. Tensil strength and resiliency vary. On the whole, patterns in the skin, which are genetically established and determined by the orientation of dermal and other factors, make their appearance early in fetal life. The patterns of folds, ridges, creases, and flexor lines thus established remain unchanged throughout life and can be altered only by damage to the underlying dermis.

The epidermis and dermis of whole skin may be cleanly separated by maceration in acetic acid or by treatment with trypsin or heat. Other methods of separation include enzymically by digestion of thin shavings, treatment with weak ammonia solution, or use of 2N sodium bromide. The enzyme method, which leaves the cells alive, permits grafting, culture *in vitro*, supravital staining, or enzymical study.

Among lower vertebrates the smooth surfaces at the dermo-epidermal junction are separated by a basement membrane, whereas in reptiles, birds, and mammals (man) epidermal cones or ridges of different sizes project downward into the dermis. Enclosed between them are dermal papillae that may contain capillary knots or encapsulated sensory receptors. The characteristic regional differences in the architecture of the underside of the epidermis can be correlated with the pattern of hair and sweat gland arrangements [17]. During old age these folds tend to flatten out. The skin of the mouse, rat, and rabbit has no epidermal ridges, and the dermo-epidermal junction is less intimate. Such folds may provide for increased cell proliferation by increasing the area of the basal layer. From the basal layer of epidermal cells delicate protoplasmic processes extend into the dermis to provide a closer union between the two layers. Anchoring roles have been assigned to all the connective tissue fibers—collaginous, elastic, and reticular.

The human epidermis, except for the palm and sole at one extreme and the cornea of the eye and the wall of the scrotal sac at the other, is remarkably constant in thickness; regional variations are attributable chiefly to the dermis. In general it is around sixty to one hundred microns thick, whereas the corneum of the palm and sole alone may reach one hundred to six hundred microns [17] and [24]. In the mouse and hamster the stratum Malpighi is two to three cells thick, the spinous and granular layers are not distinguishable, and the stratum corneum varies between five and ten layers of cells. Larger mammals possess a thicker epidermis in which layering is more distinct. Fur-bearing mammals show a thin epidermis which consists of little more than the Malpighian layer covered by a thin corneum. As no blood vessels penetrate the epidermis, all the metabolic requirements must be met solely by diffusion from the dermal blood vessels. Free nerve ends, branched or unbranched, may end in it or be associated with particular epithelial cells. Some of the changes that the epidermal cells undergo during their progression through the several layers may be correlated with the thickness of the tissue layers through which this diffusion occurs.

The supply of fresh epidermal cells, which are continually replenished, involves a complicated process of differentiation during which the cells become completely changed. For example, an internal fiber system of tonofibrils makes its appearance. Some investigators have attributed a supportive function to these fibrils. Localized thickenings, called desmosomes, appear in cell membranes and may serve to affix cells more closely together. They relate somehow to the tonofibrils, or at least form a type of attachment with them. The keratohyaline granules develop in cells which lie within the zone of the granulosum. Wherever the stratum lucidum is present (sole), the substance eleidin develops. Another structural change is the marked thickening of cell membranes. The material within these membranes is keratin, a substance that is resistant to many factors including pH, high and low temperatures, and enzymatic digestion. For more on this subject consult the references at the end of this chapter.

The stratum corneum is an interesting layer. Transparent, colorless, generally thin except in areas of the body subject to friction and pressure, it may be stripped off in layers by cellulose adhesive tape. Cells are joined together by "attachment plaques." The stratum corneum has a function in the reaction of skin to ultraviolet rays (suntanning), contributes to skin color, and is chiefly responsible for protecting the body against the diffusion of substances. Transfer of materials probably occurs in the liquid phase, and is brought about by a concentration gradient within the layer itself. The corneum is far more hygroscopic than other keratinized materials such as hair or horn. Dry skin (corneum) has a high electrical impedance to the flow of electric current and thus provides some protection. For further details on the corneum and skin as an electrical, thermal, and radiation barrier and protector and as a potential focus for multidisciplinary research, see Rushmer [24].

Keratinization in the epidermis. Keratinization is a process peculiar to the epidermis of amniotes, although to a lesser extent it may also take place in the skin of certain land-dwelling amphibians. As the differentiating cells are crowded through the several zones of the granulosum, lucidum, and outward into the corneum toward the surface of the epidermis, each undergoes a profound transformation from a nucleated, metabolizing unit to one that is dead, markedly flattened, nonnucleated and keratinized. The first of these changes may be seen in the flattening of cells that are still a part of the Malpighian layer. Further flattening has occurred in the granulosum and the nucleus is now pycnotic or fragmented, the cell membrane is thicker, and fine keratohyalin granules have become a conspicuous feature of the cytoplasm. The functional role of these is not known, although much work has resulted in various interpretations of the data [19]. This type of keratinization occurs in epidermal cells, internal root sheaths of hair follicles, and medulla of the hair. Only the thickest portions of human skin contain the lucidum type of keratin (the sole of the foot, finger pads) as do the cortex and cuticle of the hair. A different chemical compound (eleidin), possibly a derivative of keratohyalin, is visible in the semitransparent, nonstainable homogeneous-appearing stratum lucidum. The skin pigment (melanin) is present in cellular melanocytes of the Malpighian layer. Montagna has likened the entire cutaneous structure to a huge glandular system with keratin, gland secretions, and enamel of teeth and color pigments being viewed as epidermal secretions.

Desquamation. The completely keratinized cells are finally lost by desquamation from the skin surface. It has been estimated that a seventy-year-old man has thus lost some forty pounds of cornified cells. This is another example, along with blood and sperm cells, of the amazing production of cells in several regions of the body to replace those lost during body activity. In this case it is a protective feature characteristic of land-dwelling vertebrates. A regulatory mechanism controlling desquamation in man has been described by Bullough. Normally an equilibrium, conditioned upon a sensitive feedback mechanism, exists between cell proliferation in the basal layer of the epidermis and cell loss, whereby the thickness of the epidermis changes very slightly. Under environmental stress this equilibrium becomes modified and the epidermal layer, especially its corneal component, thickens markedly. Actually there is considerable variation in the equilibrium of this relationship as indicated by skin thickness in different regions of the body. Thyroid hormones accelerate, whereas adrenocortical steroids retard both cell proliferation and desquamation. A local, tissue-specific hormone has been described as inhibiting mitosis and thereby controlling the balance of cell proliferation and cell loss. When hormone concentration is low, cells produce the proteins that promote mitosis; when it is high, cell differentiation is favored.

Molting in lower vertebrates occurs periodically and may be specifically controlled. In mammals cornified cells flake off in small aggregates from the free epidermal surface (human dandruff) because a change, different from that in the reptilian molt, takes place in the intercellular cementing substance. Investigators have speculated on whether this change is simply a physical one of drying or a chemical decomposition of the mucolipoprotein. Conversely, several suggestions have been advanced to account for the accumulation of cells on the palm and sole in response to environmental stress. One of the more interesting speculations suggests a change in the differentiation process affecting the intercellular cement, at least, and a modification of the hormonal feedback pattern normally accounting for the maintenance of balance between sloughing and proliferation in the basal layer.

Growth of the epidermis. In vertebrates mitosis is confined mainly to the stratum germinativum of the epidermis, although it also occurs to a lesser degree throughout the Malpighian layer of amphibian and fish skins characterized by little or no keratinization. The rate of mitosis is variable. A thick, keratinized epidermis in the rabbit can be regenerated within two weeks from cells that are "seeded" on an epidermally denuded area. A host of different factors affect mitosis, including loss of corneal cells, shock or stress, temperature, muscular exercise, level of certain hormones, age of the animal, stage of estrous cycle, and blood supply as the source of raw materials. Epidermal growth is cyclic and exhibits a diurnal circadian rhythm along with a less defined estrous rhythm. The period of mitotic frequency in the nocturnal mouse and rat epidermis is reported to be greatest around noon to 1 PM and slightest around 10 PM. The number of dividing cells is more than double that at night (Blumfeld, 1939; Cooper and Franklin, 1940). In man the mitotic cycle is highest in the night hours. Under typical conditions human epidermis can duplicate itself in about twenty-seven days.

Growth has been described as the accretionary type (Huxley), in which the semispecialized cells of the basal generative layer retain the ability to divide mitotically and hence serve as a progenitor pool for new generations of cells, whereas cells of other layers have lost this capability. Exceptions may be found occasionally in noncornified skins of anamniotes. Clearly the generative cells are multipotential as to these different properties, but their capacity to undergo differentiation must be masked in some fashion since they can only undergo division while in the environment of the basal zone. When a daughter cell in a mitotic division appears outside the generative area, it suddenly acquires morphogenetic and physiological properties of functionally differentiating cells. However, since the basal cells give rise only to units of the epidermis, they have attained a certain level of functional specialization.

A slightly more advanced stage of differentiation of the generative cell is seen in the papillae of hairs and feathers; the daughter cells differentiate into localized cornified structures showing various specializations, but not into generalized epidermal cells. Subsequently the process of keratinization is essentially similar but the cells remain adherent through some peculiar property of the intercellular material. Other examples include specialized epidermal derivatives such as the nail, claw, hoof, horns of several types, and epidermal scales. There are instances in which highly specialized epidermal cells divide to replace lost or destroyed parts, for example, the mammary gland. In this specialized type of aleveolar sweat gland of the apocrine type, growth occurs in the secretory cells after some protoplasm is lost during milk secretion. Other examples include sebaceous glands and the mucous gland of amphibian skin.

Wound healing. Regeneration among the warm-blooded amniotes is limited to wound healing, in which the skin is involved. Much attention in the form of voluminous literature from both basic and practical standpoints has been given to this phenomenon, particularly, for obvious reasons, in man. During epithelialization and reunion of the connective tissue components, which are generally the principal processes, the adjacent epithelium migrates inward to cover the wound. Little "granulation" tissue forms if the wound has previously been sutured. Conversely when there is an open wound to be covered, marked inflammation and tissue destruction may first occur, accompanied by initial proliferation in tissues affected by the injury. As the proliferating epithelium migrates to cover the wound it moves beneath the fibrin clot to unite eventually with the dermal connective tissue; cell division is limited primarily to marginal cells. At first the wound epithelium thickens, and buds from this area grow inward only to be pinched off later as the thickening regresses. This type of skin reaction has been likened to that occurring in the healing of the adult amphibian limb following amputation. Phosphatases and proteolytic enzymes with unknown functions have been found in both amphibians and mammals. Wound healing, more rapid in the young than in adults, is, unlike amphibian regeneration, influenced by nutritional deficiencies (proteins, vitamin C). Investigators have given attention to the effects of hormones and X-radiation.

In certain portions of the mammalian body large wounds become reduced in size within a few days, as a result of the activity of the encircling connective tissue under the influence of integumental or dermal muscles (panniculus carnosus) attached to the skin. These are the muscles by which a horse twitches its skin, a wet dog shakes itself, the armadillo and European hedgehog roll themselves up into a ball, a snake moves by traction on the ground with its ventral epidermal scales, and birds fluff their feathers in regulating body temperature. Other dermal muscles, e.g., the orbicularis, are responsible for the expression of human emotions, wrinkling of the forehead, and other skin movements of the neck and head.

Dermis   Beneath the epidermis is the second and thicker layer of the human skin, the tough dermis or corium (Figure 4-1). Structurally different in every way, it consists largely of collagenous and intertwined elastic-felted fibers enmeshed in a gel-like matrix. Leather has, on occasion, been made even from human dermis. Small blood vessels and nerves penetrate this region; hair follicles and sebaceous and sweat glands are located here; and sensory organs of tactile and temperature functions are abundant. Bundles of smooth muscle fibers, the arrectores pilorum muscles of ectodermal origin, are attached to hair follicles. Smooth muscle fibers constitute a relatively continuous layer, the tunica dartos, in the dermis of the scrotum and penis. Such fibers are also abundant in the nipple and aureola of the breast (Figure 4-3) as well as in the perineal and circumanal regions. The dermis changes markedly with age as is shown by sagging and wrinkled skin. This structure is the distinctive part of vertebrate skins; it is absent from all invertebrates with the possible exception of the Cephalochordata (*Amphioxus*).

Predominantly of mesodermal origin from the dermatome and lateral somatic mesoderm of the embryo, the thickness of the dermis varies in different regions of the mammalian body, being thickest on dorsal surfaces as well as on the palms and soles of primates. Its inner surface is not clearly marked but grades off imperceptibly into the fatty subcutaneous layer. Two parts make up the dermis. An outer papillary region contains a number of specialized elements: reticular or possibly precollagenous material, collagenous and elastic fibers, abundant capillary and lymphatic vessels, nerve fibers and sensory structures, deposits of glycogen and adipose tissue along with sebaceous and sweat glands. These are all embedded in a gel-like ground substance or matrix. Also present are pigment cells, smooth muscle fibers, various kinds of dermal (scales) and epidermal derivatives (hair or feathers, glands of mucous, serous or mammary types) among the several vertebrate classes. In mammals the surface adjacent to the epidermis may be molded around the ridges and valleys of the epidermis in the form of dermal papillae. This layer also contributes to the connective tissue sheaths encapsulating hair and feather follicles as well as to the ducts of glands projecting through the papillary layer. Reticular fibers constitute or are a major component of the basement membrane underneath the epidermis.

The deeper fibrous reticular region of the mammalian dermis contains, in addition to many elements of the papillary layer, bundles of coarse, branching collagenous fibers in layers arranged horizontally at angles to each other and parallel to the epidermis. Some fibers extend downward into the framework of the underlying subcutaneous or adipose tissue, probably serving as anchors for the skin. Between the collagenous fibers is abundant elastic tissue, which sheaths any integumentary derivatives lying wholly or in part within this reticular layer. Other cellular types within the dermis include connective tissue cells such as fibroblasts, mast cells, histocytes (macrophages), pigment cells, and melanocytes. Much has been written about the histochemistry, origin, and structure of any one of these cellular units.

Evidence indicates that the ground substance has several physiological functions. Probably the reticular fibers are "precollagenous" elements, whereas fibroblasts are the progenitors of connective tissue cells such as histocytes and mast cells and, in fact, of all other types of cells found in the dermis. Mast cells contain cytoplasmic granules and stain metachromatically with toluidine blue. These granules can be demonstrated by a number of techniques, with certain differences occurring among species. Mast cells are reported to increase in various itching skin diseases and may contain histamine, as in the case of mast cell tumors. The degree of granulation responds to trauma, mechanical stimuli, thyroxine deficiency or excess, and to other hormones.

The structure, distribution, and physiology of cutaneous nerves and sensory structures have been studied by a variety of techniques. Several plexi have been investigated; a deep cutaneous plexus is present in the panniculus adiposus with fibers extending to a superficial subcutaneous nerve plexus beneath the dermo-epidermal boundary. Other nerve meshes have been reported, which indicates that the dermis is well supplied with interconnected nerves and nerve plexi. Until recently it was thought that many morphologically different types of sensory organs existed in the dermis, each of which had a specific physiological role, and studies were devoted to the identification of these roles. This view appears to be changing, with similarities being reported in the origin, histochemical and functional properties of the cutaneous receptors, as well as between species. Of the so-called sensory "end organs" the following are reported to be morphologically identifiable: Meissner and Vater-Pacine corpuscles, hederiform endings, mucocutaneous-end organs, and the dermal and hair follicular nerve networks. In regions where hair follicles are abundant the cutaneous sensory nerves are distributed among them, whereas in locations of sparse follicles the networks are profuse. Other dermal structures, such as sweat and sebaceous glands and smooth muscle fibers, affect the pattern of nerve nets.

Little can be said in the space available about the complex types of patterns in the cutaneous blood vessels. The pattern is affected by many factors, ranging from thickness of the dermis and its relation to the epidermis to types and distribution of cutaneous appendages and the relationship of the skin to underlying structures. Throughout the dermis are large and small networks of anastomosing arterioles and capillaries with minor networks associated particularly with hair follicles and sweat glands. Numerous capillary loops extend into the dermal papillary ridges, chiefly in friction areas. Associated with the networks of arterioles are venous plexi, with preferential channels between the arterioles and venules, surrounded by one layer of smooth muscle. There are also direct shunts that permit blood to bypass the capillaries. Particularly large arteriovenous anastomoses under vasomotor control are encountered in the fingers and toes, pinae of the ears, and elsewhere. These factors, together with several types of vascular shunts and the capacity of venules to contract and dilate, provide the mechanisms for cutaneous regulation of heat and blood pressure, respiration among the amphibians, and other functions of this highly versatile organ.

The Subcutaneous Layer

Beneath the dermis, and considered by some as the third component of the skin, lies the subcutaneous transitional zone characterized by the presence of abundant fatty tissue (panniculus adiposus), vascular and nervous elements, and fibrous unions with the connective tissue fascia covering the deeper lying muscles. The boundary between subcutaneous tissue and dermis is less clearly demarcated than that between the dermis and epidermis because of the accumulation of adipose tissue. This layer varies widely in thickness in different parts of the body, among individuals, and even among species. In some mammals (seals, whales, walrus) fat is abundant. Among the factors affecting the deposition of fat in man are the types and abundance of food, alcohol, drugs, neuroendocrine disturbances, genetic inheritance, stress, and bodily activity. The brown fat of true hibernators has a vital function in arousal from the state of hibernation. Another distinctive characteristic is the loose organization of the felted reticular fiber network which permits increased freedom of motion in the underlying muscles. Here the vascular network is likewise extensive and capable of holding a large fraction of the total amount of blood in the body.

Comparative Anatomy of The Skin

Protochordates

It is interesting that the transparent skin of the primitive chordate *Amphioxus*, one of the most advanced of the invertebrates (Chapter 2), foreshadows the bilaminar structure of the vertebrate skin. No recognizable predecessor of this type of organization is found in lower invertebrates. It is known that Amphioxus, often called the lancelet, possesses a number of other elementary anatomical features characteristic of vertebrates in their simplest morphology. The epidermis consists of a single layer of columnar epithelial cells, among which are sensory cells and goblet-shaped, unicellular glandular cells. Beneath this lies a thin, gelatinous, connective tissue dermis overlying the muscles. In addition, the free epidermal surface is protected by a thin noncellular cuticle, the secretion of the epithelial glandular cells. The epidermis is ciliated in the larval stage.

Another interesting protochordate skin is found in the sea squirt or tunicate, *Molgula manhattensis*, subphylum Urochordata (Chapter 2). This tunic, which is a complicated structure, exhibits considerable power of regeneration. The cellular layer, resembling the hypodermis or skin of lower invertebrates, secretes a thick, tough, protective mantle that contains tunicin as well as scattered cells and fibers. Tunicin appears to be chemically related to cellulose, a substance not found elsewhere among the chordates nor outside the plant kingdom. Stellate mesenchyme cells, fibers, blood vessels, and nerve fibers invade the cuticle.

Cyclostomes, the lowest of living vertebrates (lamprey eels, marine hagfish), possess a highly glandular skin. Unicellular beaker and granular glands occur among the layered epidermal cells. The former secret a thin layer of mucus on the surface of the skin. Unlike the cells of higher vertebrate skin, little change occurs in the shape of cells in the Malpighian layer,

whereas those in the outermost layer may appear striated. Epidermal cornification of cells takes place in the case of the horny teeth in the buccal cavity
and on the rasping tongue. A peculiarity of the hagfish is the presence of a
single row of conspicuously large multicellular, epidermal slime glands that
extend on either side of the elongated body and open exteriorly by large
pores. It has been estimated that an irritated, average-sized hagfish may
produce as much as six or seven hundred cubic centimeters of watery mucus
at one time. Some species, when in the resting state, are reported to secrete
a slime cocoon around themselves. The dermis in these descendants of the
primitive ostracoderms is thinner than the epidermis and consists of an interwoven network of connective tissue fibers.

Fish   The scaly skin of fish is relatively thin and highly glandular. In contrast to
the loose-fitting skin of amphibians and birds and the elastic, wrinkled skin
of mammals, that in fish fits smoothly and tightly over the underlying
muscles. Mucous glands of the unicellular type are confined chiefly to the
epidermal layer; even the multicellular types seldom extend far into the
dermis. The epidermis is thin and most species never develop a corneal layer.
It generally lacks color cells except for occasional irregularly distributed
melanophores (dark brown pigment). This is especially the case in shark
(elasmobranch) epidermis, which is darker than that of most fish. There are
generally two regions in the dermis of a teleost fish: a superficial layer of
compact, fibrous connective tissue tied by perpendicular bundles of connective tissue fibers to the surface of the scale, and a deeper portion consisting
of loose connective tissue with its typical content of cells, nerves, and
capillaries.

   The depth and variety of colors exhibited by many species of coral reef
fish [among these are the parrot fish (2, 9)] of the West Indies and Bermuda
are particularly striking. The color cells, all of which occur in the upper
portion of the dermis, include brown-black melanophores with short or
elongated pseudopodia, yellow xanthophores, orange-red erythrophores,
iridocytes or guanophores containing crystals of guanin arranged in a network, noncellular translucent bodies containing a blue pigment (or blue
pigment diffused through the tissue), opalescent bodies, and rod-like doubly
refractive bodies resembling guanin crystals. Blue pigment is relatively rare
among animals—in most insects, fish, and birds it results from the refraction
of light. The blue head (*Thalassoma bifasciatum*), which shows one of the
most brilliant blues among tropical coral reef fish, has no blue pigment. Its
color appears to emanate from regions of the skin supplied with melanophores overlaid by clusters of iridocytes which give an interference effect.
Chemical analysis of the blue pigment in a Mediterranean wrasse, *Crenilabrus
pavo,* has revealed the presence of a carotenoid albumin. The extraordinary
complex of color-producing tissues found among teleost fish provides an
ample structural basis for color changes. In the several types of chromatophores the concentration and dispersal of pigment, presenting smaller or
larger light absorptive surfaces and concealing or revealing the refractive
iridocytes and the blue pigment, are believed to be the mechanisms involved.
These pigments, together with the physical structure of the skin plus the
transparency of the epidermis, all contribute to the colors that make fish so

attractive. Certain fish are able to discriminate between illuminated bodies that reflect light of equal brightness though of different wavelengths. Melanophores are the melanin-bearing chromatophores largely responsible for the adaptive color changes in cold-blooded vertebrates. In teleosts these are controlled by two sets of autonomic nerve fibers: melanin-aggregating (adrenergic) and melanin-dispersing (cholinergic).

Among deep sea teleost fish of the suborders *Iniomi* and *Stomatioidei*, certain sharks, the west coast estuarine midshipmen, *Porichthys* (a relative of the toadfish), to mention a few, skin glands have become modified to form light-producing organs, or photophores [23, 29]. These have definite arrangements in patterns characteristic of the species and may serve the general functions of recognition, warning, defense, and attraction. The "cold" light they produce does not project any distance. Generally the organ consists of a glandular portion which produces a luminous secretion and is bounded on one side by a translucent lens of modified cells and on the other by a concave layer of flattened cells, called the reflector, plus a single-cell layer of pigment cells (Figure 4-5). In the shark, *Spinax,* the photophore develops

Figure 4-5. Light organs of fish: (a) the teleost, *Cyclothone* (after Brauer); (b) the teleost, *Porichthys* (after Greene).

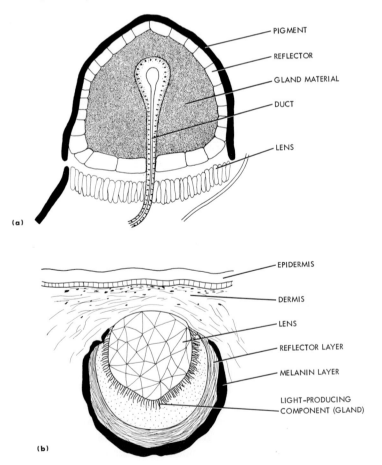

by modification of cells in the basal germinative layer of the epidermis. These gland cells form a cup that lies beneath the epidermis and, in association with other enlarged cells, forms a lens. Illumination arises through the oxidation of lucifern, a phosphorus-containing compound, by the enzyme luciferase. In some types of photophores luminous bacteria appear to be the source of illumination.

Free nerve endings and touch receptors, abundant in the epidermis and dermis, have multiple functions. They serve for thigmotactic orientation (mechanical contact and currents) and avoidance, and also may aid in discriminating between palatable and nonpalatable food. Certain avoidance reactions are mediated by the integumentary lateral line system. The common catfish possesses taste buds even in the tail skin. In fish and larval amphibians the lateral line system consists of either open or closed tubes in the skin of the head and extending tailward within the intersomitic septum. Neuromasts of sensory and supportive cells are distributed at close intervals along these grooves or tubes. The tubular type opens to the exterior by numerous pores.

A dermal armor (or remnants of one) may be found in numerous guises throughout the classes of vertebrates (cf. Chapter 6). Armored fossil fish possessed a very complete set of bony plates, and scales of dermal origin were found over the head and body. Although no trace of an epidermis has been found in the fossil record of these ancestral types, the dermal component has been identified among the sedentary bottom-dwelling ostracoderms, the mobile-jawed placoderms, the lobe-finned choanichthyes, and other fossil types. A suggestion has been advanced that probably little typical dermis was present as we know it. Remnants may be traced to dermal structures present among modern vertebrates. Workers have speculated about the function of the scales of ancient placoderm fish. Some have asked whether they served for defense or protection against dilution of internal body fluids since these animals inhabited fresh water. The absence of scales in cyclostomes, many Siluridae, and certain bottom-feeding teleosts (catfish), therefore, must be taken as a secondary modification. Although adult eels are scaleless, temporary remnants appear during development. The four chief types of scales found among modern fish, placoid, ganoid, cycloid, and ctenoid have evolved from this primary ostracoderm armor, along with teeth and such skeletal components as the dermal girdle, dermocranium, gastralia and osteoderms [23, 25, 27, 29].

The most primitive of the four types, the placoid scales of elasmobranch fish are homologous to the vertebrate tooth. Although they differ somewhat in shape and structure among the various body regions of a dogfish, for example, they have a common organizational pattern [25]. A tapering spine, capped by epidermal enamel (like a tooth) over an inner layer of hard mesodermal dentine, projects through the epidermis from a broad basal plate of dentine; probably this type of scale was compound in origin (Figure 4-6). Some have regarded the capping material as a harder vitrodentine which is also derived from mesoderm. Obvious transition from placoid scales to rows of teeth on the jaws of elasmobranchs lends further evidence for the evolution of teeth from this type of scale [23, 27].

Ganoid scales characterize the ganoid fish. In the sturgeon, *Acipenser,*

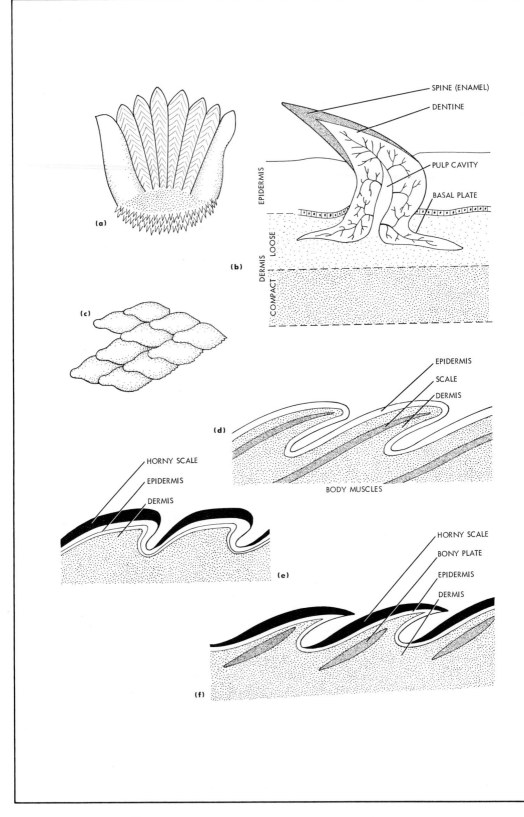

(a)

(b)

SPINE (ENAMEL)

DENTINE

PULP CAVITY

BASAL PLATE

EPIDERMIS

DERMIS LOOSE

COMPACT

(c)

(d)

EPIDERMIS

SCALE

DERMIS

BODY MUSCLES

(e)

HORNY SCALE

EPIDERMIS

DERMIS

(f)

HORNY SCALE

BONY PLATE

EPIDERMIS

DERMIS

these are large, isolated, plate-like structures, whereas in the gar pike, *Lepidosteus*, and certain related forms, the scales are hard, rhombic plates that fit edge to edge to form a complete armor. Larger plates constitute the armor on the head. In *Amia,* the bowfin or Mississippi dogfish, a living fossil-like form, ganoid scales occur on the head but cycloid scales are present elsewhere on the body. The outer surface of the ganoid scale is a hard, shiny layer of dermal ganoin which may be lacking from similar scales in certain other ganoid fish. It covers either a definite bony layer or a lower layer of vascularized connective tissue-like isopedin that contains embedded bone cells and is organized like the Haversian systems of true bone.

Cycloid and ctenoid scales differ only slightly. Both are thin layers of bone embedded in pockets of dermis covered by epidermis and overlapping each other like the shingles of a roof. The more primitive cycloid type is elongated with a smooth, inserted edge and thicker center; in contrast, the ctenoid type is rounder, with a conspicuous serrated inserted edge and tiny spines (tines) on the surface of the exposed section. *Amia*, bony dipnoans, and some teleosts have cycloid scales; most teleosts have ctenoid scales. Intermediate types have been described; among flounders, ctenoid scales occur on the dorsal side of the body and cycloid on the ventral side.

Scales are living structures and contain much intracellular material. Pigment cells are common. Because cycloid and ctenoid types may be successfully transplanted between fish, they have been employed in genetic and physiological studies as well as in studies of coloration patterns [9]. The outer layer is bony, whereas the inner is fibrillar with much calcareous material. Because growth is conditioned by an available food supply, the addition of new material by the scleroblastic cells is interrupted during a period of seasonal inactivity. The result produces rings of growth which faithfully mirror the age of the fish. The scales of the pipefish *Syngnathus* and its relative, the seahorse *Hippocampus*, are united into a body case.

Enlarged dermal spines occur commonly in fish at the anterior borders of fins. They may also serve as support for the dorsal, ventral, and even the anal fins. Fin rays may be cartilaginous (lampreys, hagfish), bony, fibrous, horny, paired, jointed or nonjointed.

Amphibians   The epidermis of amphibians is seldom more than a few cells thick and although mitoses are largely confined to the basal layer, dividing cells may occasionally be found in the upper layers (Figure 4-7). The epidermis of the frog, for example, is five to eight cells thick and rests upon a basement membrane of collagenous fibers. A single layer of flattened, nucleated cells, possibly slightly cornified in certain amphibian species, constitutes the outer stratum corneum. Beneath this is the broad layer of the stratum Malpighi, and the basal portion consists of a single layer of columnar cells. Stellate melanophores are found in the epidermis. In *Necturus,* a non-metamorphosing urodele, large, club-shaped cells occur abundantly in the

Figure 4-6 (opposite).   Types of vertebrate scales: (a) ctenoid scale of a bony fish; (b) section of a placoid scale; (c) ganoid scales of the garpike; (d) position of scales in the skin of a teleost fish; (e) horny epidermal scales of the snake; (f) diagram of a vertical section of lizard skin showing bony dermal plates beneath horny epidermal scales.

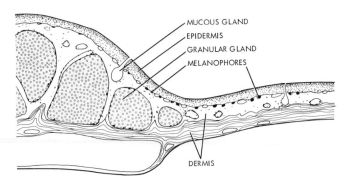

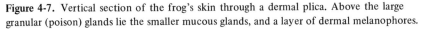

Figure 4-7. Vertical section of the frog's skin through a dermal plica. Above the large granular (poison) glands lie the smaller mucous glands, and a layer of dermal melanophores.

stratum Malpighi. Desquamation occurs in amphibians from the surface in unicellular sheets.

Some cornification of the outer cells of toads accumulates in spots to form the characteristic warts. Evidence of cornification of epidermally derived cells may be seen in the several rows of minute horny "teeth" on the lips of amphibian tadpoles, horny beaks in certain species of tadpoles, and the "claws" on the African clawed frog.

The dermis of the frog's skin (*Rana pipiens*, the grass frog) consists essentially of two layers (Figure 4-7). An outer stratum spongiosum of loose aerolar connective tissue with interlacing fibers and various cell types encloses the secretory portions of the mucous and granular glands. A layer of stellate melanophores lies just beneath the basement membrane of the epidermis. The inner layer includes compactly arranged collagenous fibers. Large dermal glands of ectodermal origin and of the simple alveolar type have ducts that penetrate the epidermis and open upon the surface of the skin. The mucous glands are lined with tall columnar epithelial cells that stain with the dye hematoxylin. Slimy mucus from the mucous glands helps maintain a moist skin, protects against friction, and contributes to the cocoon that some species of amphibians, particularly those inhabiting dry environments, secret around themselves during estivation. The whitish, acrid secretion of the granular glands is distasteful to some frog enemies and may be poisonous in certain species of tropical frogs [5]. Granular glands have a more restricted distribution in the skin, being particularly abundant in the ridges of the epidermal plicae along the dorsal lateral margins of the frog's back. Structurally each consists of a single layer of flattened cells that encloses a central cavity packed with granular material which stains with any cytoplasmic dye, e.g., eosin. Amphibians generally lack any dermal armor, except the legless caecilians in which small bands of dermal scutes are embedded in the skin.

Amphibian coloration is highly developed. Color cells include branching melanophores in the epidermis and abundant xanthophores and erythrophores in the dermis. The melanocyte-stimulating hormone (MSH) of pituitary origin produces changes in skin pigmentation through melanin dispersion. Temperature and humidity are correlative factors. The secretion of the pituitary intermediate lobe, also known as intermedin, causes darkening of the skin through dispersal of pigment in the melanophores. The removal of this melanophore-stimulating hormone from the animal's blood stream by hypophysectomy results in pigment withdrawal from the cellular processes. This pigment becomes tightly packed in the main body of the cell, and as a consequence the animal turns a lighter color. Bright light, a primary controlling factor, stimulates the release of intermedin by means of a neural reflex that involves the eyes and optic nerves. On a well-lighted background the secretion of intermedin is reduced and causes the pigment to clump; this gives the animal a lighter appearance. Darkening of the skin through dispersal of pigment follows exposure in a darkened chamber or on a dark background. Because they are primarily hormonally controlled such color changes, which occur slowly, require minutes to hours. By diffraction the guanophores produce the blue green. Yellow lipophores overlie the guanophores and filter out the blue. Their disarrangement produces yellow. Red color results from pigment in the lipophores. Changes in the melanophores also result from visual stimulation in different parts of the retina and from extracts of the pineal and other glands.

Two metamorphic periods characterize the life cycle of the spotted newt, *Diemictylus viridescens*. During each of these periods profound changes, which are hormonally controlled, cause the skin structure and other organs to adapt to the new environment. In each of these periods the skin has a characteristic structure and color. In the first metamorphic period the aquatic larval type of skin (thin, noncornified, highly glandular, living) undergoes transformation to the type of skin characteristic of the red eft stage—a thickened, cornified, nonglandular, heavily granular epidermis adapted to life on dry land. After two to three years of land life the animal undergoes a second metamorphosis during which the reddish skin changes back to the distinctly aquatic greenish amphibian type peculiar to the adult reproductive stage. The second metamorphic change in skin has been experimentally provoked within three days by injections of the hypophyseal hormone prolactin [10]. Metamorphic changes in the skin of other types of amphibian larvae may be invoked with injections of thyroid hormone [8].

Reptiles Land-dwelling vertebrates have lost most skin glands (man excepted) during their evolution to land life and have developed other types of protection in the shape of horny scales, feathers, or hair. In spite of the tough thickness of the stratum corneum, reptilian skin can suffer water loss, as reported for lizards, snakes and turtles of arid climates. Such animals, including desert amphibians, have been shown to survive arid conditions with little or no water intake because they have been able to absorb moisture from the walls of burrows and from water metabolized from food (metabolic water). Glands have almost disappeared from the reptilian thick skin; those surviving have special functions related to reproductive behavior and protection against aggressors. In the Crocodilia one pair of musk glands is located on the ventral side of the lower jaw and another within the cloacal opening in both sexes. A row of skin glands extends down either side of the back between rows of dermal plates the secretion of which has a nauseous odor. Musk glands in turtles are found along the jaw and between the carapace and plastron. On the ventral side of the thigh of most lizards lie small pits of epidermal origin, the so-called femoral and preanal glands, vestigial in females, whose viscous yellow-colored secretion acts as a sexual stimulant during copulation. Currently the several types of such pheromones among both invertebrate and vertebrate organisms are receiving much attention from biologists. Color pigment is present particularly in the Malpighian layer and outer region of the dermis. Melanophores under hormonal control account for most of the coloration.

Reptilian epidermis develops a thick stratum corneum the whole of which may periodically be shed during ecdysis in snakes and lizards, or which, as growth occurs, may accumulate through marginal rings on each scale in turtles and alligators. Between the scales of snakes a thinner, more flexible epidermis, aided by abdominal rows of keratoid plates, permits movement. Molting is hormonally controlled and hence may be induced experimentally.

Periodically mitosis ceases in snakes, for example, in the basal layer of the epidermis and the corneum simultaneously becomes dry and hard. On resumption of mitotic activity a new layer of corneum accumulates beneath the old hardened layer which is then sloughed off (molted) in entirety. In turn the soft vulnerable new corneal layer quickly hardens to an impenetrable state. Newt skins are shed in this manner, whereas snakes turn the "old" skin inside-out as it is discarded. Remnants on the tip of the rattlesnake's tail, the so-called rattles, represent previous molts. At each successive molt, possibly several times a year, a new and larger rattle is added.

Reptilian dermis shows two layers, superficial and deep, which vary in thickness among different species but otherwise are of typical vertebrate structure. Leather has been made from those types characterized by large collagenous fiber components. Man's quest for exotic materials and his disturbance of natural environments is rapidly leading to the extinction of many vertebrate species.

Birds   Avian skin is particularly adapted to the free movement of underlying muscles. The thin, delicate, loosely attached epidermis, well protected by coverings of feathers, scales, and horny beaks, serves a number of functions. Thin corneal scales are present on the legs and feet. The skin is almost devoid of glands, which are absent entirely in the ostrich, except for the common survivor, the uropygial gland on the dorsal surface at the base of the rudimentary tail in most birds. A simple, branched structure of the saccular type which is separated by a septum into two parts, this gland produces an oily secretion used to preen the feathers. This secretion, which may include cholesterol, renders the feathers impervious to water; without it an aquatic bird cannot float. Pigment is present in feathers, scales, and beak, but the skin itself will not tan. Melanocytes of the mammalian type are present in feathers, and iridescent colors are attributed to interference spectra.

The thin dermis of birds consists mostly of irregularly interlacing fibers and is rich in sensory (tactile) organs. Smooth muscle fibers raise and fluff the feathers. Modified sebaceous glands near the ear are found in a few birds, such as the rasores. Dermal ossifications are entirely lacking. The ostrich skin possesses sufficient strength to be used as leather.

Keratinized Derivatives of the Epidermis

Horny Teeth, Beaks, Epidermal Scales, and Spurs

Horny teeth within the oral funnel and on the cyclostome tongue are not true teeth but keratinized projections of the stratum corneum. Comparable structures are found on the jaws of many species of amphibian tadpoles previous to their metamorphosis. If the teeth are shed or torn off, they are replaced.

Beaks are common among higher vertebrates of the amniote group. When these are present, teeth are lacking in the adult, although tooth germs may make a transitory appearance in the monotremes and certain birds (parrots) during embryonic stages. Beaks consist of thickened, keratinized epidermis covering the jaws. Highly variable shapes are found, particularly among birds. Experimental studies of beak morphogenesis have shown that this structure is specifically induced in the head ectoderm of the embryo by the corresponding specific mesenchyme.

Epidermal scales are most often thought to be peculiar to reptiles, but in one form or another they are also found on the legs of birds (Figure 4-8), the tails and legs of rats, the bodies of armadillos, and the feet of kangaroos. They constitute the hard armor of the scaly anteater, or pangolin, on which they form overlapping plates. As in reptiles they develop as rigid masses of the stratum corneum, connected together by narrow zones of flexible epidermis. In birds and mammals the scales enlarge during development but are never shed and, if lost, are regenerated.

Horny spurs are epidermal structures of the stratum corneum present on the legs and even on wings of certain birds (tropical jacanas and screamers). Such structures are found more commonly in males of the species as one of the secondary sexual characteristics. In the rooster or fighting cock the spur is employed in defense or as an offensive weapon. The male duckbill platypus (an egg-laying monotreme mammal) has a spur on the inner surface of each hind leg which contains a duct leading from a poison gland.

Feathers

Structurally and developmentally feathers are by far the most intricate of any epidermal derivative of the stratum corneum. They occur in specific areas or tracts of the bird's skin, the pterylae, separated by featherless zones

Figure 4-8. Horny scales and spur on the leg of the fighting cock.

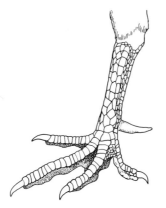

of skin, the apteria (Figure 4-9). Several types can be recognized in the chicken: flight feathers (remiges) on the wing margins, tail feathers (retrices) on the vestigial tail or uropygium, contour feathers on the body surface which contribute to the streamlined shape, and inconspicuous filoplumes or "hair" feathers distributed among the contour feathers and visible on a plucked bird. By fluffing the feathers in response to cold the bird creates a film of insulating air next to the skin's surface.

The feathers of an adult bird differ in structure within the several tracts over the surface of the body; some tracts exhibit transitions from one feather type to another, in others the types are sharply demarcated. Within these tracts feathers may also differ in the pigmentation pattern, order of embryonic development, time of development, or season of the year when the feather follicles become competent to react to hormones by producing feathers of different colors. During the molting process a characteristic order occurs in which feathers in different tracts are lost, apparently in the reverse order of their development. Feather follicles are usually arranged in rows

Figure 4-9. Feather structure: (a) pterylae, or feather tracts; (b) details of flight feather structure; (c) powder-down feather; (d) quill feather.

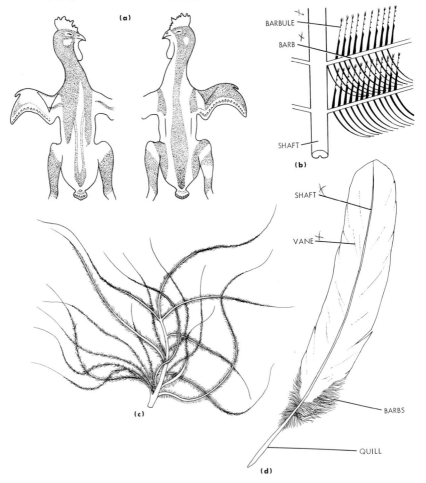

although in certain areas, such as under the wings, around the cloacal opening, and on the flanks, feathers may be arranged in a random fashion. Probably few feather follicles are added after hatching. The overlapping scales on the legs likewise appear to have a regular pattern. Although this is reported to be a less orderly development than that of feathers.

Feather color variation results from either one or both of two mechanisms: physical structure and the presence of chemical pigments. Whites, blues, and iridescent colors are structurally derived, whereas reds, yellows, and blacks are of pigment origin. There is no pigment in a white feather, the polygonal-shaped cells simply break up the light and reflect the several wavelengths equally. Structural, or Tyndall, blue results from the action of minute pores in the walls of cells located beneath the outer sheath of the feather barbs. Blue wavelengths are scattered, the longer ones are transmitted; because of this scattering such areas appear blue in reflected light. When some yellow pigment is also present in the outer sheath of such barbs, the combination of structural blue and pigmented yellow gives green. Many birds exhibit strikingly complicated variations of color patterns produced by contributions from the overlapping contour feathers. Studies by W. J. Hamilton and F. Heppner with dark-colored birds have indicated that homeothermic animals can absorb and utilize radiant solar energy and that dark pigmentation facilitates this process. It is believed that color, by reducing the metabolic cost of maintaining a constant body temperature, may be of considerable importance in the energy budget of an animal in nature. The evidence is applicable in the coloration of man when maximal absorption of solar radiation occurs in situations in which energy must be expended to maintain body temperature, as at dawn and dusk in otherwise hot climates.

Different types of feathers, from the contour feather to the filoplume with its few soft barbs attached to a short shaft lacking both quill and vane, are all modifications of a common developmental pattern of organization. A newly hatched chick (Figure 4-10) is covered with the same nestling down (plumules) consisting of fine, soft barbs and a short quill that is found among the contour feathers of adult birds. Feathers, first discovered in the earliest known fossil bird, *Archaeopteryx*, are primitive derivations of the horny reptilian scale, as are claws and beaks, with which they are homologous.

The early developmental stages of a feather and scale are similar—both show a vascularized dermal core covered by a thickened layer of ectoderm. As the feather papilla lengthens into a cylindrical cone, it grows downward into the dermis and forms a pit around its base which continues to deepen into the follicle. Concomitantly the ectodermal component of the papilla grows outward, to form the keratinized quill enclosing the dermal pulp, outer sheath, and subsequently the bundle of ectodermal barbs. As the sheath splits and the barbs become separated and spread flat, the vane of the feather is produced. Afterwards the pulp material dries up, and leaves a cavity with openings or umbilia at either end. Contour feathers grow from the same follicles as do plumules and are actually continuous with them.

Developmental patterns in all kinds of feathers are differentiations from a common basic type. On the fifth day of incubation the prospective epidermis of the chick embryo is a flat undifferentiated layer two cells thick with

Figure 4-10. Nestling down feathers on a newly hatched chick. (Courtesy Victor Hamburger, Washington University.)

a basal layer of cuboidal cells and an outer layer of flattened cells (fewer than in the basal layer). By six days the epidermis shows the beginnings of the adult condition: a basal layer of columnar cells covered by a superficial periderm of flattened cells. The seventh day shows the first indications of the dermal component of feather primordia, which are visible along the middorsal line of the back as small aggregations of dermal cells. Above each line the epidermal layer likewise has begun to thicken. Later, new aggregations form successive rows on each side of the original row. At the same time the thickened epidermis above each dermal aggregation begins to protrude, and later forms the epidermal sheath of the early feather structure. Such epidermal differentiations subsequently appear on older dermal aggregates. By eight days the more advanced feather structures have attained the form of cylindrical papillae protruding above the skin's surface. Keratin may be detected at fourteen days of incubation; the feather primordium is birefringent at twelve days.

Formation of the epidermal structure appears to be dependent upon the presence of the underlying dermal aggregate [4, 13, 22]. Thus we can speak here of an inductive interaction of epidermis and dermis. Without the formation of the dermal aggregate, brought about by localized factors at the dermal level, no differentiation of the epidermal sheath in the feather will take place. After this stage the dermis soon loses its inductive capacity. Later under the influence of the epidermis, dermal cells move into the epidermal sheath of the feather primordium. Thus the epidermis plays a major role in feather development, even controlling the caudal adjustment of feather primordium by its cephalo-caudal orientation. This has been demonstrated by growing combinations of epidermis and dermis *in vitro.* The tissue culture technique has also revealed the bipotentiality of the chick embryonic skin. It is the underlying dermis from various regions in the body that determines whether overlying epidermis remains flat and devoid of feathers, gives rise to different types of feathers in various body regions, or forms scales on the legs. Although the epidermis develops according to the nature of the underlying dermis, its histological differentiation conforms with its origin (Sengel, 1964): thus the epidermis is feather tract specific. Combinations *in vitro* of dorsal epidermis, for example, with tarsometatarsus dermis give rise to thickened epidermal scales instead of feathers. It has also been shown that dermal skin cells need not be living to produce this effect; even collagen may be substituted.

Horns   An epidermal derivative found commonly though not exclusively among male mammals is the horn, a term loosely applied to purely epidermal structures, dermal bone, or formations combining both tissues, which have roles in reproduction, protection, and offense (Figure 4-11). In vertebrate evolu-

Figure 4-11. Horns and antlers: (a)-(b) "knob horn" (giraffe); (c) fiber horn (rhinoceros); (d) pronghorn antelope; (e)-(f) cow horn; cow horn; (g) deer antler "in velvet"; (h) mature antler.

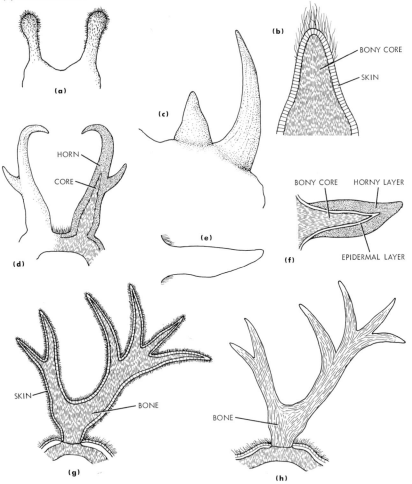

tion horns were first encountered in the skeletons of horned dinosaurs of the late Cretaceous period. In *Triceratops* (a three-horned dinosaur) all defensive mechanisms were located on the head. A broad frill of bone, presumably covered with skin, extended over the neck region, usually along with three horns on the head, two over the eyes, and one on the nose. Representatives of modern vertebrates with nose horns include several genera of lizards and the rhinoceros. Horns have attained their maximum specialization among ungulate placental mammals.

The strong horn of the rhinoceros consists of epidermal keratin fibers or hair-like filaments with a laminated structure and irregular shape, agglutinated firmly together into a pointed mass. It lacks a bony core but is fixed over a short knob on the nasal bone; a new structure is produced if needed. African and Sumatran rhinos have two slender horns—the longer one is found anteriorly, whereas a single short, broad horn characterizes the Indian species.

Antlers are borne generally by males of the deer family (deer, elk, moose), but both sexes of the reindeer and caribou develop them. Each antler of a sexually mature animal consists of a projection of the frontal bone of the skull. During development of the antler the growing core is covered with a layer of skin and the animal is "in velvet." When the antler is mature and before the onset of the mating period, the skin covering dries and is sloughed, leaving only the exposed bony core. Later the antler is lost when tissue constriction at its base of attachment on the frontal bone shuts off the blood supply and weakens the connection. This involves the breakdown and absorption of bone. Following overgrowth of the area by the surrounding skin and in hormone response to changes in light and temperature, a new antler with its covering of velvet begins to grow. This process is repeated for each breeding season. The antler enlarges during each succeeding growth period and shows an increased number of prongs. This phenomenon, obviously sex-related, is controlled by the hypothalamic-pituitary-testicular system of endocrine glands.

Another type of horn, the pronghorn, is found among two species of ungulates, the pronghorn antelope *Antilocapra americana*, and the Saiga antelope of Russia, *Colus Tatarica*. This type consists of a permanent bony core encased by a sheath of horny skin that is shed periodically and renewed each season without loss of the core. The stubby horns of the giraffe and okapi, permanent structures, remain covered by living skin throughout life. Such horns continue growth by cell addition from the germinating layer of the skin.

Hollow horns occur in both sexes among domestic and wild cattle, goats, sheep, and antelope. Horn formation of this type is similar to the ordinary process of cell proliferation from the germinal layer of the epidermis followed by cornification of the proliferated cells. Not easily impaired, the horn accumulates in thickness as a casing around a core of bone from the frontal bone of the skull. These horns are permanent, usually not branched, and may attain large size as in the Texan steer and certain breeds of African domestic cattle.

Nails, Claws, and Hooves

These homologous structures, which have a common origin, serve specialized functions among the different species (Figure 4-12). Claws form on ends of digits by action of the epidermal germinative layer. First found among living vertebrates on little-known brook salamanders and primitive frogs, they are common on modern reptiles, birds, and certain mammals. The outer plate of the claw is the unguis, possibly a modified scale, beneath which is the softer subunguis near its base. Among birds the South American koatzin also has two movable clawed digits on its wings.

Ungulate mammals show a specialization of the claw in the form of a hoof of similar origin and structure. The unguis is the hoof proper, the subunguis functions as the underlying pad. The hoof is characterized by a basic filamentous structure but, unlike the rhinoceros horn, the filaments are cemented together with cellular interfilamentous horn material. In addition,

Figure 4-12. Digital tips: (a) claw of the eagle; (b) sagittal section of a digital tip of a young child; (c) side and ventral views of the hoof of a horse.

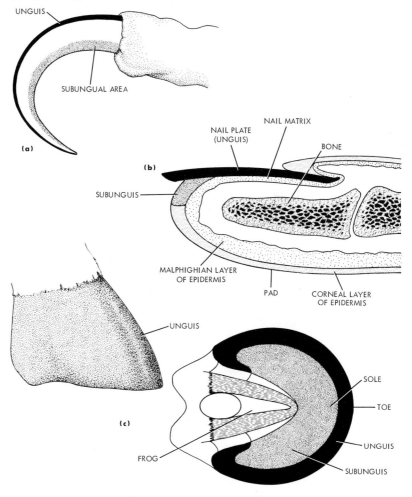

the hoof does not easily fray. The filamentous structure may contribute strength and rigidity to the hoof.

In primates the claw is replaced by a nail, the nail plate or unguis being the conspicuous component. The unguis is a narrow band between the nail plate and the epidermis of the finger tip. Cells in the nail do not progress as far as either the claw or hoof in the keratinization process which ceases at the stratum lucidum (cf. skin) stage of differentiation when cells contain the material eleidin. Nail growth takes place at its base in the upper epidermis of the digit.

Hair   Biologists have long speculated on the occurrence of human hairlessness, and the controversy is far from over. Apparently hair developed early during primate evolution, in the Triassic period according to one authority, probably as a component of the temperature-regulating mechanism of the body. Specialized types of hair are numerous: whiskers or vibrissae of the rat and cat, the effective contact receptors associated with sensory organs; the sex-linked mane of the lion; the winter fringe on the feet of the snowshoe hare; the eyelashes and eyebrows of man. The density of fur varies as shown by the fine underfur plus the longer coarse hair. Curly hair is oval and elliptical, straight hair is round, and kinky hair is flat.

Although given as one of the diagnostic characteristics of mammals, milk secretion by mammary glands being the other, hair is scanty or hard to find in rhinoceros, hippopotamus, elephant, armadillo, whale, and so on. Hairlessness in mice has been bred as a mutant. Absence or loss of hair and its distributional pattern on the body are secondary sexual characteristics. Sexual selection by the human male has been advanced as a factor in influencing hair patterns and color. Some effort has been made to associate one type of baldness with an excess of male sex hormone; however, there are several different causes of baldness.

Hair shape and structure vary over the body surface, as does its distributional pattern. The form of hairs among mammals shows numerous variations from the hard, stiff spines of the porcupine and Australian anteater to the soft, fine wool of sheep and goats. Bristles on the pig are short, straight, elastic hairs, often with split ends. Fur consists of soft, densely aggregated hairs with interspersed long coarse hairs that are removed when the skins are worked into articles of commerce. Wool hair cuticle is rough and scaly and tends to be slightly twisted, qualities which make it suitable for yarn. The late human fetus is entirely covered by abundant fine embryonic hair, the lanugo coat. Generally this is discarded before birth along with the epidermal periderm, though occasionally infants are born with a fine crop of hair.

Although hair develops from an outgrowth of the stratum corneum of the skin, its evolutionary origin differs from the reptilian scale. Essentially a hair is a compact rod of keratinized cells, showing a central cellular medulla surrounded by a cortex and, in some cases, by an enclosing cuticle (Figure 4-13). It originates at the base of an epidermal follicle from a group of germinative cells that are connected with the stratum Malpighi of the skin and lie deeply embedded within the dermis. Continuous proliferation of cells, followed by rapid keratinization, produces the column of hair cells. Associated with the follicle are a capillary network, nerve endings, an epidermal sebaceous gland with an opening into the follicle cavity, plus an arrector pili muscle of ectoderm origin (Figure 4-14). This muscle causes movement of the hair in fright, displays of anger (cat, dog), and so on. From the sebaceous gland comes the oily secretion (sebum) associated with the scalp. Size and function of these glands are controlled chiefly by androgenic hormones. They are abundant on the face and around the anogenital surfaces which they keep oily, and also on the lips and inside the mouth. The glands are small in the child, begin to enlarge in early puberty, and reach full size in the adult human (Figure 4-15).

Cellular proliferation and differentiation of the hair are affected by many factors. Among certain mammals they are interrupted when hair is discarded during various seasons of the year, as when a horse sheds its winter coat in spring in response to temperature change. In other mammals there are seasonal changes of color, texture, and/or amount, as when the weasel's winter fur coat changes from white to a summer brown (Figure 4-16). In the

Figure 4-13. Diagram of a vertical section of the human skin to show many of the different structural elements present, especially hair, glands, nerve endings, and vascular supply.

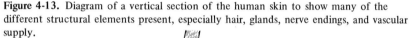

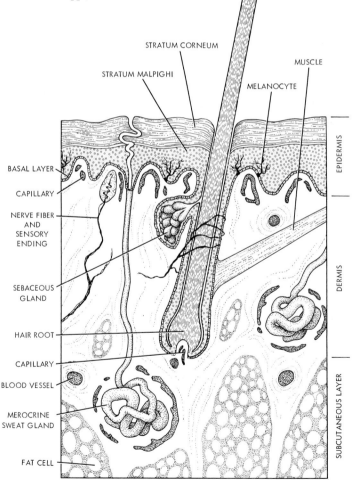

STRATUM CORNEUM

MUSCLE

STRATUM MALPIGHI

MELANOCYTE

EPIDERMIS

BASAL LAYER

CAPILLARY

NERVE FIBER
AND
SENSORY
ENDING

DERMIS

SEBACEOUS
GLAND

HAIR ROOT

CAPILLARY

BLOOD VESSEL

SUBCUTANEOUS LAYER

MEROCRINE
SWEAT GLAND

FAT CELL

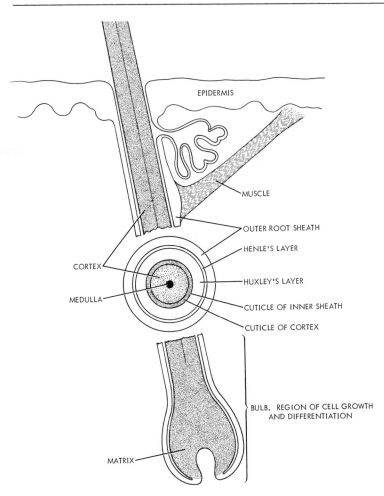

Figure 4-14. Details of the structure of a hair follicle. Cellular characteristics have been omitted, but the relationship of the layers is given in the inserted cross-section where the keratogenic zone of the follicle is not shown.

case of the cheetah of remarkable swiftness the naked cub soon develops a mantle of gray hair that is replaced by the characteristic spotted coat of the adult. Diet is an important factor for any mammal, as are the physical, emotional, and mental states of the organism. For example, morphological and color changes may result from protein-caloric malnutrition, and fiber-growth rate (merino sheep) may be affected. Adding molybdenum to the diet of sheep arrests typical pigmentation and produces a striped fleece. A copper-deficient diet changes wool texture. Hair has many specialized uses; it protects the skin from abrasions and cuts, thermal and radiant injury, and chemical irritation. Few substances can reach the skin of a furry animal.

The color of the human skin is due primarily to two components: translucency and the presence of pigments. The former permits blood in the dermal capillaries to color the skin, as in blushing. Pigments include brown which can darken to black and a yellow that may modify to red. These are diffused in the tissues. Such pigments are found in varying proportions in skins of all races and even vary within a single individual of a race. Albinos lack pigment in both skin and hair. Skin color changes during a lifetime, and the female skin is more yellow than that of the opposite sex. Pigment is present in the epidermis and hair bulb, but rarely in the outer portion of the dermis. Not until shortly after birth are pigment granules present in any amount in the stratum Malpighi. Excessive local pigmentation produces freckles, which are more common in light-skinned individuals. Cutaneous moles are composed of local elevations of both the epidermis and dermis, which may be pigmented and even involve a few hairs. When a mole is congenital and involves blood capillaries, it is known as a birthmark. Within the mammalian epidermis is a reticular system of pigment-secreting cells, the

Figure 4-15. Stereogram of an eccrine sweat gland on the right, and an apocrine sweat gland on the left of a hair follicle with its sebaceous gland. Eccrine glands are simple tubular coiled structures without connections to hair follicles; function throughout life and produce a watery secretion. Apocrine glands are connected with hair follicles, begin to function at puberty, and produce a viscous secretion. (Courtesy of Dr. William Montagna and Academic Press, New York).

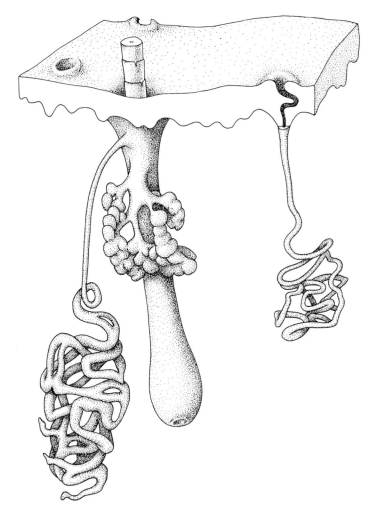

melanocytes, which constitute a self-maintaining unit. These differentiate from melanoblasts, which in turn have their origin in the embryonic neural crest cords. From such cords the melanoblasts migrate throughout the body, and on arrival at their destinations differentiate into pigment-forming cells. Those in the retina of the eye, however, have their origin in the eye primordium itself.

The color of hair is produced by pigment within the intercellular spaces of the cortex; black and red in man, brown in most other forms. White is due to an absence of pigment together with the refraction of light from air spaces between the cells of the medulla. The amount of pigment determines the shade of hair color, as brown-black usually masks the red-yellow. Dark hair lacking red is generally blue-black.

Although the neural crest origin of pigment cells among vertebrates has been well established, the mechanisms responsible for spotting patterns is not clear. For example, how does the white spotting in hair color patterns develop, such as the pigment-free areas in piebald mice?[26] Basic causative factors are reported to be genetic. Two alternative mechanisms have been proposed. One states that melanoblasts fail to reach the areas of the skin destined to be pigment-free because of a controlled migration defect at some early stage in embryonic development or as a result of cell antagonism exhibited by propigment cells. Appropriate spacing of chromatophores could produce color patterns as well as prevent the mingling of melanophores and xanthophores. A delayed time sequence of melanoblast migration in piebald mice has been reported, which possibly may be the effect produced by spotting genes. The alternative mechanism proposes that melanoblasts migrate into all areas of the skin but fail to differentiate in certain regions either through genetic factors within the neural crest cells or through the influence of the cellular environment. The question is still unanswered on the basis of current evidence from various genetic and experimental approaches. Something must be present in the colorless areas that inhibits melanoblast differentiation.

Numerous factors affecting integumentary colors among vertebrates include

Figure 4-16. Photographs of the weasel, showing the change in fur color between summer and winter seasons.

secretions of the endocrine glands (melancocyte-stimulating hypophyseal hormone—MSH or intermedin), some steroids, and hormones (corticosteroids) which influence the corticotrophin-MSH relationship. Adrenal deficiency leads to darkening of the fur. Sunlight on the human skin produces additional melanin and also causes bleached pigment already present to darken. The darkening represents the oxidation of melanin which is present in a reduced leucoform. Melanin behaves as an oxidation-reduction indicator, the oxidized form being dark, the reduced form bleached. Actually it is the thickening of the corneum rather than melanin formation that increases its screening action, and is considered to be the principal factor in the increased resistance to sunburn. Ultraviolet radiation is a major factor in human cutaneous cancer.

Skin Reactions   The skin, a mirror of body function and internal disturbance, reflects abnormal conditions of the internal environment in specific ways. A number of diseases with pigmentary indicators are known: the paper pallor of pituitary disease, the cyanotic blue of congenital heart disease or of oxygen deficiency in the newborn, the deep tan of thyroid dysfunction, and the jaundice yellow of liver disturbance. The bronze of hemochromatosis reflects a disturbance of iron metabolism that deposits iron in the skin. Many chemicals in common therapeutic and diagnostic use, including medicinal drugs and vegetable pigments, will produce skin discoloration. In exceptional amounts the yellow pigment betacarotene, a common skin component present in many vegetables, can make the skin yellowish. The carotenoid group color the serum and are associated with the fat of dermis and subcutaneous tissues. Excessive consumption of tomato products over a long period may color the skin reddish as a result of the accumulation of excessive amounts of another carotenoid pigment, lycopene. Clinical literature is a good source of such interesting information. Man's skin also reacts violently to a number of allergies and diseases such as measles and poison plant products. A skin test is employed for the detection of tuberculosis.

Among vertebrates, skin transplants usually survive for any length of time only between individuals characterized by a high degree of genetic uniformity—those of inbred strains or monozygous twins. In other cases "foreign" tissue is rejected when the host produces an antibody reaction.[3] Positive cases of successful intrasib grafts have been found, however, under certain unusual conditions, as in small natural populations of fish that have been isolated for extended periods. This has been attributed to the achievement of a high degree of genetic uniformity through inbreeding within a restricted environment. The adaptability of skin grafts from cancer patients to healthy recipients is less easily explained. Atypical behavior of skin grafts in this case may result from the attack on the mechanisms that destroy abnormal cells. Immunity mechanisms become manifested by the human fetus around the time the lymphatic system and thymus gland make their appearance. Henceforth the body is protected against foreign cells, even from tissue and organ transplants. Curiously, in some individuals the reaction is less intense than in others. Immunologic tolerance for a variety of antigens has been achieved in adult animals with immunosuppressive chemicals such as 6-mercaptopurine. Massive doses of tissue antigen, and of tissue antigen combined with chemical immunosuppressive agents, have been successful in making foreign grafts more acceptable for a time (heart, kidney).

Another type of skin reaction that is little understood is skin cancer. Chemical and physical factors of varied types may produce at first a tiny nodule long after the inducing agent has disappeared. This nodule has been observed to grow into an epidermal cancer; destructive action takes place through uncontrolled growth and cellular-tissue modification. Some kind of change has taken place in the living epidermal cells so they become, as Peyton Rous writes, "excessively proliferative, destructively uncoordinated, predatory and ungovernable; no longer capable of living in harmony with neighboring cells to maintain the natural skin." Skin and mouth cancers are far more common than is realized. The changed cells are termed neoplastic, since they form new tissue; the growth itself is a neoplasm. Coal-tar derivatives, excessive exposure to the ionizing radiation in sunlight, and myriad chemical and physical means can evoke tumors on the skin, which furnishes a visible culture medium. Skin cells are especially vulnerable to DNA damage provoked by immoderate exposure to sunlight.

Pharmacological Activity

Some vertebrate skins produce unpleasant or irritating secretions that may provide partial defense against predators. This is especially true among certain species of amphibians from whose skins compounds which possess remarkable pharmacological activity have been isolated. Often such animals have vivid pigmented colorations, as in the neotropical Family, *Dendrobatidae,* and such markings are considered to be a warning to other organisms. A number of animal groups exhibit similar warning colorations. Daly and Myers [5] describe a Panamanian poison frog, *Dendrobates pumilio,* that shows interpopulational variation in color, degree of toxicity, size, and habits. Differences in body coloration encompass the visible spectrum from red to blue, as well as achromatic black and white. Wide variations in degree of toxicity are not apparently correlated with supposed warning coloration. Skin extracts yield two toxic compounds characterized as steroidal alkaloids.

Vitamin D Synthesis by the Skin

Unlike other vitamins the "sunshine" vitamin D is synthesized in the human skin under the influence of solar rays in the ultraviolet region of the spectrum (wavelength 290-320 millimicrons) which convert the provitamin 7-dehydrocholesterol. Vitamin D mediates the absorption of calcium from the intestine and the deposition of inorganic minerals in growing bone. Naturally, children require more of it than do adults. Too little results in rickets, whereas a prolonged excess may provoke chalky calcium deposits in arteries, particularly the aorta, and "stone" formation with impairment of function in the kidney. From its source of production in the skin, the vitamin is distributed in the circulatory system.

Physiologic means of regulating the vitamin D concentration in the body is apparently through control of the rate of photochemical synthesis. Beckemeier has reported that one square centimeter of white human skin synthesized up to eighteen international units in three hours. W. F. Loomis reasons that the rate of synthesis in the stratum granulosum is regulated by the two processes of pigmentation and keratinization of the overlying stratum corneum, which allow only regulated amounts of solar ultraviolet radiation to penetrate the outer skin layer and reach the region where vitamin D is synthesized. [14] According to this view, different types of skin—white (depigmented, dekeratinized), yellow (mainly keratinized), and black (mainly pigmented)—are adaptations that maximize ultraviolet penetration in northern latitudes and minimize it in southern latitudes; hence the rate of vitamin synthesis is maintained within physiologic limits (0.01-2.5 milligrams per day) throughout man's worldwide habitat. Evidence points to a marked correlation between skin pigmentation and equatorial latitudes. Additionally, the reversible summer pigmentation and keratinization activated by ultraviolet radiation, known as suntan, represents a means of maintaining physiologic constant rates of synthesis despite the great seasonal variation in solar ultraviolet radiation in northern latitudes. In the tropics man's lightly pigmented skin can synthesize a "deadly dose," up to 800,000 units, in a six-hour exposure of his whole body. Suntanning can be overdone, as is well known when the skin "blisters" through the accumulation of tissue fluids following breakdown of tissue barriers. Heavily pigmented skin transmits around 3 to 36 percent of the rays, whereas light-colored skin may allow a 53 to 72 percent passage of the rays. Thus a dark-skinned man in northern latitudes would be less favored and would suffer in comparison to his lighter-skinned neighbor; one exception is the Eskimo, who obtains his vitamin D from the fish oils in his diet.

A deficiency of vitamin A results in atrophy of hair follicles and extensive hyperkeratosis; otherwise the skin appears normal. Conversely, excessive amounts of this essential vitamin may cause hypertrophy of the adult epidermis, in addition to various developmental defects in fetal mammals if given to pregnant females (cleft palate, thyroid disturbances, and so on).

Temperature Control

Change in the external environment is perceived by peripheral receptors in the skin which in turn send messages by sensory nerves to central receptors in the spinal cord and brain. Responses are relayed to smooth muscles and glands. Birds and mammals are homeotherms, maintaining a relatively constant internal temperature through a wide range of environmental temperature changes. In contrast, the body temperature of poikilothermic vertebrates varies only a few degrees from that of the environment. Hence poikilotherms are capable of a wide span in body temperatures, as in the case of true hibernators (bat). The skin functions in other ways in body temperature control. In man the impulses transmitted by motor nerves to the blood vessels surrounding dermal sweat glands cause them to dilate and allow more blood to reach the secretory cells. By evaporation the increased amount of secretion on the surface of the skin tends to lower the skin temperature. Conversely, undue loss of heat is prevented by reduction of the amount of blood that reaches the glandular tissue through the arterioles and dermal capillaries. Arterioles undergo vasoconstriction that results when the circular smooth muscles in the arteriole walls contract in response to messages from the temperature control center in the hypothalamus of the brain. However, some heat may continue to be lost in the arms, legs, fingers, and toes. This is controlled, in turn, by a mechanism that utilizes the principle of exchange between two currents moving in opposite directions, the counter current heat exchanger. In the extremities, arteries, veins, and their branches lie in close proximity, permitting heat transfer from arterial to venous blood.

An interesting mechanism exists in other types of human extremities such as the external ear pinna and the nose, where freezing could easily take place. Here there are arteriovenous anastomoses that bypass the capillary bed and react to stimuli by expanding both in high and low temperatures, so in each case more blood reaches the skin. This system permits both cooling at high temperatures and warming at lower ones.

Additional mechanisms provide protection for homeotherms. Heat is lost from the body by radiation, conduction, and convection. Radiation in the form of electromagnetic waves is conducted from the body by contact with air or water, the movement of which carries away the heat. People living in cold climates possess a thicker epidermis. Feathers and hair are insulating devices. Contraction of the smooth muscle associated with each hair follicle causes the hairs to "stand out" from the skin and thicken the fur coat so there is less movement of air next to the skin. In some fur-bearing mammals, coat thickness may be increased as a result of additional hair formation or replacement. Fat deposits in the subdermal and even the dermal layers also may serve as insulation.

Adaptions to
Arid Environments

Unlike reptiles, amphibians never overcame their dependence upon water in one form or another. Since the integument is permeable, it is unable to prevent the rapid evaporation that occurs readily as from a free surface[1]. Among most amphibians the loss is inversely related to the relative humidity; at low humidity this evaporation lowers body temperature, whereas a rise in body temperature accompanies dehydration. Rate of loss is independent of the skin. Normal permeability differs between various species; certain toads and the red eft land stage of the newt lose water more slowly than frogs, as evidenced by the nature of the stratum corneum. As a living membrane, frog skin has commonly been used in permeability studies. In water, frogs take up moisture by osmosis through the skin, never by the mouth, as has been demonstrated in dehydrated animals. This is an obvious advantage, as the frogs can collect necessary water from damp surfaces; in the case of desert frogs it facilitates rapid hydration from the walls of the burrows.

Australian terrestrial amphibians avoid dehydration by burrowing, during which a transparent cocoon of a single cell-layer of shed keratinized stratum corneum may reduce water loss. This cocoon completely surrounds the animal, even across the eyes and cloaca, although there may be tubular inserts into the external nares. Apparently this membrane is formed by sloughing the stratum corneum as a complete unit through intercellular separation by some unknown method. Lee and Mercer have reported passage of water through the cocoon wall of *A. albuguttatus* that amounts to 0.65-0.22 milligram of water per square centimeter per hour. Some desert-dwelling frogs have been known to spend three months or more underground where they make use of soil water. When the California spadefoot toad, *Scaphiopus counchii,* emerges from its burrow following a dry spell, it is covered by a hard material resembling dried skin. Lung fish estivate, during which they secrete a slime cocoon around themselves as they lie buried in the mud. Protection for many years may be gained in this manner, even after the mud has become a thoroughly dried mass on a scientist's laboratory shelf.

Water loss by evaporation may take place from even the thickest cornified skins like those of reptiles. In the desert tortoise, *Gupherus agassizii,* this constitutes the major proportion of water loss by the body. However, both this loss and that by respiration is far less than in lizards and tortoises from wetter regions, as reported by Schmidt-Nielsen and Bentley, 1966. It suggests that in reptiles there are adaptations of the integument associated with aridity of the environment. Birds and reptiles excrete waste nitrogen principally as uric acid so that little or no water is involved; even the fecal pellets may be almost dry. The condition of the skin aids camels to sustain a far greater degree of dehydration than in the case of humans. Some mammals in dry regions utilize metabolic or oxidation water produced from food stuffs (the deermouse, *Peromyscus,* and the kangaroo rat).

No discussion of the highly versatile skin would be complete without some mention of its role as an ecosystem with a characteristic microscopic flora and fauna and diverse ecological niches. In a fascinating article in the January 1969 issue of *Scientific American,* Dr. Mary J. Marples pictures the skin as "a kind of soil with attributes that are beneficial (temperature, food and water supplies) or harmful (slight acidity) for the organisms it supports, a discrete world where living and nonliving components, all interacting with one another, exist in equilibrium."[15]

Some of these organisms, which are potentially lethal pathogens, cause disease only if they penetrate the deeper cutaneous layers. The nonliving surface of the skin is constantly renewed from below as the flat scale-like squames of fibrous protein keratin are shed, and it is supplied with secretions of various glands upon which the cutaneous organisms feed. The eccrine sweat glands produce a weak alkaline solution containing nitrogenous substances and other nutrients, whereas the sebaceous glands associated with the hair canals exude a semiliquid sebum containing a high proportion of lipids (fatty acids, triglycerides, waxes, cholesterol and detritus from dead sebaceous cells). These glandular secretions together with the by-products from keratinization provide free amino acids as nutrients. Carbohydrates and certain vitamins are available. Except on the extremities, little variation occurs in the warmish climate of this ecosystem. Among the permanent, indiginous organisms dwelling in this environment are the follicle mite, *Demodex folliculorum,* yeasts, fungi, bacteria (such as staphylococci and Gram-negative bacilli), and possible viruses. The study of skin ecology is now considered essential to the control of skin and wound infections. Even the most innocent injection may provide entry for life-threatening infection.

References for Chapter 4

[1] Bentley, P. J., "Adaptations of Amphibia to Arid Environments." *Sci.,* **152** (1966), 619-623. In arid environments amphibia have means of acquiring water for survival.

[2] Bern, H. A., "Hormones and Endocrine Glands of Fishes." *Sci.,* **158** (1967), 455-462. Hormonal control of coloration.

[3] Billingham, R. E., "Tissue Transplantation: Scope and Prospect." *Sci.,* **153** (1966), 266-270. Immunological factors in connection with skin transplantations.

[4] Cohen, J., "Feathers and Patterns" in *Advances in Morphogenesis.* New

York: Academic Press, 1966, 1-38. Structure and development of
feathers and feather patterns.

[5]   Daly, J. W., and C. W. Meyers, "Toxicity of Panamanian Poison Frogs
(Dendrobates): Some Biological and Chemical Aspects." *Sci.,* **156**
(1967), 970-973. Pharmacological activity of the skin.

[6]   Daniels, F., Jr., J. C. van der Leun, and B. E. Johnson, "Sunburn." *Sci.
Am.,* **219** (1968), 38-46. When the human skin receives an overdose of
ultraviolet radiation, a complex series of events ensues.

[7]   *Dorland's Illustrated Medical Dictionary.* Philadelphia: W. B. Saunders,
24th ed., 1966. General reference.

[8]   Etkin, William, and Lawrence I. Gilbert (eds.), *Metamorphosis. A
Problem in Developmental Biology.* New York: Appleton-Century-
Crofts 1968. A single up-to-date source that deals in an integrative
way with the several aspects of metamophosis.

[9]   Goodrich, H. B., and M. Hedenburg, "The Cellular Basis of Colors in
Some Bermuda Parrot Fish with Special Reference to Blue Pigment."
J. Morph., **68** (1941), 493-505.

[10] Grant, W. C., Jr., and G. Cooper, IV, "Behavioral and Integumentary
Changes Associated with Induced Metamorphosis in *Diemictylus." Biol.
Bull.,* **129** (1965), 510-522. Changes in the newt's skin between land
and aquatic phases of the life cycle.

[11] Gross, J., "The Skin." *Sci. Am.,* **204**, No. 5 (1961), 120. Interesting
features and general description of the skin and its importance to man.

[12] Hertig, B. A., M. L. Riedse, and H. S. Bilding, *Advances in Biology of
Skin,* Vol. 2. New York: Pergamon Press, 1962. Advances in knowledge
of the skin.

[13] Kischer, C. Ward, "Fine Structure of the Down Feather During Its
Early Development." *J. Morph.,* **125** (1968), 185-204. Dermal-
epidermal interactions in the development of a feather.

[14] Loomis, W. F., "Skin-pigment Regulation of Vitamin-D Biosynthesis."
Sci., **157** (1967), 501-506. In man vitamin D is synthesized by the
skin.

[15] Marples, Mary J., "Life of the Human Skin." *Sci. Am.,* **220** (Jan.
1969), 108-115. The skin as an ecosystem with a microscopic flora and
fauna and diverse ecological niches.

[16] Modell, Walter, "Horns and Antlers." *Sci. Am.,* **220** (1960), 114-122.
Horns and antlers are commonly believed to be alike, but actually are
quite different: the material of horns is related to skin, that of antlers
to bone. See also Goss, Richard J., "Principles of Regeneration", New
York: Academic Press (1969).

[17] Montagna, W., "The Skin." *Sci. Am.,* **212**, No. 2 (1965), 56-66. Interesting features and a general description of the skin and its importance
to man.

[18] Montagna, W., and W. C. Lobitz (eds.), *The Epidermis.* New York:
Academic Press, 1964. A detailed discussion of the epidermis, its
structure and function.

[19] Montagna, W., *The Structure and Function of the Skin.* New York:
Academic Press, 1962. A more detailed description of the skin:—its
role, structure, importance, and unsolved problems.

[20] Montagna, W. (ed.), *Advances in the Biology of the Skin, Vol. 6.* Long Island City, New York: Pergamon Press, 1966. Further information on the structure and function of the skin.

[21] Odland, G. F., and R. O. Greep (eds.), *Histology.* New York: McGraw-Hill, 2nd ed., 1966. Histological structure of the skin.

[22] Rawles, M. E., "Tissue Interactions in Scale and Feather Development as Studied in Dermal-Epidermal Recombinations." *J. Embryol. Exptl. Morphol.,* **11** (1963), 765-789. A study of the interactions of the epidermis and dermis during development of the skin.

[23] Romer, Alfred S., *The Vertebrate Body.* Philadelphia: W. B. Saunders, 3rd ed., 1963. Comparative anatomy of the skin and its derivatives.

[24] Rushmer, R. F., K. J. K. Buettner, J. M. Short, and G. F. Odland, "The Skin." *Sci.,* **154** (1966), 343-348. Use of the skin to show the diversity of problems that can be approached by investigators with widely different backgrounds.

[25] Sayles, L. F., and S. G. Hershkowitz, "Placoid Scale Types and Their Distribution in *Squalus acanthias." Biol. Bull.,* **73** (1937), 51-66.

[26] Searle, A. G., *Comparative Genetics of Coat Colour in Mammals.* New York: Academic Press; London: Logos Press, 1968.

[27] Smith, Hobart M., *Evolution of Chordate Structure.* New York: Holt, Rinehart and Winston (1960). Evolutionary development of skin structures.

[28] ——, "The Phylogeny of Hair and Epidermal Scales." *Turtox News,* **36** (March 1958), 82-84. The evolutionary origin and development of hair and scales.

[29] Weichert, Charles K., *Anatomy of the Chordates.* New York: McGraw-Hill, 1951. Comparative anatomy of the skin and its derivatives.

5

The skeletal system: a physiological and biomechanical perspective

Functional Definition of the Skeletal System

The organization of the vertebrate skeletal system is best understood by considering the functions of both the skeletal tissues and the skeletal organs. The primary role of all skeletal systems is *biomechanical:* to provide protection, support, and motion. The size, shape, and position of the skeletal organs, as well as their internal and external structural arrangements and modes of articulation, accurately reflect this primary functional requirement. Biomechanical demands are similarly reflected in the histological composition of the skeletal organs. Vertebrate skeletal tissues, which include all possible variations of fibrous, cartilaginous, and osseous tissue types, form a continuous spectrum of connective tissues that individually respond to a specific functional demand. Bone is the most common skeletal tissue. As a tissue, it fulfills another major role in the mineral homeostasis of most vertebrates by serving as a reservoir of calcium, phosphate, and citrate ions, among others. As an organ, bone serves as a location within which hematopoesis (the formation of red blood cells and granulocytes) may occur. The bones of some birds have a pneumatic function, for they enclose extensions of the air sacs.

Origin of Vertebrate Skeletal Tissues

Phosphorus is a relatively rare element environmentally. One probable reason bone developed in vertebrates was to serve as a storehouse of this energy-rich material, the ADP-ATP cycle being the body's principal source of metabolic energy. The section "Dermal Armor" in the following chapter suggests additional adaptative influences, as well as the probable evolutionary sequence of skeletal tissues.

The earliest known vertebrate fossil, fragmented dermal armor from the Middle Ordovician agnathan fish, contains well developed bone and dental tissues. The fossil record indicates that the earliest fish may be classified into two principal types on the basis of the histological nature of their bone tissues. One type, the *Osteostraci,* possessed bone with enclosed osteocytes, whereas the *Heterostraci* had an acellular bone totally devoid of enclosed osteocytes. Because the probable antecedents of these fish are unknown, it is impossible to speculate meaningfully on the precise stages by which vertebrates acquired these two types of bone tissue. In any case, the fossil record also makes it clear that subsequent vertebrate evolution to amphibians, reptiles, birds, and mammals involved only cellular bone. Indeed, the *Heter-*

176

ostraci seem to have had no significant role in the phylogeny of the higher fish. Acellular bone disappeared in the lower fish, as in all higher forms, only to reappear once again in the advanced teleosts. It is apparent, therefore, that the histological structure of bone has no significant part in fish evolution. Cellularity of bone tissue may be a functional necessity in these vertebrates above the fish that possess a parathyroid gland along with the concomitant endocrinologically controlled processes of mineral homeostasis.

Skeletal tissues have biomechanical as well as homeostatic functions. Both their microscopic and gross structural arrangements reflect these two functional requirements. In mammals it is relatively simple to distinguish among (1) dense collagen fiber bundles arranged as tendinous cords or the broad sheets of aponeuroses, (2) cartilage, of a number of types, and (3) bone. In the lower vertebrates, particularly among fish, this sharp distinction is blurred; the many "intermediate" skeletal tissues which are found establish the fact that skeletal tissues are not organized as a parallel series of discrete entities but instead form a continuous spectrum of tissue types. As a general rule the distinctiveness of the skeletal tissues becomes apparent when a terrestrial mode of life is attained. Seemingly the added function of weight-bearing confers some selective advantage upon certain skeletal tissues and renders many of the intermediate types nonadvantageous. However, in pathological situations, such as the healing of fractures, this spectrum of intermediate tissues reappears, and it is clear that these cells are still potentially capable of forming the whole spectrum of skeletal tissue.

Organization of the Skeletal System

It is customary to separate the skeletal system into *cranial* and *postcranial* divisions. The cranial skeleton (or *skull*) consists of two portions that are functionally independent and to a considerable degree phylogenetically separate. These are (1) the *neural* skull (neurocranium), which protects and supports the enclosed brain, associated membranes, and cerebrospinal fluid, and (2) the *facial* skull (splanchnocranium and dermocranium) which surrounds the oral cavity and provides a movable digestive lever in all vertebrates except agnathan fish. The splanchnocranial elements are covered externally in all vertebrates, except chondrichthyian fish, by the dermocranial elements. Associated with the neural skull is a series of capsules for the organs of special sense (nose, eye, ear) (Figure 5-1).

The postcranial skeleton can also be subdivided. There is a *somatic (axial)* skeleton consisting of the vertebral column and ribs (both thoracic and abdominal, when present); an *appendicular* skeleton with both free (fins, limbs) and embedded (pectoral and pelvic girdles) portions; and a *visceral* (branchiomeric) skeleton that serves the organs and spaces derived from the pharyngeal region.

A second type of classification of the skeletal system stresses the ontogenetic processes by which bones are formed. In such a classification, which cuts across the topographic system, skeletal tissues may be classified as endochondral (preformed in a cartilaginous model that is later replaced, more or less completely, by bone) or membranous (dermal). The dermal skeleton is an outer protective system that varies in its structure from the dense layers of fibrous collaginous tissue of the mammalian dermis to actual plates of bone

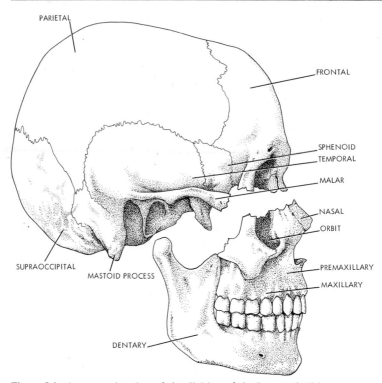

Figure 5-1. An approximation of the division of the human skull into a neural skull (upper) and a facial skull (lower). Technically these are termed the neurocranium and splanchnocranium respectively. (After Pernkopf.)

(often surmounted by teeth). Many intermediate types of dermal skeletal tissues are known, including all varieties of fish scales, calcified plates of tendinous tissue, or bone plates in fish (box-fish, seahorse), and calcium salt deposits in some amphibians (*Bufo*). These types of skeletal tissue will be discussed further in the following sections. Here we will consider briefly the composition of the cranial skeleton.

Neural Skull   The brain of the earliest vertebrate was probably completely enclosed within a continuous cartilaginous casing to which were joined the cartilaginous capsules of the organs of special sense. Above this box-like structure was a superficial shield of dermal bone. This unitary chondrocranium covered with dermal bones, or tooth-like denticles in the case of the cartilaginous sharks and rays, is still found in some recent fish.

The neural skull customarily is divided into a skull vault and a skull base. The general vertebrate pattern of organization of the neural skull is observed during early cephalic development. In the base a series of cartilaginous sensory *capsules* (olfactory, optic, and otic) are formed independently and subsequently fuse with a series of basal midline cartilages. These midline masses are divided by the site of the pituitary gland and its enclosure, the sella turcica, into a *presella* and *postsella*. They form the polar, trabecular, and parachordal cartilages respectively (Figure 5-2). Dorsally, the original vertebrate structural pattern involved an upward growth of the cartilaginous

tissues to enclose the brain within a series of pilae (walls) and a tectum
(roof). As the relative size and complexity of the brain increased, this dorsal
roofing became incomplete and was replaced by a series of intramembranous
flat (*calvarial*) bones. In mammals the vault of the neural skull is membranous in origin except for the supra-occipital region, which still retains the
earlier cartilaginous origin. In the higher vertebrates bone, by the processes
of endochondral ossification, replaces almost all the embryonic and fetal
cartilage of the neural skull.

The calvarial bones arise from independent centers of intramembranous
ossification. Although they become attached to the neurocranium, they are
truly dermal elements that have sunk beneath the surface of the skin during
the course of evolution. They remain separated by a series of soft-tissue
areas, the *sutures*, even in the adult skull. The sites of these sutural lines are
not genetically predetermined, but arise as a result of the differing relative
growth rates of adjacent bones. A general trend in the vertebrate skull has
been for a reduction in the number of the calvarial bones, a matter that
provides a useful index in taxonomic and phylogenetic studies. Sutures,
which serve several mechanical functions in the skull, act primarily as stress-
breakers to reduce the loads normally imposed upon the neural skull by the
action of attached muscles. Sutures, again acting to relieve imposed stresses,
permit a slight degree of relative motion to occur between adjacent bones.
The position of the suture lines also is biomechanically significant, in that it
reflects the position of underlying areas of highly organized fiber tracts of
the outer meningeal coat of the brain, the dura mater (Figure 5-3). This
functional type of union aids the concomitant growth of brain and skull
during primate infancy and early childhood.

Facial
Skull

The nasal, oral, and pharyngeal cavities require both protection and support
in order to maintain their functional patency. The skeletal tissues, tendon,
cartilage, and bone, related to this role comprise the facial skull. All vertebrates, except the agnatha, have an additional requirement—the facial skull
must provide some means of articulation by which jaws can move. Those
forms in which both the upper and lower jaws are mobile are said to possess
kinetic skulls (chiefly some fish, reptiles, and birds); in all others only the
lower jaw is capable of motion. As in the neural skull, evolution of the vertebrate facial skull is marked by a general reduction of the number of bones
present. Further details of the incorporation of the articular elements of the
jaw into the middle ear of mammals are described in the following chapter.

In cartilaginous fish the facial skull, like the neural skull, is composed
totally of cartilage. These facial cartilages belong to the gill-arch (branchial)
series. In higher forms those areas of the facial skull chiefly surrounding the
oral cavity are formed of the same elements, but these become increasingly
covered by intramembranous, or dermal, bones. The pharyngeal, and later
the laryngeal, regions continue to be protected by branchial arch cartilages.
However, these originally cartilaginous elements become increasingly replaced
by endochondral bone substitution, and in higher vertebrates the role of the
endochondral elements is gradually superseded by the dermal elements.
Examples of dermal bones in the facial skull are the dentary, maxillary,
premaxillary, and nasal illustrated in Figure 5-1.

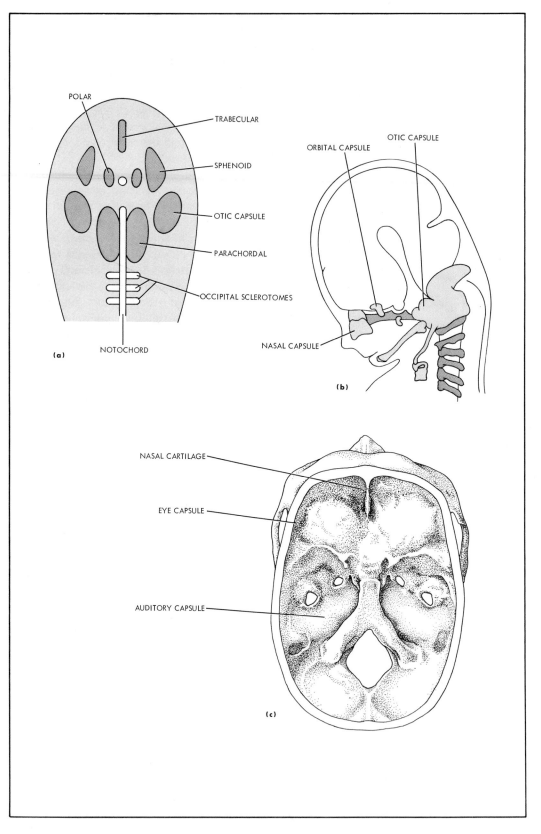

Figure 5-2 (opposite). (a) The skull begins as a series of isolated cartilaginous capsules serving to protect the organs of special sense, centrally located nasal, orbital and otic, together with similar tissues associated with the support of the central nervous system. (After William and Smith.) (b) Subsequently these cartilaginous masses coalesce and form in man what is in essence the base of the skull. This lateral view also shows the development of a series of visceral (branchiomeric) cartilages which play a transitory role in the formation of the jaws. (After Patten.) (c) When this figure of a much later stage of human fetal development is compared with (a), the completeness of the fusion of the sensory capsules with the central elements is seen. This stage does not differ essentially from that of the adult. All of this cartilage will be replaced by bone. (After Keith.)

The Biomechanical Role of Skeletal Tissues

The skeletal system is structured as a response to a wide variety of biomechanical demands. It may serve to protect and support enclosed soft-tissue organ systems, such as the brain or orbital contents. In this case, flat, plate-like arrangements that allow little motion between the several portions of these skeletal enclosures are best. However, another equally important demand is that the several units of the skeletal system permit motion between them. Because of this basic structural requirement, *joints* that articulate one skeletal part to another are formed. In this sense the skeletal system may be said to consist of a number of levers. Attached to the lever

Figure 5-3. The vault of the neural skull is not preformed in cartilage. Rather, bone tissue forms *in situ*; see Figures 5-6 (a) and (b). The several sutures demarking these bones are seen in this dorsal view of the adult human skull. (After Pernkopf.)

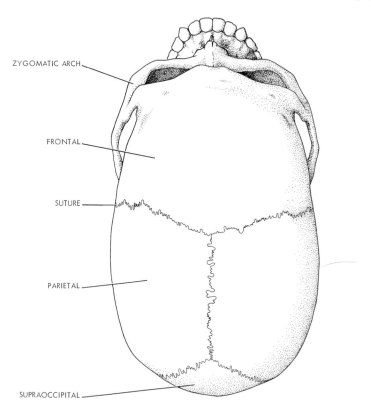

ZYGOMATIC ARCH

FRONTAL

SUTURE

PARIETAL

SUPRAOCCIPITAL

arms are the contractile elements, the muscles, the activity of which moves the skeletal lever arms as well as the often interposed connective tissues and ligaments. Although locomotion, the movement of the body through its environment, is a very common type of motion, there are also other important types of skeletal motion, such as the movement of the gill-arch mechanism in fish, of the thoracic cage in terrestrial vertebrates and of the vertebral column or jaws in all vertebrates.

Structural Modifications

The composition and structural arrangement of skeletal tissues accurately reflect the external biomechanical forces usually imposed upon them. Bone provides a relatively high degree of structural rigidity as well as mechanical protection in certain cases, whereas cartilage is more useful in situations requiring elasticity. In other sites, such as intermuscular septa, where skeletal tissues serve primarily for the attachment of muscles, sheets of dense fibrous connective tissues may be found as substitutes for osseous tissue. In all of these skeletal tissue types further refinements of histological composition are also functionally related. For example, hyalin cartilage is well suited to withstand compressive forces, and thus is found on the articular surfaces of most long bones. Where shearing forces are applied, however, fibrous cartilage is encountered, since this tissue type best withstands such forces. In other areas of observation we find structural reflections of functional demands. The preferential arrangement of both collagen fiber bundles and of interspersed cells in all skeletal tissue types is an excellent indication of areas upon or through which external forces are applied. Random arrangements of these same structural elements, on the other hand, are a good general indication of areas that are subjected to minimal external loadings.

Structurally, bone tissue is subject to modifications that are functionally related. Bone is a vital, dynamic tissue, not in any way to be regarded as "dead" or fixed in either its structure or composition. In a real sense bone is in a constant state of flux, in terms of both its composition and structure. The histological differences between reticular or woven bone, trabecular (cancellous or spongy), and compact bone indicate osseous response to differing functional demands. The usually transitory masses of woven bone are laid down rather rapidly and have no significant biomechanical function, whereas compact bone, either lamellar or osteonal, is formed more slowly. The thin trabeculae, serving as internal trajectories, are easily reconstructed if the nature of the imposed external loads varies. The ease of resorption and redeposition of trabecular bone makes it admirably suited to serve as a mineral reservoir in egg-laying vertebrates that have periodic, but heavy, demands for mineralization of both egg shells and fetal skeletons; birds are particularly good examples of this relationship.

Mineral Homeostasis

Bone is composed of an organic and inorganic phase. The former consists almost entirely of a ubiquitous vertebrate fibrous protein, collagen, together with a small but biologically significant amount of "ground substance" containing sulfated mucopolysaccharides. The inorganic phase has the general chemical structure of a specific type of calcium-phosphate salt, a hydroxy-apatite, $CA_{10}(PO_4)_6(OH)_2$. Biological apatites differ in many significant ways from their mineralogical homologues; they have a smaller crystallite size and their chemical formulation is such that they are said to be "calcium deficient," that is, they contain fewer calcium ions per unit of structure than do the mineralogic apatites. These two characteristics go far toward explaining the role of bone tissue in mineral homeostasis because (1) biological apatites provide relatively large surface area potential or actual contact with body fluids, and (2) this calcium deficiency renders the bone salts capable of taking up additional ambient ions that can easily substitute for calcium (strontium, lead, and so forth). At the same time it is in this "imperfect" state of crystal composition that bone salts can be most easily dissolved.

Bone formation is a dual process. The cells responsible (the osteoblasts) first lay down the organic matrix, upon which the subsequent deposition of the mineral phase occurs. An increasing body of evidence indicates that the first deposited form of this calcium phosphate salt is amorphous (noncrystalline), and further, that a very significant amount of the salts in any bone at any age may be in this amorphous stage. This is important since amorphous salts are more easily mobilized by the body than are crystalline salts. Subsequent mineral maturation of the newly formed bone entails first a conversion of the amorphous calcium phosphate salts to a crystalline state. Maturation of any mineralized area is marked by an increasing "perfection" of the crystalline structure and a concurrent increase in crystallite size. More mature bone salts are relatively less available for homeostatic purposes than newly formed salts. To understand the general vertebrate process of mineral homeostasis, a few principles must be clarified.

The concept of homeostasis is a general one. In the present context, we imply that the serum of the vertebrate body has a relatively constant range of concentration of calcium and phosphate ions (among others). Whenever the serum concentration of these ions falls below critical levels, the bone tissue gives up the required ions from its supply. When an excess of these ions is present, they must be eliminated generally by the urinary system. Additionally the skeletal store of mineral ions is drawn upon in certain circumstances such as fracture healing or when, in pregnancy, the developing fetus places a high priority demand upon the mineral salts of the mother.

The now classical depiction of the mechanisms of mineral homeostasis is simple (Figure 5-4). The average concentration of calcium ions in the blood

Figure 5-4. Homeostasis is the means by which the body regulates and controls its own level of functioning. In this figure the horizontal lines express a desired, but never static, level of a particular activity. At left, the actual level at any time (which progresses horizontally from left to right) is too high. This function is then decreased but, as is normal, does not terminate at the desired level, and rather falls below the line. A time-lag period ensues before the body can sense this lowered level of activity and then attempt to raise it. The cyclic nature of homeostasis is thus perpetuated.

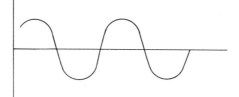

is 10 mg percent. About this average value is a normal homeostatic fluctuation that varies in a regular and roughly sinusoidal manner (Figure 5-5). When the calcium concentration falls below the average value, the parathyroid gland is stimulated to release parathormone. The effect of this hormone on the enclosed vital osteocytes is to signal for the release of calcium from the hydroxyapatite of the skeletal system. When this release phenomenon succeeds in raising the ionic concentration of calcium above the mean value, the parathyroid gland ceases to release parathormone. This is the essence of a "feedback" mechanism. Actually there are two distinct modes of regulating mineral ion concentration. If the parathyroid glands are removed from a mammal, the serum calcium concentration falls to about 7 mg percent. Accordingly, only the last 30 percent of mineral homeostasis is under endocrine regulation; 70 percent is accounted for by a relatively rapid, nonvital physicochemical process of ion exchange. The remaining 30 percent requires the activity of a vital cell, primarily the enclosed osteocyte, which itself is sensitive to the slower effect of circulating parathormone.

In terms of homeostatic availability, bone tissue is classified as either *stable* or *labile*. The former makes up approximately 96 percent of the total bone volume, whereas the labile fraction is the remaining 4 percent. Despite this

Figure 5-5. A specific example of mineral homeostasis is shown. The desired level of calcium ion concentration in the blood is 10 mg per 100 ml (10 mg percent). This is subject to constant homeostatic regulation. About 70 percent of this amount is accounted for by simple chemical equilibrium with newly formed bone. The other 30 percent is homeostatically regulated by the parathyroid gland. When the concentration of calcium ion falls below 10 mg percent, this is sensed by the parathyroid glands which then release a hormone (Parathormone, PTH). This acts on the somewhat older, stable bone mineral, via the osteocytes, to cause a release of calcium ions. Such a release always exceeds the desired level. This, too, is sensed by the parathyroid gland which acts as a calcium ion monitor, and causes it to cease releasing PTH. This cycle is endlessly repeated. (The role of calcitonin has been omitted deliberately.) (After McLean and Urist.)

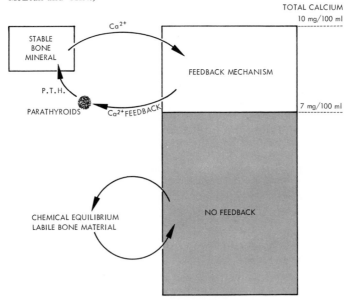

great relative disparity the smaller labile fraction is more available for homeostatic purposes, furnishing about 70 percent of the calcium content of the serum. This same labile fraction is not affected by the slower processes of endocrine activity, but rather is made available by the more rapid process of physicochemical dissolution.

The labile fraction consists of the most recently laid down and mineralized bone tissues. This is precisely the area where the hydroxyapatite crystallites are at once smaller and less perfect in their structure. Since all new bone tissue matures in time, formerly labile areas eventually become stable. It is the stable portion that is affected by parathormone. In order to ensure a constant supply of labile bone, the skeletal system undergoes a constant process of structural reorganization, with older bone being resorbed and new bone being laid down. This type of remodeling may be quite independent of the remodeling that occurs during growth and in response to altered bio-mechanical conditions.

Calcitonin
In recent years, data have accumulated indicating that an additional endocrine factor is probably involved in mineral homeostasis. The glandular source of this hormone still remains in dispute, hence a variant term, cal-citonin; however, most workers agree that the thyroid gland is the source of this hypocalcemic factor. It appears that this hormone inhibits bone resorp-tion or promotes bone formation, and quite possibly does both. In any event, its activity is directly opposite to that of the bone-resorbing potential-ity of the parathyroid hormone. The probably correct assessment of the activity of this hormone does not detract from the biological feedback mechanism proposed before, but merely adds to the complexity of the inter-actions necessary to assure the vertebrate organism of a satisfactory calcium and phosphate ion level.

True parathyroid glands are not found in fish. Although some workers feel that the piscine ultimobranchial body may be a functional analogue, data suggest that calcium metabolism in fish is carried out by other processes that possibly involve ionic movements through the gills or through the skin. Certainly, because vast numbers of fish species contain bone without enclosed osteocytes, it would be useless for most fish to secrete a hormone unless a responding target cell were present. The apparent correlation between a terrestrial mode of life and the appearance of the parathyroid is suggestive but, because parathyroids continue to function in vertebrates that have become secondarily marine, implies no direct causative mechanism.

Growth of
Skeletal Tissues
Skeletal growth can be defined in several ways. It may mean a change in size or shape, with concomitant changes in tissue volume, or it may mean a change in spatial position. The former is the most commonly used definition, although the latter, as we shall soon see, is even more significant. Cartilage and other nonosseous skeletal tissues increase their size in the same two ways: by mitosis of already differentiated cells and by the differentiation or modulation of other connective tissue cells into a skeletogenic mode.

As we have seen the osseous system can be divided into *endochondral* and *membranous* bones according to the way in which the bones are formed. In the former a cartilaginous model is formed first and subsequently replaced almost entirely by bone, whereas in the latter no such model ever exists. All the axial and almost all of the appendicular skeleton, as well as the chondocranium, are endochondral bones; the skull vault, the facial bones, and a few of the appendicular bones are almost totally membranous in origin.

Membranous
Bone Formation

In certain areas of the soft tissues covering the brain or the oronasal cavity of the developing organism, for example, a group of previously undifferentiated connective tissue fibroblasts alter their internal biomechanical activity and become functional osteoblasts. This *modulation* causes these cells to begin to secrete a now calcifiable matrix that surrounds the cells themselves, and in a sense now traps the new osteocytes within the newly formed bone. Intramembranous ossification spreads from these *primary ossification centers* by the same process of fibroblastic modulation. In this way relatively large areas of the human fetal skull are rapidly covered with protecting and supporting bone tissues (Figure 5-6). These are the *dermal bones*. As the bone tissues of adjacent bones approach each other, the rate of growth slows perceptibly and a new osteogenic process begins the formation of a covering layer of soft tissue, the periosteum, about all the surfaces of the bone. This enveloping tissue has an outer, thick fibrous layer, and an inner osteogenic layer formed by the functional osteoblasts. Periosteal osteogenesis is a slower, more regular process than that of modulation and tends to produce layered (laminar or lamellar) bone tissue structure. As bone is produced, some of these osteoblasts are "left behind," as it were, and become enclosed functional osteocytes.

After membranous bone formation has ceased the periosteum remains and the osteogenic layer becomes inactive, although it is fully capable at all ages of responding to a wide variety of stimuli and becoming active again.

Endochondral
Bone Formation

In the embryo, masses of blastemal cells form precartilaginous condensations that mark the sites of the adult endochondral bones. Further cytodifferentiation and growth lead to the formation of a large cartilaginous model that is surrounded by an enveloping *perichondrium,* homologous to a periosteum. This model is capable of growth both interstitially by chondrocytic mitosis, as well as appositionally by the activity of the inner layer of perichondral chondroblasts. At certain sites (nutritive) a vascular invasion of the cartilage model occurs, usually, but not necessarily, concurrent with the transformation of the perichondrium at that level into an active periosteum and the subsequent formation of a ring of bone tissue external to the cartilage model. This vascular invasion is followed by an active erosion of the internal cartilage and the formation of the primitive marrow cavity. The area of erosion spreads rapidly in all directions, paralleled by a spread of a bony shaft. Some masses of cartilage are not eroded immediately, but instead become sites of cartilaginous growth plates. In mammals these are situated at the ends of the long bones where they form the epiphyseal growth plates. In other vertebrates, such as fish, these growth plates may be more centrally

Figure 5-6 (opposite). Intramembranous bone formation in the human skull is shown in (a) an early and (b) a late stage. Continued growth leads to that depicted in Figures 5-1 and 5-3. (After Patten.)

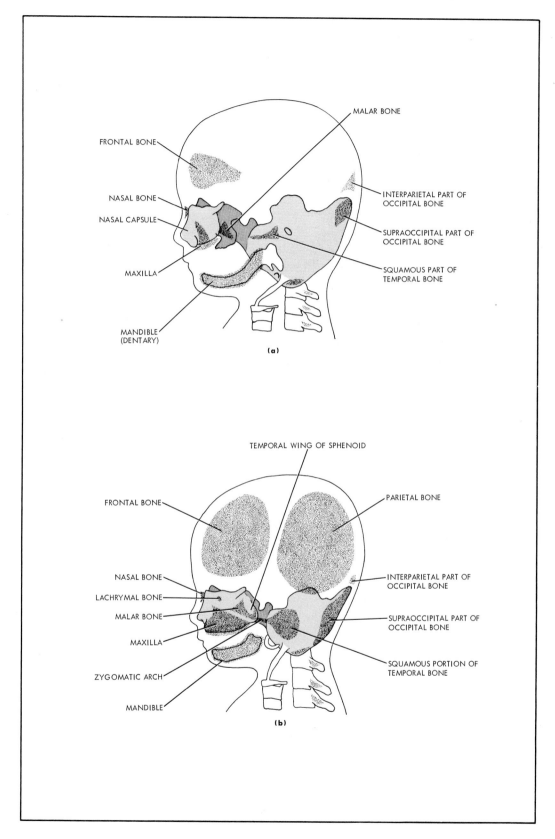

(a)

MALAR BONE

FRONTAL BONE

NASAL BONE

NASAL CAPSULE

MAXILLA

MANDIBLE
(DENTARY)

INTERPARIETAL PART OF
OCCIPITAL BONE

SUPRAOCCIPITAL PART OF
OCCIPITAL BONE

SQUAMOUS PART OF
TEMPORAL BONE

(b)

TEMPORAL WING OF SPHENOID

FRONTAL BONE

PARIETAL BONE

NASAL BONE

LACHRYMAL BONE

MALAR BONE

MAXILLA

ZYGOMATIC ARCH

MANDIBLE

INTERPARIETAL PART OF
OCCIPITAL BONE

SUPRAOCCIPITAL PART OF
OCCIPITAL BONE

SQUAMOUS PORTION OF
TEMPORAL BONE

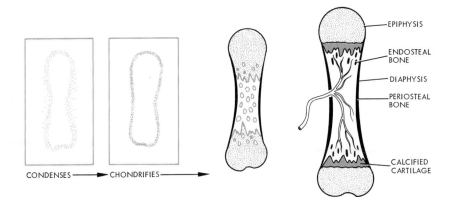

CONDENSES ⟶ CHONDRIFIES ⟶

EPIPHYSIS

ENDOSTEAL BONE

DIAPHYSIS

PERIOSTEAL BONE

CALCIFIED CARTILAGE

Figure 5-7. Four characteristic stages of endochondral ossification are shown. Here the growing cartilaginous model is continually replaced by bone. (After William and Smith.)

situated; they also may be in some cranial regions of mammals. Regardless of their site, all growth plates function in a similar way. The cartilage becomes polarized with a maturational gradient that is usually unilaterally, although it may be bilaterally, directed. There is first a so-called reserve zone of small chondrocytes. Next comes a zone of active mitosis, the zone of proliferation. Typically, rows or columns of chondrocytes are formed. It is here that the major elongation of these bones continues, brought about by the increase in the number of cells and the volume of their surrounding matrix. The next developmental stage is a zone of cellular hypertrophy. This chondrocytic enlargement is correlated with biochemical and biophysical changes that now permit calcification to occur in the matrix, longitudinally between the chondrocytic columns but not between the cells of any given column. In the final zone, that of vascular invasion, the lacunar walls of the lowermost chondrocytes are broached, the horizontal uncalcified matrix eroded, and on the remaining longitudinal bars of now calcified cartilage matrix osteoblasts deposit a transitory bone tissue. Subsequent growth changes will ultimately include the resorption of all of these mixed skeletal tissue bars (Figure 5-7).

Longitudinal growth will continue as long as these growth plates are present. In some vertebrates they are present throughout life; in others they fuse usually in a definable sequence most probably under endocrine control, ending this type of bone growth.

It must be emphasized that all bone tissue is homologous. Endochondral bone formation is that type of replacement of the cartilage model by bone whether complete or incomplete. Once bone tissue is formed, its growth processes by osteoblastic deposition and by resorption are the same in both membranous and endochondral bone. These osteogenic processes essentially are identical in all vertebrates.

The articular ends of all bones in which any biomechanically significant degree of motion occurs are covered with cartilage, whether the bones are endochondral or membranous. In the endochondral bones this articular cartilage is derived from the original mass of prenatal cartilage. In membranous bones another tissue type is found, the secondary cartilage, which differs from the prenatal cartilage in topographic as well as in some minor histological details. Although in most cases this secondary cartilage is replaced by vascular erosion without the formation of a growth plate, in some significant instances, as in the mammalian mandibular condylar process, a typical growth plate is found.

Linear and volumetric increases in skeletal tissues by osteogenic processes do not satisfactorily account for all growth phenomena. Although it is often assumed tacitly that osteogenesis by itself is a sufficient explanation for the skeletal growth, and indeed it is thought to be the primary cause of such growth, there are alternative theories. Skeletal tissues form, grow, and continue to be maintained while completely embedded within their surrounding soft tissues. Substantial data strongly suggest that the growth of these embedding soft tissues, broadly defined, is the primary morphogenetic event in skeletal-tissue growth. The observed histological processes of transforming osteogenesis, in this view, are secondary and mechanically compensatory events by means of which the skeletal tissues respond appropriately to the functional demands placed upon them. The vertebrate neurocranial vault is a good example of this second type of bone growth, *translative growth.* These membranous bones arise, grow and are maintained while embedded in a neurocranial capsule that is capable of both expanding and protecting the enclosed neural mass as the latter enlarges. As the capsule expands, the embedded calvarial bones are passively carried outward. Transformative osteogenic processes along with bone deposition and resorption occur within these bones. However, such transformative growth is not the primary event that causes the bones to grow outward. Rather it is the secondary and compensatory remodeling process by which the bones respond to the need to cover increasing large neurocranial vault areas and also to compensate for changes in vault curvature.

In summary, there are two types of bone tissue growth: transformative and translative. The former is an active process that alters the size, shape, and structure of the bone tissue, whereas the latter is a passive process by means of which this bone tissue is relocated in space, even while it is being transformed simultaneously.

Bone Architecture

Skeletal tissues can be subjected to only four types of external forces: compression, tension, shear, and torsion (Figure 5-8), or to any combination of these. The organization of skeletal tissues and organs reflects their adaptation to the dynamic conditions normally produced by such external loading. We can best discuss the question of the adaptation of bone form to function at two levels of macroscopic observation: the external and internal morphology.

Figure 5-8. All physical bodies can be subjected to only four principal types of external loading. These are, in order, compression, tension, shear, and torsion.

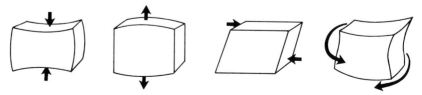

In order to do so, it is necessary to review briefly the appropriate bio-mechanical principles.

Two terms require definition. *Stress* is a measure of force per unit area and *strain* is a measure of the change in the shape of a physical body in reaction to an imposed stress. Now let us assume that we have a physical body in the form of a sphere and we impose a compressive stress upon it. The body tends to deform by strains into an ellipsoid. The planes along which maximal internal compressive and tensile stress occur are shown (Figure 5-9) crossing each other at right angles. These same two lines (or axes) also indicate the lines of maximal internal strain, the axis of compressive strain lying vertically to resist the externally applied forces, whereas the horizontal axis shows the maximal resistance to tensile deformation. These two sets of internal axes are also called *trajectories*. To illustrate further the principle of trajectories, let us consider the case of a beam projecting horizontally from the wall in which one end is embedded (Figure 5-10). The force of gravity tends to

Figure 5-9. (a) To illustrate this principle let us imagine a spherical form which is either vertically loaded by compressive forces, or horizontally loaded by tensile forces. The deformation that might result is illustrated. The two lines which intersect at right angles represent the axes of maximal extension and compression; the former is horizontal, the latter vertical. (After Murray.)

(b). Expanding on the example shown in (a) we now see the effect of vertical com-pressive loading. The linear deformations, both in a compressive and tensile sense, are easily seen, as are the several major axes. It is now obvious that the axes of both major compressive and tensile strains are so arranged as to resist maximally their respective linear deformation. (After Kummer.)

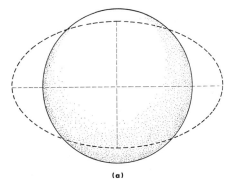

(a)

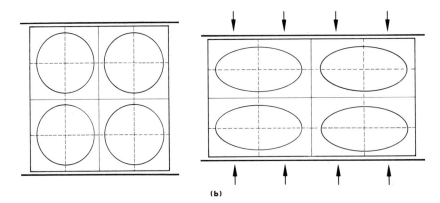

(b)

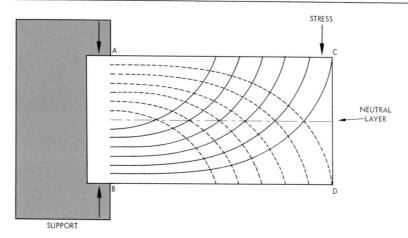

Figure 5-10. The principle expressed in Figure 5-9 is illustrated in another way. A beam of homogeneous composition is suspended in a wall at only one end. Gravity alone tends to deform (to bend) this beam so that the upper side (AD) tends to elongate, and the lower side (BC) tends to shorten. These stresses are resisted by the internal structure of the beam. Lines of principal compressive stress arise on the lower (compressive) side, but rise up to meet and oppose any upper pushing force. Similarly, lines of principal tensile stress arise on the upper (tensile) side and seem to oppose any downward pulling force. These lines are called trajectories, and they are quantitatively greater at each surface. Obviously as one passes deeper into the beam, the tendency to either compress or stretch is reduced until the neutral axis of both forces balance out. Note that, in theory, these trajectories should cross each other at right angles. (After Murray.)

deflect this beam so that side AB is lengthened (the tensile side) while side CD is shortened (the compressive side). The trajectories of internal compressive strain (that resist the compressive stress) arise on the compressive side and rise up to meet the potentially deforming source. The reverse is true for the trajectories of tensile strains. Note also that the tensile and compressive trajectories are closely grouped near the surfaces of the beam, and as we pass toward the center they become more widely separated and finally disappear. This is because at the center of this beam we finally arrive at a region in which the tendency to elongate matches equally the tendency to compress; this is the *neutral axis*. If this beam were a bone (in the sense of the discrete named elements of formal osteology) we would expect bone tissue to be found only where it is necessary, and in the amount necessary, to meet the forces normally imposed upon it. Thus, we would have a structure in which the shaft of the bone would have a solid rim while its internal volume could well be empty of bone tissue. Further, at the end of this bone the interior would be filled with a series of thin curving *bone trabeculae* that tend to cross each other at right angles as they run to either side of the bone. The beam illustrated does not correspond closely to any usual vertebrate skeletal construction. We can better continue this demonstration if we consider a column of homogeneous material in which a vertical stress is loaded asymmetrically (eccentrically). This condition tends to compress sides AB and elongate sides CD. Note that the maximal tensile and compressive trajectories are at the outermost surfaces (and parallel to them), and that both of these

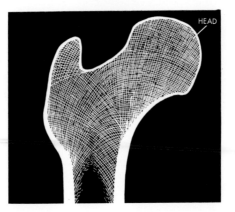

Figure 5-11. The trajectorial theory of bone structure is illustrated in this figure and in Figure 5-12. At the head of the human femur the weight of the body is passed eccentrically directly from the pelvis to the femoral head. The vertical set of osseous bars are the compressive trajectories. Those running roughly at right angles, and horizontally, are the tensile trajectories. In this partial view of the right human femur the shaft of the bone on the right is the compressive side, while the tensile side is at the left since the line of weight-bearing lies outside the bone. (After Hall.)

forces decrease as we move toward the internal neutral axis. This explains why most vertebrate long bones tend to be *tubular* in construction and have hollow shafts. The compact bone tissue is found where there is the greatest need to resist deformation, and it is not found where the magnitude of these same forces is too low to be of any practical biological importance. The remaining hollow space is now available for hematopoietic or pneumatic functions.

The human femur is a good example of an eccentrically loaded long bone. With the imposed loading of external forces at the upper end of the head, we easily perceive that the medial aspect of the bone tends to be compressed, whereas the lateral aspect tends to be stretched. The trabecular bone patterns at each end of the femur accurately reflect the differential loading patterns that exist there. In the proximal end two clearly discernible sets of trabeculae are found. One arises from the compressive side to meet the loading forces at the head of the femur. The other set, arising from the tensile side, crosses the first at approximately right angles and serves to prevent lateral distortion of the femoral head when it is loaded (Figure 5-11). At the distal end the forces imposed upon the femur are now passing through the center of the shaft, having altered from their previously eccentric position at the proximal end. Accordingly, the internal trabeculae are found in a grid-like pattern, with the compressive set lying vertically and the tensile set horizontally (Figure 5-12).

Weight-bearing in tetrapods has a very significant effect on the determination of long bone structure. The typical tetrapod weight-bearing limb bone, therefore, has a long, essentially cylindrical shaft of compact bone surrounding a hollow medullary cavity; at each end trabecular bone, arranged in a trajectoral fashion, serves to transmit the forces usually applied at the two cartilage-covered articular ends. In those vertebrates that formerly led a terrestrial existence but who have subsequently returned to an aqueous environment, the whole bone shaft is filled with a dense mass of bone tissue and both marrow cavity and trabecular bone have disappeared (cetacea and penguins are good examples of such pachyostosis).

The form of all nonappendicular bones is equally capable of a functional explanation. The several types of vertebrae found in the vertebrate axial skeleton closely reflect the specific biomechanical demands placed upon them. The human condition serves as a useful example. The small, rudimentary coccygeal vertebrae contrast strongly with the adjacent solid, fused sacral members. The differences in size, shape, and angulation of articular facets of the lumbar, thoracic, and cervical vertebrae are so strikingly related to their specific functional capabilities as to make further discussion unnecessary (Figure 5-13).

The Protective Function of the Dermal Skeleton

Skeletal tissues have a most significant role in providing mechanical protection for the body from the external environment. This may be accomplished in many ways: by the use of plates of dense collagenous tissues, bones, scales, dermal ossicles, shells, bony plates, and so on. In most cases, locomotor needs require a flexible articulation between such superficial skeletal elements; in the case of shells the protective function is predominant.

Vertebrates alone possess a composite skeletal tissue that is formed by the integrated activity of both ectodermal and mesodermal tissue types. All such vertebrate tissues are located superficially, and they originate as the result of the inductive interaction between basal ectodermal cells and subjacent mesenchyme (ectomesenchyme). The earliest known composite dermal skeletal tissues in vertebrates are tooth-like structures, containing all the tissue types associated with vertebrate teeth; indeed they are truly dental in structure as well as formation. All other vertebrate dermal skeletal tissues are formed by homologous odontogenetic, inductive, interactive processes. The structural diversity of vertebrate dermal skeletal tissues, scales, and osteo-

Figure 5-12. The lower end of the human femur has its sets of principal trajectional axes arranged differently from the upper end seen in Figure 5-11. Here the weight of the body passes directly (concentrically) down through the center of the bone. The trajectional response is exactly that shown in Figures 5-8 and 5-9. (After Hall.)

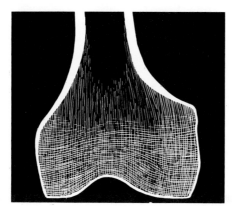

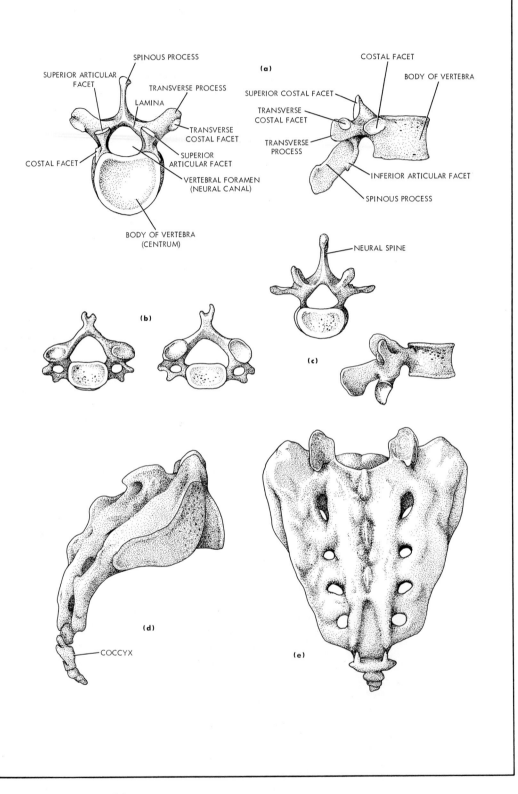

SPINOUS PROCESS

SUPERIOR ARTICULAR FACET

TRANSVERSE PROCESS

LAMINA

COSTAL FACET

BODY OF VERTEBRA

SUPERIOR COSTAL FACET

TRANSVERSE COSTAL FACET

TRANSVERSE PROCESS

COSTAL FACET

TRANSVERSE COSTAL FACET

SUPERIOR ARTICULAR FACET

VERTEBRAL FORAMEN (NEURAL CANAL)

INFERIOR ARTICULAR FACET

SPINOUS PROCESS

BODY OF VERTEBRA (CENTRUM)

(a)

(b)

NEURAL SPINE

(c)

(d)

COCCYX

(e)

194

derms and their phylogenetic relationships are discussed in the following chapter. Yet, despite their specific structural variation, they all share a common ontogenetic ancestry and this basic homology continues to be expressed both in their ontogeny as well as in their composition.

It is customary to designate as the *exoskeleton* that portion of the skeletal system related to the protective function. More properly this should be called the dermal skeleton because the skeletal tissues themselves are to be found within the dermal layers of the skin. However, dermal skeletal tissues also contain some component, variously structured, that is derived from the activity of the overlying epidermis. In some vertebrates we find the protective skeletal function being fulfilled by epidermal products alone; the scales of the pangolin, the keratinized teeth of the lamprey, and the horn of the rhinoceros are familiar examples. Further, the designation of the dermal skeleton as the protective organ system must be broadened conceptually to allow for such structures as the antlers of the deer. In some vertebrates the exoskeleton has a dual structure, in which the epidermal and dermal components are well formed. The alligator and the turtle exhibit types of such a composite exoskeleton.

The Pattern of the Appendicular Skeleton The appendicular skeleton is the main system for locomotion and weight bearing. In the basic vertebrate body there are two pairs of appendages or pterygia, generally termed the pectoral and the pelvic. All vertebrate limbs have a proximal embedded portion (girdle) and a distal free portion. Typically the girdle consists of both dorsal and ventral elements that variably combine to articulate the limb to the axial skeleton, and also to serve as areas of attachment of muscles that either attach the body to the limb skeleton or serve to move the more distal parts of the limb. The distal free portion of the limb demonstrates a remarkable structural consistency in tetrapod vertebrates. There is a single proximal long bone (propodium), and a pair of intermediate long bones (epipodia) which articulate typically to two rows of small bones from which arise five rows of osseous rays in the most basic vertebrate pattern. Variations from this pattern, such as the partial fusion of the paired intermediate long bones or variations in the number and shape of bones in the intermediate series or in the digital rays, are related to the specific functional adaptation of the limbs in a given species.

The paired appendages of fish are superficial rayed skeletal structures, the fins, which combine the functions of protection and locomotion in a variable manner. Fin structure is almost, but not exclusively, related to locomotion. Basically, fish fins provide a means of controlling both the pitch and yaw of an elongated body as it moves through water (Figure 5-14). Both pectoral and pelvic fins serve this function, as do the anal and dorsal fins which are

Figure 5-13 (opposite). The striking morphological differences between the several portions of the vertebral column are totally related to their specifically different functional demands. The varying demands for support and motion, i.e., for dynamic and static functions, produce these vastly different forms. (a) Lower thoracic vertebrae, cranial and lateral aspects; (b) cervical vertebrae, cranial and caudal aspects; (c) middle lumbar vertebrae, superior and lateral aspects; (d) sacrum, lateral aspect; (e) dorsal aspect. (After Wolf-Heiddeger.)

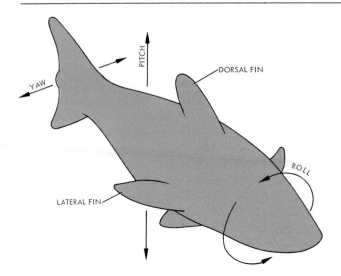

Figure 5-14. A schematized view of a fish. The vertical and horizontal fins obviously serve to prevent both pitch and yaw of the body as it moves through the water.

not portions of the appendicular skeleton but are modifications of the axial skeleton as are all piscine tail structures. Both amphibians and reptiles may possess homologous nonappendicular fins that no longer function as loco- motors and may not even be related to protection. Such flippers are clearly derived from the tetrapod limb structure.

Articulation of the Skeletal System

Biomechanically, bones serve two functions: (1) to protect and to support functionally related soft tissues and biological spaces; and (2) to provide leverage systems for locomotion, posture, maintenance, and feeding and respiratory mechanisms. To fulfill the latter function, bones act as lever arms that are activated by attached contractile elements, the muscles. Where one bone meets another, there is an articulation (a *joint*) which is capable of functional classification. When a relatively free degree of motion occurs, the joint is *diarthrosis;* an articulation with a limited range of motion is an *amphiarthrosis;* an articulation with virtually no motion is a *synarthrosis*.

The articulations between adjacent limb bones are examples of typical diarthroses, whereas the mammalian pubic symphysis is a good example of an amphiarthrosis. The cranial suture lines are synarthroses, with the exception of the *kinetic* skulls of some vertebrates that permit motion of upper jaw components as well as those of the lower jaw.

Diarthroses

All diarthrodial joints have a number of common characteristics. (1) When- ever two bony lever arms articulate freely relative to each other, the articu- lating ends are covered with an articular cartilage. The histological type of this cartilage is related to the forces normally imposed at that joint. Hyalin cartilage is found where compressive forces predominate (the majority of diarthroses), whereas fibro-cartilage is adapted to shearing forces. We find that any diarthrodial joint has both functional and nonfunctional surfaces;

only the former is covered with cartilage. (2) The two opposing diarthrodial joint surfaces are reciprocally convex and concave, although not necessarily congruent in shape. (3) All diarthroses are surrounded by a joint capsule, within which is a viscous synovial fluid that both lubricates and helps to nourish the joint cartilages. (4) The range of activity at any joint is observed when the two joint surfaces are tightly compressed. This compression is the first function of the muscles that provide motion at a given joint. (5) In some joints an additional feature is found. This is the interposition of a disc (or meniscus) of dense fibrous connective tissue. Such a disc divides the joint cavity into separate compartments, completely or incompletely. The menisci provide stability for the lever arms at certain critical points of the range of motion and also permit motion of the individual lever arms relative to the disc without necessarily involving motion of this same disc relative to the other articulating surface. By this means the functional capacity and range of motion of the joint are increased.

An interesting relationship exists between the size and shape of joint surfaces and the type and amount of motion that may occur there. Any diarthrosis is a structural compromise between mobility and stability. The comparison between the human shoulder and hip joints is a case in point. In the hip joint, the rounded femoral head is coupled to a hemispherical acetabular fossa of approximately equal size; this arrangement provides good stability for bipedal locomotion, with a concomitant loss of some degree of freedom of motion. In the shoulder joint a large humeral capitular head is approximated to a relatively small osseous glenoid fossa. In itself, the osseous structure provides little stability. However, in life, a large strong tendinous cuff, composed of the attachments of the scapulo-humeral muscles, completes the hemispheric concave shape and so provides an adequate degree of stability while also permitting a relatively great range of motion (Figure 5-15).

Amphiarthroses
Where great stability must be combined with the possibility of some motion between adjacent bones, or where there is need for periodic separative motion between bones (as in the pubic symphysis), we find bands of dense fibrous connective tissue connecting adjacent bony surfaces. In some mammals it is known that the pubic symphyseal amphiarthrosis of the females becomes loosened under the influence of the endocrine system to permit parturition. Although they are not usually considered as such, cranial sutures that are still open function as amphiarthroses. This function is particularly well seen in mammals during birth, when the head may be severely molded as it passes through the pelvic canal.

Synarthroses
This term is useful only to indicate that after cranial growth has ceased, the adjacent membranous bones may fuse together at their mutual sutural areas. Such fusion obviates any possibility of motion, and such immobility is characteristic of a synarthrosis.

Synchondroses
For the sake of completeness we should note certain masses of cartilage usually restricted to the vertebrate skull base. These masses are remnants of the formerly totally cartilaginous cranial base. They are found between two

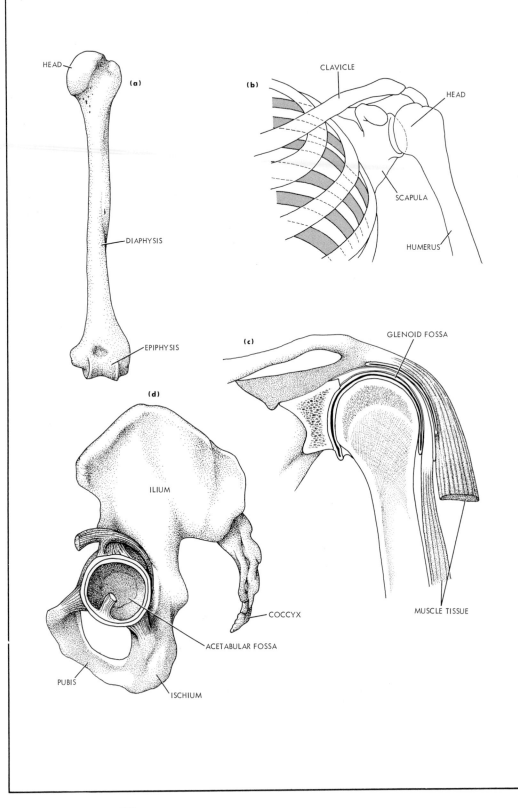

Figure 5-15 (opposite). The human upper limb articulates at the shoulder in such a way as to provide maximum mobility with a sufficient but minimal security. The head of the humerus (a) does not differ much from that of the femur (Figure 5-11). However the amount of bone tissue with which it articulates on the shoulder blade (the scapula) is relatively small (b). As seen in (c), the small size of this osseous glenoid fossa (g) is added to, in the living and functioning state, by a very large cup-like mass of musculo-tendinous (M-T) tissues. In effect, then, there is a flexible ball-and-socket joint at the shoulder. In the hip joint (d), the round head of the femur is firmly seated within a deep bony cup, the acetabular fossa. The resulting gain in stability and mechanical security is paid for by a loss of mobility, relative to that enjoyed at the shoulder. (After Wolf-Heiddeger.)

adjacent endochondral bones and frequently contain either one or two epiphyseal-like growth plates. These growth plates, like the cranial sutural areas and the mandibular condylar cartilages, are the sites of secondary, compensatory growth rather than sites of primary, expansive cranial growth.

References for Chapter 5

[1]   Moss, M. L. (ed.), Comparative Biology of Calcified Tissue." *Ann. N.Y. Acad. Sci.*, **109** (1963), 1-410. A review of many aspects of skeletal tissues with emphasis on the universality of the vital calcification processes.

[2]   Sognnaes, R. F., "Calcification in Biological Systems." Washington: *Publ. No. 64 A.A.A.S.* (1960). Here again, vertebrate and invertebrate modes of calcification reveal a basic commonality of process.

[3]   Person, P. (ed.), "Biology of the Mouth." Washington: *Publ. No. 89 A.A.A.S.* (1968). Particular emphasis on oral structures with a broad comparative statement.

[4]   McLean, F. C., and M. R. Urist, *Bone.* Chicago: University of Chicago Press, 3rd ed., 1968. The best review of the entire subject.

[5]   Ørvig, T. (ed.), *Some Current Problems of Lower Vertebrate Phylogeny.* Stockholm: Almquist and Wiksell, 1966. This report of a recent Nobel Symposium is the best available on the origin and significance of skeletal tissues.

6

The musculoskeletal system: an evolutionary perspective

The Relationship of the Muscular and Skeletal Systems

The musculature and the skeleton form a single co-adapted mechanism. Temporally the two units interact ontogenetically and have interacted phylogenetically. Spatially, body movement results from the interaction of the two units. The ontogenetic and spatial interactions of the skeletal system has been discussed previously (Chapter 5). This chapter will deal with the phylogenetic interactions of these two units.

The skeletal system is ideal to demonstrate evolutionary trends for, unlike all other organ systems, it has a good fossil record. The muscular system also shares in this evidence through the strong influence that muscles have on the form and function of bones. However, a fossil record is not absolutely necessary for the construction of the evolutionary history of an organ system or one of its components (remember the discussion in Chapter 1), since the probable phylogenetic history can be reconstructed through comparative observations of the structure and function of the systems in extant animals. It is essential in the reconstruction of the evolutionary sequence of an organ system to remember that the system has not evolved *in vacuo* but was an integrated part of the entire organism and was functional throughout its entire history. It is helpful, therefore, for a better interpretation of the evolution of the animal, to relate the function and structure of an organ system to its habits and ecology.

Divisions of the Musculoskeletal System

Four general functions are served by the musculoskeletal system of vertebrates: locomotion, ingestion, respiration, and protection. These functions tend to correspond to the classical divisions of the muscular and the skeletal systems (Table 6-1). The muscular system is characteristically divided into three large subunits, the somatic, the visceral, and the integumentary (Figure 6-1). The somatic musculature forms the bulk of the muscles associated with the trunk and appendages. Embryologically it is derived from the myotome and develops only into striated muscle tissue. Somatic musculature is innervated by somatic sensory and somatic motor neurons and thus is under voluntary control. In contrast, the visceral musculature is derived from the hypomere and is innervated by visceral sensory and visceral motor neurons; this type of innervation is normally associated with involuntary control. There is, however, an exception to the association of involuntary control with visceral innervation. Visceral muscular tissue is of two types, smooth and striated. The former tissue is directly associated with the digestive tube

200

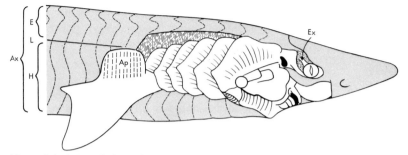

Figure 6-1. A lateral view of the cranial end of a shark, illustrating the major divisions of the muscular system. Visceral muscles, muscle fibers included; somatic muscles, no fibers included. Ap, appendicular muscles; Ax, axial muscles; E, epaxial muscles; Ex, extrinsic eye muscles; H, hypaxial muscles; L, position of lateral line and horizontal skeletogenous septum.

and is under involuntary control, whereas the striated tissue, branchiomeric musculature, encloses the skeleton of the gill arches and their derivations and can be controlled voluntarily.

The integumentary musculature also contains smooth and striated muscle tissue, intrinsic and extrinsic respectively. The intrinsic muscles lie in the dermis and are derived from the dermatome. They occur only in birds and mammals, where they function in thermoregulation by altering the position of the feathers or hair to increase or decrease the thickness of the insulation layer. The extrinsic muscles extend between the dermis and trunk musculature and are derived from either the myotomic or branchiomeric musculature. Because of its derivation, the extrinsic integumentary musculature is striated. Reaching its greatest elaboration in mammals it forms a thoracic cutaneous sheet, the panniculus carnosus, and a craniocervical sheet, the platysma, of myotomic and branchiomeric derivation, respectively. The platysma is further modified in many mammals to form the facial muscles.

Table 6-1. The divisions of the musculature and skeleton with an indication of their usual function.

Musculature	Skeleton	Function
Somatic	Somatic	
Axial	Axial	Locomotion
extrinsic eye muscles	cranial	
trunk	postcranial	
epaxial		
hypaxial		
Appendicular	Appendicular	Locomotion
dorsal (extensor)	girdles	
ventral (flexor)	pterygial	
Visceral	Visceral	Feeding and respiration
Branchiomeric		
Splanchnic		
Integumentary	Integumentary	Protection
Extrinsic	primary dermal armor	
Intrinsic	secondary dermal armor	

By means of dermal muscles, a snake erects the ventral scales in movement, bird flight is aided, a horse twitches a fly from its skin and moves its ears, and an armadillo rolls himself into a ball.

Evolution of the Vertebrate Locomotor Apparatus

It is generally recognized that the ancestors of chordates were sessile organisms, and the lower chordates still retain fairly sedentary habits; some are entirely sessile. Even Amphioxus, the most streamlined lower chordate, spends much of its time buried in the sand with only the front end protruding. In contrast vertebrates tend to be active, motile organisms, and their musculoskeletal system reflects this activity.

Vertebrates display two forms of locomotion, axial and appendicular. Propulsion is produced by flexing the body and/or tail in axial locomotion, and the movement of the appendages generates the propulsive force in appendicular locomotion. Axial locomotion is usually associated with aquatic habits and appendicular locomotion with subaerial and aerial habits. Axial locomotion is generally considered the primitive locomotor pattern. The distribution of the two locomotor forms is illustrated in Figure 6-2.

The Evolution of Vertebrate Locomotion

The evolution of chordate locomotion probably began with a pelagic larval stage and a sessile adult. Movements of this larval type were produced by bands or tufts of cilia. For some reason this mode of locomotion was replaced by body flexure. The appearance of axial locomotion may have occurred concurrently with the trend toward a motile adult stage, or it may have resulted from the presence of an axial locomotor larval stage that permitted a paedogenetic trend. At any rate, the first vertebrates, the ostracoderms, possessed axial locomotion. The placoderms were also dependent upon this form of locomotion; however, their stability while swimming was improved with the development of paired appendages. Axial locomotion is characteristic of the osteichthyian and chondrichthyian fish, although some members of each group have developed appendicular locomotion. The latter is particularly evident in the skates and rays with their greatly enlarged pectoral fins. [1, 2]

The development of terrestrial vertebrates, the amphibians, involved the shift from axial to appendicular locomotion. Concomitant with this behavioral shift was a major structural reorganization of the vertebrate body. Most amphibians, reptiles, birds, and mammals still move by appendicular locomotion. Nonetheless, each tetrapod lineage except the birds has one or more groups that have re-evolved axial locomotion (Figure 6-2).

Segmentation

The origin of metamerism has frequently been linked with undulatory locomotion, i.e., axial locomotion. Recent investigations have shown that segmentation and axial locomotion are functionally correlated in the chordates but not in the protostomous invertebrates; these findings indicate that segmentation arose independently in these two lineages. In the invertebrates the

Figure 6-2 (opposite). The phylogenetic distribution of the two major forms of vertebrate locomotion. Nearly every vertebrate class possesses both axial and appendicular locomotion; however, one form is usually dominant in each class.

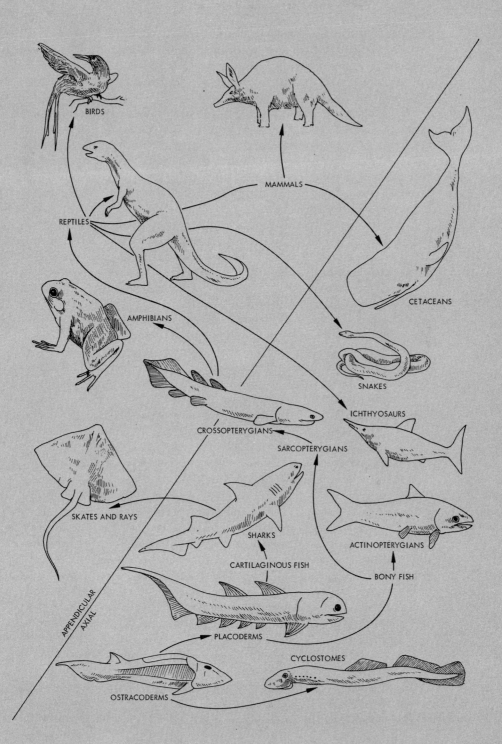

BIRDS

MAMMALS

REPTILES

CETACEANS

AMPHIBIANS

SNAKES

ICHTHYOSAURS

CROSSOPTERYGIANS

SARCOPTERYGIANS

SKATES AND RAYS

SHARKS

ACTINOPTERYGIANS

CARTILAGINOUS FISH

BONY FISH

PLACODERMS

CYCLOSTOMES

APPENDICULAR

AXIAL

OSTRACODERMS

forces of muscular contraction act longitudinally on a fluid skeleton to flex the body, and therefore body undulation can be generated without segmentation. In contrast, the forces of contraction in chordates act transversely on a solid skeleton and segmentation is a prerequisite to the generation of body undulations. [3]

The tadpole-like larva of tunicates is the usual model for one of the final morphological stages in the transition from a visceral animal to a somatic animal, viz., from a protochordate to a vertebrate. Because it is likely that the vertebrate lineage did pass through such a stage, the caudal structure of the tadpole larva must be examined. The tail contains a notochord and longitudinal muscle bundles that are not segmented. The initial axial locomotor pattern was, thus, a sculling motion of the tail; the notochord stiffened the tail and the reduced caudal flexibility produced a larger resistance surface. Selective pressures to streamline the body would act toward segmentation. If the anterior end of the body is reduced, a sculling mode of locomotion becomes progressively less efficient because the surface areas on the two sides of the muscular pivot are approaching equality. If they are equal, there is no progression, only a stationary flapping.

To continue with this hypothesis, the notochord probably elongated with the development of segmentation of the musculature. Previously the notochord was restricted to the tail owing to the mechanics of sculling, which require that the muscles attach anteriorly beyond the pivot. Muscular segmentation and elongation of the axial skeleton would have improved the quality of undulatory locomotion and increased the agility of the animal. Improved locomotor ability would be of positive selective value to its possessor. The ostracoderms, with a segmented musculature and an unsegmented axial skeleton, may be considered the end point of this trend. Although ostracoderm fossils show no axial skeleton, it may be assumed that they possessed a notochord that did not fossilize.

Axial Musculature and Locomotion

Because the embryonic origin of myomeres in the extant agnathans and gnathostomes is nearly identical it can be assumed that the ostracoderms had a segmented axial musculature. However, the structure of the myomeres and the ontogenetic pathways in the latter two groups are distinctly different. Rather than speculate on the structure of the ostracoderm myomere, we will state that it gave rise to two distinct myomeres, both functionally and morphologically distinct, and we will provide evidence for this statement.

Three types of myomeres occur in adult chordates (Figure 6-3). The amphioxine myomere of the cephalochordates is > -shaped with the wings oblique to the sagittal plane; the dorsal wing leans craniad, the ventral wing caudad. The cyclostomine myomere as seen in the lampreys and hagfish is ⋛-shaped, although the flexures are smooth, not angular. The entire cyclostomine myomere leans caudad. In contrast, the piscine myomere of chondrichthyian and osteichthyian fish is ⋛-shaped with sharp, angular flexures and wings of alternating inclinations. Generally, the arms of the W slant craniad and the center caudad. This obliquity is not fortuitous but has functional significance. Since the myomeres are oblique, each one encompasses several vertebral segments, although attached only to one, and each overlaps a number of other myomeres. These two features allow a wave of contraction

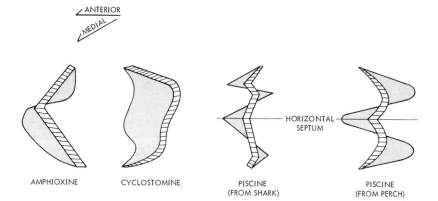

Figure 6-3. Lateral views of single myomeres from fish-like chordates. The horizontal lines indicate the muscle fibers at the lateral surface of the myomeres. (After Nursall.)

to pass smoothly along the myomeric chain, with the result that the body undulations are smooth waves. If the myomeres were perpendicular to the longitudinal body axis, the body undulation would be somewhat jerky as it passed from segment to segment. Because the myomeres of agnathans are slanted only caudad, body waves can pass only in that direction, whereas in fish with amphioxine or piscine myomeres the waves can proceed either craniad or caudad, for these myomeres are oblique in both directions. [4]

All three types of myomeres develop from a myotomic block. The amphioxine and cyclostomine myomeres appear to pass directly from the rectangular myotome to their final form. The piscine myomere, in contrast, passes through an amphioxine stage in its ontogeny, during which the horizontal skeletogenous septum appears and divides the axial musculature into epaxial and hypaxial units. Neither the functional nor the adaptive significance of this septum is clear. It does provide an additional site of attachment for each myomere, which may improve the leverage upon contraction.

Both chondrichthyian and osteichthyian fish possess piscine myomeres and epaxial and hypaxial divisions of the musculature. It is likely that the placoderms had a similar structural arrangement of the axial musculature. We cannot, however, make the same assumption for the ostracoderms because their two derivative lines, the cyclostomes and the gnathostomes, have distinctly different muscular arrangements. The cyclostomes have no horizontal skeletogenous septum and have a cyclostomine type of myomere. To suggest the condition of the axial musculature for the ostracoderms would be pure speculation. An attempt to use Haeckel's Biogenetic Law is likely to lead us astray. The piscine myomere does go through an amphioxine-like stage, but this similarity probably results from convergence and not relationship. In osteichthyian fish the amphioxine stage is passed before hatching and the obliquity of the osteichthyian's amphioxine myomere is different from the obliquity of the cephalochordate's amphioxine myomere.

With the evolution of the tetrapods the role of the axial musculature changed from locomotion to support. As might be expected, with this shift in function there was a corresponding alteration of the axial musculature. Initially the epaxial musculature retained its segmental arrangement, whereas

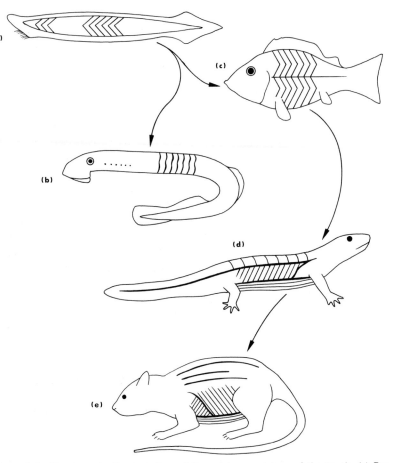

Figure 6-4. The stages in the evolution of the axial musculature of the trunk. (a) Pre-vertebrate condition: no horizontal septum; amphioxine myomeres; occurs in cephalochordates and embryonic chondrichthyians and osteichthyians. (b) Cyclostomine condition: no horizontal septum; cyclostomine myomeres; occurs in cyclostomes. (c) Piscine condition: horizontal septum with epaxial and hypaxial divisions; piscine myomeres; occurs in post-larval chondrichthyians and osteichthyians. (d) Early tetrapod condition: epaxial musculature retains segmentation; loss of segmentation in hypaxial musculature and development of thin muscular sheets; in salamanders and probably early amphibians. (e) Advanced tetrapod condition: epaxial segmentation lost with formation of longitudinal bundles; sheets of hypaxial muscles; in anurans and amniotes.

the hypaxial musculature became reduced to thin muscular sheets, the oblique and transverse abdominal muscles, with little indication of segmentation. This condition presently exists in the amphibians. In the amniotes, the epaxial musculature loses its segmentation and forms longitudinal bundles traversing several vertebral segments (Figure 6-4).

Several amniote groups, e.g., snakes and cetaceans, have returned to axial locomotion. In the snakes, locomotion is by lateral undulation, and segmentation of the musculature has become a necessity. Myomeres have not reappeared, but instead muscular slips extend between adjacent vertebrae or over several vertebral segments. The cetaceans swim by dorso-ventral undulations.

The axial musculature retains its longitudinal organization. Caudally, however, the muscle tissue is replaced by tendons that extend across the caudal peduncle and the tail undulates by alternate contraction of dorsal and ventral muscle bundles.

Axial
Skeleton

The postcranial axial skeleton is composed of three units: the vertebral column, the ribs, and the sternum (Figure 6-5). Phylogenetically, the sternum is of recent occurrence, as it first appeared in the amphibians. Its site of origin was the ventral skeletogenous septum in association with the evolution of appendicular locomotion and the correlated changes in the pectoral girdle. Its original function may have been to provide additional surface area for appendicular muscle attachment and in extant animals (anurans and birds) the sternum has this function. The amniote sternum provides a ventral attachment site for the ribs and because of this union is, at least partially, associated with respiration. The sternum of birds and mammals is usually bony and in amphibians and reptiles is cartilaginous.

Although ribs may have occurred in the ostracoderms, they were certainly present in the placoderms. Ribs are present in all extant classes of vertebrates; however, in some groups they do not exist as free entities. Often the ribs are fused to the transverse processes of the vertebrae. In fish, two types of ribs occur [Figure 6-5(b) and (c)] : dorsal ribs within the myosepta at their junction with the horizontal skeletogenous septum, and ventral ribs also in the myosepta but at their junction with the peritoneum. Ribs may occur along the entire body axis, although they are generally restricted to the trunk. Dorsal ribs are characteristic of all vertebrates as one of the major components of the axial locomotor apparatus, whereas the ventral ribs occur as ribs only in fish; however, their serial homologues, the haemal arches, are found in both fish and lower tailed tetrapods. The ventral ribs form a stiff basket that supports and protects the viscera. In fish the dorsal ribs form part of the locomotor mechanism, while in the tetrapods they are an important part of the respiratory apparatus. (This is discussed in some detail in the section on the respiratory mechanism.) Fish ribs tend to be single-headed (unicipital) in association with their lack of movement. The primitive tetrapod condition is a bicipital dorsal rib. This type of rib still occurs in reptiles and birds, which use a costal suction-pump respiratory mechanism. Unicipital ribs exist in mammals, and the ribs of amphibians are either lost or greatly reduced.

The vertebral column is primitively and developmentally preceded by a nonsegmented structure, the notochord, which is slowly replaced by the segmental vertebrae. There are usually three parts to a vertebra: a dorsal neural arch enclosing the spinal cord dorsally and laterally; a central spool-shaped centrum supporting the spinal cord ventrally, replacing the notochord and providing an articulation with adjacent vertebrae; and in lower tailed vertebrates a ventral haemal arch enclosing dorsomedial blood vessels [Figure 6-5(c)] . A variety of articular facets are present on the vertebrae; these facets develop a firm interlocking union between vertebrae as well as between vertebra and rib.

It is more difficult to decipher the phylogenetic history of the vertebral column (Figure 6-6) than that of the axial musculature because of the great structural diversity of the column. Initially the vertebral column was represented by the notochord which was probably restricted to the tail, but with the development of segmented musculature in the prevertebrate the notochord extended into the trunk, at least the posterior half, and head. This condition probably was present in the ostracoderms. Although it is negative evidence, the absence of fossilized vertebral columns in ostracoderm fossils suggests the column possessed either cartilaginous vertebrae or only a notochord. It is likely that the axial support was furnished by the notochord, since the column of the extant agnathans is composed of a notochord and small bilateral cartilaginous blocks beside the spinal cord. These blocks may be the anlage of the neural arches of gnathostomes, although they certainly do not completely enclose the spinal cord.

The vertebral column of the placoderms was similar to that of the ostracoderms. The notochord extended longitudinally beneath the spinal cord; however, neural arches and haemal arches were present. The arches were arranged segmentally and thus indicate the beginning of segmentation in the axial skeleton. The presence of a notochord is again based on circumstantial evidence, because there are no impressions of centra in placoderm fossils.

In the two piscine lines (chondrichthyians and osteichthyians) derived from the placoderms, centra appear and the entire vertebral column is segmented. In spite of the presence of neural and haemal arches in placoderms, the homology of chondrichthyian vertebrae with those of osteichthyian fish is questioned. The embryological development of the centra is similar, but the development of the arches and the intercalary plates is sufficiently dissimilar to suggest that they are homoplastic rather than homologous structures. In addition, the chondrichthyian vertebral column differs from the similar structure in all other extant vertebrates in three ways. The entire column is cartilaginous throughout life. The arrangement of the arches and intercalary plates forms a completely interlocking column with no gaps. Nerves and blood vessels exit and enter the column through foramina in the plates and arches rather than through fenestrae between vertebrae, as in the bony fish and tetrapods.

Within the bony fish, a wide range of vertebral diversity exists. In general, the three grades of actinopterygians illustrate three levels of vertebral evolution. The chondrostean vertebral column is usually composed of a notochord and neural and haemal arches; the extant sarcopterygians share this condition. At the holostean level the vertebral column has undergone a large amount of evolutionary experimentation, with vertebral structure ranging from no centrum to the presence of two centra. If present, centra are of various architecture and intercalary plates may be absent or present. Vertebral

Figure 6-5 (opposite). The postcranial axial skeletons of a fish and a tetrapod. (a) Lateral view of *Amia calva*; note lack of regional differentiation. (b) Cross-section through the trunk of *Amia*; note the number of myomeres in this single section demonstrating the overlapping and obliquity of piscine myomeres. (c) An anterior view of an *Amia* vertebra. (d) A lateral view of a mammal, *Parablastomeryx*; note the regional differentiation of axial skeleton. C, centrum; CV, cervical vertebrae; DR, dorsal ribs; HA, haemal arch; HSP, haemal spine; LV, lumbar vertebrae; M, myomere; NC, neural canal; NS, neural spine; S, sacral vertebrae or sacrum; ST, sternum; T, caudal vertebrae; TV, thoracic vertebrae; VR, ventral vertebrae. [(a)-(c) after Goodyear; (d) after Matthew.]

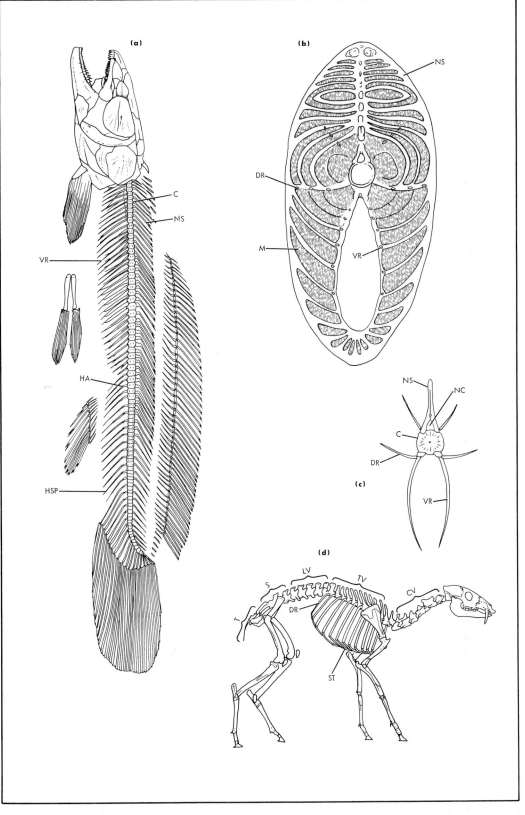

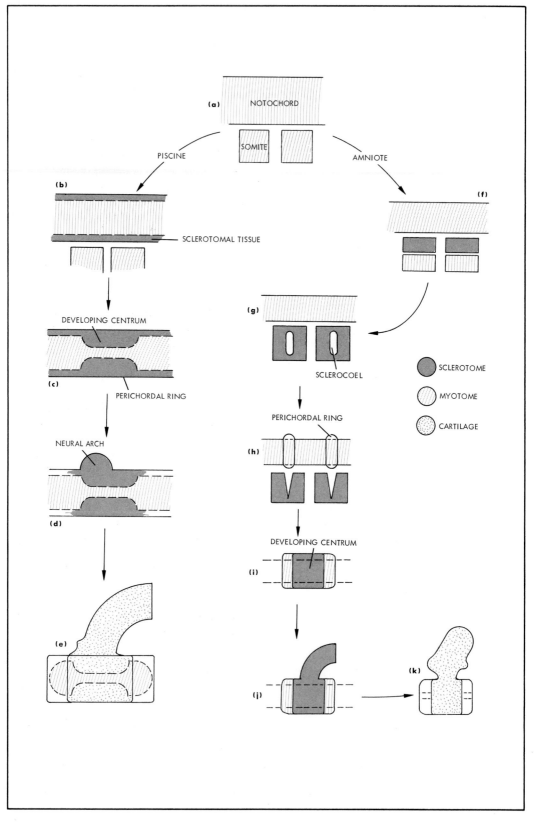

(a) NOTOCHORD
SOMITE
PISCINE
AMNIOTE

(b)
SCLEROTOMAL TISSUE

(f)

(g)

DEVELOPING CENTRUM
(c)
PERICHORDAL RING

SCLEROCOEL

SCLEROTOME
MYOTOME
CARTILAGE

NEURAL ARCH
(d)

PERICHORDAL RING
(h)

DEVELOPING CENTRUM
(i)

(e)

(j)

(k)

structure has become stabilized in the teleosts. In this group each vertebra is composed of a single centrum, a haemal arch, and a neural arch with zygapophyses. The notochord is constricted in the region of the centra. This constriction, however, is characteristic of fish central structure, and the notochord is generally occluded from the centra only in tetrapods.

The fossil crossopterygians, unlike their extant relative, had ossified centra. Of particular interest is the rhipidistian line in which there is considerable diversity. One group had a double centrum with a single anterior annular element, the intercentrum, and a pair of dorsoposterior elements, the pleurocentra. This diversity in the vertebral structure of osteichthyian fish indicates that centra evolved and were lost independently in many lines of piscine evolution. Nonetheless, the similarity in central ontogeny of extant fish and tetrapods suggests that the vertebrae of all osteichthyians and tetrapods are homologous.

It is not enough simply to assert that the vertebrae in these two groups are homologous. The embryological evidence must be presented to illustrate their evolutionary relationships. [5, 6] Vertebral development in teleosts [Figure 6-6(b)-(e)], a highly specialized taxon well separated from the tetrapod line, is initiated by a migration of cells from the ventromedian wall of the epimere or somite to and around the notochord [Figure 6-6(b)]. There the sclerotomic cells form the perichordal tube. In addition, a mass of sclerotomic tissue migrates to the myoseptum to form the neural and haemal arch anlagen, each pair of which is derived from a single epimere. The tissues of the arch anlagen begin to condense and take on the form of arches. Simultaneously, condensation begins in the perichordal tube [Figure 6-6(c)] but this occurs unevenly throughout the tube in centers that are localized in the vicinity of a myoseptum. These centers are the anlagen of centra. They are separated from one another by rings of tissue, the perichordal rings, the development of which lags behind the remainder of the perichordal tube. The perichordal ring and enclosed notochord will form the intervertebral ring or disc. The centering of the condensation around the myosepta produces a resegmentation of the developing vertebrae so that they alternate with the myotome. Ossification can and does occur in two ways; either there is a direct ossification of condensed vertebral rudiments, or ossification is preceded by chondrification.

The preceding is generalized description, of course, as a result of the diversity of vertebral structure in the osteichthyians. A similar pattern is found in the tetrapods, differing mainly in the inclusion of several new steps [Figure

Figure 6-6 (opposite). A schematic illustration of the two main patterns of vertebral development in vertebrates. (a) Shared embryological condition. (b)-(e) Developmental pathway in bony fish. (f)-(k) Developmental pathway in amniotes. All views are dorsal except (d), (e), (j), and (k), which are lateral. (b) Early perichordal tube stage; sclerotome completely encloses notochord. (c) Late perichordal tube stage; condensation of sclerotome and constriction of notochord. (d) Precartilage stage; further compaction of sclerotomal tissue with establishment of basic vertebral shape. (e) Cartilage stage; vertebra chondrifies, but not intervertebral body. (f) Sclerotome stage; sclerotomal cells migrate from somite and form sclerotome. (g) Sclerocoel stage; sclerocoel forms in sclerotome. (h) Early perichordal tube stage, sclerotomal cells around sclerotome detach and surround restricted area on notochord. (i) Late perichordal tube stage. (j) Precartilage stage. (k) Cartilage stage.

6-6(f)-(k)] . In all tetrapods the sclerotomic tissue does not migrate directly to and around the notochord and spinal cord, but amasses lateral to them in a block, the sclerotome [Figure 6-6(f)] . The sclerotome then disperses; this dispersal in amniotes is preceded by the formation of a sclerocoel [Figure 6-6(g)] . First the middle of the sclerotome migrates to the notochord and forms the perichordal ring [Figure 6-6(h)] , dividing each sclerotome into a cranial half and a caudal half. The cells from the cranial and caudal halves of adjacent sclerotomes migrate to the notochord and form the perichordal tubes [Figure 6-6 (i)] . In contrast to fish, resegmentation in tetrapods occurred earlier in development and not in contact with the notochord. This manner of resegmentation is termed sclerotomic resegmentation. Amniotes differ slightly from the amphibians with the appearance of the sclerocoel in the middle of the sclerotome; the sclerotome simply marks the division into cranial and caudal halves. The remaining steps to ossification are the same and as varied as in the bony fish. Owing to the sclerotomic resegmentation, the fate of various parts of the sclerotome can be traced in tetrapods. Of particular interest is the constant origin of the neural arch from the caudal half of the sclerotome.

In the phylogenetic development of the vertebrae (Figure 6-7), you will recall that certain crossopterygians had double centra pierced by the notochord. The earliest amphibians had a similar condition, although a tendency toward reduction of the notochord and an increase in the size of the central elements, single intercentrum and paired pleurocentra, is noticeable. Also, zygapophyses developed on the neural arches. Soon the notochord was occluded from the centrum. In the line leading to the extant amphibians, it is suspected that the intercentrum gave rise to the single centrum, but the lack of "missing link" fossils prevents confirmation. In contrast, the vertebrae of the labyrinthodonts are well documented with fossils. In some early labyrinthodonts the paired pleurocentra had fused into a single annular centrum of approximately the same size as the intercentrum. Within another later labyrinthodont line, the pleurocentrum was gradually reduced in size until it was completely replaced by a single large intercentrum.

The opposite trend was observed in the line leading to the amniotes. In the early reptiles the intercentrum began to decrease in size with a corresponding enlargement of the pleurocentrum. In later reptiles and the reptilian derivatives, birds and mammals, the intercentrum was lost and only the pleurocentrum remained.

These phylogenetic modifications of the vertebral column can be explained, at least to some degree, upon functional grounds which may hint at the adaptiveness of the structure. The appearance of the arch was likely to have been associated with an increased area of muscle attachment as much for improved axial locomotion as for protection and support of the spinal cord and blood vessels. The development of centra, likewise, may be correlated with axial locomotion and the development of a flexible but sturdy column. In the evolution of tetrapods, the function of the column shifted from loco-

Figure 6-7 (opposite). Various phylogenetic stages in the evolution of the vertebrae of vertebrates. I, intercentrum; IC, intercalary cartilage; NA, neural arch; P, pleurocentrum. (From Williams, in part.)

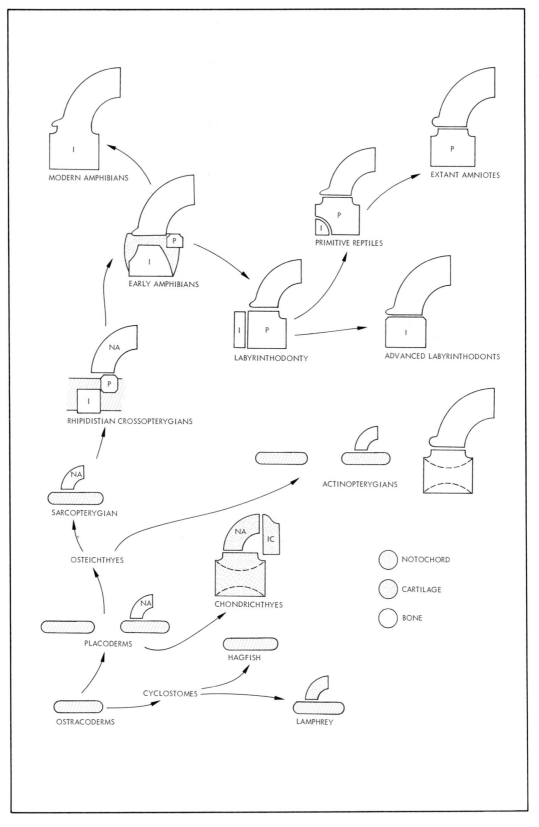

MODERN AMPHIBIANS

EARLY AMPHIBIANS

EXTANT AMNIOTES

PRIMITIVE REPTILES

LABYRINTHODONTY

ADVANCED LABYRINTHODONTS

RHIPIDISTIAN CROSSOPTERYGIANS

SARCOPTERYGIAN

ACTINOPTERYGIANS

OSTEICHTHYES

CHONDRICHTHYES

NOTOCHORD

CARTILAGE

BONE

PLACODERMS

HAGFISH

OSTRACODERMS

CYCLOSTOMES

LAMPHREY

213

motion to support. The appearance of zygapophyses provided a firmer inter-locking column. The change between amphibians and reptiles from a double to a single central condition cuts the number of joints in half and provides a more rigid arch.

Appendicular Locomotion and Structure

Vertebrates possess two classes of appendages: unpaired and paired. The paired appendages or pterygia are the pectoral and pelvic fins of fish and the fore- and hindlimbs of tetrapods. The following discussion will be restricted to paired appendages, not because unpaired appendages, i.e., dorsal fins, anal fins, and so on, have little functional value, but rather because they are absent in most tetrapods. Likewise, not all vertebrates have paired append-ages; they are absent in agnathan fish, snakes, and caecilians.

Since pterygia are present or secondarily lost in all gnathostomes, the manner of their origin must be investigated. In attempts to provide an explanation three theories have been promulgated. The first and least plaus-ible is Gegenbaur's gill arch theory, which suggests that the paired fins were derived from the posterior gill or visceral arches. With such a theory, the origin of both the girdle and the fin skeleton is explained; the gill arch became the girdle and the supports in the gill formed the fin skeleton. Facts that make this explanation untenable are the neural crest origin of the visceral arch skeleton and the hypomeric origin of the girdle and fin skeleton. The body-spine or armor theory is more acceptable, but it also leaves some points unexplained. This theory suggests that the series of ven-trolateral spines observed in some ostracoderms [Figure 6-8(b)] provided the material for fin evolution. The spines aggregated into a series of groups and developed membranous covers. The aggregations of spines were reduced to an anterior and a posterior pair, thereby producing the typical vertebrate pattern. This theory aptly explains the appearance of an appendicular skeleton, but the skeleton would be dermal since it is derived from dermal spines. Most of the appendicular skeleton is endochondral, and in contrast to the direct ossification of dermal bone, it passes through the cartilaginous stage. The fin-fold theory takes its origin from the ventrolateral metapleural folds of cephalochordates. It is hypothesized that similar folds existed in a lightly armored ostracoderm [Figure 6-8(a)]. The membranous folds develop-

Figure 6-8. The body form of two early fish, illustrating the possible initial stages in the evolution of paired appendages: (a) *Pterygolepis*, an anaspid ostracoderm (fin-fold theory); (b) *Euthacanthus,* an acanthodian placoderm (body-spine theory). (After Romer.)

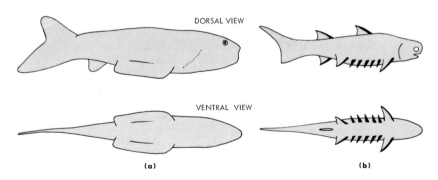

DORSAL VIEW

VENTRAL VIEW

(a)   (b)

ed internal support either before or after the folds were interrupted into a series of paired appendages. As in the body-spine theory, most of the paired appendages were lost. The problem that remains in this theory is an explanation of the origin of the appendicular skeleton, particularly the girdle.

None of these theories is satisfactory; however, a combination of the fin-fold and body-spine theories provides at least a workable model. Nonetheless, the important question remains unanswered. What were the selective advantages to the evolution of fins? If we examine the function of fins and compare it with the modification of body structure in ostracoderms that appears to have developed to serve the same function, we find a clue. Initially fins were relatively immobile and served simply as stabilizers to prevent or lessen the locomotor deviations of pitching and rolling. To accomplish the same ends, the anterior quarter of the ostracoderm body was frequently dorsoventrally compressed. This body form restricted the mobility of the fish.

Appendicular Skeleton and Musculature†

The most primitive fin consisted simply of a bony spine with a broad base, supporting a membranous flap (Figure 6-9). The anterior or preaxial edge contained the spine and was firm and inflexible, but it is doubtful that the membranous flap behind the spine contained any skeletal elements or musculature. This type, the fin-fold fin, acted simply as a stabilizer. From a fin with a single skeletal support a new fin evolved in the placoderms that possessed small plates or rods, pterygiophores, behind the spine. The pterygiophores formed a longitudinal series that were embedded in the body wall and served as an attachment site for appendicular musculature that consisted of a dorsal and a ventral muscle mass that were, at least initially, simply slips from the axial musculature. Extending laterally into the membranous fin were fin rays, the dermatotricha, that provided support to the fin which still had a broad base and little mobility.

Within the placoderms, the fin-fold fin continued to be modified, although it still maintained its broad base and lack of mobility. The pterygiophores differentiated into large plates proximally, the basals, and a series of longitudinal rods distally, the radials. The basals remained imbedded in the body wall; there were usually three, propterygium, mesopterygium, and metapterygium, anterior to posterior. The basals served as attachment sites for the appendicular musculature, and if their size is any indication, the appendicular musculature had also increased in extent. The radials extended perpendicularly from the basals in the fin and beyond them were the fin rays.

The fins of chondrichthyian fish are also fin-fold fins (Figure 6-9). They have the same basic internal structure as the most advanced placoderm fin-fold fin; the major modification is a narrowing of the base and a lateral elongation of the basals. The basals thus are no longer embedded in the body wall, and musculature has again increased in size. The dorsal musculature can actually extend the fin and the ventral musculature flexes it. The fin is still acting mainly as a stabilizer, but its slight mobility allows it to act partially as a hydroplane.

In osteichthyian fish, two fin types are derived from the placoderm fin-

†Because of the structural similarity and the serial homology of the pterygial skeleton, the following discussion will not differentiate between anterior and posterior appendages.

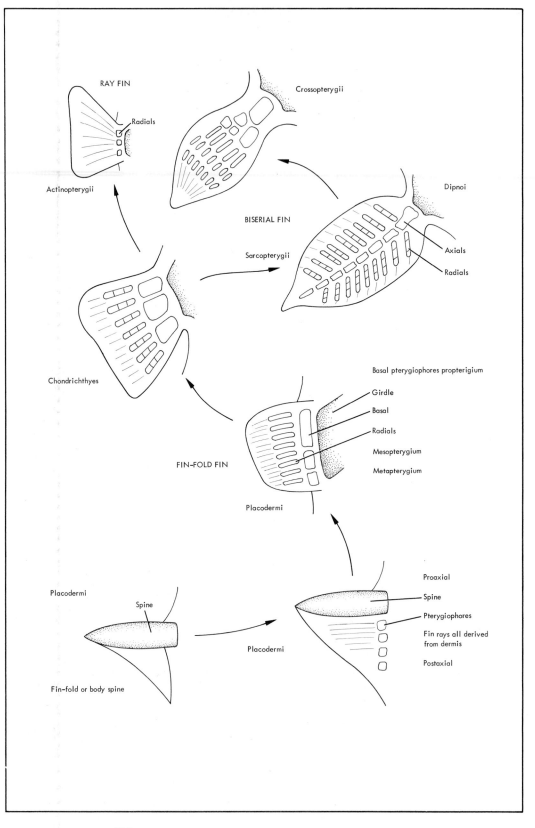

RAY FIN

Radials

Actinopterygii

Crossopterygii

BISERIAL FIN

Dipnoi

Axials

Radials

Sarcopterygii

Chondrichthyes

Basal pterygiophores propterigium

Girdle

Basal

Radials

Mesopterygium

Metapterygium

FIN-FOLD FIN

Placodermi

Placodermi

Spine

Proaxial

Spine

Pterygiophores

Fin rays all derived from dermis

Postaxial

Placodermi

Fin-fold or body spine

fold fin. The actinopterygian line possesses a ray-fin fin and the sarcopterygian line a biserial or lobed fin (Figure 6-9). In both lines the base of the fin is greatly constricted, and the fin has a high degree of mobility. The fins definitely act as rudders and are responsible for steering and braking the fish. In some fish, the fins become the major propulsive elements. In the ray-fin fin, the pterygiophores are greatly reduced and restricted to the body wall, the basals are seldom present, and the radials are few in number and occasionally are lost. The fin is very flexible and can be folded like a fan. Its internal support consists of elongated fin rays, but the appendicular musculature is restricted to the body and does not extend into the fin. Even though the musculature is proportionately reduced, it is differentiated into smaller subunits and is able to provide finer control of the fin movements.

The biserial or lobed fin has followed a converse evolutionary pathway. Not only are the pterygiophores present in large numbers, but they extend into the fin and compose most of it. The dipnoan biserial fin shows the primitive condition with the basals forming a longitudinal axis and the radials radiating from this axis. Short fin rays extend from the radials to the edge of the fin. In contrast, the longitudinal basal axis of the crossopterygian fin has shifted to the posterior, postaxial border of the fin. The radials extend towards the preaxial and distal borders. The musculature in both of these biserial fins projects outward into the fin and is sufficiently differentiated for precise movements.

With the transition from an aquatic to an amphibious or terrestrial life, the crossopterygian fin became a limb. The same basic limb structure is found in all tetrapods and in both the fore- and hindlimbs (Figure 6-10). The limb is divided into five units: propodium, epipodium, mesopodium, metapodium, and phalanges. The propodium consists of a single element, the humerus (in the forelimb) or femur (in the hindlimb) which articulates proximally with the appropriate girdle. In the epipodium there are two elements, the radius and ulna (in the forelimb) or the tibia and fibula (in the hindlimb). A series of small bones occurs in each mesopodium; these constitute either the carpus (wrist) or tarsus (ankle). The metapodial elements are the metacarpals or metatarsals; together with the phalanges they form the skeleton of the digits. Within the tetrapod limb the appendicular musculature retains its basic division into dorsal (extensor) and ventral (flexor) groups. These groups, however, are finely subdivided so that a wide range of movement is obtainable. Without going into much detail, abductor and adductor muscles extend from the girdle to the propodial and epipodial elements; they move the limb away from and toward the body respectively. The extensors and flexors lie within the limb. The fine subdivisions of the extensor and flexor muscle masses permit such movements as rotation (supination and pronation) of the lower limb and independent movement of the digits. A general summary of the appendicular musculature is presented in Figure 6-11.

Two theories have been promulgated to account for the evolution of the limb (Figure 6-12). Both use the crossopterygian fin for its derivation. They differ, however, in the arrangement of the basal pterygiophores of the

Figure 6-9 (opposite). A morphological series of fins illustrating the probable phylogenetic history of vertebrate fins.

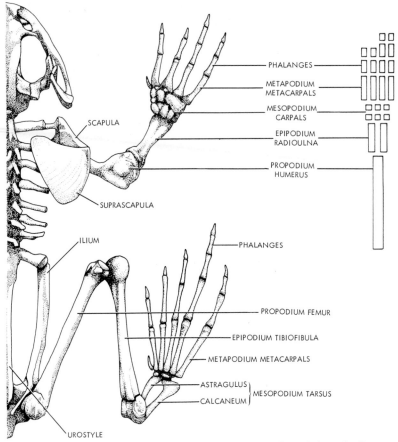

Figure 6-10. The appendicular skeleton of a tetrapod. (a) Dorsal view of a frog skeleton. (b) A schematic representation of the tetrapod limb.

biserial fin as it was derived from fin-fold fin. In the basal theory, the basal pterygiophores form the proximal two rows of plates in the crossopterygian fin. Because of this arrangement the humerus and femur are derived from a mesopterygium, radius or tibia from propterygium, and ulna or fibula from metapterygium. The mesopodial, metapodial, and phalangeal components of the limb are derived from radials. The axial theory suggests that the basal pterygiophores formed the longitudinal axis of the biserial fin. Therefore, in the crossopterygian fin the basals lie along the entire postaxial margin of the fin. The humerus or femur, ulna or fibula, and mesopodial, metapodial, and phalangeal elements of the postaxial border are derived from basals. The radials form the radius or tibia and all the remaining mesopodial, metapodial, and phalangeal elements. The basal theory fails to include the dipnoan type of biserial fin in its derivation of the limb, and fossil evidence shows that the crossopterygian fin was derived from the dipnoan type. Although the axial theory provides the correct morphological sequence in its derivation of the limb, the complete reorientation of the basals is difficult to perceive.

With the appearance of paired appendages and their associated musculoskeletal components, the internal supportive apparatus, the girdles, were developed. Unlike the pterygia, the architecture of the pectoral (anterior) and the pelvic (posterior) girdle is dissimilar, and their components cannot be serially homologized. Therefore, it is necessary to discuss the structure of each girdle separately.

The pectoral girdle is composed of two sets of bony elements, dermal and endochondral or cartilaginous (Figure 6-13). All elements are bilaterally paired. While the dermal elements appear to have been derived from the dermal armor of the ostracoderms, the origin of the endochondral elements is unknown and only Gegenbaur's gill arch theory has suggested the source of their origin. In placoderms the endochondral elements are (ventral to dorsal) the coracoid, scapula, and suprascapula. The glenoid fossa, the articular surface for the head of the humerus, lies on the suture between the coracoid and scapula. The dermal elements include (ventral to dorsal) the clavicle, cleithrum, supracleithrum, and posttemporal. The posttemporal is firmly articulated with the dermal bones of the posterodorsal margin of the skull, and the dermal and endochondral elements articulate with one another and form a solid girdle. In general, the dermal elements tend to lie anterior of the endochondral ones. In chondrichthyian fish all dermal elements have been lost. The sarcopterygian and chondrostean fish have a pectoral girdle with the same components as those of placoderms. In contrast, the clavicle

Figure 6-11. Evolutionary trends in the appendicular musculature. Because of the diversity of vertebrate appendages and the associated musculature, the dendrogram attempts only to show the general trends.

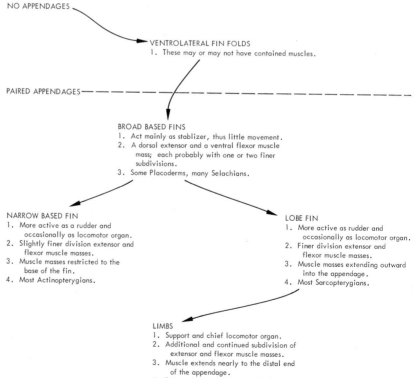

NO APPENDAGES

VENTROLATERAL FIN FOLDS
1. These may or may not have contained muscles.

PAIRED APPENDAGES

BROAD BASED FINS
1. Act mainly as stablizer, thus little movement.
2. A dorsal extensor and a ventral flexor muscle mass; each probably with one or two finer subdivisions.
3. Some Placoderms, many Selachians.

NARROW BASED FIN
1. More active as a rudder and occasionally as locomotor organ.
2. Slightly finer division extensor and flexor muscle masses.
3. Muscle masses restricted to the base of the fin.
4. Most Actinopterygians.

LOBE FIN
1. More active as rudder and occasionally as locomotor organ.
2. Finer division extensor and flexor muscle masses.
3. Muscle masses extending outward into the appendage.
4. Most Sarcopterygians.

LIMBS
1. Support and chief locomotor organ.
2. Additional and continued subdivision of extensor and flexor muscle masses.
3. Muscle extends nearly to the distal end of the appendage.
4. Tetrapoda, except for secondarily reduced limbed and limbless forms.

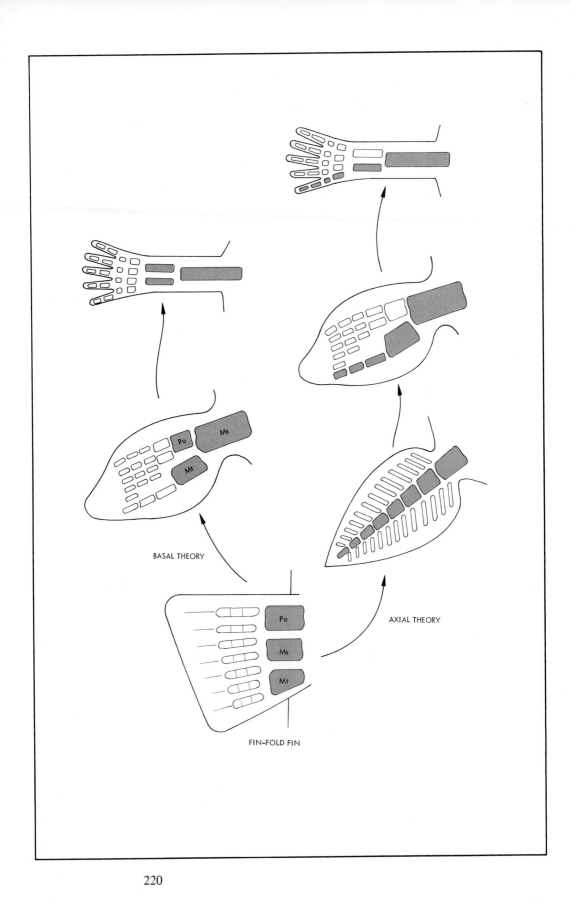

BASAL THEORY

AXIAL THEORY

FIN-FOLD FIN

Po

Ms

Mt

220

Figure 6-12 (opposite). The presumed role of the basal pterygiophores (shaded) in the evolution of the vertebrate limb according to the axial and basal theories. Po, propterygium; Ms, mesopterygium; Mt, metapterygium.

and the suprascapula are usually absent in the advanced actinopterygian fish, the holosteans and the teleosteans.

The transition from fish to tetrapod involved a structural modification of the pectoral girdle (Figure 6-13). The posttemporal was lost, and so also the girdle's articulation to the skull. With the loss of this dermal element on each side, a ventromedian, dermal element, the interclavicle, became important. In addition, the glenoid fossa shifted from its coracoscapula position to an entirely scapular position, which has been retained throughout all tetrapods. The extant tetrapod amphibians show a continual reduction of dermal

Figure 6-13. A morphological series of pectoral girdles illustrating the various stages in evolution. Only one side is shown. CLA, clavicle; CLE, cleithrum; CO, coracoid; IC, interclavicle; PC, postcoracoid; PT, posttemporal; S, scapula; SC, supracleithrum; SS, suprascapula.

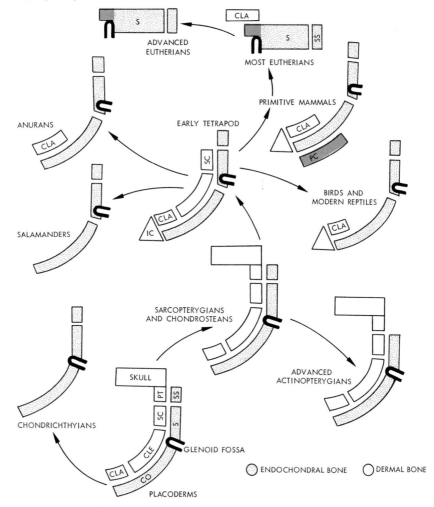

elements but no loss of endochondral elements, and the girdle of salamanders is composed only of the endochondral elements. In anurans, the only dermal element remaining is the clavicle. The avian and reptilian girdles have retained all endochondral elements, plus the interclavicle and clavicle.

The mammalian girdle has also gone through a series of reductions of the primary units. Primitive mammals have lost the dermal cleithrum and supracleithrum, and a new endochondral element, the postcoracoid, has appeared on each side. In most extant eutherian mammals the interclavicle has disappeared and the coracoid and suprascapula have been lost. The postcoracoid is greatly reduced and fused to the scapula. In some eutherian mammals, no dermal element persists.

The pelvic girdle is entirely endochondral and as such the origin is unknown. In placoderms it is represented simply by a pair of ventral plates which are fused medially through a pelvic symphysis (Figure 6-14). Each

Figure 6-14. An arrangement of pelves from extant vertebrates to suggest the probable evolutionary history of the pelvic girdle. All are shown in ventral aspect. IM, ilium; IS, ischium; P, pubis.

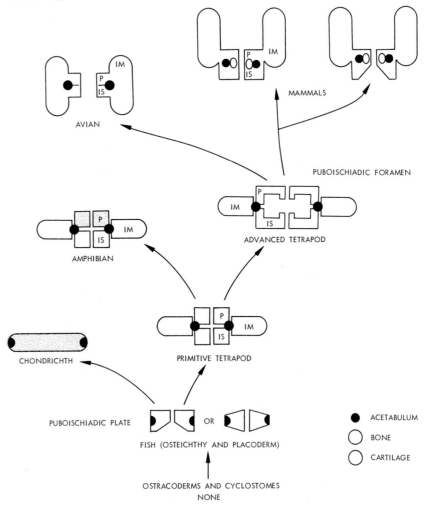

plate had a single ossification center plus a very small dorsal process, and laterally possessed an articular surface, the acetabulum, for the femur. In osteichthyian fish the pelvic girdle has retained essentially the same form as in the placoderms. The two ventral plates are fused into an inseparable bar in chondrichthyian fish.

The transition from axial to appendicular locomotion involved many structural modifications of the pelvic girdle (Figure 6-14). Within each ventral plate two ossification centers developed, the anterior one became the pubis, the posterior one, the ischium. The bilateral halves of the girdle are joined through the pubic and ischial symphyses. A large dorsal projection, the ilium, develops on each side from its own ossification center. The tetrapod girdle, unlike that of the piscine, establishes contact with the axial skeleton by means of an articulation on each side between the ilium and a sacral rib. The acetabulum lies at the junction of the ilium, ischium, and pubis.

The pelvic girdle of extant tetrapod amphibians is identical to that of ancestral amphibians except that the pubes of the former remain cartilaginous. The reptilian pelvis develops a large puboischiadic foramen in each half of the puboischiadic plate, and the ilium generally articulates with two pairs of sacral ribs, occasionally more but never less. The avian pelvis differs greatly in form from the reptilian. Both pubis and ischium are reduced in size and do not contact their mates of the opposite side. The ilium is elongated anteroposteriorly. All three elements are inseparably united with one another as well as dorsally with the synsacrum, a fused series of lumbar, sacral, and caudal vertebrae. The mammalian pelvis has undergone a fusion of ilium, ischium, and pubis to form a single innominate bone on each side. Accompanying these changes there has occurred a proportionate increase in the size of the ilium, which has taken on a strongly anterior orientation. The puboischiadic foramina have become reduced in size. A puboischiadic symphysis is present in many mammals, but in some the ischia do not meet.

The preceding discussion has attempted to illustrate the evolutionary trends within the appendicular musculoskeletal system. Because of its limited goal, this has been superficial in some respects and particularly so for the muscular system. The main evolutionary trend in the appendicular muscles has been a finer subdivision of the dorsal and ventral muscle masses to attain a precise control of movement. To illustrate more than this general trend in muscles, it would be necessary to name individual muscles, but because the homology of muscles between vertebrate classes is poorly understood this was avoided.

Probably all the evolutionary modifications of the skeletal system can be explained entirely on mechanical or functional grounds. One of the most obvious modifications is the transfer of the appendicular-axial skeletal attachment from the pectoral to the pelvic girdle with the development of appendicular locomotion and terrestrialism. Because it is more effective to push than to pull, the hindlimbs become the major propulsive elements in appendicular locomotion. This is comparable to steering, where an anterior steering mechanism is more effective. The posterior appendages develop an attachment with the axial skeleton and a forward thrust is applied directly to the axial skeleton and not through a muscular sling. For increased mobility of

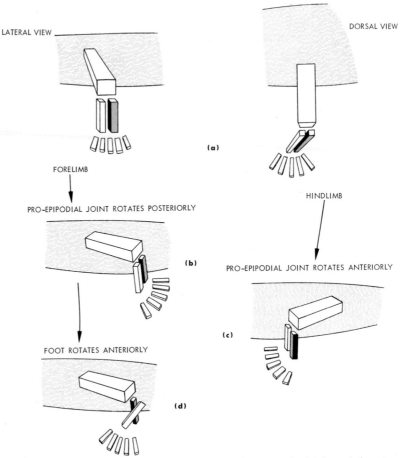

Figure 6-15. The modification of limb posture in the tetrapods. (a) Sprawled posture; the fore- and hindlimb posture of the early tetrapods. (b) and (c) The change in forelimb posture; the two rotations occurred concurrently. (d) The change in hindlimb posture; there is no torsion of epipodial elements.

the anterior appendages the firm union to the skull is lost, and a muscular sling comes into operation. In addition, this modification allows the anterior appendages to act as shock absorbers and reduce the shock to the skull.

The initial limb posture of tetrapods was a sprawl with the limbs held perpendicular to the longitudinal body axis. There has been a tendency in amniotes for the limbs to be brought under the body (Figure 6-15); this has occurred independently at least three times, in dinosaurs, birds, and mammals. The reorientation of the limbs results from the rotation of pre-epipodial joints of the forelimb posteriorly [Figure 6-15(b)] and of the hindlimb anteriorly [Figure 6-15(d)]. The rotation of the hindlimb causes the hindfoot to point anteriorly, but that of the forelimb would cause the forefoot to point posteriorly. The latter, of course, has been avoided, and the forefoot is directed anteriorly. To obtain this orientation, the epipodium has become twisted upon itself [Figure 6-15(c)]. The position of the ulna remains stationary as does the distal end of the radius. The proximal end, however, slides over the ulna toward the postaxial border of the limb.

The appendicular skeleton shows many other modifications associated with locomotor habits. Saltatorial and cursorial vertebrates usually have an elongated limb skeleton, and frequently there is a reduction by fusion and loss of epipodial, mesopodial, metapodial, and phalangeal elements. Fossorial tetrapods have a short, robust appendicular skeleton, and often the pedal elements are enlarged. A convergent evolutionary trend can frequently be observed by comparing vertebrates of similar locomotor habits from several separate classes.

The Evolution of Vertebrate Feeding and Respiratory Mechanisms

The earliest vertebrates and their predecessors were small, probably the size of Amphioxus or just slightly larger. Like the cephalochordates, they certainly depended upon cutaneous respiration, i.e., the skin functioned as a respiratory surface. They possessed gill arches (visceral arches); however, gill arches are a misnomer because they formed a pharyngeal or branchial basket that acted as a strainer to collect food. As vertebrates became progressively larger and as armor began to develop, cutaneous respiration became less and less adequate for metabolic needs. A high selective premium would then have been placed on additional respiratory surfaces. Gills probably were the result of this selective pressure and probably existed in all ostracoderms. The branchial basket, thus, was effective as a respiratory as well as a feeding apparatus.

The feeding function of the gill arches was lost or reduced by the modification of one of the anteriormost pairs into jaws. In chondrichthyian and osteichthyian fish, the gill arches with the associated gills are primarily respiratory, and the jaws are the major feeding apparatus. Tetrapods, likewise, depend upon the jaws for feeding. The respiratory surface in tetrapods has, of course, been shifted from the pharyngeal region itself to an outgrowth of this region, the lungs. Surviving elements of the visceral skeleton are found in the skull, auditory ossicles, tongue, larynx and upper trachea.

The Respiratory Apparatus

There is little question that the visceral or gill arches of the vertebrates were derived from the pharyngeal bars of the branchial basket. The structure of the pharyngeal bars of cephalochordates is probably similar to that of the prevertebrates. However, it is doubtful that the prevertebrates had the enormous number of pharyngeal bars that are typical of extant cephalochordates. Prevertebrates probably had no more than twenty on each side and perhaps even fewer, and most vertebrate embryos possess only seven arches. Embryologically the highest number appears to be twelve or thirteen in some cyclostomes; an ostracoderm, *Pharyngolepis,* had sixteen. Each primary pharyngeal arch of a cephalochordate possesses a cartilaginous bar which does not appear to be jointed, nor does muscular tissue exist. The internal surface bears a heavy coat of cilia that creates the water current passing through the pharyngeal basket. Structurally similar arches probably existed in the prevertebrates and earliest ostracoderms. [7]

As the bony armor of ostracoderms developed the visceral arches began to replace the skin, at least in part, as the major respiratory surface (see Table 6-2 for a summary of vertebrate respiratory surfaces). The lateral walls of

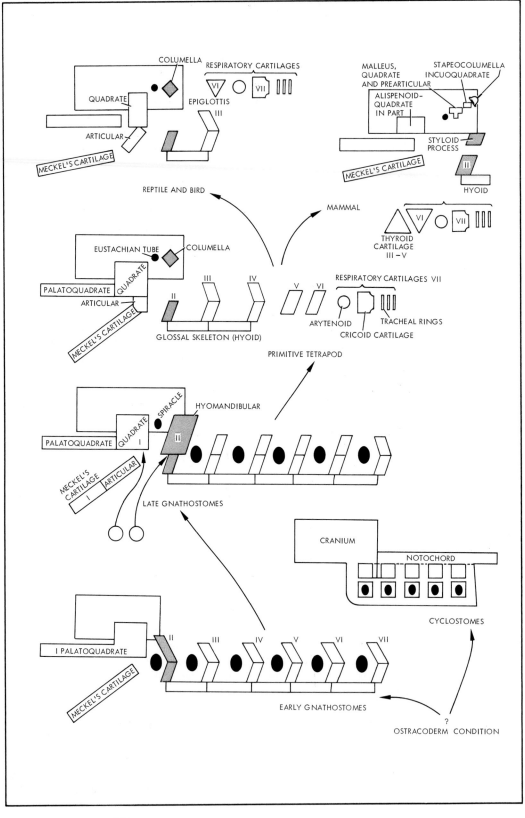

Figure 6-16 (opposite). A schematic representation of the visceral arches and their evolutionary history.

the arches became laminated and gills were developed; filter feeding was still retained. Initially the cilia were probably capable of generating an adequate flow of water through the gills for feeding and respiration, but later the ciliary mechanism was replaced by a musculoskeletal pumping mechanism for moving water through the pharyngeal basket. However, the cilia probably remained as a feeding mechanism to transport the food-trapping mucus down the gut. Musculoskeletal pumps appear to have arisen independently twice among the ostracoderms, for the cyclostomes and the gnathostomes have structurally different gill arch systems. Since there are extant members of both groups, descriptions of the structure and function as they presently exist can be helpful. The reader can extrapolate the condition of ostracoderms and placoderms from this information.

The cartilaginous gill arches of cyclostomes are not jointed; in fact, there are no joints between successive gill arches so an entirely unjointed pharyngeal basket is formed (Figure 6-16), and they are united dorsally to the notochord. By this means the pharyngeal cavity is completely encircled by a firm but flexible skeletal network. The musculature of the gill arches, the branchiomeric muscles, lies internal to the skeletal arches. While extant cyclostomes have a lingual skeleton and musculature, the homologies and origin of this lingual apparatus are unsettled. Furthermore many paleontologists believe that this skeleton did not exist in ostracoderms.

The jointed gill arches are cartilaginous in chondrichthyian fish and generally bony in osteichthyians (Figure 6-16). Each is usually divided into at least three segments and is joined to its bilateral mate and the ipsilateral arches by a ventromedial, longitudinal series of bars. Dorsally they are usually embedded in the body musculature but do not contact the axial skeleton except for the anteriormost one or two arches. In these types the branchiomeric musculature lies external to the arches except for a few small

Table 6-2. Respiratory mechanisms of vertebrates. These are the major respiratory surfaces and pumping mechanism of the vertebrates.

Group	Respiratory surface	Pumping mechanism
Prevertebrates	Skin	None
Ostracodermi	Gills	Branchial suction pump
Cyclostomata	Gills	Branchial suction pump
Placodermi	Gills	Branchial suction pump
Chondrichthyes	Gills	Branchial suction pump and buccal pressure pump
Osteichthyes	Gills	Branchial suction pump and buccal pressure pump
Amphibia	Skin	None
	Lungs	Buccal pressure pump
Reptilia	Lungs	Costal suction pump
Aves	Lungs	Costal suction pump
Mammalia	Lungs	Costal suction pump, diaphragmatic suction pump

slips. The jaw, which is a derivation of the anterior visceral arches, will be discussed later.

Although cyclostomine and piscine branchial structures are dissimilar, the manner of operation as suction pumps is nearly identical [Figure 6-17 (a)-(c)]. Water is drawn into the branchial chamber by the expansion of the cavity and is forced out by its contraction. The direction of flow is normally into the mouth, through the buccal cavity to the branchial cavity, then over the gills to the outside via the gill slits. This is a generalized model, and the structural differences do produce functional differences. In contrast to the piscine mode in which muscular activity is responsible for the expansion and contraction of the branchial cavity, the nonjointed arches of cyclostomes have an elastic recoil action. This recoil expands the cavity, and muscular activity contracts the cavity. The piscine ventilation system has, in addition to the branchial pump, a buccal pump. The buccal pump serves to draw water into the buccal cavity; its main function, however, seems to be to force water into the branchial or pharyngeal cavity. Therefore the buccal pump operates as a pressure pump.

The development of a pumping mechanism had a profound effect on the musculature of the visceral arches. It is likely that little or no muscle tissue was associated with the arches when flow was maintained by ciliary action. When muscle tissue appeared in the arches, it was smooth muscle, because that is the type of tissue in the remainder of the digestive tract. The increased muscular activity associated with the development of a branchial pump appears to have caused a shift to striated muscle tissue, which is stronger and more active than smooth muscle. A similar modification of hypomeric muscle tissue occurred during the evolution of the heart. Striated cardiac tissue, however, is histologically unlike any other muscle tissue, whereas the branchiomeric musculature is histologically identical to somatic musculature. The derivatives of the branchiomeric musculature are summarized in Table 6-3.

In the chondrichthyian and osteichthyian fish the first visceral arch forms the jaw and has no function in respiration. The second arch frequently acts as part of the jaw suspensorium, but in addition it supports a gill on its posterior surface. The remaining arches, the third through seventh, support the gills and pump water over them.

Gills are not suitable for aerial respiration because they collapse on one another, reducing the surface area available for gas exchange and yet maintaining a large surface area for excessive water loss. With the increasing importance of lungs and the loss of gills, the visceral arches took on new functions in the tetrapods. The second through sixth arches (or at least their ventral portions) form the hyoid apparatus in these organisms. Al-

Figure 6-17 (opposite). Stylized models of the respiratory mechanisms in vertebrates. (a) Ventilation cycle of a lamprey when attached to its prey; inspiration results from the elastic recoil of the visceral skeleton. (b) A single-pump mechanism of some bony fish; both inspiration and expiration are powered by muscular contraction. (c) The double suction pump operating in most osteichthyian and chondrichthyian fish. (d) The buccal force or pressure pump of amphibians. (e) The costal suction pump of some amniotes; in mammals, the diaphragm is used instead of the rib cage. (In part, after Hughes.)

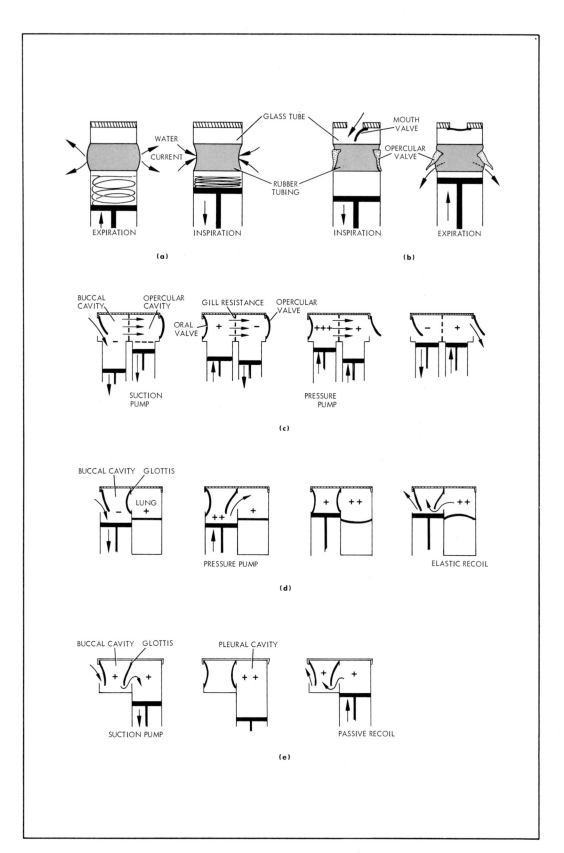

though arches no longer support the gills, their function is still primarily respiratory. Amphibians ventilate their lungs by means of a buccal force or pressure pump [Figure 6-17(d)]. Air enters the buccal cavity to equalize the partial vacuum created by the depression of the hyoid apparatus. The hyoid apparatus is then raised, and air is forced into the lungs. Expiration is passive, for the elastic nature of the lungs forces out the air. Because it forms a series of small elements supporting the anterior end of the respiratory tube the seventh arch is also associated with respiration.

The second and third arches of reptiles and birds, but only the second in mammals, enter into the formation of the hyoid apparatus (Figure 6-16). In these forms it has become associated with the tongue as the glossal skeleton that no longer serves any respiratory function but acts only as an attachment surface for lingual muscles. The fourth and fifth arches of reptiles and birds have no skeletal derivatives, and the sixth and seventh arches form a series of cartilages and bones that support the anterior part of the respiratory tube. Mammals have lost the third arch, and a series of respiratory cartilages and bones have been derived from the fourth, fifth, sixth, and seventh arches. The buccal pressure pump of amphibians has been replaced by a costal suction pump [Figure 6-17(e)], in which the ribs, with certain exceptions (turtles, birds), are freely movable. Upon contraction of the obliquely oriented intercostals, the ribs move forward and upward, thereby enlarging the thoracic cavity in which a partial vacuum exists. The enlargement causes the elastic lungs to expand and fill this partial vacuum, and the air flows inward. The elastic nature of the lungs is the main force for exhalation. A muscular diaphragm has developed in mammals from the oblique and transverse septa. By contracting, the diaphragm flattens and thus the volume of the thoracic cavity is increased. In general, mammalian ventilation is more dependent upon the diaphragm than on the costal suction pump mechanism.

The Feeding Apparatus   As we saw earlier, the feeding habits of the prevertebrates probably were like those of extant cephalochordates. The cilia lining the pharyngeal basket and buccal cavity created a current through the basket, and food particles were

Table 6-3. Some of the main derivatives of the branchiomeric musculature, which indicate their evolutionary divergence. The musculature is finely divided into many muscle bundles that can be readily observed in any student laboratory guide.

Prevertebrates	Associated with pharyngeal basket	↑ Smooth Muscle
		Striated Muscle
Agnathans	Branchial musculature	
Gnathostomous fish	Branchial musculature Mandibular musculature	↓
Tetrapods	Mandibular musculature Hyoid musculature Cervical musculature	
Mammals	Mandibular musculature Hyoid musculature Facial musculature	

entrapped on a mucous sheet that was flowing to and down the esophagus. The ostracoderms became larger, and it is likely that this increase in size occurred concurrently with the evolution of a new feeding mode, suctorial feeding. We are led to believe this because filter feeding by ciliary action is always restricted to small animals. In suctorial feeding, large amounts of detritus are drawn into the mouth and pass back to the branchial cavity. The gill arches possess gill rakers or their analogs, which prevent the larger items from passing through. These items are swallowed. Thus, the branchial pumping mechanism would become equally important in feeding as in respiration. However, some paleontologists believe that a velum, a buccal modification of the cyclostomes, was also present in ostracoderms and preceded the visceral arches as the pumping mechanism. [8]

The suctorial mechanism appears to have led to the enlargement of the mouth and in some ostracoderms to a scoop-like modification of its ventral portion. Both adaptations were probably associated with the development of selective feeding habits rather than with random "vacuum cleaner" feeding. In addition, these adaptations seem to have been associated with the development of jaws. The origin of the jaws is thought to be the result of an ever-increasing enlargement of the mouth; as the mouth was crowded backward, it encompassed the first and then the second gill arch. During the course of this change the second gill arch was converted to the palatoquadrate of the upper jaw and Meckel's cartilage of the lower jaw. Although the mandibular arch is clearly derived from the second visceral as shown by its innervation, it is labeled the first arch since the premandibular arch is absent in most gnathostomes.

Placoderms are considered to be the first fish with jaws, but it is likely that jaws were present among their ostracoderm ancestors. The first jaws were probably entirely cartilaginous and bore dermal scales that were the predecessors of teeth. The first jaws consisted of the palatoquadrate (upper) and Meckel's (lower) cartilages and these elements along with their derivatives later became intimately associated with the skull as the splanchnocranium. At the earliest stage, however, the jaws were entirely free of the cranium and were enclosed in the musculature. This type of jaw suspension, paleostyly (Figure 6-18), with no extrinsic support, does not permit a very strong bite. Selection certainly favored a firmer jaw suspension as is shown by the development of two general types of suspension (Figure 6-18). In autostyly, the palatoquadrate articulates with the neurocranium; in hyostyly, the palatoquadrate articulates with the hyomandibular, i.e., the dorsal part of the second visceral arch that is joined to the neurocranium. In the primitive paleostylic state the jaws were cartilaginous, but this condition was replaced in the more advanced placoderms by various patterns of ossification of the first visceral arch. The palatoquadrate in one placoderm group ossified from three centers, Meckel's cartilage from two, and the latter furthermore was braced externally by a splint-like dermal bone.

Chondrichthyian fish have what may be considered a neotenic condition; the palatoquadrate and Meckel's cartilage are cartilaginous throughout life, only occasionally calcifying but never ossifying. Jaw suspension is hyostylic in most cartilaginous fish. Both the upper and lower jaws support whorls of teeth.

Unlike the chondrichthyians and placoderms, the upper and lower jaws of

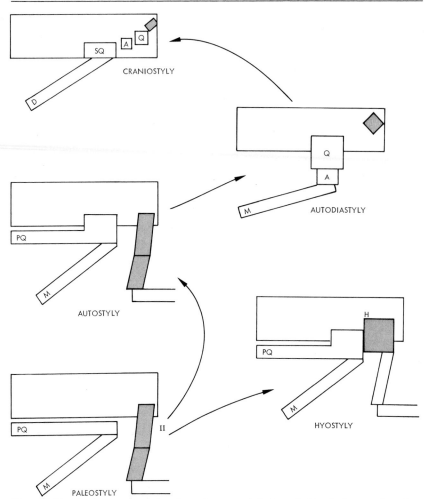

Figure 6-18. The jaw suspensoria of vertebrates and their probable phylogeny. A, articular; D, dentary; H, hyomandibular; M, Meckel's cartilage; PQ, palatoquadrate; Q, quadrate; SQ, squamosal.

osteichthyian fish [Figure 6-19(g) and (h)] are largely dermal in origin and as such are part of the dermocranium, the part of the cranial skeleton derived from ostracoderm dermal armor. The derivatives of the first visceral arch are present. Meckel's cartilage develops a small posterior ossification center that forms the articular bone, while the remainder retains its cartilag-

Figure 6-19 (opposite). Various aspects of the cranial skeleton of the bowfin, *Amia calva*, showing the interlocking of the dermocranial, neurocranial, and splanchnocranial elements. (a) A lateral view of the cranium. (b) A dorsal view of the cranium; note the complete encasing of neurocranium by dermocranial elements. (c) A dorsal view of the neurocranium; a large portion remains cartilaginous. (d) A ventral view of the neurocranium. (e) A lateral view of the neurocranium. (f) A lateral view of the mandibular arch (first visceral arch); much of the mandibular arch remains cartilaginous. (g) A mesial view of the lower jaw. (h) A mesial view of the lower jaw with coronoid and prearticular removed. See Table 6-4 for explanation. (After Allis.)

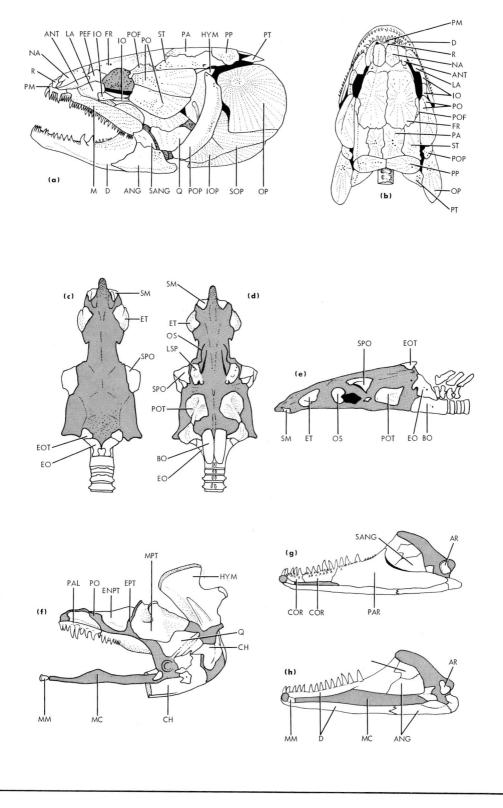

233

inous state and is completely enclosed by dermal bones [Figure 6-19(f)] . The number of these dermal bones varies. The largest one, the dentary, occupies the anterior half to two-thirds of the lower jaw. The palatoquadrate is variously ossified; a posterior ossification center, the quadrate, is always present and the anterior part frequently remains cartilaginous, although occasionally one or two "suprapterygoid" may appear. The dermal elements of the upper jaw, especially the premaxillary and maxillary, form the major part of the upper jaw and bear the teeth as does the lower dentary. Most osteichthyians have a hyostylic jaw suspensorium.

In the amphibians the quadrate is ossified and firmly united to the skull (autostyly). Meckel's cartilage of the lower jaw is cartilaginous and completely encased by dermal elements. The lower jaw articulates with the cranium through the quadrate and articular bones. Because amphibian autostyly is distinctly different from that of the fish, it is termed autodiastyly. The hyomandibular is freed from its feeding role and/or respiratory function and becomes associated with the reception of sound. With this new function, it is given a new name, the columella.

Birds and reptiles have essentially the same jaw structure as the amphibians. The dermal elements form the major part of the jaw, with the quadrate and articular serving as the articular surfaces. Meckel's cartilage persists and is encased in dermal bone. In the evolution of mammals, the jaws underwent considerable modification from the typical tetrapod condition. A remnant of Meckel's cartilage remains, but the small dermal elements are absent and the lower jaw consists of one bony element, the dentary. The latter articulates with the cranium through the squamosal, also a dermal element. This association is also a form of autostyly but, because the first visceral arch no longer is a part of the jaw suspensorium, this mammalian type of autostyly is termed craniostyly. The columella or stapes is an ear ossicle that in nonmammalian tetrapods transmits vibrations from the tympanic membrane to the inner ear. In mammals it is joined by two other bones the incus and malleus; the incus is derived from the quadrate and the malleus from the articular and the dermal prearticular. These three elements form a bony chain across the middle ear chamber for the transmission of vibrations. [9]

Evolution of Musculoskeletal Protective Devices

The musculoskeletal system provides two types of protection. The dermal skeletal system acts as a shield and prevents penetration of the body. This type of protection, present in one form or another in most vertebrates, arose early in the evolution of the group. In a few fish muscle tissue has been modified to form an electric organ; an electrical discharge repels the predator.

Dermal Armor

Among the chordates dermal armor, or its derivatives, is a unique characteristic of vertebrates. The armor consists of dermal or membranous bone that arises directly in the connective tissue. Endochondral bone, in contrast, is preformed in cartilage (the ontogeny of bone formation was described in the preceding chapter). Dermal armor made its first appearance in the ostracoderm, where it developed supposedly either to maintain the animal's water balance in its new fresh-water habitat or to protect it from predation by the eurypterids, large aquatic arthropods. The first fossil record of vertebrates consists of the remains of ostracoderm dermal armor, and the evidence shows that these fish were almost completely encased in plates and scales of bone. The head and anterior part of the trunk were enclosed in a series of firmly articulating plates, the cephalothoracic shield, while the remainder of the body was covered by scales that permitted flexing of the body and thus locomotion. The structure of this dermal armor is unlike that of any dermal elements in extant vertebrates. It had a superficial enamel layer covering denticles of a dentine-like material, which was supported by vascular or spongy bone and a lower layer of lamellar or compact bone. The dermal elements of all vertebrates can be derived from these four layers (Figure 6-20).

The most primitive dermal scale, the denticulate scale, had these four layers; it occurred in both ostracoderms and placoderms. Scales, which had

Figure 6-20. The evolution of the dermal armor and its derivatives in the vertebrates. (After Bertin, in part.)

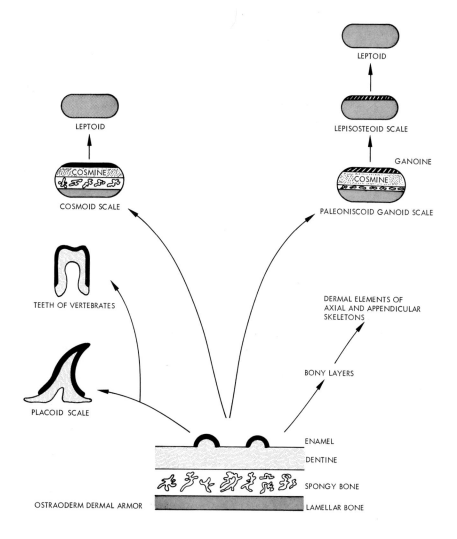

lost the two layers of bone, appear to have acted as teeth, and vertebrate teeth still retain the enamel and dentine layers. The placoid scales of chondrichthyian fish share a similar history and have the same two layers. Two types of scales developed in early osteichthyian fish (Figure 6-20). The sarcopterygian line has a cosmoid scale that is similar in structure to the denticulate scale, but lacks the denticles and has a continuous enamel coat and a cosmine instead of dentine layer. This scale was modified in later sarcopterygians by the loss of the superficial layers until only the lamellar layer remained, to become the leptoid or elasmoid scale. In the actinopterygians the earliest scale was the paleoniscoid ganoid scale. It possessed cosmine instead of dentine, a thick ganoine layer instead of enamel, and a reduced spongy bone layer. The paleoniscoid scale was replaced by the lepisosteoid scale of two layers, ganoine and lamellar bony. The ganoine layer is absent in the teleostean fish, which have leptoid scales like the extant sarcopterygians.

Dermal scales were present in some of the early amphibians. In the extant amphibians, they are found only in the caecilians. Because they are buried in integumentary folds, dermal scales in these amphibians do not provide any protection. They do not exist in amniotes, although some amniotes do have bony plates, osteoderms, in the dermis. Osteoderms are probably secondarily derived and not homologous to fish scales.

With the development of paired appendages in vertebrates, the posterior margin of the cephalothoracic shield appears to have been incorporated into the pectoral girdle. These elements, clavicle, cleithrum, supracleithrum, and posttemporal, were discussed in the appendicular section. The union of the pectoral girdle with the skull is thus a primitive feature that has been retained in osteichthyian fish.

The dermocranium of later vertebrates is derived from the anterior part of the cephalothoracic shield of the ostracoderms. The cranium or skull of most vertebrates consists of three components: the dermocranium is the external encasing unit; the neurocranium supports and protects the brain ventrally and laterally; the splanchnocranium forms, at least embryologically, the mandibular framework, as was explained in the discussion of the first visceral arch. The history of the dermocranium can easily be determined, but this is certainly not true for the neurocranium. Because the neurocranium is preformed in cartilage, it may have been cartilaginous throughout its early history and thus has left no fossil record of its existence.

This speculation leads to the persistent argument over which skeletal tissue is the most ancient. The decision has seesawed back and forth between bone and cartilage. The evidence for bone is the presence of dermal armor in the earliest ostracoderms; for cartilage the fact that cartilage precedes bone embryologically. This sort of argument is fruitless for bone and cartilage probably appeared nearly concurrently and the types of bone are not distinguishable. In addition, the notochord is obviously the oldest skeletal tissue; it appears early in ontogeny. Its histological structure in vertebrates is identical to that of the protochordates and suggests its existence in their common ancestor. Dermal bone occurs in the ostracoderms, and there is no evidence of an endoskeleton. This could be taken as evidence for the development of dermal bone prior to cartilage. But later ostracoderms have ossified cranial skeletons. Because the cranial skeleton is endochondral, cartilage must have existed in the earliest ostracoderms beneath the dermal armor. The best arrangement of skeletal tissue in order of appearance would be notochord, dermal bone and cartilage concurrently and, finally, endochondral bone.

The neurocranium is always preformed in cartilage and frequently is only partially ossified in adult vertebrates. Our first record of the neurocranium is from the osteostracan ostracoderms in which the neurocranium was one solid bony unit enclosing the brain and inseparably fused to the visceral arches. The extant cyclostomes show a similar condition except that the neurocranium remains cartilaginous and forms only a ventral plate beneath the brain. In both agnathans and gnathostomes, the olfactory and otic capsules are part of the neurocranium, a feature that has been retained in all vertebrates. Generally the neurocranium of placoderms was cartilaginous. Like that of the ostracoderms, it formed a completely enclosing braincase. One major difference does exist between the two; in the placoderms the visceral arches may contact the braincase but they are definitely not fused to it. Only the form of the neurocranium of the chondrichthyian fish differs from that of the placoderms.

The neurocranium of osteichthyian fish has made a major shift in structure. It is no longer a solid piece, but is composed of a number of ossifications. The number of elements varies, but it is necessary only to recognize the major groupings (see Table 6-4). The occipital group forms the posterior part of the braincase encircling the foramen magnum, the aperture for the spinal cord. A sphenoid group forms the middle of the braincase and the ethmoid group and olfactory capsule the anterior end. Elements of the otic group lie laterally between the sphenoid and occipital groups. The neurocranium was highly ossified in the early osteichthyians. There was a trend for a reduction of ossification, so that in extant bony fish the eight bony neurocranial elements are embedded in a cartilaginous matrix [Figure 6-19(c)-(e)].

This reduction trend seems to be reversed in tetrapods; the amniotes have firmly ossified braincases. The olfactory capsule, which is rarely ossified elsewhere, forms the turbinal bones in mammals. The tetrapods have the same grouping of neurocranial elements. While the neurocranium provides some protection for the brain, it appears, however, to function mainly in support. The major protection is provided by the dermocranium. The three pairs of sensory capsules are also encircled and protected by the dermocranium.

The structure of the cephalic shield, which is very diverse in both the ostracoderms and placoderms, ranges in composition from a mass of small bony elements to a single bony unit. This diversity and the incompleteness of the fossil record have thwarted the determination of homologies with the dermocranium of later gnathostomes. Nonetheless, this structure is derived from the bony layers of dermal armor. Of the extant vertebrates only the cyclostomes and chondrichthyian fish lack a dermocranium.

Within the osteichthyian fish the dermocranial architecture becomes "standardized." This is not to say that the arrangement of elements is identical in all bony fish, but that a general pattern of seven series of bony elements is established [Table 6-4 and Figures 6-19(a) and (b)]. A rostral series surrounds the nares at the anterior end of the skull. A median roofing series extends from the rostral series to the dermal elements, posttemporal and supracleithrum, of the pectoral girdle. The eye is surrounded by an orbital series that abuts anteriorly with the rostral series and posteriorly with the temporal series. This series laterally encloses the otic capsule and articulates posteriorly to the opercular series forming the skeletal covering over the gills. The mandibular series has an upper and a lower jaw division. A palatal series forms the roof of the mouth.

The terminology for the individual elements, whether in fish or tetrapods, is derived from that of man and other mammals. The homology of elements has been fairly well established in the tetrapods and their crossopterygian ancestors; therefore the parietal of an extant mammal is derived from the same ancestral element as a parietal of a labyrinthodont amphibian. Such is not the case in the actinopterygian and dipnoan fish. Elements bearing the same name may or may not be homologous within the different actinopterygian lineages, and homologies between tetrapods and actinopterygians are even more tenuous. Because of this, the following discussion will be restricted to the presentation of general trends.

Table 6-4. The cranial components of vertebrates with emphasis on *Amia*. All elements paired unless otherwise indicated.

Dermocranium	Dermocranium	Neurocranium
Dorsal Roofing elements	*Mandibular Elements*	*Ethmoid Elements*
Median Series	Upper jaw series	Sphenethmoid (1)
Rostral (1) (R)	Premaxillary (PM)	Ethmoid (ET)
Nasal (NA)	Maxillary (M)	Septomaxillary (SM)
Frontal (FR)	Jugal	Mesethmoid
Parietal (PA)	Quadratojugal	*Sensory Capsule Elements*
Postparietal (PP)	Lower jaw series	Otic
Posttemporal (PT)	Dentary (D)	Epiotic (EOT)
Orbital Series	Coronoid (COR)	Prootic (POT)
Antorbital (ANT)	Prearticular (PAR)	Sphenotic (SPO)
Prefrontal (PEF)	Surangular (SANG)	Opisthotic
Lacrimal (LA)	Angular (ANG)	Optic
Infraorbital (IO)	Splenial	Sclerotic ring
Postfrontal (POF)	Postsplenial	Olfactory
Postorbital (PO)		Turbinals (Restricted to
Temporal Series		mammals)
Intertemporal		
Supratemporal (ST)	**Neurocranium**	**Splanchnocranium**
Squamosal	*Occipital Elements*	*Mandibular Arch*
Opercular Series	Supraoccipital (1)	Upper jaw
Preopercular (POP)	(Restricted to	Palatoquadrate (PQ),
Opercular (OP)	amniotes)	cartilaginous
Subopercular (SOP)	Exoccipital (EO)	Entopterygoid (ENPT)
Interopercular (IOP)	Basioccipital (BO)	Metapterygoid (MPT)
Ventral Roofing Elements	*Posterior Sphenoid*	Quadrate (Q)
Median Series	*Elements*	Lower jaw
Parasphenoid (1)	Basisphenoid (1)	Mentomeckelian (MM)
Prevomerine	Laterosphenoid (LSP)	Meckel's cartilage (MC)
Pterygoid	*Anterior Sphenoid*	Articular (AR)
Lateral Series	*Elements*	
Palatine (PAL)	Orbitosphenoid (OS)	**Splanchnocranium**
Ectopterygoid (EPT)	Presphenoid (1)	*Hyomandibular Arch*
		Hyomandibular (HYM)
		Ceratohyal (CH)

In the earliest osteichthyian fish, the dermocranial series was composed of numerous small bony elements. There was a tendency in both the sarcopterygian and actinopterygian lines to reduce the number and increase the size of the elements. This reduction was accomplished by loss and fusion of ossification centers, and the resulting dermocranium was sturdier because it had fewer sutures.

The reduction trend continued in the tetrapods, with the entire opercular series being lost early in their evolution. The number of elements, especially in the rostral, orbital, and mandibular series, decreased; the lower jaw went from approximately seven elements in early amphibians to a single element in mammals; and the orbital and rostral series did likewise. The primitive condition of dermocranial elements enclosing the neurocranial ones was gradually replaced by interdigitation and interlocking of neurocranial and dermocranial elements. Initially bones of both the mandibular and palatal series bore teeth, but with few exceptions the amniotes have teeth only on the elements of the mandibular series. In the amphibians the internal nares open directly into the buccal cavity. The elements of the palatal and mandibular series of amniotes tend to form a ventral shelf of bone on the dermocranium. This shelf, the secondary palate, reaches its greatest development in crocodiles, birds, and mammals, although it is present to a lesser degree in other reptiles such as sea turtles. Its taxonomic distribution indicates that it arose independently several times.

Electric Organs
Convergence is nowhere more striking than in the evolution of electric organs in fish. Electric organs are found in six unrelated families of fish, two families of chondrichthyian fish and four teleostean. In all fish the electric organ is composed of a large number of disc-like cells, electroplates, arranged in columns. Each electroplate is a multinucleated cell embedded in a thick extracellular gelatinous coat, and both are enclosed in a connective tissue sheath. During discharge, each electroplate generates a small voltage, 150 millivolts. The dorsal surface of each electroplate is positive, the ventral surface negative. Because electroplates are stacked in a column, the current passes dorsally as batteries arranged in a series. The columns discharge in parallel. In the electric eel, the total discharge may reach a maximum of 500 volts; however, the discharge in most electric fish is much lower. [10]

Although electric organs are strikingly similar histologically (histological differences do exist), they are, owing to the wide variety of locations and origins (Figure 6-21), clearly convergent organs. In all electric fish except the African catfish, *Electrophorus,* the organ is derived from muscle tissue and occurs in place of muscle bundles. Extrinsic eye muscles, branchiomeric, epaxial or hypaxial muscles, may give rise to electric organs, and thus the organ may be cranial or caudal, dorsal or ventral (Figure 6-21). The electric organ of *Electrophorus* lies between the integument and the axial musculature. Since no muscle bundles are replaced by the electric organ and the axillary gland is absent in *Electrophorus,* the electric organ is thought to be a derivative of the axillary gland. Strangely enough, no one has investigated the embryology of the electric organ in *Electrophorus.*

The protective function of a 500-volt discharge or even of a fifty-volt discharge can easily be realized. But how does such an organ evolve from

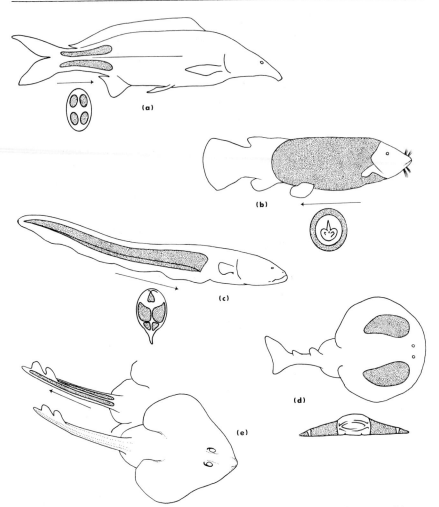

Figure 6-21. The location of electric organs in some electric fish: (a) *Mormyrus*; (b) *Malapterurus*; (c) *Electrophorus*; (d) *Torpedo*; (e) *Raja*. (After Grundfest.)

muscle tissue that is capable of producing a discharge registered only in millivolts? What is the function of an electric organ that produces a discharge of less than a volt, the discharge of most electrical fish? The answer to the last question has only recently been discovered. With this discovery, the probable evolutionary steps in the development of electric organs as a protective device are also suggested. Experiments have shown that fish, for example *Gymnarchus niloticus* with weak discharges, enclose themselves in a weak electrical field. This field definitely does not act as a shield against predators but as a perception field. Any object in or entering the field causes an irregularity of the field and thus can be detected by the fish. Just as we have a visual perception, the fish, no doubt, has an "electrical" perception that enables it to recognize prey or predator. The selective advantage of such a mechanism is apparent.

If we are to understand the evolution of this new mode of perception, we must remember that the electric organ produces only signals and does not act as a receptor. The lateral line system was originally thought to be the receptor and the discovery of electroreceptors in the lateral line proves it. Electric perception is analogous to the radar of bats or the sonar of porpoises. The signal is produced, received, and interpreted by the individual fish. It is intrinsic rather than extrinsic perception; the signal is not produced by an external source, only modified by it.

References for
Chapter 6

[1] Gray, J., *Animal Locomotion.* London: Weidenfeld & Nicolson, 1968, 479 pp. Discusses the mechanics of locomotion.

[2] "Symposium on Vertebrate Locomotion." *Am. Zool.,* **2** (1962), 127-208.

[3] Clark, R. B., *Dynamics in Metazoan Evolution.* Oxford: Clarendon Press, 1964, 313 pp. Chapter 5 discusses the origin of chordate locomotion.

[4] Nursal, J. R., "The Lateral Musculature and the Swimming of Fish." *Proc. Zool. Soc. London,* **126** (1956), 27-43.

[5] Schaeffer, B., "Osteichthyian Vertebrae." *J. Linn. Soc. London,* **47** (1967), 185-195.

[6] Williams, E. E., "Gadow's Arcualia and the Development of Tetrapod Vertebrae." *Quart. Rev. Biol.,* **34** (1959), 1-32.

[7] Hughes, G. M., *Comparative Physiology of Vertebrate Respiration.* Cambridge: Harvard Univ. Press, 1963, 145 pp.

[8] "Symposium on Evolution and Dynamics of Vertebrate Feeding Mechanisms." *Am. Zool.,* **1** (1961), 177-234.

[9] "Symposium on The Vertebrate Ear." *Am. Zool.,* **6** (1966), 368-466.

[10] Keynes, R. D., "Electric Organs" M. E. Brown (ed.), *The Physiology of Fish."* New York: Academic Press, 1957, pp. 323-343.

7

Digestion and nutrition

Like the epidermis, cells which line the gastrointestinal tract have direct encounter with the external world. A major function of the epidermis of most vertebrates (amphibians excepted) is to limit strictly the entry of chemical substances and parasitic organisms from the outside, while permitting egress from the body of specialized secretions (slime, oil, sweat, and so on). In striking contrast, the major function of the epithelium of the digestive tract is to facilitate the entry of a wide range of chemical substances into the body. This is not an easy task. It involves the formation of enzyme-containing secretions needed for the chemical breakdown of food materials. Often it must be supported by the mechanical breakdown of food objects, and transfer processes are needed to bring nutrients into suitable relationship to the surfaces where entry takes place. Various self-protective devices are present which, in general, limit to a certain extent the ingress of harmful substances and invading organisms.

The digestive system also has other, somewhat less conspicuous, roles. It removes undesirable substances from the body through the excretory processes of the liver and the mechanical egestion of food materials taken in but undigested. Relatively large masses of bacteria and of dead cells lost from the walls of the digestive tract itself are also discarded. As will be noted later, the tract contains structures important for a wide range of additional important bodily functions—search for and selection of food, self-defense, respiration, reproduction, and kidney excretion—through activities of some of its specialized regions (*buccal cavity, pharynx, aboral intestine, cloaca*).

The structures of vertebrate gastrointestinal systems reflect the variety and complexity of their functions. In all vertebrates digestive tracts include spaces (e.g., stomach, intestinal chambers) where ingested food materials are subjected to enzyme-catalyzed reactions that break them down to individual molecules. These processes depend on formation by secretory cells of fluids that contain a range of enzymes and ions dissolved in water. The secretory cells exist individually in the epithelium or are grouped into glandular organs (including the pancreas and the massive liver in all vertebrates, and salivary glands in most vertebrates except fish). In some of the digestive chambers micro-organisms flourish, and there break down nutrients by enzymatic reactions that supplement the effects of the animal's own enzymes. Such microbial processes are exploited to a particularly high degree in ruminant mammals.

There are relatively huge surface absorptive areas across which exchanges occur from the luminal environment within the digestive tract, but still outside the epithelial boundaries of the body, to the neighboring blood stream. These absorptive areas, lying chiefly in the intestines, are characterized by a single epithelial cell layer with rich underlying meshes of blood and lymph capillaries. The transfer of materials across this cellular layer is partly passive—by diffusion from the gastrointestinal lumen—and partly by active, energy-requiring processes within the cells themselves.

The mechanical breakdown of food materials and the transfer of nutrients depend chiefly on the specialized muscles built into or associated with the digestive system (Figure 7-1). Ciliated surfaces play some part in transfer, too, especially in lower vertebrates. Characteristically, secretory cells in the

Figure 7-1. Diagram representing some features of the digestive tract of vertebrates. The tubular structure (gut) varies greatly in different animals, and in any one animal from one part to another, in shape (e.g., expanded stomach chamber, narrow intestinal region), function, pattern of lining epithelium and glands, etc. Some features which are quite generally found include: (1) The *tunica mucosa*, an inner lining of epithelial cells underlaid by connective tissue. The mucosa may be deeply folded, or modified by the presence of many special processes, *villi*. The epithelial cells of the mucosa secrete a variety of substances (water, salts, mucus, enzymes), and also carry on the absorptive activities of the intestine. (2) The *tunica submucosa* is a connective tissue layer under the mucosa. It may contain complex glands with ducts leading to the mucosal surface. (3) *Muscle* layers, made up of smooth muscle cells, are usually arrayed in part along the circumference and in part along the major axis of the gut (circular and longitudinal muscles), although other arrangements of muscle cells may occur as well. In general, contraction of the muscle cells in the circular layer results in narrowing and lengthening of the gut segment, while contraction of the longitudinal muscle cells shortens the gut segment. (4) A delicate sheath, the *serosa*, covers the digestive tract when the tract lies free in the body cavity. In those conditions, the gut is attached to the wall of the body cavity by the thin, sheet-like mesentery traversed by large blood and lymph vessels, and by nerves. Rich nets of blood vessels, lymph vessels (except in cyclostomes and elasmobranchs), and nerves lie in and between the connective tissue and muscle cell layers.

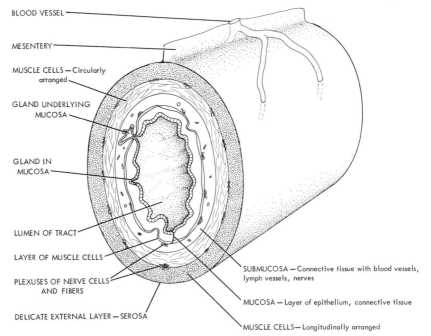

BLOOD VESSEL

MESENTERY

MUSCLE CELLS — Circularly arranged

GLAND UNDERLYING MUCOSA

GLAND IN MUCOSA

LUMEN OF TRACT

LAYER OF MUSCLE CELLS

PLEXUSES OF NERVE CELLS AND FIBERS

DELICATE EXTERNAL LAYER — SEROSA

SUBMUCOSA — Connective tissue with blood vessels, lymph vessels, nerves

MUCOSA — Layer of epithelium, connective tissue

MUSCLE CELLS — Longitudinally arranged

epithelium form *mucus*, a slimy, often quite complex protein-containing fluid that plays an important part in lubricating the nutrient masses in transit and in protecting the delicate epithelia from mechanical and chemical damage.

There is provision for storage in all vertebrate digestive systems. More or less unworked food materials can be held in distensible esophagi or stomachs (most vertebrates), *crops* (expanded chambers in the esophagi of many birds) or skin-lined cheek pouches (some mammals). Molecular-sized nutrients (e.g., glycogen, iron, some fats, and vitamins) are stored in various places—chiefly in the liver. Ingested material that has been thoroughly worked over in upper areas of the tract may be stored in the aboral part of the intestine or in the cloaca, pending completion of water absorption and an appropriate time for its expulsion from the body as feces.

Thus, a complex of basic processes—ingestion, digestion (chemical breakdown), absorption, mechanical transfer, self-protection, excretion, and egestion—are carried out by all vertebrate digestive systems in closely integrated patterns. The fundamental origin of the patterning is the structure of the tract itself, with its supporting vascular systems (blood, lymph). This structural organization is modulated and supplemented by sensitive responses of the individual epithelial and muscle cells of the tract and by adaptive nervous and endocrine control. The overall patterning may be visualized best, perhaps, by reviewing in some detail the form and function of the relatively simple digestive systems of amphibians. Following this, variations and adaptive mechanisms in members of the other vertebrate classes will be noted more briefly.

Digestive Systems of Amphibians: *Necturus maculosus*

Figure 7-2 shows some characteristic features in the anatomy of the urodele amphibian, *Necturus maculosus*. Typically in amphibians the opening of the mouth into the buccal cavity is surrounded by epidermally lined lips. Small, conical teeth are set along the margins of the jaws, and sometimes also in additional rows or groups on the roof of the mouth (Figure 7-3). These function chiefly in holding the slippery, squirming organisms that are the typical prey of amphibians. Generally there is a muscular tongue attached to the floor of the mouth that aids in securing nutritive material and guiding it into the pharynx. An especially interesting tongue structure occurs in anuran amphibians (frogs, toads). The tongue is attached only at its anterior region. It can be flicked out of the mouth to trap a flying insect, then quickly retracted by contraction of its muscles to bring the prey back with it into the buccal cavity. In the roof of the mouth are the respiratory openings or internal nares (*choanae*). Thus in amphibians, as in some fish and all higher vertebrates, a common channel through the buccal cavity leads to the respiratory and digestive organs.

In most amphibians, much of the buccal cavity is lined with ciliated epithelium. Beating continuously in the direction of the pharynx, the cilia carry particles of food and secretions toward the aboral region of the tract. There are numerous mucus-secreting cells in the epithelium lining the mouth cavity. Larger and more complex salivary glands lie adjacent to the buccal cavity and their ducts open into it. Richly supplied with blood vessels, like the buccal mucosa itself, these glands are capable of secreting large amounts of fluid. They are absent in some aquatic amphibians, and it is inferred that their chief role in terrestrial forms is to provide the fluid that is so helpful in swallowing food. Amphibian salivary glands may also produce starch-splitting enzymes, the importance of which is doubtful as most digestion of carbohydrates and other food components occurs in the intestine. By complicated muscular contractions involving the tongue and the floor of the mouth, ingested food is thrust into the pharynx. This is an expanded chamber, lined with ciliated, multi-layered and mucus-secreting epithelium, which leads into the next part of the digestive system (the esophagus), and also carries air to the lungs. During swallowing, the transit of food into the lungs is prevented by muscular contractions that close off the glottis, the entryway into the lungs (Chapter 8).

From the pharynx, food passes into the *esophagus*, a relatively short, thin-walled tube lined with ciliated, stratified epithelium. Scattered gland cells in

Figure 7-2. *Necturus maculosus* (a) is an aquatic, tailed (urodele) amphibian possessing both lungs and external gills as respiratory organs. The digestive tract in *Necturus* is structured in a manner which is fairly representative of the amphibians in general. It is shown in ventral view in (b) (the lower surface of the body, including the lower jaw and ventral wall of the pharynx, have been removed).

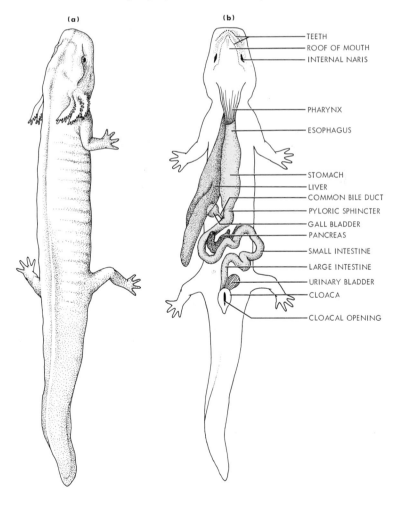

(a)

(b)

TEETH
ROOF OF MOUTH
INTERNAL NARIS

PHARYNX
ESOPHAGUS

STOMACH
LIVER
COMMON BILE DUCT
PYLORIC SPHINCTER
GALL BLADDER
PANCREAS
SMALL INTESTINE
LARGE INTESTINE
URINARY BLADDER
CLOACA
CLOACAL OPENING

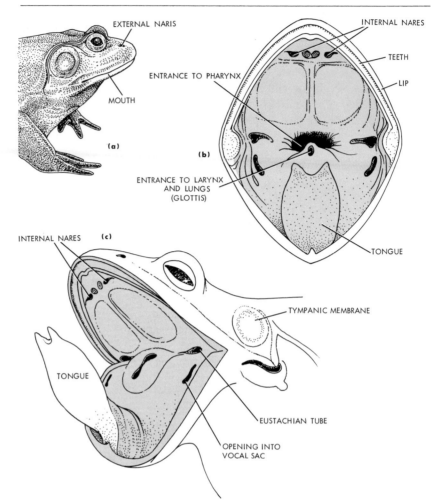

Figure 7-3. The structure of the mouth in representative anuran amphibians: (a) head of the frog *Rana catesbiana*; (b) mouth of the frog *Rana catesbiana*, opened to show structure; (c) mouth of the frog *Rana esculenta*, open mouth seen from side to show tongue attachment. [Parts (a) and (b) are modified from Dickerson; part (c) is from Bolk.]

the mucosa form mucus and proteins that can change to proteolytic enzymes (pepsinogens). Layers of muscle cells in the wall contract rhythmically in waves that move toward the stomach (this contractile pattern is termed peristalsis). Food in the esophagus travels with these peristaltic waves and generally cannot go back into the mouth because the esophagus has a thick band of circularly arranged muscle cells (a *sphincter*) at its junction with the pharynx. By contracting, this can effectively close off the route back into the upper part of the tract. Once the food mass has reached the stomach, it is restrained from re-entering the esophagus by contraction of a second sphincter at the junction between the esophagus and stomach. In passing, it may be noted that such sphincters, muscular structures guarding entry or exit at particular regions of the tract, are important features of all vertebrate digestive systems.

The stomach of amphibians is an expanded chamber of a simple, long spindle-shape in *Necturus* and other urodeles, and of similar form though often wider and somewhat curved in the shorter-bodied anurans. Here the food mass is retained and flooded with gastric juice secreted by the epithelial lining and the organized glands of the wall. At the aboral end of the stomach is the pyloric sphincter, which can contract and effectively seal off the stomach from the adjacent intestine. Much of the time, while digestion proceeds, this sphincter is indeed closed. From time to time, in correlation with waves of contraction sweeping over the stomach walls, it relaxes and allows the passage of some gastric contents into the upper intestine. At this point it may be well to consider more specifically the role of the stomach. In amphibians and other vertebrates with stomachs (later it will be noted that in some groups of fish the stomach is absent) this organ appears to have a major common function: the maintenance of collected food materials and their regulated supply to the dominant digestive-absorptive organ, the intestine. This storage function is correlated, in almost all normal vertebrates, with the secretion of gastric juice rich in hydrochloric acid. It has been inferred that the original role of this strongly acid gastric secretion may have been to prevent bacterial action on nutrients in the stomach. This is especially important in vertebrates which store food in the stomach for relatively long periods of time (from one to several days in fish, amphibians, and reptiles). At the same time, the low pH is important in protein digestion. This is another function of the stomach, inferred by some zoologists to be a more recent innovation in evolution. For, in addition to hydrochloric acid and the ubiquitous mucus, gastric secretory cells form *pepsinogens* which quickly turn into proteolytic enzymes (pepsins) on egress from cells and exposure to acid. Optimally active at the low pH of the stomach contents, pepsins catalyze the breakdown of proteins in the ingested food materials. Generally, considerable protein digestion has occurred by the time the gastric contents are ejected from the aboral (pyloric) region of the stomach into the oral region of the small intestine.

In *Necturus* and other urodele amphibians, the small intestine is a short, somewhat coiled tube with a relatively narrow diameter (Figure 7-2). It tends to be longer and more coiled in anurans. The mucosa lining its walls is folded or ridged in patterns that vary from one species to another but always functions to increase its active surface area. Sometimes the surface shows multiple tiny, finger-like extensions, each termed a *villus*. Within the villi, ridges, and folds, and everywhere else under the surface, are rich networks of blood and lymph capillaries. Lining the surface are cells of characteristic fine structure, with membranes facing the intestinal lumen, that are modified to increase surface area by the formation of myriad tiny projections, or *microvilli* (Figure 7-4). These give the impression of "striation" commonly seen at the magnification of the light microscope. Mucus-secreting cells and simple glands are present as well. Into the small intestine lead ducts from the *gall bladder* and pancreas, bringing bile from the liver and pancreatic juice from the pancreas. With the intermittent contractions of the muscles of the intestinal walls, the material within the intestinal lumen is thoroughly mixed with the variety of enzymes, bile salts, ions, and secretions of the intestine, liver and pancreas, and digestion is carried nearly to completion.

At the same time, nutrients and components of the mixture traverse the epithelial lining of the intestine into the tissue spaces, and from there into the blood and lymph vessels underlying the epithelium.

Beyond the small intestine the contents are moved by contractions of the muscular walls into the short, wide-bored large intestine. Here digestion continues and may be supplemented by bacterial decomposition. Absorption of water and salts condenses the gut contents, conserving these valuable inorganic constituents. It is not known whether absorption of organic materials also occurs in the large intestine of amphibians, but in general such absorption is not a function of this region of the digestive tract of vertebrates.

Finally, moving from the large intestine the now useless remnants of the ingesta—fragmented chitinous skeletons of insects, undigested bones and skin of small vertebrates, cellulose fibers from plants, bacteria, bits of dead cells—enter the cloaca. The cloaca is a short, broad chamber with connections from the ureters, reproductive system, and the urinary bladder, as well as from the major inlet from the large intestine. Through its single orifice, the egesta of the digestive tract (feces) as well as sperm, ova, and urine gain exit from the body.

The liver, as shown in Figure 7-2, is a large gland of somewhat irregular form, lying along the stomach and upper part of the intestine. Into it, through the hepatic portal vein, flows the venous blood draining the absorptive surfaces of the intestine. This blood traverses a vast series of irregular channels lying among and in intimate proximity to the liver cells (Figure 7-5). Newly absorbed nutrients pass from the blood into the liver cells, there to be reprocessed (as in the synthesis of blood proteins from absorbed amino acids by liver cells) or stored (as in the deposition of liver glycogen, formed in part from glucose absorbed from the intestine). Some of the nutrients bypass the liver cells, of course, and travel through the great hepatic veins toward the heart, from there to be distributed throughout the body. The liver cells also form the special secretion, *bile*. This contains components of importance in the overall digestive process: bile salts that aid in the attack of enzymes on fats, various ions, and water. It should be mentioned, too, that bile formation participates in the process of excretion (this major regulatory

Figure 7-4 (opposite). (a) In cross-section, the small intestine of the amphibian *Amphiuma* (photomicrograph, enlargement 225×) shows deep folds of the inner surface lining the lumen. This inner surface is a layer of lightly staining epithelial cells, where much of the production of enzymes takes place. Mucus is formed here too, and absorption of water, salts, and nutrients occurs across the luminal boundary of the cells.

(b) A small section of the intestinal wall of *Amphiuma* is shown in a micrograph, magnified 442×. The luminal surface shows a characteristic *brush border*. Several specialized cells may be seen in the process of discharging large masses of mucus into the intestinal lumen.

(c) Further details of the amphibian intestinal cell are indicated in this diagram derived from electron micrographs of amphibian intestinal tissue. The brush borders, when seen at high magnification, prove to consist of great numbers of fine processes, *microvilli*. At very high magnification these are seen to be embedded in and covered by a surface coat which is thought to have a protective function. Within the cell lie characteristic structures important in absorption and in synthesis of digestive enzymes, e.g., smooth and rough endoplasmic reticulum, Golgi apparatus, and numerous vacuoles.

The histological material shown in (b) was made available through the kindness of Mrs. Deborah Christensen.

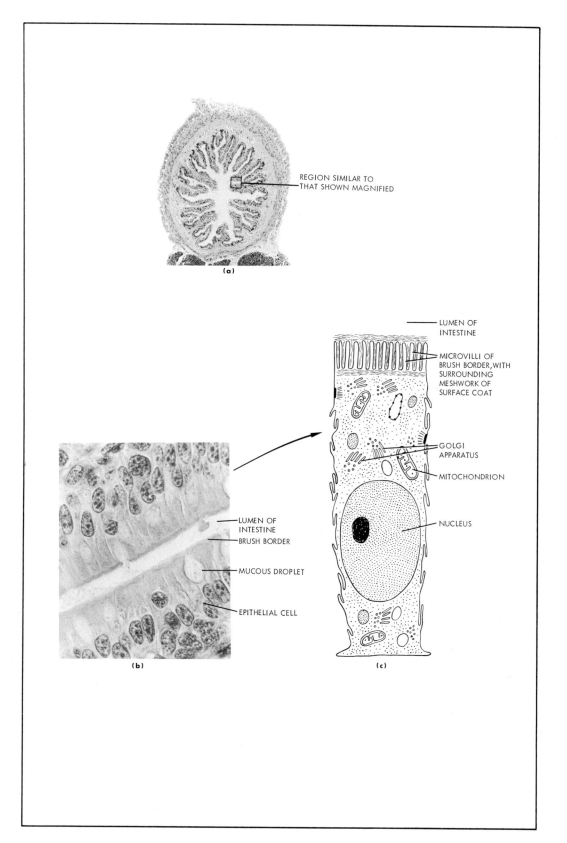

REGION SIMILAR TO
THAT SHOWN MAGNIFIED

(a)

LUMEN OF
INTESTINE

MICROVILLI OF
BRUSH BORDER, WITH
SURROUNDING
MESHWORK OF
SURFACE COAT

GOLGI
APPARATUS

MITOCHONDRION

NUCLEUS

LUMEN OF
INTESTINE
BRUSH BORDER

MUCOUS DROPLET

EPITHELIAL CELL

(b)

(c)

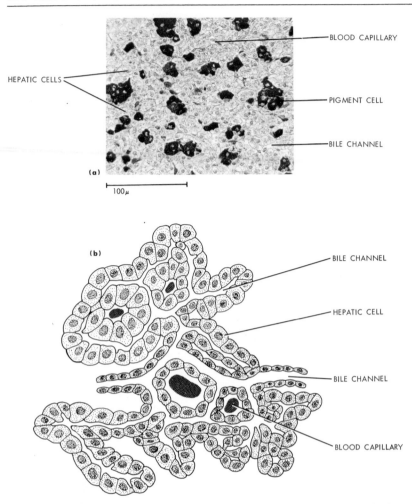

BLOOD CAPILLARY

HEPATIC CELLS

PIGMENT CELL

BILE CHANNEL

(a)

100μ

(b)

BILE CHANNEL

HEPATIC CELL

BILE CHANNEL

BLOOD CAPILLARY

Figure 7-5. Detail of structure of the amphibian liver. (a) Photomicrograph (96×) of a section of liver of *Amphiuma*, showing dense arrangement of hepatic and pigment cells. Numerous blood and bile channels can be distinguished among the hepatic cells. (Histological material prepared by Deborah Christensen.) (b) Redrawing of a classic illustration by Eberth, showing details of the arrangement of cells and blood and bile channels of the liver of a frog.

function will be discussed more fully in Chapter 9). Thus liver cells extract from the blood and secrete into the bile certain waste organic compounds, for instance, breakdown products of hemoglobin metabolism (bile pigments). Traveling from the liver to the intestine, these compounds then move down the digestive tract and eventually are discarded from the body.

As bile is formed it accumulates in special channels, bile capillaries, which lie among the liver cells in patterns roughly parallel to, but separate from, the blood capillaries. The secretion then passes from the bile capillaries into larger and larger ducts, finally into the hepatic duct leading out of the liver. Shortly after emerging from the liver, the hepatic duct joins a second duct (cystic duct) from the gall bladder, a spherical storage chamber for bile. The duct emerging from the confluence of the hepatic and cystic ducts (common bile duct) leads to the intestine (Figure 7-2). The mechanisms of the verte-brate gall bladder and bile ducts have been studied fully only in the case of mammals. It seems, however, that the system may function similarly in other classes, since the general structure and the functions of bile appear to be closely parallel among vertebrates. Even the lack of a gall bladder in certain birds and mammals is not a major exception to the generality of bile pro-cessing, since the absence can be interpreted as an adaptation to the special dietary patterns of these animals. In any case, for lack of adequate studies on amphibians, most of the rest of this account of bile formation and transport must be based on observations of mammals but with the impli-cation that it is relevant to amphibians as well. At the junction between the common bile duct and the intestine, a specialized array of smooth muscle cells acts as a sphincter. This is of functional importance, since contraction of these muscles (closure of the sphincter) blocks the flow of bile into the intestine and thus forces bile back into the gall bladder where it is stored. While in the bladder the bile may be concentrated and changed in composi-tion by activities of the cells of the bladder wall. When partially digested food (especially if rich in fatty materials) enters the duodenum, hormonal and nervous stimuli act on the gall bladder and sphincter. Bile is driven out, by contraction of bladder muscles, through the common bile duct and the now opened sphincter into the intestine. As a whole, these structures—bile ducts, gall bladder, and sphincter—provide a means of supplying bile to the intestine in close correlation with digestive demands.

The pancreas is an irregularly-shaped gland, far smaller than the liver, yet conspicuous as it lies close to the small intestine (Figure 7-2). In amphibians, as in other vertebrates, it is made up of cellular structures, the *acini*, of a tubular or roughly spherical shape (Figure 7-6). The pancreatic cells that form each acinus lie in close association with a rich capillary network and produce a large volume of secretion which is poured into an associated duct system. The secretion contains enzymes capable of attacking organic compounds of all the major classes occurring in food. Besides these specific chemical agents, mucus, water, and ions (including bicarbonate ions, important in the adjustment of intestinal pH) make up the pancreatic secretion. Each acinus opens into a tiny duct; the ducts converge, then join larger ducts until, at last, they form the main pancreatic duct (or ducts—more than forty-five are found in individuals of some amphibian species). Besides its conspicuous digestive role, the pancreas functions as an endocrine gland. Special cell masses, termed islets (or *islets of Langerhans*), form blood-borne hormones of great importance in metabolic control. This point will be discussed further in Chapter 12.

The pancreas, like the liver and in fact the entire stomach and intestine, is attached by a *mesentery*, a thin, transparent tissue sheet to the body wall. Within this travel the nerves and the blood and lymphatic vessels. Embryo-logically, the mesenteries arise from the lining of the coelom, but they are expanded and modified in shape and attachment to the body wall with the growth and final assumption of the adult form of the tract and its associated glands.

The entire gastrointestinal tract is richly supplied with arteries. These will be described in more detail in Chapter 8. The vascular supply is important

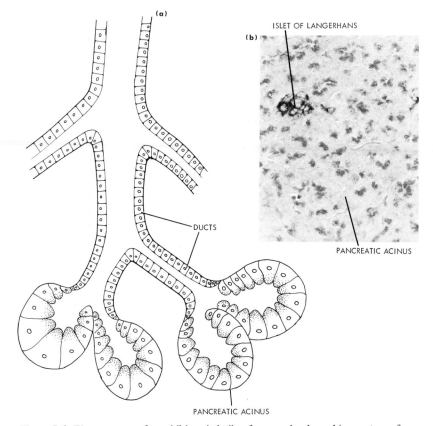

Figure 7-6. The pancreas of amphibians is built of a complex branching system of cellular ducts leading into acini where the secretion is formed. This is diagrammed in (a). (b) is a photomicrograph (magnification 224X) of pancreatic tissue of the toad *Bufo bufo*, stained to show the endocrine tissue (islets of Langerhans) and secretory granules of the exocrine tissue of the pancreas (acini). (Histological material kindly supplied by Dr. August Epple.)

because of the high energy demands of the secretory, absorptive, and muscular activities of the tract. With the exception of its oral and aboral ends, the digestive system is drained through a special system of veins into the great *hepatic portal vein*, which leads to the liver. Thus it brings directly to the liver cells the venous blood heavily enriched with the many substances absorbed through the intestinal mucosa. In amphibians, as in some fish and all higher vertebrates, the intestinal surface is also drained by a second transport system, the complex of lymphatic vessels. Lymph capillaries under-lying the mucosal epithelium are the chief route of entry into the body of fatty materials. Lymph, often termed *chyle* when laden with fats during digestion, flows from the mucosa through lymphatics (*lacteals*, a name suggesting the milky appearance of the fat-rich chyle) of increasing size. These eventually reach the great lymph vessels (*cisternae chyli*, single or paired *thoracic ducts*) which, bypassing the liver, deliver lymph directly to the great veins draining into the heart.

Changing
Structure

It is of interest to consider the changing pattern of digestive tract structure through the course of the individual animal's life. The lining (epithelium and glands) of the digestive tract of *Necturus* and other amphibians originates embryologically from endoderm lining the *archenteron*. Only the most anterior and posterior sections of the tract (mouth, salivary glands, part of cloaca) have epithelia formed by inturning of the surface ectoderm. Thus, during development the archenteron lengthens and progressively takes on rudiments of form, with an expanded forechamber (pharynx), a narrower posterior section of the foregut, and a narrow hindgut region. From the body surface anteriorly a pit (*stomodeum*) deepens towards the pharynx. Subsequently this stomodeum becomes the buccal cavity. Where it fuses with the pharyngeal wall a membrane forms and then breaks down so that the buccal cavity opens directly into the pharynx, at which point there is a junction between ectoderm and endoderm. Similarly, at the posterior end of the body a surface pit (*proctodeum*) forms and deepens. Its ectoderm fuses with the hindgut and the membrane between them breaks through so that the gut opens directly into the proctodeum (differentiating as the cloaca) and through it to the outside. Surrounding the endodermal regions of the gut are mesodermal derivatives—muscles and connective tissue making up the bulk of the digestive system. Differential growth molds the tract into its characteristic form; accessory glands, which originally budded from the endoderm, grow to adult mass and function as liver and pancreas; and the definitive patterns of blood supply, gland secretion, and neural control are established.

In other vertebrates, too, the glandular and absortive surface is of endodermal origin, with much of the rest of the tract arising from mesoderm. The details of gastrointestinal development vary greatly among vertebrates, depending on the amount of yolk in the egg and the pattern of development characteristic of the particular vertebrate class (refer to Chapter 3). Often young vertebrates have patterns of digestive form and function quite different from those of adults of the same species. The most dramatic change is seen in fish and amphibians that have discrete larval and adult stages, separated by clear-cut processes of *metamorphosis*. For instance, the lamprey's larva (Ammocoete), feeding by a filtration process on algae, bacteria, and other tiny particles, changes into an active, predatory adult that attaches by a sucker to another organism (e.g., a teleost fish) and travels with it, rasping away at its flesh and sucking its blood. This transition involves complete reorganization of the mouth and pharyngeal region (Figure 7-7). The intestine lengthens, twists, and develops the characteristic folding of the internal surface. Both liver and pancreas undergo structural change. The process as a whole has been observed to occur rapidly—in the course of a few weeks in the case of the lamprey *Lampetra*, for instance. It is a straining and dangerous time of structural revolution, involving not only the digestive tract but the entire body as well. The anuran amphibians, frogs and toads, with aquatic, filter-feeding larvae (tadpoles), and terrestrial, carnivorous adults also show a dramatic change in gastrointestinal structure and activity at metamorphosis. The narrow, simple foregut of the larva changes into the esophagus and expanded stomach, the midgut shortens and widens as it becomes the adult intestine, and the surface and gland cells break down to be replaced by adult structures. In urodele larvae, though the general anatomy of the digestive tract is less drastically altered at metamorphosis, the surfaces and the glands undergo as thorough a cellular reorganization as they do in anuran amphibians. In other vertebrates, too, adjustments occur

Figure 7-7. (a) The simple digestive tract of the Ammocoete larva undergoes significant modification during relatively abrupt metamorphosis to the adult form [(b) and (c)]. Conspicuous adult features are the elaborate, "toothed," cup-shaped mouth apparatus, and the "tongue." In (b) the "tongue" has been removed to reveal the underlying structures, but it is shown in place, viewed from the side, in (c). A single passageway traverses the branchial region in the larva, whereas separated esophageal and branchial passages are seen in the adult [the branchial foregut wall has been slit lengthwise in (b) to reveal the more dorsal esophageal passageway]. The simple tubular midgut of the larva differs markedly from the adult's more elaborate intestine with spiral valve. [(a) and (b) redrawn from classic illustrations by Pernkopf; (c) from *Chordate Morphology*, by M. T. Jollie, copyright (C) 1962, by permission of Van Nostrand Reinhold Company.]

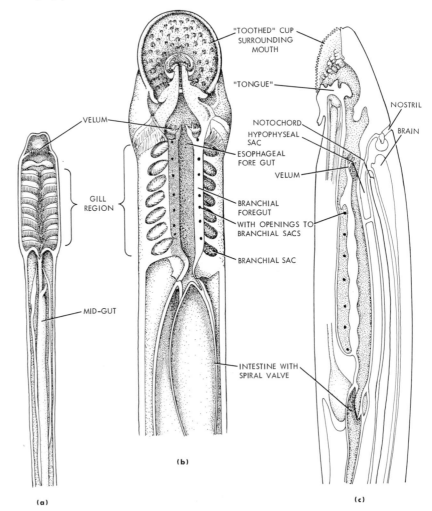

between young and adult life, but these generally are less striking and far reaching. Two specific cases may be cited. In some reptilian species, the dentition changes with age (immature *versus* adult animal), apparently in correlation with changing patterns of nutrition (e.g., insectivorous *versus* herbivorous habits). In mammals, the type of cellular enzymes formed by the stomach changes with maturation (predominance of infantile *rennin,* an enzyme specific for attacking milk protein, *versus* adult type *pepsin*).

Once growth has reached an advanced stage or is complete, the basic structure of the gastrointestinal tract generally shows little further change. In all vertebrates, however, the moment-by-moment form of the gut varies with the degree of distension of various chambers, and the intermittent, often rhythmic contractions of the muscular walls. Internally, the delicate mucosa is subject to continuous replacement of its cells. Unfortunately, very little is known about this process in nonmammalian vertebrates. In mammals, it has been studied extensively with estimates of the average lifetime of individual cells obtained from observations of average frequencies of mitosis or by the use of radioactive substances incorporated into the cellular structure. The cells of the buccal epithelium are replaced in the course of about 8.5 days (rabbit), and the stomach surface and gland cells in periods ranging from 6.5 to 1.8 days. The lining of the small intestine turns over relatively rapidly, with replacement times measured as approximately 1.4 to 2.8 days in various mammals. In view of these rapid cell replacement cycles, and the great energy demands placed on the intestinal mucosa in absorption of nutrients and formation of secretions, it is understandable that this structure is one of the most metabolically active of all mammalian tissues (details in other vertebrates are still few and far between). It is also one of the most sensitive to disease and damage, e.g., from starvation, ionizing radiations, and so on.

Digestive Systems of Fish   Turning now to a comparison of gastrointestinal tracts among different vertebrate classes, the most striking generalization to note, perhaps, is the basic similarity of plan among all vertebrates. The protochordates, too, show some striking features of their digestive apparatus in common with vertebrates. This may be appreciated best by reference to diagrams (Figure 7-8) of urochordate and cephalochordate digestive systems.

The cyclostomes have a relatively simple gastrointestinal system (Figure 7-7). The mouth is, of course, jawless, and is little more than a round opening into the pharynx. It may be surrounded externally by tentacles (as in the hagfish *Myxine*) or by a more elaborate, funnel-shaped "hood" (as in the lamprey *Petromyzon*). The latter may be studded with small, horny tooth-like projections containing keratin. It serves as a sucker, an organ of attachment to the lamprey's prey. At the entrance to the mouth is a muscular structure, often called a "tongue," carrying keratin "teeth." This is used to scrape or tear away at the dead or dying tissues of organisms (hagfish) or fish and other living prey (lampreys). Associated with the toothed tongue of lampreys are paired glands that secrete an anticoagulant substance into the host.

The pharynx of the hagfish has numerous (six to fourteen) gill openings on each side and, as is classically the case in vertebrates, it is shared by the respiratory and digestive systems. This sharing may have originated within the group of chordate animals by adaptation of the pharynx from its primary nutritive role to allow exploitation of its structure in respiration. Evidence for such a primary role of the pharynx and its mucus-secreting endostyle exists in the lamprey larva and in protochordates. The manner in which the pharynx operates in respiration and the structure of the gills will be considered in more detail in the next chapter. In lampreys, although the pharyngeal region participates in both feeding and respiration, the processes are structurally differentiated. Here, a shelf-like membrane develops in the pharyngeal region of the larva, dividing it into two adult structures—an upper esophagus (digestive) and a lower gill (respiratory) section.

In the simple tubular channel that follows the esophagus, there is nothing comparable with the stomach as described, for instance, in the case of amphibians. Zoologists generally infer that the primitive vertebrate ancestors were stomachless, like the cyclostomes of today. Gastric storage of nutrients would be of little adaptive value in jawless organisms feeding exclusively and more or less continuously on small particles—plankton, detritus, and the tissue and blood rasped and sucked from prey. Beyond the esophagus, the digestive tract is typically lined with a single-layered epithelium with many gland cells. Here the main secretory, enzymatic, and absorptive work of the digestive system is done. For part of its length the inner surface of the intestine shows a deep, longitudinal fold (sometimes called a *spiral valve*, or *typhlosole*) that functions to increase the active surface area of the tract. Beyond this region the intestine expands somewhat towards the posterior end of the body, then opens through a small orifice, the anus, into a cloacal groove, thence to the surface of the body. A well formed liver, with a gall bladder, is present. There are pancreatic cells, but these are not collected into a single digestive gland. Rather, they are found in scattered groups embedded in the walls of the intestine.

Among the jawed fish, sharp divergences are seen from the tract structure as it occurs in cyclostomes, and there is perhaps as much variation in the forms of digestive tracts among fish as in all other vertebrate classes (Figure 7-9). The mouth opening is framed by jaws that may carry teeth ranging in form from simple conical teeth through long, sharply pointed fangs to blunt, plate-like tools for crushing shells and other hard objects (Figure 7-10). These teeth may be restricted to the jaw margins, as in sharks, or occur grouped or in rows on the palate and the floor of the buccal cavity. In some teleosts, teeth arise from the bones of the gill arches in the pharynx. The mouth cavity of jawed fish is devoid of a tongue and glands comparable with the salivary glands of tetrapod vertebrates.

The pharynx, with its gill openings, shows marked variation in contour

Figure 7-8 (opposite). Digestive systems of representative protochordates. I(a) Diagram of an ascidian. The body wall and branchial sac have been cut away to show the position and structure of the digestive tract, and its relationship to the body apertures. Arrows indicate the direction of movement of fluid. (Modified from W. A. Herdman, *The Cambridge Natural History*, Vol. VII.) London: Macmillan and Company Ltd., 1922. I(b) Simplified diagram of an ascidian *Herdmania momus*. (Redrawn from Van Name, courtesy of the American Museum of Natural History.) II. Cephalochordate *Branchiostoma lanceolatum*, seen from the ventral view with part of the body wall removed. (Redrawn from Pernkopf.)

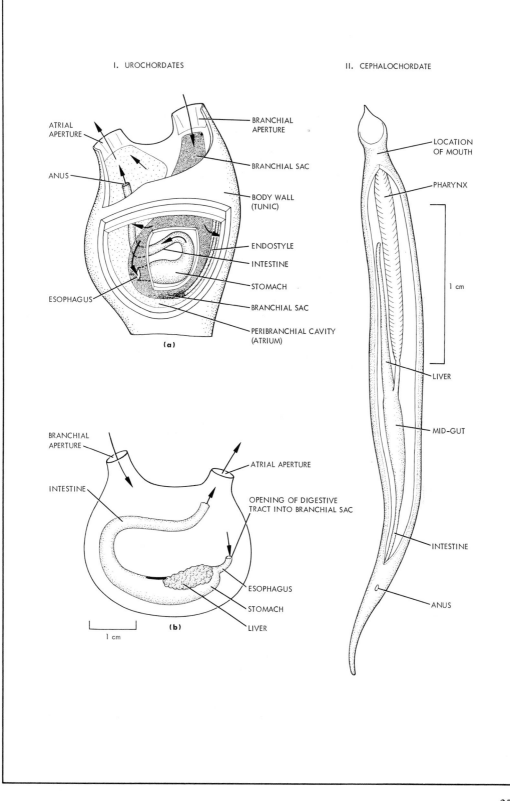

I. UROCHORDATES

ATRIAL
APERTURE

ANUS

ESOPHAGUS

BRANCHIAL
APERTURE

BRANCHIAL SAC

BODY WALL
(TUNIC)

ENDOSTYLE

INTESTINE

STOMACH

BRANCHIAL SAC

PERIBRANCHIAL CAVITY
(ATRIUM)

(a)

BRANCHIAL
APERTURE

INTESTINE

ATRIAL APERTURE

OPENING OF DIGESTIVE
TRACT INTO BRANCHIAL SAC

ESOPHAGUS

STOMACH

LIVER

1 cm

(b)

II. CEPHALOCHORDATE

LOCATION
OF MOUTH

PHARYNX

1 cm

LIVER

MID-GUT

INTESTINE

ANUS

257

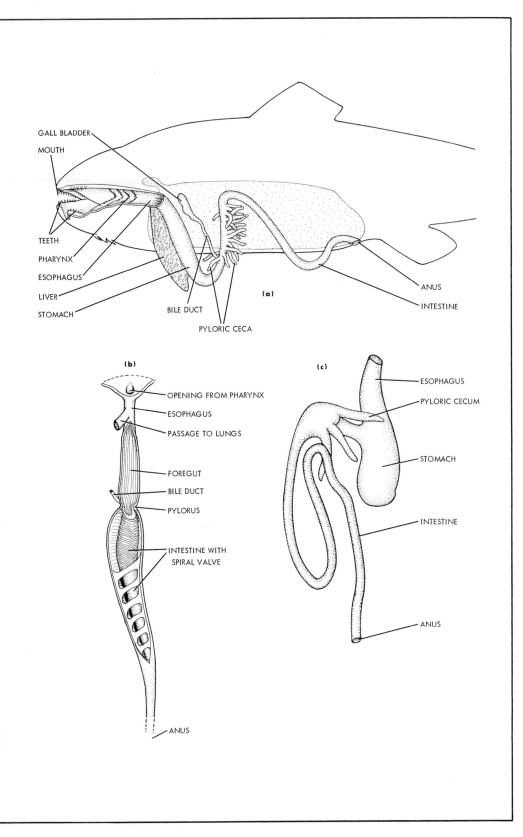

(a)

GALL BLADDER

MOUTH

TEETH

PHARYNX

ESOPHAGUS

LIVER

STOMACH

BILE DUCT

PYLORIC CECA

ANUS

INTESTINE

(b)

OPENING FROM PHARYNX

ESOPHAGUS

PASSAGE TO LUNGS

FOREGUT

BILE DUCT

PYLORUS

INTESTINE WITH
SPIRAL VALVE

ANUS

(c)

ESOPHAGUS

PYLORIC CECUM

STOMACH

INTESTINE

ANUS

(Chapter 8). The esophagus is a relatively short, simple tube lined with mucus-secreting cells, and it is often ciliated. Beyond it, in most fish groups, lies a stomach (Figure 7-9). This is reasonably interpreted as an evolutionary adaptation to the ability of these jawed vertebrates to capture and swallow, intact or in large pieces, other organisms of significant size. In a few groups (including lungfish and a few teleosts), however, there is no stomach. Because of the inferred close evolutionary relationships of these forms to animals with well developed stomachs, most zoologists agree that stomach-lessness in these exceptional fish is a secondary adaptation. The walls of the stomachs of fish are lined with secretory cells forming hydrochloric acid and pepsinogens.

Great variety exists in the external form and internal structure of the intestine among fish. Throughout there is a trend toward increasing surface area, either by elaboration of the internal surface, by increase in the length of the intestine, or by use of both of these structural devices. Where the intestine lengthens, it tends to coil back upon itself within the confined space of the body cavity. In many bony fish, elongate blind sacs—pyloric ceca—open from the intestine near its junction with the stomach. They vary in number from a few up to a thousand. In these ceca, as within the intestine itself, digestion and absorption take place. Of the various arrangements for increasing active intestinal surface, the internal elaboration and folding of the mucosa is thought to be most primitive, since it occurs in cyclostomes and elasmobranchs and rarely in fish considered more advanced from an evolutionary standpoint. Thus, elasmobranchs often have elaborate outfoldings of the intestinal mucosa, curving in a spiral valve about the inside of the tract. Sometimes such a spiral valve is coiled around upon itself so that it nearly fills the lumen of the intestine, offering a greatly expanded surface for secretion and absorption (Figure 7-11). By contrast, the spiral valve is absent in teleosts, but as in amphibians the intestine shows a trend towards increased length. Teleost intestines may be more than twice as long as the entire body, and lengthening is particularly notable in the case of her-bivorous fish. At least in part, this is believed to represent a functional adap-tation to the special problems of digestion of refractory plant materials. Comparable trends, originating independently, are seen in other vertebrate classes in which some forms adopted a diet of plant material (see, for instance, the discussion of mammalian digestive tracts later in this chapter).

The intestine opens into a wider large intestine (or a short terminal chamber, the *rectum*), which is similar to comparable structures in amphibians. The large intestine or rectum then leads into a cloaca (sharks) or directly to the

Figure 7-9 (opposite). Drawings showing some aspects of digestive systems of fish. (a) is an overall lateral view of the digestive tract of a teleost, *Salmo fario*. Note the structur-al arrangements for increasing the surface area of specific parts of the tract (pyloric ceca; intestine longer than body cavity). (b) the position of the spiral valve in the intestine of the dipnoan fish. *Protopterus annectens,* has been displayed by removal of the ventral wall of the gut. Note also the absence of a stomach in this fish. (c) shows further relative lengthening of the intestine, and large pyloric ceca in the teleost *Perca sp.* [Redrawn from classical illustrations by Parker and Haswell, (a); Pernkopf, (b); and Wiedersheim, (c). (a) and (c) from T. W. Bridge, "Fishes," in *Cambridge Natural History*, Vol. III. London: Macmillan and Co., 1922.]

(a)

(b)

28 cm

(c)

TEETH

10 cm

(d)

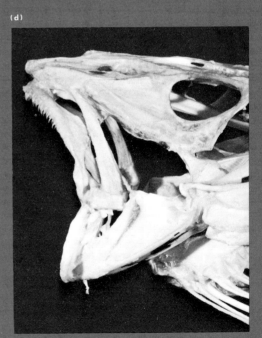

outside through a small anal opening (bony fish). The liver, with its gall bladder, is a large consolidated organ, and the pancreas is usually recognizable as a single glandular structure, although its tissue is scattered along the intestinal walls and in the mesenteries of a number of fish, including lungfish and some teleosts. There is also great variation in detail of form, duct structure, and blood supply of these digestive glands.

Digestive Systems of Reptiles and Birds

Reptiles resemble terrestrial anuran amphibians in many aspects of their gastrointestinal structure. The jaws are rimmed with teeth that usually are conical in form (teeth have disappeared in turtles). In some species the stomach is larger and considerably more elaborate than in amphibians (Figure 7-12). An example is the alligator's stomach, with a heavy-walled, muscular forechamber differentiated from a more delicate, aboral pyloric chamber. The large intestine, too, is often greater in size and complexity than that of amphibians. At the junction between the small and large intestines, there may be a sac-like extension of the large intestine. This *cecum* presumably functions to increase the overall volume and surface area of this part of the tract. In some reptiles, the cloaca at the termination of the digestive system, is found to be quite specialized. Partially separated cloacal chambers receive the egesta (*coprodeum*), urine and reproductive cells (*urodeum*). In common, these chambers lead into a terminal cloacal region and from there to the outside.

In birds, as might be expected from their unique exploitation of the possibilities of flight, the mass of machinery surrounding the mouth and in the buccal cavity is greatly reduced. Teeth, which were present in primitive birds (*Archeopteryx, Hesperornis*), are replaced functionally by horny beaks, as well as by other adaptations of the aboral gut (to be discussed later). As compared with other vertebrates and their toothed ancestors, modern birds show a general lightening and reduction of the jaws. The esophagus is relatively long and narrow, in correlation with the functional importance of the neck in these animals (Figure 7-13), and often there is an aboral region of great expansion to form a crop. Food can be stored here, a feature of adaptive value in birds with their exceptionally high energy demands for flight and the physiological control of body temperature.

The stomach of birds tends to be elaborate. It usually has an orally located section with delicate walls lined with secretory cells (*proventriculus*), and a more posterior section with heavy walls differentiated as a muscular grinding

Figure 7-10 (opposite). Great variety exists in the dentition of fish. (a) and (b) show views of the teeth of the carnivorous elasmobranch, the mako shark, *Isurus glaucus*. The sharply pointed teeth with wide bases are attached by connective tissue to the cartilaginous jaws. Many of the teeth shown would not be seen in the open mouth of the living animal, since they would be covered with the oral mucous membrane. They are replacement teeth, which progressively move into position along the jaw margins as older functional teeth are shed. (c) and (d) show dentition of a teleost, the cod *Gadus*. The teeth are fine and numerous, serving in the retention of captured prey (invertebrates, small fish) in the mouth. (Shark jaws prepared by Arthur D. Welander; cod skull obtained from Richard C. Snyder; photographs by Sigurd Olsen.)

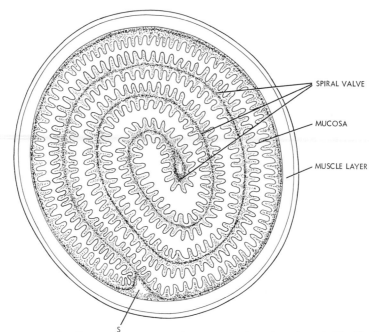

Figure 7-11. Cross-section through the intestine of an elasmobranch (*Scyllium*) showing the elaborate structure of the spiral valve, which folds away from the gut wall at S, and is wound upon itself to fill much of the space within the intestine (Redrawn from the classic illustration by Jacobshagen.)

organ. This thick-walled *gizzard* is of great importance in aiding mechanical breakdown of food prior to digestion. Needless to say the toothless bird is unable to use mouth-chewing in the preparation of food for digestion. Instead, strong contractions of the gizzard wall, often accompanied by the grinding action of small stones swallowed by the bird and lodged in this organ, provide the mechanical trituration necessary for subsequent extraction of nutrients from resistant food sources such as seeds and insects. The presence of the gizzard, like the loss of teeth, appears to be an important adaptation that serves to decrease the weight of the head. At the same time the trend towards aggregation of food storage functions in the thoracic and upper abdominal regions (in crop, proventriculus, and gizzard) may aid in adjusting the bird's center of gravity for special flight requirements.

Comparing the rest of the gastrointestinal tract of birds with the tract of reptiles, the observer is apt to be impressed most by the greater lengthening of the small intestine. In the bird, too, the tract is highly active, with rapid muscular movements and fast digestive processes correlated with high body temperature. At the junction between the small and large intestine elaborate

Figure 7-12 (opposite). (a) Drawing of the digestive system of a lizard, *Iguana sp*. The stomach is U-shaped, and in life it surrounds several loops of intestine, but in this illustration the intestine has been pulled away from the stomach so that its general form may be seen more clearly. The urinary bladder, which opens into the cloaca on its ventral aspect, is shown in outline. (b) shows the stomach of *Alligator mississippiensis* (redrawn from a classic illustration by Pernkopf).

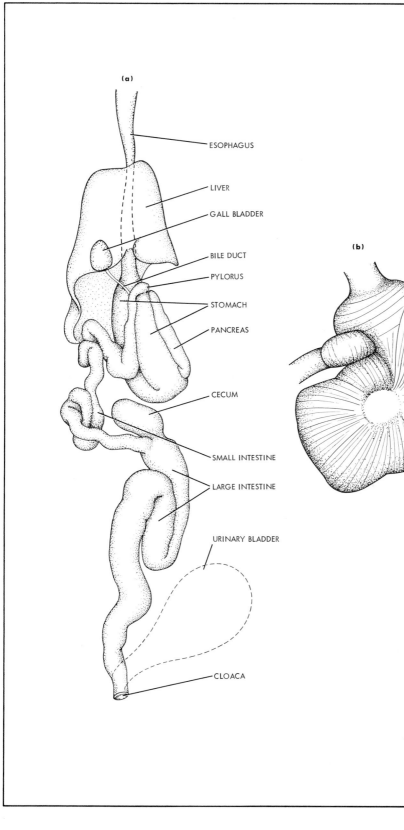

(a)

ESOPHAGUS

LIVER

GALL BLADDER

(b)

BILE DUCT

PYLORUS

STOMACH

PANCREAS

CECUM

SMALL INTESTINE

LARGE INTESTINE

URINARY BLADDER

CLOACA

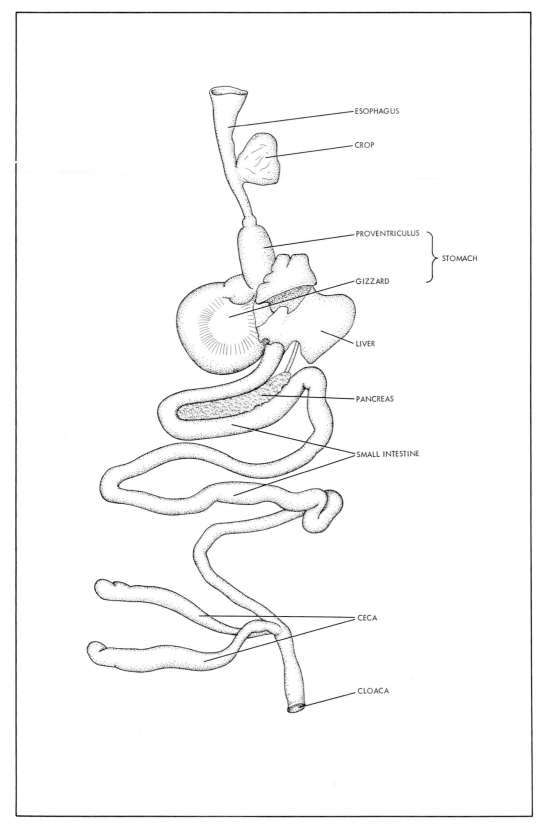

ESOPHAGUS

CROP

PROVENTRICULUS

STOMACH

GIZZARD

LIVER

PANCREAS

SMALL INTESTINE

CECA

CLOACA

264

Figure 7-13 (opposite). Digestive tract of a bird, the Japanese quail *Coturnix coturnix japonica*, seen from the ventral view. The liver has been pulled back to show details of the stomach structure, and the intestine and the ceca have been displaced from their normally compact arrangement in the abdominal cavity to show the length and continuity of these structures.

ceca may be found, although these are not present in some species, including hummingbirds and some pigeons. The pancreas and liver are generally similar to these organs in other vertebrates, although the gall bladder is sometimes absent. As in reptiles, the cloaca is differentiated into a coprodeum and urodeum. Especially in the coprodeum and adjacent regions of the aboral large intestine, water is reabsorbed from urine entering from the ureters and urodeum. This is significant in birds with physiological requirements for water conservation (see also Chapter 9).

Patterns of Dentition   Mammals differ strikingly from birds in the complexity and importance of the buccal cavity with its array of teeth. These latter may be elaborated into defensive or offensive weapons—*incisors*, fangs, and tusks—or be specialized for such functions as grinding leafy plant material (herbivores) or gnawing hard objects, i.e., chiefly wood (rodents, see Figure 7-14). At this point it may be well to review some major features of vertebrate dentition before proceeding in a brief survey of the teeth of mammals, for teeth are of great interest to comparative anatomists. They are durable structures that have contributed much to the study of paleontology. In a certain sense, teeth are conservative in form so the comparison and contrast between teeth in indi-

Figure 7-14 (next two pages). (a) Skull of a fox, *Urocyon*. On each side of the upper jaw, beginning most anteriorly, there are three small conical *incisor* teeth (I—two of these appear to be superimposed in this photograph); a long *canine* tooth (C); four *premolar* teeth (P); and two *molar* teeth (M) of more complex form. On each side of the lower jaw there are three incisor, one canine, four premolar, and three molar teeth. Anatomists describe dentition patterns of mammals by a series of numbers representing first the upper jaw (I-C-P-M) and then the lower jaw in a *dental formula* given in the form I-C-P-M/I-C-P-M. Thus, for this fox, the dental formula is 3-1-4-2/3-1-4-3.

(b) Drawing of a ground section (oriented in the plane tongue-cheek) of a human maxillary molar tooth. The roots are normally attached to the socket in the jaw bone by a special bony substance, *cementum*. (Redrawn from D. Permar, *Manual of Oral Embryology and Microscopic Anatomy*, 3rd edition, Philadelphia: Lea and Febiger, 1963, with the kind permission of Professor Permar and the publisher.)

(c) *Left:* A molar tooth of a horse, *Equus caballus*, showing elaborate patterning of enamel ridges. These function in the grinding of the plant material that makes up the horse's diet. *Right:* The skull and lower jaw of an insectivore, the Townsend mole *Scapanus townsendii*. The dental formula is 3-1-4-3/3-1-4-3. The teeth are relatively unspecialized in form. To appreciate this, compare the incisors with those of the nutria (f), the canines with the canine teeth of the bear (e), and the premolars and molars with those of the sheep (d). Note that the horse tooth and mole skull were photographed simultaneously, so their comparative sizes are represented accurately.

(d) Lower jaw and skull (seen from the palatal aspect) of an artiodactyl, the domestic sheep *Ovis aries*.

(e) Skull of the black bear *Euarctos americanus*.

(f) Skull of a rodent, the nutria *Myocastor coypu*.

(Skeletal material obtained from Richard C. Snyder. Photographs by Sigurd Olsen.)

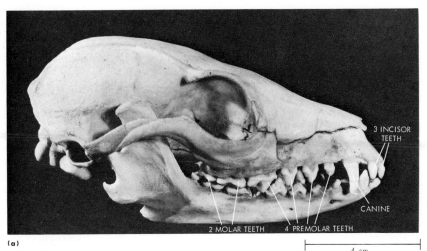

3 INCISOR TEETH

CANINE

2 MOLAR TEETH   4 PREMOLAR TEETH

(a)

4 cm

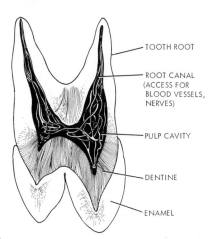

TOOTH ROOT

ROOT CANAL (ACCESS FOR BLOOD VESSELS, NERVES)

PULP CAVITY

DENTINE

ENAMEL

(b)

4 cm

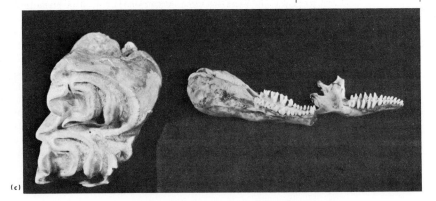

(c)

266

(d)

4 cm

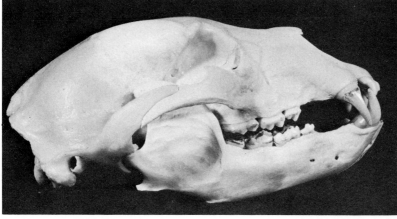

(e)

4 cm

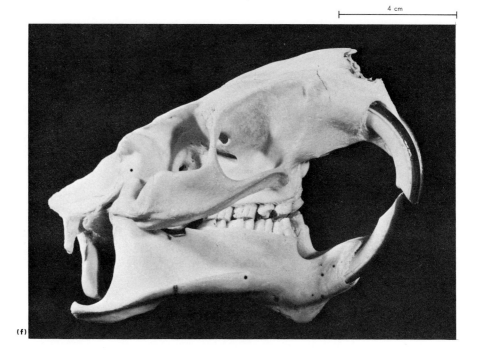

4 cm

(f)

267

viduals and in members of differing species, genera, and higher taxonomic groupings provide significant evidence about relationships and divergencies. At the same time teeth show beautiful functional adaptiveness in relation to their capture of prey, crushing and maceration of food materials, and other processes. Thus, they are a productive source of information about the feeding and related activities of animals. Indeed, there are few structures that demonstrate more clearly than teeth the intimate interplay and interdependence of form and function. In the brief treatment necessitated by the limitations of space and objectives of this book, facets of tooth anatomy can only be touched upon. The interested reader will find references to more comprehensive discussions of dentition at the end of this chapter. Further study of this subject is sure to increase the comprehension of broad principles as well as narrower details of comparative anatomy.

In a review of the dentition of vertebrate animals, it may be recalled that teeth are or once were present in gnathostome fish and in some orders of all higher vertebrate classes. They have been lost secondarily, however, in some amphibians (toads), some reptiles (turtles), and in all modern birds. In fish and amphibians, teeth are entirely mesodermal in origin. They develop in the dermis of the jaws, palate, and/or pharynx with a hard, mineralized *dentine* forming the main body of the tooth. Dentine varies in composition from one animal to another, but in general it has a low content (about 30 percent) of water and organic materials (proteins, organic acids and so on). Its main constituents are inorganic salts, which are in crystalline form; a complex inorganic calcium phosphate salt, hydroxyapatite, resembles dentine in structure. Often dentine is highly organized in the form of parallel arrays of tubules. It surrounds a pulp cavity lined with special dentine-building cells (*odontoblasts*) where blood vessels and nerves come into close proximity with the inner layers of dentine. In reptiles and mammals, dentine is covered with a layer of very hard mineralized material, *enamel*, secreted by cells of ectodermal origin. These cells, *ameloblasts*, are lost after the growing tooth erupts into position in the mouth, so that enamel, once fully formed, cannot grow or be replaced. Enamel consists of salts to the extent of about 96 percent of its mass, chiefly in crystalline form, and is seen in mammals in clearly prismatic arrays. Calcium, magnesium, sodium, phosphate, and carbonate have been identified as constituents of enamel. It provides an exceedingly resistant covering for the underlying dentine and contributes to the long life of definitive mammalian teeth. In all vertebrates except mammals, formation of new teeth is more or less continuous throughout the animal's life. In contrast, mammals generally develop two sets of teeth, the early "milk" or deciduous teeth that are formed first and then replaced by a not quite full complement of permanent teeth. These latter generally function throughout the major part of the animal's life. In mammals the teeth may, but rarely do, continue to grow from their roots throughout life. This is the case, for instance, with the incisors (front gnawing teeth) of rodents.

Vertebrates in general show quite a wide range of placement of teeth and in the means of their attachment to the supporting structures. Often the teeth adhere firmly to the underlying bone through fibrous and cement attachments, but in certain fish and reptiles the attachment may be ligamentous and thus less rigid. When dentition is "hinged" in this manner, it may be quite movable. In some species teeth are set in sockets in bone (thecodont pattern), whereas in others they are attached on top or along the inner (tongue) side of the jaw (patterns termed respectively acrodont and pleurodont). In fish, teeth may occur in rows along the jaw margins, over the entire palate, and on gill arches in the pharynx. They may be very numerous, numbering in some cases hundreds or thousands in a single individual. Typically in amphibians and reptiles the teeth are fewer, acrodont or pleurodont in arrangement, and more restricted than in fish in placement along the jaw margins; palatal teeth occur in some reptiles. In mammals, the number of teeth is relatively small (generally forty-four or less) and their position is restricted to the jaw margins (Figure 7-14). The one or several roots of each tooth are set in bony sockets. If it is possible to speak of a typical form of tooth in fish, amphibians, and reptiles, this could be described as conical. Mammals have some conical teeth as well (the complement of front incisors and the *canine* teeth), but the cheek teeth (*premolars* and *molars* along the sides of the jaws) are far more complex in structure. Their opposing surfaces have multiple cusps and ridges with patterns that are constant within a given species, though varying from species to species. Superimposed on the basic tooth forms and patterns are features correlated with function. Among fish and reptiles, some species feeding on hard, resistant material (e.g., plants, shelled invertebrates) show flattened, plate-like grinding teeth. Herbivorous mammals have specialized premolars and molars with ridged and very resistant grinding surfaces. In carnivorous mammals, the canine teeth may be elongated and sharply pointed, serving as weapons for attack on prey. Some other tooth adaptations will be touched on later in this chapter.

Digestive Systems of Mammals   The tongue of mammals is often highly specialized, functioning in the capture of prey, in the grasping of food, and in vocalization. The esophagus tends to be long and slender, but no specialized crop is found in mammals. The stomach differs from the bird's stomach, showing no division into proventriculus and gizzard. Rather, the stomach of mammals is often a relatively compact organ, though it may be differentiated by contour and by patterning of the tissues of the wall into regions located orally (cardiac region), centrally (fundic), and aborally (pyloric), this latter part lying adjacent to the pyloric sphincter (Figure 7-15). As in other vertebrates the mammalian pyloric sphincter, which opens and closes depending on the degree of filling and the digestive condition of the stomach, has an important part in controlling the supply of nutrients to the small intestine. Perhaps the most striking adaptations of mammalian stomachs are seen in the case of herbivores with their enlarged and specialized stomach chambers where symbiotic micro-organisms are maintained (Figure 7-16). Bacteria and protozoans are of great importance to the mammal because of their unique biochemical capabilities. Supplementing the limited enzyme syntheses of their mammalian hosts, these organisms form cellulases and other enzymes that break down the resistant chemical compounds of plant cell walls and fibers, and thus increase greatly the efficiency of use of plant materials by herbivorous mammals.

As in birds, the small intestine of the mammal tends to be extremely long.

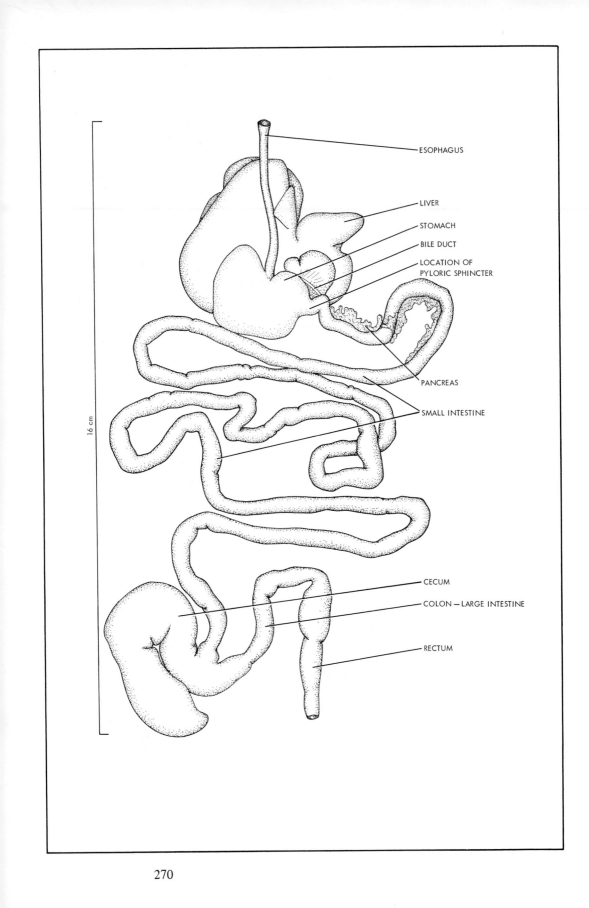

ESOPHAGUS

LIVER

STOMACH

BILE DUCT

LOCATION OF
PYLORIC SPHINCTER

PANCREAS

SMALL INTESTINE

SMALL INTESTINE

CECUM

COLON — LARGE INTESTINE

RECTUM

16 cm

Figure 7-15 (opposite). Digestive system of a mammal, the Norway rat, *Rattus norvegi-cus*, seen in ventral view, and freed of mesenteries. The liver has been reflected back and orally, to reveal the stomach and intestine. There is no gall bladder in the rat; rather, bile flows through the delicate bile duct into the small intestine in the region of the pancreas.

The internal surface is further increased by the presence of innumerable villi, tiny finger-like projections of the mucosa into the intestinal lumen. Often considerable specialization in structure and function is seen from oral to aboral end of the small intestine. The *duodenum*, the region nearest the pyloric sphincter, is relatively short and thick-walled and has the highest rate of muscle activity, absorption, and secretion of any region of the tract. In some mammals a middle section (*jejunum*) can be easily differentiated, and beyond this the terminal section (*ileum*) is also distinctive in contour, structure, and function (for instance, bile salts are strongly absorbed in this section of the intestine alone). Both the small and large intestines are far more elaborate in herbivores than in carnivores. All these structural features are correlated with the high energy demands and specialized dietary requirements of these homeothermic vertebrates.

The general structure of the liver and pancreas is comparable with that

Figure 7-16. The stomach of a sheep, a representative herbivore. The large chambers lying between the esophagus and the abomasum-pylorus region (parts which are closest in function to simpler mammalian stomachs) are specialized for culture of hugh colonies of microorganisms. The routes of the ingested material is suggested by the white arrows. Food is swallowed, passing from the esophagus into the rumen where mechanical breakdown and attack by microorganisms is initiated (arrow path marked ①). Repeatedly, the partially digested material is regurgitated from the rumen, up through the esophagus, to the mouth for further chewing (arrow path marked ②), swallowing, and further digestion. These elaborate chemical and mechanical processes result in exceptionally efficient use of plant material by the sheep. (This figure is slightly modified from the classical illustration by Pernkopf.)

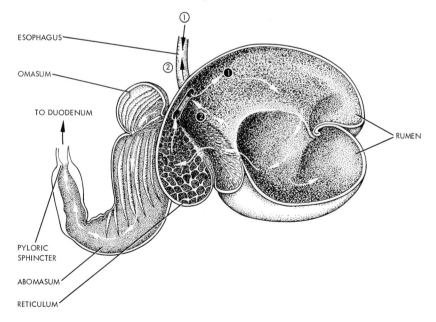

seen in most other vertebrates, although in some birds and in certain mammals (e.g., deer, horses, some rodents) the gall bladder is absent. It has been suggested that this peculiarity may be correlated with the lack of a need to store and concentrate bile during times of gastrointestinal inactivity.

A large semiblind chamber, the cecum, is generally attached to the large intestine at its junction with the small intestine, and at its opposite end may terminate in a further blind extension, the *appendix*. These structures appear to function as digestive ceca generally do, to provide additional volume for processing of the nutrient mass by digestive enzymes and micro-organisms and to give additional absorptive area. The structures are particularly well developed in herbivores, and are smaller (the appendix may even be greatly reduced and essentially nonfunctional) in carnivores and primates, including man.

As in all other vertebrates, the mammal's large intestine functions chiefly as a site of water and ion absorption. Only in monotremes and marsupials does it lead into a cloaca. In more advanced mammals, its contents pass into the *rectum*, a smaller, simpler chamber lined with stratified epithelium, and thence through a sphincter-bounded opening, the anus, to the outside.

In this account, similarities among vertebrate digestive systems have been emphasized. Needless to say, the detailed functioning of the gastrointestinal tract is highly varied and sensitive to the environmental conditions under which the individual lives. The tract is richly supplied with nerves, some operating independently, some controlled by the central nervous system. Most of the extrinsic control is from the autonomic division of the central nervous system. Often, however, the extreme oral and extreme aboral ends of the tract are powered by striated (voluntary) muscle, and are under the animal's voluntary control. Though the smooth muscle cells of the digestive tract show a great deal of intrinsic contractility, shortening more or less rhythmically and so mixing, churning, and moving the contents along the tract, the overall patterns of movement are integrated by nerve plexuses within the gut wall or by nerves connecting with the central nervous system. Thus, the waves of contraction that sweep in a consistent direction along the tract wall (peristalsis) depend on both intrinsic and extrinsic nerves. Further, autonomic nerves (chiefly the paired vagus nerves) take part in integrating the motility of different regions of the tract. Examples are the relaxation of the stomach walls as food approaches it from the esophagus and stomach contractions that eject the contents into the small intestine when the oral regions of the intestine have emptied. In a wide range of vertebrates the stomach makes strong, repeated contractions when it has been empty for some time. In man, these contractions are often recognized consciously as "hunger pangs," and they seem to play a part in signaling the need for food (onset of hunger). Though we cannot, of course, know whether vertebrates other than ourselves feel hunger as we do, some experimental results suggest that similar gastric contractions precede the onset of feeding behavior in a variety of vertebrate animals. Thus, nerves have a function in signaling the need for food, as well as in coordinating feeding behavior and digestive processes.

Neural control of the gastrointestinal tract is supplemented by chemical control. The food materials themselves, especially after partial digestion, may stimulate gland secretion. Cells of the walls of the small intestine, stomach, and other gastrointestinal regions form endocrine secretions (*secretin*, identified in all vertebrate classes, and *gastrin, enterogastrone, cholecystokinin*, and so on, studied thus far chiefly among mammals). These endocrine hormones travel through the blood to the gland and muscle cells of the stomach, small intestine, liver, gall bladder, and pancreas, and modulate the responses of these structures with respect to current digestive demands. Hormonal control is specific and may be quite complex. For instance, the hormone secretin is absorbed into the blood from the duodenal mucosa when acidic materials enter the duodenum from the stomach. Secretin then travels through the circulation and stimulates increased secretion by the pancreas and liver. In contrast, when fatty materials enter the duodenum from the stomach, the inhibiting hormone *enterogastrone* is released from the intestinal mucosa and acts on the stomach to inhibit gastric secretion; this mechanism has been studied fairly adequately only in mammals. The person who wishes to appreciate fully the structure of the gastrointestinal tract must take into account its dynamic organization. The anatomy of the tract fluctuates with its changing pattern of activity. Thus, for instance, the color, length, contour, and position of the intestine, and the appearance of its blood and lymph vessels, change greatly from time to time, depending on the animal's current state of gastrointestinal function, and neural and endocrine control.

Diversity of Functions Though much more could be said of the basic structural characteristics of the digestive system, the preceding account may give an adequate introduction to gastrointestinal tracts from the point of view of their primary role in animal nutrition. Before completing this chapter, however, it may be useful to refer briefly to some of the accessory roles that the system has taken on from time to time in the course of vertebrate evolution. In some cases the variety, adaptiveness, and uniqueness of these roles are quite surprising. They are a reminder of a very important characteristic of evolutionary adaptations— the tendency of these adaptations to be "opportunistic," that is, to take advantage of existing structures and functions to arrive at solutions to new biological problems.

Thus, the arming of the mouth cavity with teeth or beaks, of adaptive value in capturing prey, is completely compatible with the use of the mouth cavity and teeth as defensive weapons as well as tools for nest building (fish, birds), and for burrowing or gnawing trees (rodents). The salivary glands, evolved chiefly in connection with the formation of lubricating fluids, are adapted in certain reptiles as poison glands. In some birds salivary glands function in producing cementing substances for nest building, that recalls a very widespread association of the digestive tract with reproduction and care of the young. In some fish species the fertilized eggs are retained in the mouth of one of the parents till they have developed far enough to be capable of independent existence. Many birds and some mammals feed their offspring with food regurgitated from the crop or stomach, and in pigeons the crop has a special secretion (crop milk) used for feeding the young. Widely throughout the vertebrate series the reproductive and digestive systems are also intimately associated where they share the common exit chamber, the cloaca. Universally the digestive and respiratory systems are interwoven in the buccal-pharyngeal region. Correlated with this is the widespread use of the buccal cavity, with its teeth and tongue, in vocal signaling. The buccal cavity plays an important part as a site of sensory receptors (Chapter 10). Although these function chiefly in food selection and in the integration of the activities of the entire digestive tract, they also have wider roles in the economy of many vertebrates. In animals of most vertebrate classes, the walls of the tract contain aggregations of lymph cells that are important in protecting the organism against invading micro-organisms. Sometimes these are found at the junction of the buccal cavity and pharynx, as in the case of the mammal's *tonsils*. The walls of the small intestine, too, often show lymphocyte aggregates or lymph nodes (mammals). Finally, red blood cells are formed in the intestinal walls (cyclostomes, lungfish) and in the liver (fish, amphibians, vertebrate embryos). All in all, the digestive system is a remarkably versatile participant in the complex interplay of vertebrate organ systems.

References for Chapter 7   *General anatomical and physiological references cited at the end of the Introduction to the Reader may be consulted. Additional information will be found in the following publications.*

Bonneville, M. A., "Fine Structural Changes in the Intestinal Epithelium of the Bullfrog during Metamorphosis." *J. Cell. Biol.,* **18** (1963), 579.

Brauer, R. W., "Liver Circulation and Function. *Physiol. Rev.,* **43** (1963), 115.

Ito, S., "Structure and Function of the Glycocalyx." *Fed. Proc.,* **28** (1969), 12.

Pernkopf, E., "Beiträge zur vergleichende Anatomie des vertebraten Magens." *Zischr. Anat.,* **91** (1930), 329-390.

Peyer, B., *Comparative Odontology.* Chicago: University of Chicago Press, 1968.

Porter, K. R., "Independence of Fat Absorption and Pinocytosis." *Fed. Proc.,* **28** (1969), 35.

Sellers, A. F., and C. E. Stevens, "Motor Functions of the Ruminant Forestomach." *Physiol. Rev.,* **46** (1966), 634-661.

8

Respiration and circulation

Introduction:
How Success
Depends Upon
Joint Efforts
Just as division of labor and specialization characterize successful modern society or a smaller unit of a successful enterprise, so the success of the vertebrate animal is dependent upon a division of labor among specialized cells, tissues, and organs which serve specific functional tasks. Structure and function become inseparable, and the student of morphology or structural patterns must never lose sight of the functional objectives of the various structural components.

Respiration, unfortunately, does not have a single well defined meaning in biological contexts. In its widest interpretation it incorporates all operations that effect the exchange of respiratory gases between the external environment and the metabolizing cells. Sometimes it is used in reference to the biochemical degradation of substrate in cellular metabolism. That meaning of the term will not be treated in this text. External respiration is that part of the exchange of gases with the external environment which is responsible for loading oxygen and unloading carbon dioxide. This process takes place in the specialized structures referred to as respiratory organs, and the design of these organs is our present concern. Two equally important processes, the unloading of oxygen and the loading of carbon dioxide at the transport terminal serving the metabolizing cells, occur in the fine-bored, thin-walled capillaries of the vascular system. How the capillaries are designed to promote efficient exchange will be considered in the section on circulation. It will become increasingly apparent, however, that the efficiency of these processes depends inseparably on the joint functions of the organs of respiration and circulation. Both organ systems are designed to promote effective transport between the external environment and the living cell.

It is important to realize that the ultimate physical process that completes this transport chain is simple, passive diffusion. Diffusion is the random movement of matter (molecules) from regions of high concentration to regions of low concentration. The rate of diffusion depends on several factors formally expressed in Figure 8-1. You will see throughout these chapters that the objective of both the respiratory and circulatory organs is to aid the process of diffusion. Figures 8-2 and 8-3 indicate the principal ways in which the structure of these organs can promote effective diffusion exchange. A comparison is made of diffusion through an unspecialized body surface and a surface specialized for gas exchange. Similarly, Figure 8-3 shows the difference between avascular and vascular tissues for the transport of diffusible matter like gases, water, heat, ions, and so on.

The following example provided by the late Nobel Prize winner, August Krogh, emphasizes the profound importance for gas exchange of the respiratory and circulatory organs. Krogh estimated that a hypothetical spherical organism with a radius of one centimeter needs an oxygen pressure of twenty-five atmospheres or more than 125 times the oxygen pressure in ambient air at sea level, in order to supply the center of the organism with oxygen by diffusion alone unassisted by a respiratory and circulatory system. Krogh calculated that an aquatic organism living in air-saturated water cannot have a radius greater than 0.5 millimeter if it is to be supplied by diffusion alone. Another theoretical example shows that it would take a

Figure 8-1. Diffusion is governed by the equation

$$\frac{S}{T} = DA \frac{C_1 - C_2}{l}$$

where S = the amount of substance diffused, T = time, D = a diffusion constant, A = the surface area over which diffusion takes place, C_1, C_2 = the concentration of the substance at the points considered and l = the length of the diffusion path. The rate of diffusion depends on the steepness of the concentration gradients, where

$$\text{Concentration gradient} = \frac{\text{Concentration difference}}{\text{Distance} (= l)}.$$

A large area
  allows more molecules to pass.

A short diffusion path
  allows more molecules to pass.

A large concentration difference
  will cause more molecules to pass.

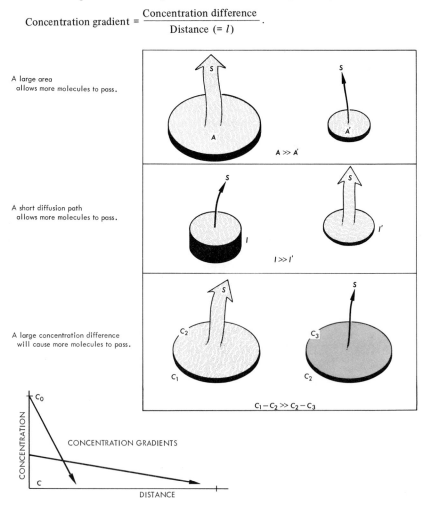

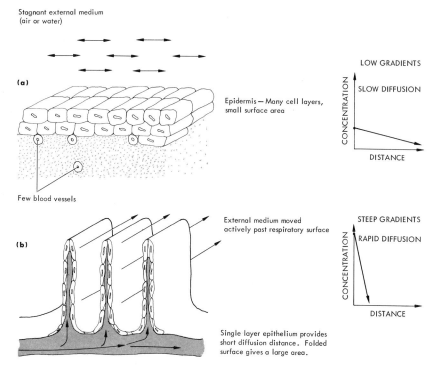

Stagnant external medium
(air or water)

(a)

Epidermis — Many cell layers,
small surface area

Few blood vessels

LOW GRADIENTS

SLOW DIFFUSION

CONCENTRATION

DISTANCE

(b)

External medium moved
actively past respiratory surface

Single layer epithelium provides
short diffusion distance. Folded
surface gives a large area.

Many blood vessels branching
into thin walled capillaries

STEEP GRADIENTS

RAPID DIFFUSION

CONCENTRATION

DISTANCE

Figure 8-2. (a) An unspecialized body surface is inefficient in gas exchange because it provides a small surface area and low concentration gradients. The gradients are low because of the long diffusion distance, the sparse blood circulation, and the stagnant external medium. (b) A body surface specialized for gas exchange is efficient because of a large surface area and steep diffusion gradients. The short diffusion distance, the rich blood circulation, and the active movement of the external medium cause the steep diffusion gradients.

Figure 8-3. (a) Tissue without blood circulation. If masses of cells (tissues) receive nutrients and exchange gases and metabolites by diffusion only, the transport is slow and inefficient and cannot support the metabolic activity of an active tissue. (b) Tissue with blood circulation. If blood capillaries penetrate tissues to the vicinity of individual cells, transport is rapid and efficient. Interruption of the blood supply to metabolically active tissue causes the cells to die or be damaged irreversibly.

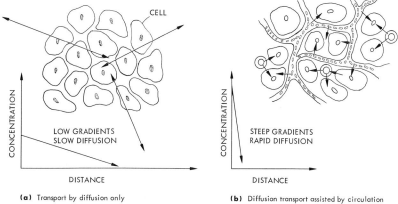

CELL

CONCENTRATION

LOW GRADIENTS
SLOW DIFFUSION

DISTANCE

(a) Transport by diffusion only

CONCENTRATION

STEEP GRADIENTS
RAPID DIFFUSION

DISTANCE

(b) Diffusion transport assisted by circulation

molecule of oxygen several years to be transported from your lung to your toe if the transport depended only on diffusion unassisted by a circulatory system. If a molecule of oxygen, however, was brought within ten microns of living cells via the vascular system, the diffusion time would be reduced to fractions of a second.

The need for assisted diffusion transport by specialized organs of respiration and circulation in the vertebrate animal should therefore be obvious. The architecture and bio-engineering of these organs at representative levels of vertebrate organization form the basis for the following two sections.

Section One: The Respiratory System	External respiration or gas exchange in chordates as a rule takes place in specialized organs called respiratory organs. These include various forms of gills and lungs designed for aquatic and aerial gas exchange, respectively. Gas exchange can also take place through nonspecialized parts of the general body surface, the skin. In some amphibians such nonspecialized body surfaces constitute the primary or only site for gas exchange.
The Physics of Respiratory Media	Air and water differ in essential respects as media for external gas exchange. It should be noted, in particular, that the concentrations of oxygen in air and in air-saturated water differ about thirty-fold at normal room temperature. Similarly, the density of water is about 1000 times that of air. These differences serve to emphasize that the energy cost of moving water past the respiratory exchange surfaces, i.e., the work of breathing, will be markedly higher for the water breather than the movement of air for the air breather. It is important to realize these differences in order to understand the design and functional properties of respiratory organs.
The Organs for Aquatic Gas Exchange	Functional gills are found in all fish, although much reduced in some of the air-breathing forms such as the lungfish and several tropical fresh-water teleosts. Gills can be external, protruding directly from the branchial region into the ambient water, or internal, protected by specialized skin folds in teleosts or the general pharyngeal wall in cyclostomes and elasmobranchs. External gills are generally vulnerable to injury from mechanical contact or from predation by enemies. External gills can be moved in a wave-like action by specialized muscles to effect convection or stirring of the external water. However, much more effective stirring occurs in internal fish gills by active ventilatory movements that renew the water passing the respiratory exchange surfaces. Functional external gills are also present in larval amphibians and are retained in some neotenic adult Urodeles.
The Structural Design of Gills	How can the structure of gills promote exchange diffusion between the external environment and blood? We would anticipate the following structural factors to be important: (1) a large surface area for diffusion; (2) short diffusion distances and low diffusion barriers; (3) effective structural support for renewal of the water facing the external exchange surface (optimal conditions require that the foregoing factors be complemented by the blood vascular structures in the matching process between the respiratory water current and the blood); (4) numerous, small calibered and thin-walled vascular channels or blood spaces in gills with a large surface area and a large ratio of surface to volume in the matching of water and blood; (5) effective structural support for continued passage of blood past the exchange surfaces; (6) a spatial arrangement of the water current and blood current in a counterstreaming fashion.

Let us examine typical elasmobranch and teleost gills in the light of the foregoing considerations. In fish the gill structures are supported by, and attached to, a series of symmetrically placed branchial arches. In the more primitive fish, the elasmobranchs, the two rows of primary filaments of a

Figure 8-4 (opposite). (a) Successive branchial arches showing relationship of gill filaments and secondary lamellae to the interbranchial septum in an elasmobranch fish.
Note that two successive hemibranchs between interbranchial septa make up one
respiratory unit. The arrows indicate the pattern of waterflow. (b) Relationship of
bloodflow and waterflow in a respiratory gill unit. The solid arrows indicate blood
flow, open arrows the water flow.

typical branchial arch are attached to opposite sides of a supportive interbranchial septum. In teleosts this interbranchial septum is reduced or absent
and each primary filament is supported by an independent gill ray.

The tips of the primary filaments in all types of gills are usually in contact
with the tips of the primary filaments of the neighboring branchial arches
(Figure 8-4). The individual filaments, which look something like the
leaf of a book, are stacked on top of each other. Both sides of each primary
filament bear numerous secondary lamellae (Figure 8-4). The secondary
lamellae are the actual site of gas exchange. In active species of fish they are
extremely numerous and provide a surface for exchange that may exceed the
entire surface area of the fish itself by more than ten times (Table 8-1). In
some fish the distance from water to blood is less than one micron. Note
also that the water will pass on both sides of the secondary lamellae and
thus the diffusion distance between water and blood is further reduced
(Figure 8-4). It is of equal importance that the large number of secondary

Table 8-1. Dimensions of fish gills in relation to normal activity habits. [From G. Hughes
(1966)]

	Toadfish	Fluke	Sea Robin	Tautog
Behavior	sluggish	sluggish	moderately active	moderately active
Weight (g)	305	404	365	466
Total number of filaments	656	1706	1996	1580
Total length of all filaments (mm)	4752	9747	14,022	12,537
Secondary lamellae (per mm)	11	19.3	20	19
Gill area (mm^2/g body weight)	151	247	432	450

	Butterfish	Mullet	Mackerel	Menhaden
Behavior	moderately active	very active	very active	very active
Weight (g)	261	250	226	525
Total number of filaments	1548	2190	2814	2298
Total length of all filaments (mm)	9855	16,399	19,271	25,138
Secondary lamellae (per mm)	32	26.5	29.4	27
Gill area (mm^2/g body weight)	461	1010	1040	1241

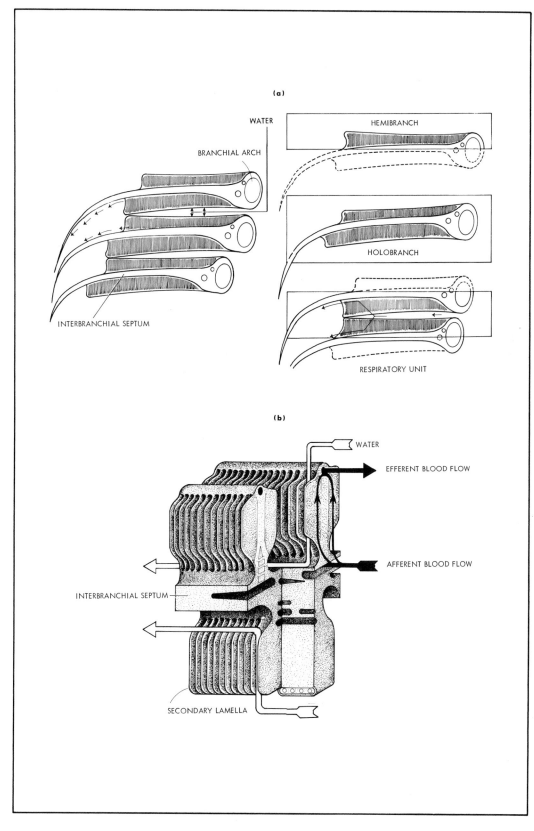

(a)

WATER

BRANCHIAL ARCH

HEMIBRANCH

HOLOBRANCH

INTERBRANCHIAL SEPTUM

RESPIRATORY UNIT

(b)

WATER

EFFERENT BLOOD FLOW

AFFERENT BLOOD FLOW

INTERBRANCHIAL SEPTUM

SECONDARY LAMELLA

281

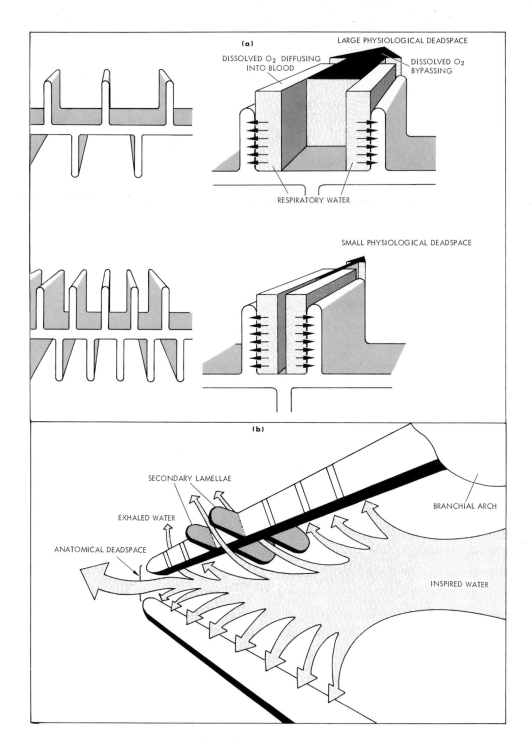

Figure 8-5. (a) *Large physiological deadspace.* A large distance between secondary lamellae makes the diffusion path from water to blood too long for all the dissolved O_2 molecules to diffuse into the blood. *Small physiological deadspace.* A short distance between secondary lamellae allows most O_2 molecules to diffuse into the blood. (b) *Anatomical deadspace.* If the tips of gill filaments do not make contact, some water will escape without having been directed past the exchange surfaces of the secondary lamellae. This water is labelled anatomical deadspace.

282

lamellae reduces the distance across which the gases must diffuse in the water. This is important because water may otherwise become too distant from the exchange surfaces to participate in actual gas exchange with the blood. When exchange is limited by diffusion distance, this is referred to as functional or physiological deadspace as distinct from a direct bypass of water referred to as anatomical deadspace (Figure 8-5). The water taken into the mouth during breathing is guided through progressively smaller channels. When passing between the secondary lamellae, the width of the water channel can be as short as one-fiftieth of a millimeter in some fish.

The large number of secondary lamellae results in a large total cross-sectional area irrigated by the water flow and a low velocity of the water past the exchange surfaces of the gills. Both of these factors will promote an efficient exchange diffusion.

In many active fish such as a mackerel, the number of secondary lamellae can be extremely high and exceed forty per millimeter. Their shape is asymmetrical with their greatest height facing the water current (Figure 8-5). This will help to assure that the water flow is broken up to eliminate possible stratification that would reduce the diffusion rate. The resistance to water flow in each of these narrow channels can be considerable, but the remarkably large number, more than a quarter million in a small fish, will assure an adequate flow of water at acceptable energy cost to the fish. However, it is important to realize that the low concentration of oxygen in water compared to that in air will necessitate a ventilation volume past the gills many times the volume of air that an air breather needs to ventilate to extract a comparable amount of oxygen. Also remember that the 1000 times higher density of water compared to air will additionally increase the energy cost of breathing in water. In accordance with this high energy cost, the ventilatory reserve allowing increased ventilation during periods of increased need for gas exchange is much smaller in water breathers than in air breathers.

Some structural features of gills reduce the apparent disadvantage of breathing in water compared with air. The counterstreaming arrangement of the water and blood flow is one very important factor. Figure 8-6 compares schematically a countercurrent and a concurrent exchange system with diagrams of their exchange efficiency.

The unidirectional path of the respiratory water current is indispensible to a countercurrent exchange. Water enters the mouth or spiracles and continues past the gill surfaces before it is expelled from the gill slits or the opercular openings. Unlike conditions in air-breathing vertebrates, the unidirectional water passage results in a continued renewal of water at the exchange surfaces. In the bidirectional airway of lung breathers, freshly inspired air is prevented from reaching all the way to the exchange surfaces of the lung before it becomes admixed with the gas trapped in the airways. The latter are designated as deadspace.

The continued passage of the unidirectional water current past fish gills is achieved by the rhythmic activity of skeletal musculature which causes a double pumping action. A buccal or orobranchial pressure pump and an opercular parabranchial suction pump, aided by valves in the mouth or spiracle and at the opercular or gill slit openings, assure a fairly continuous and steady passage of water. Water is prevented from entering the esophagus by a sphincter valve demarcating the posterior end of the pharyngeal cavity. The passage of the water from the buccal cavity across the gill surfaces is illustrated in Figure 8-7 (a) and (b).

Note that the direction of the water flow between the secondary lamellae depends on the close apposition of the distal tips of succeeding primary gill filaments. This apposition will prevent the discharge of water before it has made contact with the gas-exchanging surfaces of the secondary lamellae. Such closure becomes crucial for the efficiency of the gas exchange. It is structurally supported by specialized abductor muscles of each branchial unit (Figure 8-7).

After having traversed the secondary lamellae where the gas exchange takes place between the water and the blood, the respiratory current continues behind the operculum for final discharge or, in the elasmobranchs, is guided in channels between interbranchial septa before being expelled from the gill slits.

The gills make up a delicate organ vulnerable to mechanical injury from external objects or predators. Consequently, in adult fish they are confined to the protected pharyngeal cavity. In this location, however, the gill surfaces are in danger of being smothered by ingested food. Among the structural measures to circumvent this are the lateral position of the gills and the presence on the branchial arches of gill rakers which act as filtering devices. The gill rakers are developed to various degrees in different fish in apparent coordination with their habitat. Bottom-living species from muddy habitats have well developed gill rakers. They can also be secondarily well developed in forms that actually depend on them as filters for feeding purposes, such as in the large basking sharks. These fish feed on plankton and their flattened, tapering gill rakers may be more than ten centimeters long, resembling in appearance the filtering devices in plankton-feeding whales.

It is important to realize that gills are structurally built to function in water that gives the fish approximately neutral buoyancy. When fish gills are exposed to gravitational effects in air, their fine secondary lamellae rapidly collapse and become ineffective in gas exchange.

The gills in fish are perfused with oxygen-deficient blood channeled directly from the heart via the ventral aorta to the afferent branchial arteries. Many features of blood circulation through gills will be described in the subsequent section. Those aspects of branchial circulation essential to the understanding of the architecture of gills as respiratory-exchange organs will be discussed in the following paragraphs.

The secondary lamellae are supplied with blood by the afferent branchial arteries [Figures 8-4 (b) and 8-9] which pass along the primary filaments on

Figure 8-6 (opposite). (a) Countercurrent exchange between water and blood in fish gills. (b) Blood and water meet in a counterstreaming arrangement in the secondary lamellae. (c) In a countercurrent arrangement the arterial blood can reach O_2 tensions higher than those in expired water. On its way through the gill, blood continues to make diffusion contact with inhaled water. (d) When water and blood meet in a concurrent exchange, the arterial blood can only reach O_2 tensions approaching those in expired water. Oxygen gain is hence much less than in a countercurrent system.

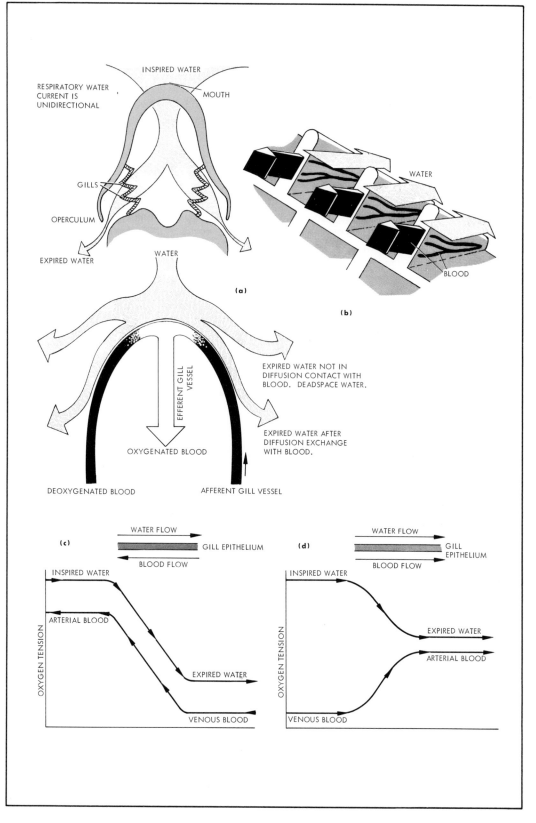

INSPIRED WATER

RESPIRATORY WATER CURRENT IS UNIDIRECTIONAL

MOUTH

GILLS

OPERCULUM

EXPIRED WATER

WATER

(a)

WATER

BLOOD

(b)

EFFERENT GILL VESSEL

EXPIRED WATER NOT IN DIFFUSION CONTACT WITH BLOOD. DEADSPACE WATER.

EXPIRED WATER AFTER DIFFUSION EXCHANGE WITH BLOOD.

OXYGENATED BLOOD

DEOXYGENATED BLOOD

AFFERENT GILL VESSEL

(c)

WATER FLOW

GILL EPITHELIUM

BLOOD FLOW

OXYGEN TENSION

INSPIRED WATER

ARTERIAL BLOOD

EXPIRED WATER

VENOUS BLOOD

(d)

WATER FLOW

GILL EPITHELIUM

BLOOD FLOW

OXYGEN TENSION

INSPIRED WATER

EXPIRED WATER

ARTERIAL BLOOD

VENOUS BLOOD

285

the side facing the effluent water (e.g., along the interbranchial septum in elasmobranchs). In the secondary lamellae the blood ceases to circulate in well defined vessels because the blood spaces are more akin to lacunae or irregular interconnecting spaces than to a network of true vascular capillaries. Each secondary lamella in turn empties into the efferent primary filament artery running along the margin of the primary filament on the side facing the incurrent water. Figures 8-6 (a)-(c) and 8-9 illustrate that the direction of the blood passage inside the secondary lamella is opposite to that of the water, and thus a structural possibility for countercurrent exchange of gases is provided.

Detailed experiments on eels permit us to evaluate the total external surface of the secondary lamellae. The analysis illustrates the remarkably large area of respiratory epithelium available for gas exchange. In a 500 gram eel, the total number of filaments was found to be 2100. The average length

Figure 8-7. The gill filament musculature is important in positioning the filaments to maintain a curtain or sieve between filaments of successive branchial arches. This will ensure efficient ventilation of the gas exchange area of the secondary lamellae. At time of excessive water inflow through the mouth the adductor muscles may open the "curtain" slightly and thus protect the delicate lamellae from damage by the pressure of inflowing water.

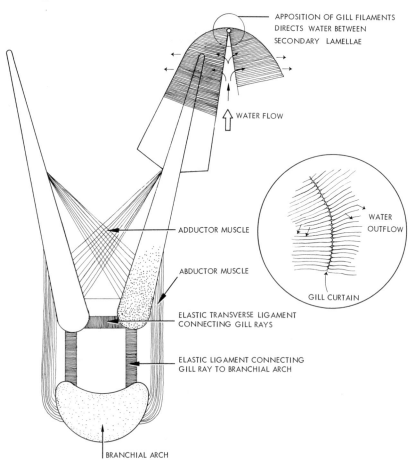

APPOSITION OF GILL FILAMENTS DIRECTS WATER BETWEEN SECONDARY LAMELLAE

WATER FLOW

ADDUCTOR MUSCLE

ABDUCTOR MUSCLE

ELASTIC TRANSVERSE LIGAMENT CONNECTING GILL RAYS

ELASTIC LIGAMENT CONNECTING GILL RAY TO BRANCHIAL ARCH

BRANCHIAL ARCH

WATER OUTFLOW

GILL CURTAIN

of each filament was seven millimeters and there were eighteen secondary lamellae per millimeter. This gives a total of 264,600 lamellae (2100 X 7 X 18). Each lamella was approximately 0.60 millimeter along its long axis and 0.45 millimeter along its short axis. A lamella has roughly the shape of a triangle, giving it a surface area of 0.45 X 0.6 X 2 = 0.135 square millimeter. However, only 75 percent of the lamellar area is thought to be involved in actual gas exchange. Since each lamella effectively offers two sides for gas exchange, we get a total available surface equal to 264,000 X 0.101 X 2 = 52,920 square millimeters, or approximately 530 square centimeters. This area represents many times the general body surface area of the fish itself. Because of the internal pillar cells supporting the frame of the internal lamellar space the blood inside the lamellae will be dispersed over an area less than that available for irrigation by water from the outside. Consequently, the surface area of the internal blood space is estimated to be about 50 percent of the external surface.

We contended early in this chapter that an important design requirement for a respiratory organ was to provide a close matching of water and blood over a large exchange surface offering minimal diffusion distance and resistance. Figure 8-8 shows schematically how the water and blood when matched in the lamellae of the gills have been distributed across remarkably large areas. This not only serves to provide a large exchange surface area and a very short diffusion path between water and blood, but the matching process is also favored by an expansion of the cross-sectional areas of the fluid columns and thus by a marked reduction in the velocity of the flowing water and blood. This velocity relationship follows from the simple principle of continuity in flowing incompressible fluids. We have all observed how the water slows down when a creek widens. The decreased velocities of water and blood are of obvious advantage by allowing more time for the gas exchange diffusion.

Recent work on circulation through the primary filaments of teleost gills by Steen (see References) has brought new evidence for views expressed by earlier anatomists that blood circulation through the gill filaments may follow alternate routes either around the tip of the margin of the filament or through a central nonrespiratory compartment and thus avoids contact with water at the respiratory exchange area [Figure 8-9 (a) and (b)]. The important inference to be made from such an arrangement is that the fish may be able to execute some kind of regulation as to the portion of blood directed to the respiratory exchange spaces or directed past these to the efferent side of the branchial circulation. One important advantage of such branchial vascular shunts in fish may be related to osmotic regulation. The blood and other body fluids in both fresh and salt-water fish are not in osmotic equilibrium with the surrounding medium but have an osmotic concentration intermediate between fresh and salt water. During passage through the respiratory exchange spaces in the gills, the blood will thus be subjected to osmotic gradients and the result will be an undesirable flux of water into the blood of fresh-water fish and out of the blood of salt-water fish. Hence the salt-water fish will constantly lose water that has to be compensated for by intake of external sea water, which in turn will pose problems of ionic imbalance because of the high salt content in sea water. Paradoxically, then, we can say that a fish in sea water lives in a dry environment. Conversely, the fresh-water fish will be constantly diluted and will have the problem of retaining enough salts. It is interesting that cells in the respiratory epithelium of teleost fish gills have specialized for active excretion or absorption of salts in marine and fresh-water fish, respectively (see Chapter 9). The vascular shunts of the secondary lamellae just described may be important in allowing blood to be shunted past the exchange spaces and thus minimize the stress on osmoregulatory mechanisms. Such shunting must, however, be compromised with the actual needs of the fish for respiratory gas exchange.

Fish gills show structural adaptations to environmental conditions and to general activity and behavior. Thus many fish in oxygen-deficient waters show especially well developed lamellae that provide a large surface area for gas exchange. However, many teleost fish in tropical oxygen-deficient waters have developed accessory means for gas exchange—utilizing the atmospheric air. In these forms the gills show a tendency to degenerate and become less

Figure 8-8. Structural factors important for the matching of water and blood in fish gills. (a) The surface expansion of the blood and water columns in the gills promotes efficient gas exchange by providing a large surface area and (b) a low velocity of the flowing fluids.

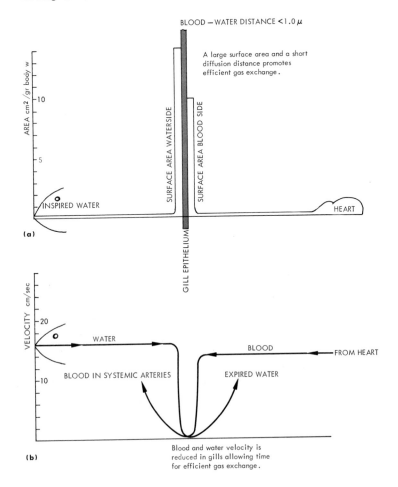

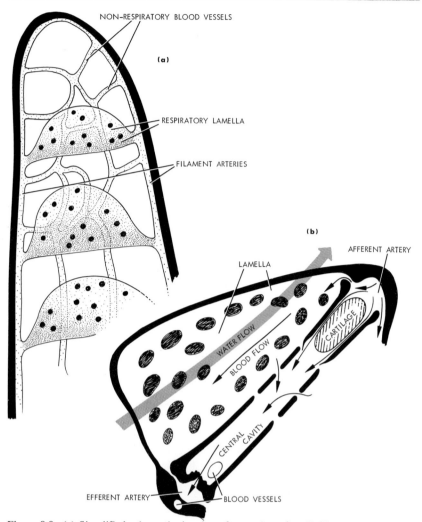

NON-RESPIRATORY BLOOD VESSELS

(a)

RESPIRATORY LAMELLA

FILAMENT ARTERIES

(b)

AFFERENT ARTERY

LAMELLA

WATER FLOW

BLOOD FLOW

CARTILAGE

CENTRAL CAVITY

EFFERENT ARTERY

BLOOD VESSELS

Figure 8-9. (a) Simplified schematic drawing of a portion of a gill filament showing the respiratory and nonrespiratory (shunt) blood paths. (b) Drawing of a gill filament showing a secondary lamella in cross-section. The vascular channels are marked with arrows; the large gray arrow indicates blood circulation through the respiratory part of the lamella and the small arrows indicate circulation through the shunt or the non-respiratory portion.

useful in aquatic gas exchange. Pelagic fish, which often are very active swimmers, show structural adaptations resulting in large gill areas and short diffusion paths. Mackerel and herring are good examples of this category. In some fast-swimming fish like the swordfish, a peculiar gill structure has developed to withstand the deforming forces of a high swimming speed. Table 8-1 summarizes data on the surface area and diffusion characteristics of a number of teleost gills related to their ecological situations.

The Ultrastructure
of Gill Lamellae

The ultrastructure of the gas-exchanging surfaces of the secondary lamellae is made up of two epithelia that become continuous along the distal margin of the lamella. The two epithelia are held apart by a special type of cell, pillar cells, which are spaced randomly and extend from one epithelium to the other. The resulting space between the two epithelia takes the form of a lacunar compartment. This is the compartment that constitutes the blood space. Below each epithelium lies the basement membrane. Figure 8-10 (a) and (b) show electron micrographs of a secondary lamella from the teleost, *Gadus pollachius*. One can see that the blood space is uniformly delineated by a thin sheath growing out from the main body of the pillar cells. This outgrowing lining is called a pillar flange and is less than 0.5 micron thick. The flanges of adjacent pillar cells interconnect and thus come to represent the continuous boundary of the blood space. The average cell body to cell body distance of the pillar cells in this particular fish is about ten microns. The width of the lacunar blood space is, in general, just large enough for the red blood cells to pass through (Figure 8-10). Between the pillar flanges and the epithelia is a basement membrane that typically contains collagen fibers. The basement membrane shows a tendency to become thickened where it is juxtaposed to the pillar cell body. The epithelia facing the waterside of the lamellae are often made up of single cell layers but may also constitute several cell layers in complex interdigitation. The flat nuclei of the epithelial cells characteristically tend to be located on a common axis with pillar cells and the nuclei of epithelial cells on the other face of the lamella. This arrangement is of obvious advantage since the denser cellular elements then come to exert a minimal resistance to diffusion between the blood space and the water. The electron micrograph (Figure 8-10) reveals the remarkably short and direct diffusion path between the water and the blood. Several recent authors report an average water to blood diffusion distance of less than one micron. It has also been suggested that the pillar cells may have an additional importance in regulating local blood flow through the lamellae by intermittent shortening and thus restricting the blood passage. The presence of distinctly fibrillar material in these cells offers a structural basis for this suggestion.

The Phylogeny of
Vertebrate Gills

In embryological life all vertebrates develop a series of lateral visceral clefts and separating arches in the pharyngeal region. There is a tendency for the number of clefts to be higher in the more primitive forms. Some cyclostomes may have as many as fourteen whereas teleost fish show only five or six pairs. Among air-breathing tetrapods the visceral clefts disappear in adult life, with the exception of the first cleft which is homologous with the Eustachian tube and parts of the middle ear. The clefts are formed when the endodermal pharyngeal pouches push through the mesenchyme and meet ectodermal invaginations. The gills formed in the clefts are, in general, considered to be of ectodermal origin (Figure 8-11).

Although the most primitive of vertebrates, the cyclostomes have gills that in many respects differ from the basic design apparent in other vertebrates. We shall begin a brief survey of gills in vertebrates, therefore, with the elasmobranch fish which are considered to represent archaic conditions. Vertebrate gills are formed in successive bilateral branchial clefts or perforations between the pharynx and the exterior. The structural supports for the gills are the branchial arches or gill arches. These arches make up the part of the

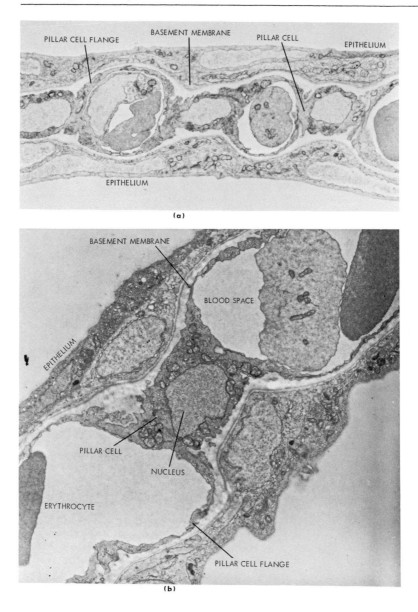

Figure 8-10. Ultrastructure of blood-to-water diffusion path in a teleost fish gill (*Gadus pollachius*). (a) Low power electron micrograph showing the general structure of a secondary lamella. Three pillar cells can be seen, with their flanges meeting and joining to delimit the blood space. Erythrocytes and a white blood cell are present. Note also the basement membranes and epithelia (4,000X). (Courtesy Professor G. M. Hughes.)

(b) An approximately median section of a pillar cell body and its flanges. Note the large nucleus, and the abundant mitochondria and tubules set in a dense cytoplasmic matrix. A column is present, enclosed in an infolding of the plasma membrane. Note the junction of one of the pillar cell flanges with that of an adjacent pillar cell. In the epithelia, note the location of the nuclei opposite the pillar cell body and the presence of more than one cell layer. Both nucleus and cytoplasm in the outermost cell of the lower epithelium are markedly denser than those of the other cells (10,000X).

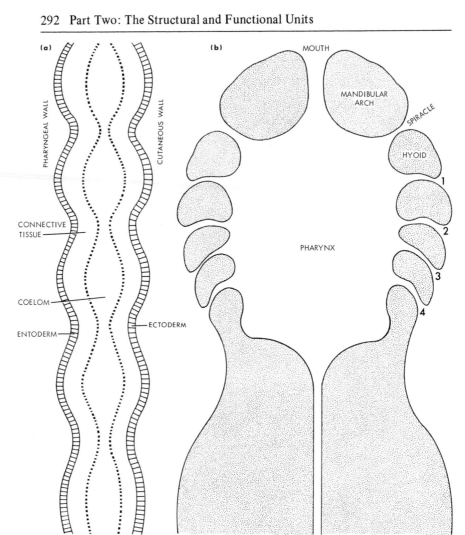

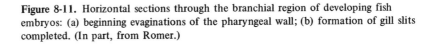

Figure 8-11. Horizontal sections through the branchial region of developing fish embryos: (a) beginning evaginations of the pharyngeal wall; (b) formation of gill slits completed. (In part, from Romer.)

tissue space between the successive branchial clefts. The first pair of clefts in elasmobranchs has become highly specialized and is called the spiracles. Functionally the spiracles are a site of entrance for the respiratory water current in addition to the mouth opening. Fast moving sharks commonly swim with their mouths partially open; their habits have largely eliminated the need for spiracles which have become vestigial or lost. On the other hand, the mouth of bottom-dwelling forms among sharks and skates could easily be smothered with mud and debris, and in such forms the spiracles have become very large and are the primary entrance for the respiratory water current.

The first branchial arch, the mandibular arch, occupies a region between the mouth and the specialized spiracular opening. Typically in sharks there are five pairs of branchial clefts behind the spiracles. The number may be larger in some primitive sharks; for example, members of the primitive genus *Heptanchus* show seven clefts. The branchial arch between the spiracle and the first regular branchial cleft is referred to as the hyoid arch (Figure 8-12). In sharks each of the branchial clefts, except the spiracles, has a wide internal connection with the pharynx, whereas the external opening is commonly narrowed to a slit-like aperture placed laterally. In some sharks, like the large basking sharks, the slits may be larger and traverse most of the dorsoventral aspect of the fish. In the dorsoventrally flattened skates and rays the external gill slits are located on the ventral side. Characteristically, in sharks [Figure 8-12 (a)] the gill slits are separated by membranous outgrowths from the arches. These structures, called interbranchial septa, represent the boundary between each gill cleft and the next (Figures 8-4, 8-12, 8-13). The distal ends of the septa, which are usually thin, make up an epithelial cover over the succeeding gill cleft. The gills are represented by a folded stack of plates or filaments radiating from the branchial arch. These filaments, in turn, project secondary lamellae from their upper and lower sides. The blood vessels and nerves supplying the respiratory portion of the gills run along the branchial arches. The arches also provide the basis for variously placed supporting structures referred to as gill rods or rays. In elasmobranchs each typical branchial arch projects a double row of gill filament piles located one on each side of the interbranchial septum. Such a gill is called a holobranch. On some of the branchial arches only one side has developed filaments; this is a hemibranch. The common classification of a structural gill unit as one complete holobranch does not correspond to a functional gill unit that consists of two hemibranchs from succeeding branchial arches [Figure 8-4 (b), 8-12 (a)].

The markedly modified spiracular opening among the elasmobranchs sometimes carries a rudimentary hemibranch on its anterior wall; this structure is known variously as a mandibular or spiracular pseudobranch. Its function is not known but it can hardly be respiratory since the blood supplying it, with few exceptions, comes from the efferent side of the branchial circulation and thus has been arterialized already by passage through gills. The hyoid arch usually bears only a posterior hemibranch. The last gill slit has only one hemibranch projecting from the preceding branchial arch.

Members of the Holocephali, which are related to the elasmobranchs and with them make up the chondrichthyian order, differ from the elasmobranchs by lacking the spiracle altogether, and also by having one gill slit less than the elasmobranchs. Notably, the Holocephali also have a large skin fold protecting the branchial region. This skin fold or operculum has its origin in the hyoid arch and grows posteriorly over the gill clefts. The operculum unites dorsolaterally and ventrally to the body wall, but the lateral posterior margin is free and is the site of discharge for the expired water.

In the bony fish a number of differences stand out from the basic gill structure of the elasmobranchs. The more primitive Chondrostei have retained the spiracles, but the interbranchial septum has been further reduced so that the gill filaments project freely beyond the outer margins of the septa. This development progresses further in teleosts, and in some the

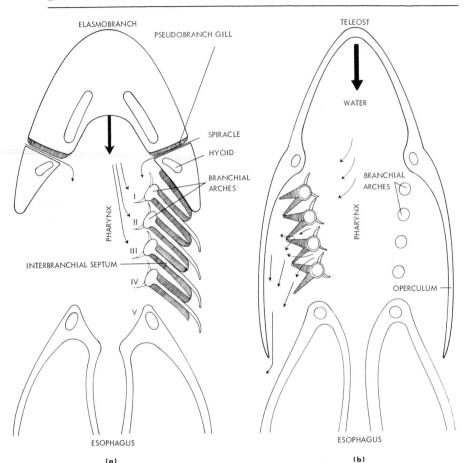

Figure 8-12. (a) Horizontal section through the head of an elasmobranch fish. (b) Horizontal section through the head of a teleost fish.

interbranchial septum is reduced to almost nothing (Figure 8-13). With this development the gill rays have an increased structural importance in support and orientation of protruding hemibranchs. The fifth branchial arch usually remains gill-less. There are, however, several variations in the distribution of hemibranchs on the various branchial arches among different fish. Many attempts have been made to relate these differences to phylogenetic ranking, but the discussions are mostly speculative.

   An important structural change of major functional consequence in the bony fish is encountered in the operculum which becomes well developed, movable, and structurally supported by specialized opercular bones and muscles for movement. The opercula in bony fish are more than the protective covering in Holocephali. They are essential in the breathing mechanism, providing a branchial chamber suction pump which, linked with

Figure 8-13 (opposite). Transverse sections of branchial arches in fish showing the relationship of the primary filaments to supporting structures such as the interbranchial septum and gill rays. (a) Elasmobranch (*Selache*); (b) chondrostean (*Acipenser*); (c) teleost (*Salmo*); (d) teleost (*Esox*).

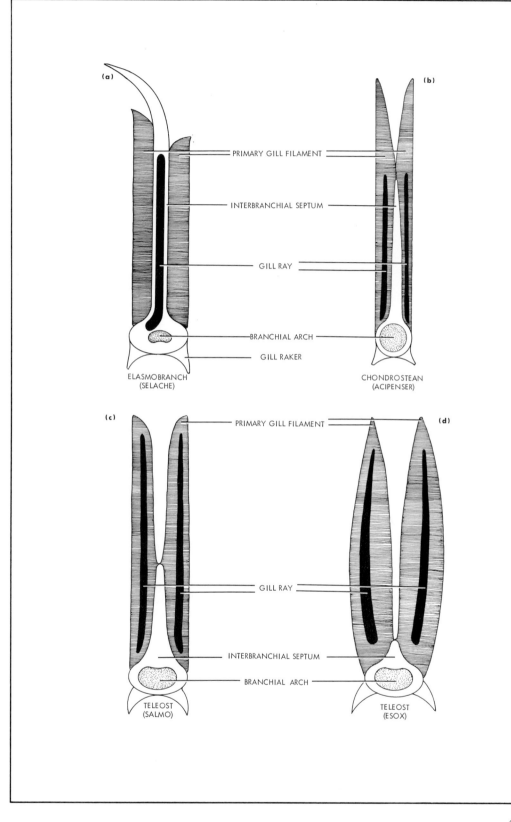

(a)

PRIMARY GILL FILAMENT

INTERBRANCHIAL SEPTUM

GILL RAY

BRANCHIAL ARCH

GILL RAKER

ELASMOBRANCH
(SELACHE)

(b)

CHONDROSTEAN
(ACIPENSER)

(c)

PRIMARY GILL FILAMENT

(d)

GILL RAY

INTERBRANCHIAL SEPTUM

BRANCHIAL ARCH

TELEOST
(SALMO)

TELEOST
(ESOX)

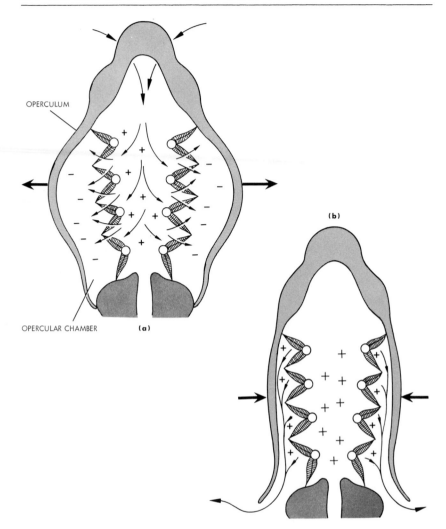

Figure 8-14. Horizontal section through head of teleost fish showing how the pharyngeal and opercular pumps propel the respiratory water current. Pressures indicated by + and − relative to the ambient pressure surrounding the fish. (a) Dilatation of opercular chamber will cause a suctional attraction for water across the gills. (b) Contraction of opercular chamber will cause water to escape along a pressure gradient from the buccal chamber to the outside.

the pharyngeal pressure pump, is responsible for propulsion of the respiratory water current (Figure 8-14).† The gills of *Neoceratodus,* the only lungfish that is primarily an aquatic breather, conform to the basic plan of elasmobranchs. There are five branchial clefts and the hemibranchs are largely attached to well developed interbranchial septa. A specialty of the gills in *Neoceratodus* is the extension of the branchial filaments to the dorsal and ventral walls of the branchial clefts; thus the hemibranchs are continuous between interbranchial septa. In the other genera of lungfish, *Protopterus*

†Figure 8-15 shows the path of the respiratory water current in elasmobranchs.

and *Lepidosiren*, a marked gill reduction accompanies an increased development of lungs in accord with the dominance of aerial breathing. In both genera the gill reduction results in two branchial arteries passing to the efferent branchial side without the intervention of gills (see the next section, on circulation).

Gills of
Cyclostome Fish

The gills in cyclostomes are said to be specialized and to have little apparent structural homology to gills in other fish. Their unique features may result from the semiparasitic feeding habit of attaching their heads to the prey. In addition, the entire muscular apparatus of these jawless cyclostomes involved in moving the respiratory water current is a variant from

Figure 8-15. Diagram of a dogfish in side view (anterior) and horizontal section (posterior) to show the path of the respiratory current. The flow is unilateral. The horizontal sections pass through the external gill slits and illustrate the changes in volume of the parabranchial and orobranchial cavities. Pressures in these cavities are indicated with respect to zero pressure outside the fish. Full line arrows show the movements of the mouth and branchial regions, with their thickness indicating the relative strength of contraction. Valve in spiracular channel (a) open and (b) closed. (After G. M. Hughes, 1963.)

WATER ENTERING SPIRACLE

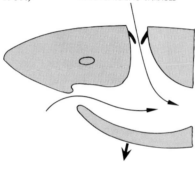

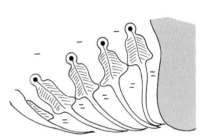

(a)

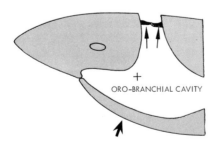

ORO-BRANCHIAL CAVITY

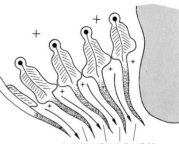

(b)

PARABRANCHIAL CAVITIES

systems in other fish. The cyclostomes, comprising the lampreys and the myxinoids, are also referred to as marsipobranchs because of their peculiar gill structure. The gills are contained in spherical pouches, that connect either internally with the pharynx through individual openings (myxinoids) or by union with a special diverticulum of the pharynx that ends blindly and is located ventrally (lampreys). This diverticulum, referred to as the branchial canal, lies below the regular pharynx and communicates anteriorly with the esophagus. In adult lampreys all the gill pouches open separately to the exterior through small orifices covered by fine skin folds that act as valves. In the myxinoids the expired water is discharged through one external

Figure 8-16. (a) Horizontal section through the branchial region of the cyclostomes *Petromyzon* and *Myxine* showing the gill pouches and inflow and outflow channels of the respiratory water current. (b) Respiratory tract of Myxine showing the respiratory water passage. The velum represents a unique pumping structure propelling the water into the gill pouches. These in turn are also contractile and contribute further to the movement of water. (c) Detail of a gill pouch in Myxine illustrating the counterstreaming arrangement of blood and water.

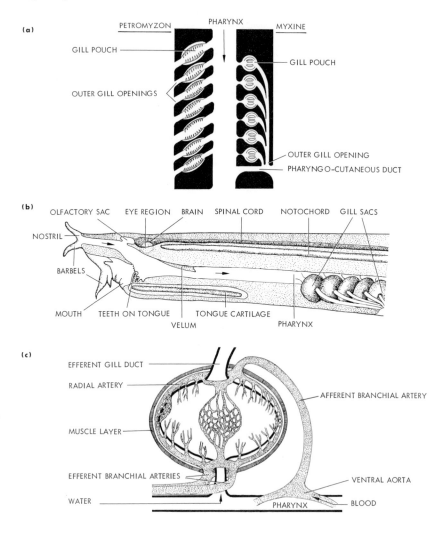

aperture terminating in a common duct from each side. These ducts in turn are formed from the fused canals leading from the gill pouches on each side [Figure 8-16 (a)]. The branchial filaments in cyclostomes are represented by a continuous system of tightly packed epithelial ridges investing the entire internal surface of the gill sacs. This epithelium is reported to be partially ciliated in lampreys, a feature that is typical of their very specialized larval form, the ammocoete. The interbranchial septa are thick and well developed and constitute the external boundaries of the gill units. Each of these units includes a specialized branchial cartilaginous skeleton and branchial muscles in addition to a complicated system of vascular channels that include some large peribranchial sinuses. When well developed muscles of each sac rhythmically constrict, water is discharged through the external orifices. During inhalation the water current enters the pouches through the same orifice from which it is expelled. The forces involved in inhalation are thought to result from a passive recoil of the branchial pouches after the very active constriction during expiration. In this way the lampreys employ a bidirectional respiratory passageway that is a unique practice among water-breathing vertebrates.

In myxinoids a fairly wide nasal aperture provides entrance for the water current even when the mouth parts are imbedded in prey during its semi-parasitic feeding. An effective water current is maintained by the rhythmic velar movements aided by contractions in the muscular walls encircling the gill pouches. As in teleosts and elasmobranchs the matching of blood and water in myxinoid gills takes place in countercurrent fashion [Figure 8-16(c)] .

The Rise of Air Breathing

More than 350 million years ago in the Silurian and Devonian geological periods the prevailing climatic conditions brought about a marked reduction in the oxygen concentration of large fresh-water basins. As a result aquatic respiration became marginal for many forms of life and a direct utilization of atmospheric oxygen became necessary for survival and further evolution of the vertebrates. Fossil evidence, as well as a variety of extant bony fish, show several types of structural adaptations for the direct utilization of atmospheric oxygen. These adaptations include modifications of the buccal cavity or arborizations from pharyngeal and opercular cavities for direct gas exchange between blood and rhythmically ingested air. In another modification diverticula from the upper gastrointestinal tract developed as functioning receptacles for air. The stomachs or cloacae of other fish developed specialized parts that functioned in aerial gas exchanges; still others developed a marked vascularity of the skin that was effective in direct aerial gas exchange.

Today many fish show these and other structural adaptations for air breathing, but only one of the early types has evolved further in vertebrate evolution, i.e., the diverticulum of the foregut, later referred to as lung, air bladder or swim bladder, as a rhythmically ventilated respiratory organ. Why this solution was favored in the further evolution of vertebrates remains speculative. However, with the development of a separate vascular circuit to the new gas exchange organ (see the next section, on circulation) one important advantage of this structure was soon obvious. Without such support from the cardiovascular system the efficiency of pulmonary breathing in terms of oxygen delivery to the tissues would be far too low to support the increasing metabolic levels and the higher operational ability of tetrapod vertebrates.

A structural homology between the air bladder of fish and the lungs of lungfish and tetrapods seems well established. The swim bladder in fish has been credited with at least four different functions. First, it serves as a hydrostatic organ in buoyancy control; this is its primary function in modern teleosts. Second, the swim bladder may function as a respiratory organ or as an oxygen storage organ. Third, it is important as a sense organ for pressure perception and as an amplifying structure in sound perception. Last, the bladder itself can be an organ of sound production.

Figure 8-17. Phylogeny of the swimbladder. Schematic cross-sections and longitudinal sections of various air bladders: (a) typical physostome teleosts, (b) holostean type, *Amia* and *Lepidosteus.* (c) *Polypterus*; (d) *Neoceratodus*, the Australian lungfish; (e) *Protopterus,* the African lungfish; (f) amphibian.

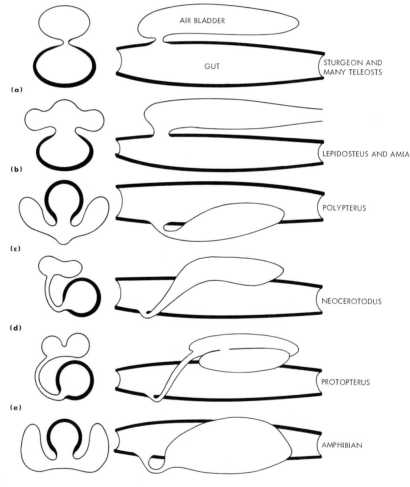

Cyclostome and chondrichthyian fish show no trace of a swim bladder. The swim bladder of fish as well as the lungs of tetrapods are of endodermal origin and develop as an outgrowth from the gut. In some fish, it may retain a connection with the gut, the pneumatic duct, and is called a physostomous air bladder. In others the pneumatic duct degenerates and the bladder is called physoclistous. In still others the entire swim bladder atrophies and disappears. Figure 8-17 shows the various types of air bladders and their connection with the gut.

In this chapter we are primarily concerned with the structural design principles of respiratory organs. We shall concentrate on the air bladder as a respiratory organ and as a forerunner of the higher vertebrate lung. It seems well established that the air bladder was an accessory respiratory organ when it first appeared with certainty in the early crossopterygian fish. This view is supported by the early evolution of these fish in swampy, oxygen-deficient tropical waters. Their accessory respiratory organs were probably essential and permitted survival while other fish became extinct. The presence of lung-like air bladders is also suggested in fossil evidence, particularly from the Devonian period. Although a respiratory function of the air bladder has been lost in the great majority of modern fish, it has been retained in some archaic forms like *Polypterus, Amia, Lepidosteus*, and the lungfish. In the latter it has become the principal effective organ of gas exchange. The diversity in adaptive adjustment and the many modes of accessory air breathing displayed by modern tropical fresh-water fish all indicate that the transition to aerial breathing was gradual and that the original means of aquatic gas exchange with gills regressed slowly and assisted the new mode of aerial gas exchange in its development. Because of the differences in the physical properties of oxygen and carbon dioxide in their relation to water and air as respiratory media, the developing air-breathing organs initially were primarily oxygen-absorbing organs, and the retained aquatic organs assisted effectively in the elimination of carbon dioxide. The long and gradual development of air breathing was probably crucial for selection of the final structural design of lungs and for the drastic change in the piscine pattern of blood circulation that was necessary for efficient oxygen transport.

The Structural Design of Lungs   It was noted earlier that the oxygen concentration in the atmosphere is about thirty times greater than that of air-saturated water. This reduces the requirement for ventilation or renewal of the external medium to the respiratory surfaces in air breathers. On the other hand, their departure from water gave the truly terrestrial vertebrates a new problem of water balance caused by desiccation. This was different from the problems of maintaining osmotic and fluid balance in both fresh and salt-water aquatic animals. Finally, exposure to air creates entirely new conditions in terms of gravitational effects and differences in density of the media and the tissues involved in gas exchange. The aquatic fish is under no significant gravitational stress because of the nearly uniform densities of water, blood, and the tissue intervening between them. Thus only minimal forces are acting to deform the extremely delicate respiratory surfaces suspended in water. Conversely, in the air breather, blood, air, and the tissues separating them are all of different densities, and the resulting vertical pressure differences and shearing forces act to deform the respiratory surfaces.

The hazards of desiccation and the need for mechanical protection and structural support to minimize these gravitational effects required that the air-breathing organ be internal. This, in turn, required an elaborate system of passageways connecting the internal gas-exchanging membranes with the external air. Since the gas-exchanging surfaces must be moist, the geometry and other characteristics of the airways had to meet this need. The problem of water conservation is probably the reason why no air-breathing vertebrate has developed a unidirectional airway system in which the inhaled air passes across the respiratory surfaces and escapes via tubes different from those by which it entered the organ. One important consequence of the bidirectional airway is the inevitable presence of a gas volume trapped in the airways after an expiration and before the next inspiration. This nonfunctional or dead air space is referred to as the anatomical deadspace. The presence of such a deadspace will cause oxygen tension inside the lung to be lower than in outside air; conversely, the carbon dioxide tension in the lung will exceed that of ambient air.

In the following description of the mammalian lung, we will see how these general requirements have influenced its design. In a later section we will discuss the phylogenetic development of the lung and its relation to special environmental conditions. It was emphasized earlier that the respiratory system shares responsibilities with the circulatory system in the transfer of gases between the external environment and the immediate cellular environment. This is done by matching large volumes of gas with large volumes of blood in the gas-exchanging organ. This organ, in turn, is designed to effect the rapid transfer of gases by diffusion between the two media.

The respiratory system in air-breathing vertebrates is made up of two main parts; a system of conducting and distributing tubes and the small, thin-walled air sacs, the alveoli, in which the actual gas exchange takes place. The upper airway or respiratory tract includes the nasal and mouth passages. Air taken in through these openings converges into the trachea. The trachea, in turn, divides into a right and a left bronchus. Each of these divides again into two, and so on, until in man there are more than twenty subdivisions. You can calculate that from the single primary tracheal tube there arise about 1,000,000 terminal tubes or bronchioles connecting to the alveolar system (Figure 8-18). For each of these terminal airways, there are many blind, thin-walled alveolar sacs [Figure 8-18(c), (d)]. Man has about 30,000,000 alveoli in his two lungs. Their diameter ranges between 75 to

Figure 8-18 (opposite). (a) Gas exchange in the lung depends on matching blood and air over large surface areas. (b) Air flow to the lung and alveoli is bidirectional. Air enters by the same route it leaves. The blood flow through the lung is unidirectional. The blood volume in the lung is effectively replaced with incoming blood at each heart beat. (c) In the human lung the trachea divides into two bronchi which by twenty or more subdivisions make up a million bronchioles terminating in about 300 million dead-end air sacs, the alveoli. (d) Gas exchange takes place in the alveoli where the diffusion path between blood and gas is about 0.5 micron. Human alveoli vary in size from 75 to 300 microns.

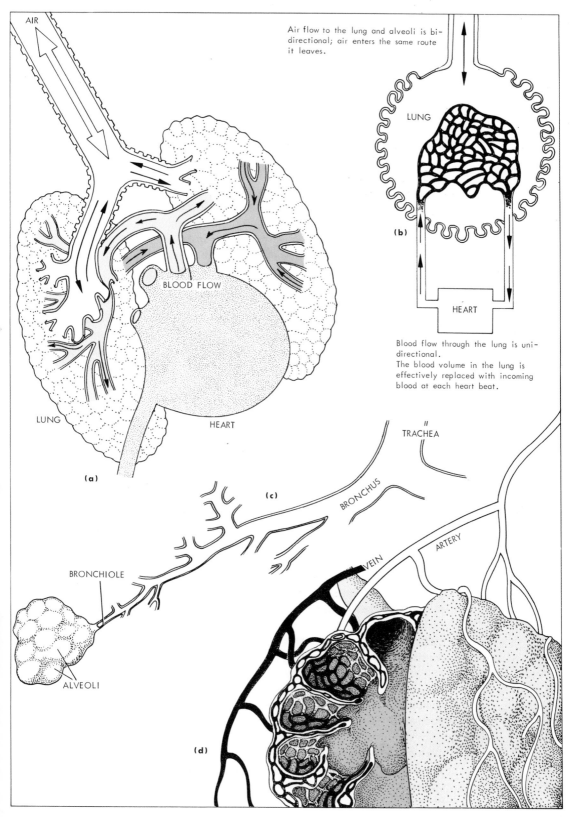

AIR

Air flow to the lung and alveoli is bi-directional; air enters the same route it leaves.

LUNG

(b)

HEART

Blood flow through the lung is uni-directional.
The blood volume in the lung is effectively replaced with incoming blood at each heart beat.

BLOOD FLOW

LUNG

HEART

(a)

TRACHEA

(c)

BRONCHUS

BRONCHIOLE

VEIN

ARTERY

ALVEOLI

(d)

300 microns, and their total surface area can be as much as eighty square meters, or more than forty times the general body surface area. It has been shown in mammals that the alveolar surface area increases in proportion to the general body mass from late embryonic life to full maturity. Work on several mammalian species also revealed that the ratio of alveolar surface to body weight is nearly constant between species.

In both gills and lungs the initial column of water of inspired air is distributed to cover remarkably large areas for diffusion exchange. In gills the inspired water ventilates the exchange surfaces directly whereas in lung breathers the inspired air reaches the exchange surfaces of the lung by diffusion. There are important differences in how the surface expansion is structurally supported. Because the density of the respiratory medium and tissues is uniform in the water breather, there are no deforming forces and it is thus possible to obtain a large surface expansion simply by guiding the water through finer and finer gates. Note that this is not a system of tubes or channels, but of gates provided by the spaces between the secondary lamellae. Note also that in the tubular airway system there are more than twenty subdivisions of the airways from the trachea to the terminal bronchioles [Figure 8-18 (c)]. Another important difference is related to the bidirectional passage of the external medium in the air-breathing animal. The air has to leave the same way it enters [Figure 8-18(b)]. No actual gas exchange is made in the connecting airways in lungs, and it is important to keep down the volume of air held so that as much as possible of the air inhaled reaches the terminal air spaces. However, if the tubes are made very narrow in order to reduce the deadspace, the breathing muscles will be required to work too hard to pump the air in and out. The moved air must reach as many alveoli as possible; but as long as the lungs occupy a sizable space, the distance from the trachea to the actual alveoli will differ in various portions of the lung. Another important task of the distributing system of tubes is to correct these differences in length by varying their diameter and hence the resistance to air flow in various portions of the lung. This process is structurally aided by the presence of smooth musculature around the finer tubes, the bronchioles. Contraction and relaxation of this musculature are important to the distribution of air inside the lungs.

A factor of great importance in maintaining the structure and functional integrity of the lungs is the secretion of substances by the alveoli that reduce the surface tension and thus help prevent collapse of the alveolar gas exchange surfaces.

Other important functions are performed by the upper respiratory tract, consisting of the nose, mouth, pharynx, larynx, and the trachea. First of all, this portion of the respiratory system serves to condition the air with respect to humidity and temperature before it reaches the alveoli. It also has been demonstrated that many vertebrates use evaporation from their upper airway tract to increase the heat loss; this is the reason for fluttering in birds and panting in dogs. The airways are also tremendously important in filtering and cleaning the inspired air. This is a continuous process involving the hairs in the outer nasal passages and powered by the active movements of cilia in the trachea and bronchi. Particles in the inspired air are trapped in a continuously secreted mucous layer that is moved upward by ciliary action. In man the effective velocity of the mucous film can be as high as sixteen millimeters per minute. The efficiency of the process is remarkable; all particles down to about two microns in diameter may be transported up the airway tract and removed via the nose or the mouth.

The muscular activity responsible for the movement of air in and out of the lungs differs at different levels of vertebrate organization. In the lower vertebrates, lungfish and amphibians, a positive intrapulmonary pressure empties the lungs and buccal swallowing of air refills them under positive pressure. In higher tetrapods respiratory muscles actively expand the chest and thus lower the pressure within the respiratory chamber and secondarily within the lungs to draw air into them.

The pulmonary artery, constituting the inflow channel to the pulmonary circuit, divides and subdivides much like the arborization of the airway system and finally at the capillary level the surface area approximates the area of the alveoli or about eighty square meters in an adult man (Figure 8-18). The internal diameter of the pulmonary capillaries is approximately that of a red blood cell. In mammals the red cell diameter ranges between seven and twelve microns, whereas in lower vertebrates, notably amphibians, diameters are as much as seventy to eighty microns. The small pulmonary capillary diameter forces the red cells, one after the other, to be exposed to the air in the alveoli, separated only by membranes that are less than one micron thick on the average (Figure 8-19). Even though the length of a capillary is extremely short it is remarkable that in a resting man five liters of blood can pass through the capillary bed in each minute. Because only one red cell at a time can pass through each capillary, there must be billions of capillaries. During the same one-minute period the air pump provides an air volume approximately equal to the blood volume for the matching process.

We have all experienced the varying demands for oxygen according to our physical activity. During hard exercise we need more oxygen in order to metabolize more foodstuffs to provide for the increased energy. It is surprising that the organ systems are capable of changing their performance to allow for such sudden increases in our activities. Man, for example, can increase the blood flow through his lungs ten times during hard exercise. A corresponding increase in the volume of air ventilated must accompany this response. These facts emphasize the remarkable efficiency in the structural design of the lungs.

The submicroscopic structure of the tissues separating blood from gas has been clarified in recent years with the aid of electron microscopy. An important parallel to conditions in gills is represented by the continuous epithelial lining of the pulmonary alveoli. Figure 8-20 shows how the cytoplasm that envelops the epithelial cell nucleus forms flattened extensions that reach out to cover the pulmonary alveoli. These nuclei bulge into the alveolar recesses with the important result that the thin cytoplasmic extensions will cover the contact surface of the pulmonary capillaries where the actual gas exchange takes place. It has been estimated that approximately two-thirds of the total surface of one alveolus will represent a direct interface with blood capillaries and thus this area constitutes the maximum actual respiratory surface. However, relative modifications in this exchange area are considered to be one of the adjustments that air-breathing verte-

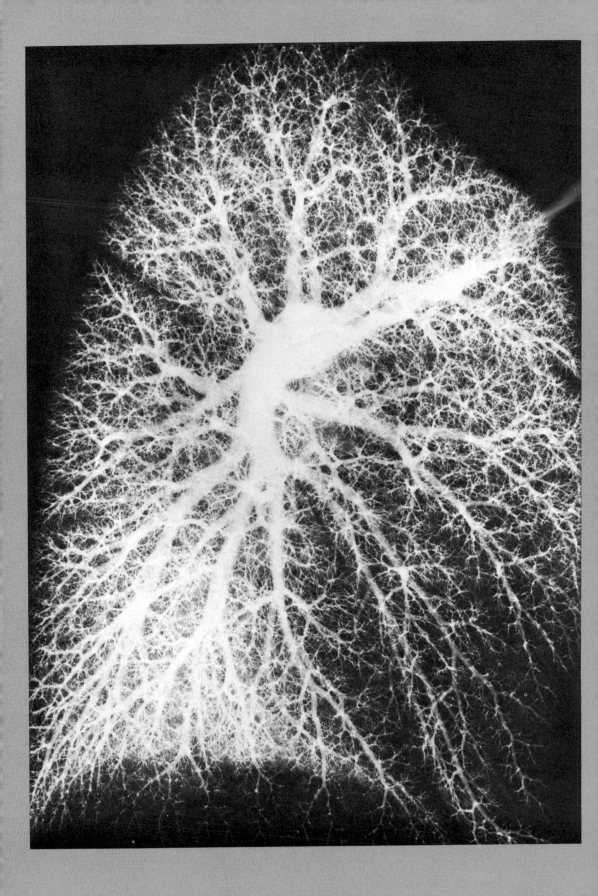

Figure 8-19 (opposite). X-ray photograph of the arterial system of a human lung. The pulmonary capillaries are actually finer than the smallest branches visible in the photograph. Their diameter is from 5 to 10 microns, their length is less than 0.5 millimeter, and their wall thickness is about 0.1 micron. If they were placed in series, rather than in parallel as they are in the arterial system, their total length would exceed several hundred miles. (Courtesy Dr. Julius H. Comroe, Jr., *Scientific American*, February, 1966.)

brates make when their demands for gas exchange are drastically increased. The blood-to-air pathway is extremely thin and the boundary is made up of three different layers. Facing the blood side is the endothelium of the pulmonary capillary. Between this endothelium and the cytoplasmic extensions of the alveolar epithelium is a homogeneous basement membrane (Figure 8-20). Table 8-2 provides a comparison of the thickness of these three layers in four representative vertebrate classes. The pigeon shows by far

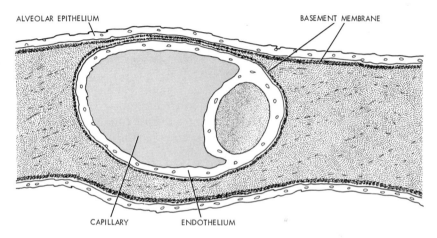

Figure 8-20. The distance separating blood and air in an alveolus is extremely short. Only three layers intervene between air and blood in the most direct diffusion path: the alveolar epithelium, a basement membrane, and the endothelium of the blood capillary. The total diffusion distance in a human lung may be as short as 0.2 micron. [After Frank N. Low, *Anatomical Record*, Vol. 139 (Jan.-Apr., 1961), p. 106.]

Table 8-2. Approximate length of the normal diffusion pathway in respiratory organs of representatative vertebrates. [From H. Schulz (1959)]

	Fish (airbreather, haplochromia)	Amphibian (toad)	Bird (pigeon)	Mammals (rat)	(human)
Capillary endothelium (angstroms)	1000-4000	2000	385-750	180-1000	200-4000
Basement membrane (angstroms)	600	7000-23,000	295-470	650	1100-1600
Alveolar epithelium (angstroms)	1500-15,000	4000-5000	145-175	500-1000	400-650
Total diffusion pathway (microns)	0.31-2.0	1.3-3.0	0.1-0.14	0.13-0.26	0.36-2.5

the shortest diffusion distance, less than 0.14 micron. Among the species studied the toad has the longest blood-to-air pathway, up to three microns. Data in Table 8-2 suggest that the thickness of the blood-to-air distance shows adaptive adjustment to the respiratory demands of the different species more than to their phylogenetic ranking.

There is one barrier to the exchange diffusion of the respiratory gases that we have not yet discussed: the red cell itself. Recent studies have suggested that the diffusion barriers in the blood-to-air pathway are so small that the resistance to gas movement into the red cell itself may be the greater and actual limiting factor in the whole diffusion process. The remarkable chemical, hemoglobin, which is located inside the red cells and gives blood its red color, increases the capacity of man's blood to carry oxygen by almost forty times. The reason for the relatively slow exchange of oxygen and carbon dioxide with the hemoglobin in red cells is that the gases react chemically with the hemoglobin in addition to being transferred by simple physical diffusion. This process requires considerably more time than diffusion alone and becomes an important consideration when we compare vertebrates, inasmuch as the red cells change more than ten-fold in density and in size from amphibians to mammals.

The Phylogeny of Vertebrate Lungs
Paleontological evidence suggests that lungs were present in certain freshwater placoderms and in most crossopterygian fish. Lungs are also present in extant dipnoans and some primitive living actinopterygian fish. They appear in all vertebrates as a ventral outgrowth from the foregut or lower pharynx. In some forms the developing lungs resemble the gill pouches in their early outgrowths from the pharynx. On this basis you will read in some textbooks that primitive lungs may have developed as a modified pair of posterior gill pouches.

The Lungfish
In *Neoceratodus*, the Australian lungfish, the lung has not assumed an important role as a respiratory organ but functions merely as an accessory organ to the gills when the surrounding water becomes severely hypoxic or rich in carbon dioxide or when the fish swims vigorously. It is an unpaired, richly vascularized, thin-walled sac located dorsal to the gut and extending the entire length of the body cavity. If the lung is cut open along a midventral, nonvascular strip of connective tissue, transverse septa are seen which divide the lung bilaterally into a series of compartments. Medial reticulated septa further increase the internal surface (Figure 8-21). The pulmonary arteries follow the medial strips and give off lateral branches that supply fine vessels to the internal surface of the lung, including all the septa. The lung narrows anteriorly and connects, on the right ventrolateral side, with the pharynx through the pneumatic duct. A slit-like muscular glottis marks the entrance from the pharynx to the pneumatic duct.

Histologically the lung contains an epithelium, connective tissue, and smooth muscle, in addition to the blood capillaries. The smooth muscle is present in the lung wall but is more prominently developed in the septa. Its function in the mechanics of breathing is to maintain the prevailing positive pressure, essential for exhalation, inside the lung. It may have an additional role in buoyancy control by changing the volume of the lung.

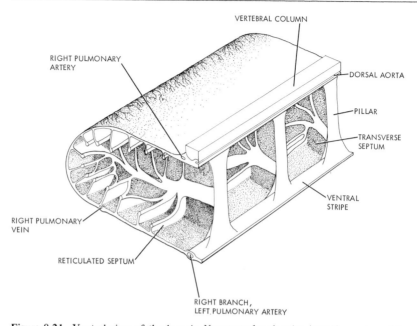

VERTEBRAL COLUMN

RIGHT PULMONARY
ARTERY

DORSAL AORTA

PILLAR

TRANSVERSE
SEPTUM

VENTRAL
STRIPE

RIGHT PULMONARY
VEIN

RETICULATED SEPTUM

RIGHT BRANCH,
LEFT PULMONARY ARTERY

Figure 8-21. Ventral view of the lung in *Neoceratodus* showing how the septa and trabeculae compartmentalize the lung and increase the internal surface area.

The lung structure of the African (*Protopterus*) and South American (*Lepidosiren*) lungfish shows a considerable advance over *Neoceratodus*. This development correlates with the greater emphasis on pulmonary breathing that has become the main method of oxygen absorption in these forms. In contrast to *Neoceratodus*, these lungfish can subsist on pulmonary breathing alone. The lung is a paired structure except for a fused anterior section, and the external surface of the lung is correspondingly much larger than that of *Neoceratodus*. Moreover, the internal septation and compartmentalization are far more developed and the gas exchange sites are more akin to alveoli than are the compartments between the septal ridges of the *Neoceratodus* lung (Figure 8-22). Note that in the actual gas exchange areas of the lung the blood is separated from the alveolar air only by the capillary wall and by thin extensions of the alveolar epithelial cells. The nuclei of the epithelial cells show a clear tendency to be removed from the most direct diffusion path between blood and gas. This tendency, which is also apparent in fish gills, is typical of tetrapod lungs as well.

A comparison of the lungfish thus shows that increased dependence on aerial breathing is correlated with an increased surface area available for gas exchange in the lung. Simultaneously, the blood vascular system shows an increase in the vascularization of the lung, matching the increase in the blood-air interface for gas exchange. Third, the diffusion barriers and the length of the diffusion path between blood and air tend to become smaller.

The Lungs in
Tetrapods

Amphibian lungs are marked by a great diversity in structure in apparent correlation with multiple modes of breathing; gills, skin and buccal mucosa supplement gas exchange in the lung. Some forms show a clear dominance of one method of breathing and have entirely discarded another. Thus, we find lungless salamanders relying on gills or skin for gas exchange. Accordingly, lung structure in amphibians varies markedly and shows, in general, little advance over conditions in lungfish. Internal septal arrangements increase the surface area of the lung, but the internal divisions of the lung fail to provide direct narrow passageways from the external environment to the gas exchange surfaces. Such direct communication seems essential for an efficient renewal of fresh air to the lungs. Yet, in amphibians we see the earliest phylogenetic manifestation of a trachea, although not differentiated into the tracheobronchial tree typical of the higher tetrapods (Figure 8-23).

The mechanics of breathing are similar to those in lungfish; a buccal positive pressure pumping or swallowing mechanism forces air into the

Figure 8-22. (a) Ventral view of lung in *Protopterus aethiopicus*, (b) Schematic drawing of the anterior region of the lung in the African lungfish, showing how the trabeculation creates alveolar-like pockets. (c) Close-up photo of the dense trabeculation inside the lung of the African lungfish. [Parts (a) and (b) redrawn and part (c) reproduced from Monique Poll, "Étude sur la structure adulte et la formation des sacs pulmonaires des Prototypères" (*Ann. in 8vo Zool.* 1962, **108**) by kind permission of Dr. H. Poll, Musée Royal de l'Afrique Central, Tervuren, Belgium]

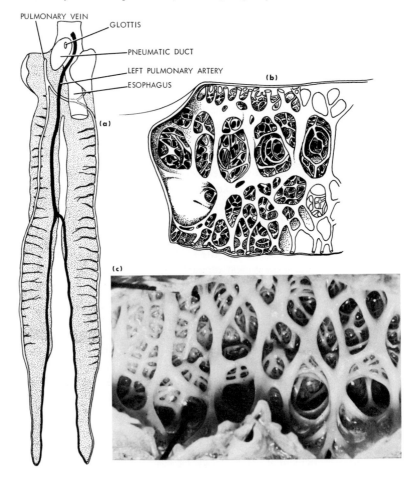

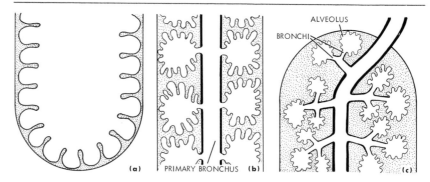

Figure 8-23. The evolutionary development of the internal lung surface and connecting airways in tetrapods. (a) In the primitive amphibian stage, ridges and septa provide surface expansion, but there are no direct passageways to bring the inhaled air into rapid communication with the gas exchange surfaces. (b) The stage represented by some reptiles shows further compartmentalization of the lung, and more direct communication from the primary bronchi to the gas exchange surfaces. (c) In the mammalian stage, further bronchial subdivisions provide large surface areas for gas exchange, and direct airways (leading through many orders of bronchi) route the inhaled air to the alveolar surfaces.

lungs. Expiration occurs in response to an opening of the glottis, and the air escapes because of a positive pressure inside the lung. This pressure is, at least in part, created and maintained by the contraction of smooth muscle in the lung itself, as well as by extrapulmonary compression forces from the body wall or, if the animal is partly immersed in water, by external hydrostatic pressure.

Reptiles, like the amphibians, constitute a diverse group; however, in these animals the lung has become the principal and, with few exceptions, the only organ for gas exchange. Consequently we see both structural and functional changes that increase the efficiency of the lung. The structural subdivision of the internal lung space has advanced considerably from the amphibian stage, although primitive reptiles like Sphenodon show a far smaller ratio of surface area to lung volume than do advanced forms of lizards and crocodilians. Asymmetry in the size of the paired lungs appears generally in vertebrates, but it is most explicit in reptiles where elongated forms like snakes and some lizards show one lung to be completely atrophied or much smaller than the other. Many reptiles, snakes and lizards, also tend to have the gas exchange surfaces concentrated in the anterior end of the lung. Typically, the trachea may extend halfway down the length of the lung. In such cases the anterior portion is referred to as a tracheal lung. The posterior portion of these lungs is conspicuously free from vascularization and appears to function as a storage chamber for air (Figure 8-24).

In Chelonia (turtles) and crocodilians the lung shows a more uniformly distributed parenchyma. In line with this the airways seem to be more structurally complex, with more distinct secondary bronchi branching off from the primary bronchi that extend from the trachea (Figure 8-24).

Of perhaps greater functional advantage than the structural features of the lung itself are the supporting structural changes that allow reptiles, turtles excepted, to inhale air by suctional attraction. This is accomplished by an

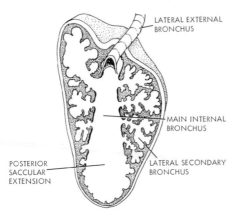

Figure 8-24. A longitudinal section through a snake or lizard lung shows an anterior portion where alveoli are dense and in direct communication with primary bronchi. In its posterior part this type of lung becomes sac-like with sparse vascularization.

expansion of the general body wall brought about by muscular action on the ribs. The resulting internal pressure changes draw air into the lungs. Expiration is effected either by passive recoil of the body wall or by active contraction. This method of ventilating the lungs is far superior to the positive pressure breathing in lungfish and amphibians. Figure 8-25 illustrates the mode of breathing and the muscular support in a turtle. Breathing in turtles, where the ribs are fused to the compact shell, is of necessity different from that in other reptiles. Thus, an important advance in pulmonary breathing of reptiles is in the mechanism of ventilation. A further improvement depends on a more efficient transport function by the cardiovascular system. This will be discussed in the next section, on circulation.

Bird lungs are the most specialized of all vertebrate lungs. Their structural design meets the demands of flight and allows the rapid adjustments that are required by the changes in the metabolic requirements for gas exchange.

Differing from the usual organization of vertebrate lungs into airways and gas exchange surfaces, the bird lung also shows an additional structural component—its unique system of air sacs. These make up the terminal air spaces which communicate on the one hand with the exterior through the lungs and tracheobronchial system (Figure 8-26) and on the other with spaces in some of the larger bones. The air sacs are thin-walled with smooth nonvascular surfaces. They surround most of the viscera and their total volume capacity exceeds by far that of the lungs themselves. The matching of blood and gas for actual gas exchange takes place in the lungs, which are relatively small, situated dorsally in the thoracic region and closely adhered to the overlaying ribs and thoracic vertebrae. The two primary bronchi branching from the trachea pass through the two lungs where they lose their cartilagenous support and give rise to a branching system of tubes, the secondary bronchi. From these tubes a third-order system of bronchi begins, the parabronchi, which finally give rise to a fine system of thin-walled air tubes. These are all interconnected and have a network of blood capillaries interlaced on their internal walls [Figure 8-26(c)]. Gas exchange takes place within the air tubes. The alveoli in mammalian lungs have a corresponding function but differ in being dead-end spaces.

The large-caliber airways, nonfunctional in actual gas exchange, continue through the lung parenchyma into the two abdominal air sacs; other air sacs have smaller connections with second- or third-order bronchi of the lungs. Secondary connections with the system of parabronchi are sometimes referred to as recurrent bronchi. In birds the mechanics of respiration and the passage of air through the lungs into the air sacs and back is not adequately understood. Through a bellows action by the rib musculature on the extensive air sacs, the air flow can reach very high values. The system appears to offer a unique structural advantage in that the deadspace and residual air volumes of the gas exchange portion of the lung can be kept very low. Moreover, the interdigitating system of exchange tubes which allows air to flow

Figure 8-25. (a) Schematic drawing of muscles used in the breathing movements of a turtle. (b) Volume changes of the lung and surrounding cavity during a breathing cycle. (From McCutcheon, 1943.)

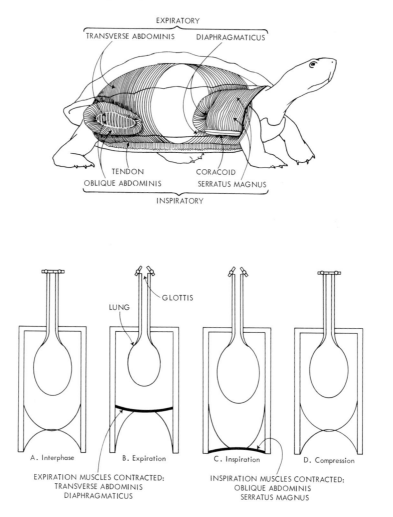

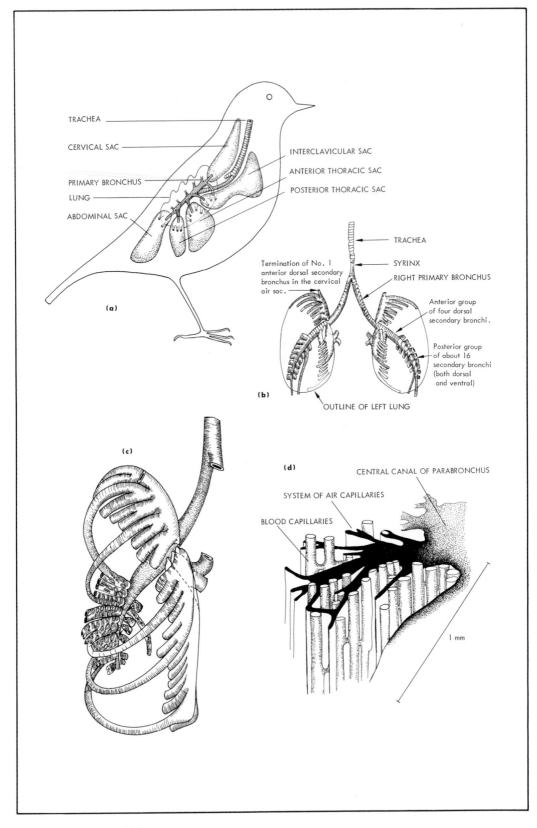

TRACHEA

CERVICAL SAC

PRIMARY BRONCHUS

LUNG

ABDOMINAL SAC

INTERCLAVICULAR SAC

ANTERIOR THORACIC SAC

POSTERIOR THORACIC SAC

(a)

TRACHEA

SYRINX

RIGHT PRIMARY BRONCHUS

Termination of No. 1 anterior dorsal secondary bronchus in the cervical air sac.

Anterior group of four dorsal secondary bronchi.

Posterior group of about 16 secondary bronchi (both dorsal and ventral)

OUTLINE OF LEFT LUNG

(b)

(c)

(d)

CENTRAL CANAL OF PARABRONCHUS

SYSTEM OF AIR CAPILLARIES

BLOOD CAPILLARIES

1 mm

314

constantly in both directions is an excellent and efficient structure for diffusion exchange of the respiratory gases. In addition to the usefulness of the air sacs in increasing the total air capacity and facilitating the exchange in flow through tubes, they help to reduce the specific weight of birds and to regulate their body temperature.

The mammalian lung appears to have evolved from structures most closely represented by those in crocodilian-like reptiles. In addition to internal septation by repeated subdivisions of the airways connected to the trachea and terminating in the blind alveoli, the lungs of mammals are distinctly lobulated. The human lung which typifies the mammalian lung was described in detail in the early part of this chapter. It should be emphasized, however, that the powerful muscular diaphragm that separates the thoracic and abdominal cavities in mammals provides the structural basis for a very efficient suctional attraction of air. The ventilatory capacity of mammals probably exceeds that of all other vertebrates.

Figure 8-26 (opposite). Structure of the lung and airways in birds. (a) Birds hold a large volume of air in their extensive systems of air sacs. The air channels penetrate a large part of the avian skeleton. In addition to serving in gas exchange, the large air content is important because it reduces the specific weight of the bird.

(b) The complicated system of primary and secondary bronchi serve as connecting channels to the air sacs as well as to the parabronchi (tertiary bronchi) where the actual gas exchange takes place.

(c) The parabronchi are tubes about 1 millimeter in diameter. These tubes form numerous arcades between secondary bronchi and anastomose freely.

Dimensions of the various ducts that make up the avian lung.
(The diameters are approximations and refer to a full-grown fowl.)

Duct	Maximum diameter, mm (except for capillaries)
Primary bronchus	
Anterior end	4
Middle	4.5
Posterior end	1
Anterior dorsal secondary bronchi	
At their points of origin from the	
primary bronchus, numbers 1-4	2
At their points of maximum diameter	
Number 1	8
Number 2	5
Number 3	5
Number 4	3
Posterior secondary bronchi	3
Tertiary bronchi	1
Air capillaries	10 microns

(d) When air flows through the parabronchi, it is distributed over the large surface of the air capillaries that radiate from the central canal. The walls of the air capillaries are laced with interdigitating blood capillaries. Gas exchange occurs between the air and blood across the epithelium of the air capillaries and the endothelium of the blood capillaries.

The cardiovascular system is responsible for the transport of materials and
energy within the vertebrate organism and between the exterior environment
and the organ systems. A closed system of tubes, the blood vessels,
constitutes the transport channels. Energy for the propulsion of blood, the
actual carrier in the transport operations, comes from a rhythmically
contracting heart. It is common to all the different transports carried out by
the cardiovascular system that sites for pick up and delivery are represented
by a remarkable arborization of the vascular channels into fine capillary
networks that bring the blood within a short distance of the external
environment in the respiratory organs and to the internal environment of
tissue fluids which bathe the cells.

In the last section we described how the respiratory and circulatory
systems jointly exchange the respiratory gases, oxygen and carbon dioxide,
with the external environment. The other terminal of this vital transport
operation lies in the fine-bore capillaries that perfuse all living tissues. The
final linkage between the capillaries and the cells occurs by simple diffusion
via the interstitial or extracellular fluid. These tissue-capillary networks, the
systemic capillaries, also function as terminals for the delivery of nutrients,
the metabolic fuel, absorbed from ingested food in the gastrointestinal
system. The transport proceeds through important processing plants such as
the liver and other glands before the absorbed nutrients are carried farther to
their destination in the metabolizing cells. The cardiovascular system also
transports enzymes, hormones, and other biogenic regulators between their
production sites and the cellular environment.

Carbon dioxide is not the only metabolic end product carried by the
cardiovascular system. Heat is constantly being produced and must be
distributed and eliminated from the animal in order to maintain its internal
temperature requirements. Excess water and electrolytes are transported to
the kidneys, the main plant for adjusting the fluid balance of the body.
Kidney function requires that the cardiovascular system maintains the blood
pressure needed by the filter units, the glomeruli, which free the blood of
unwanted waste. This filtering process does not, however, discriminate
adequately between substances that need to be eliminated and many that
need to be retained. Consequently an important function of the cardiovascular system in the tubular portions of the kidneys is to take back or
reabsorb into the blood those essential constituents lost in filtration. Details
of the structural basis for these processes will be described in the chapter on
excretion.

Finally, the cardiovascular system performs a vital service to the health of
the organism by providing transport in immunological reactions. The blood
itself serves as substrate for many such reactions and also as a reservoir for
leucocytes and other bacteriophage elements used in defense against disease.
The structure and morphology of the blood, the transport carrier, are in
many respects equal in importance to the structure of the transport network,
the blood vessels and the heart. The cardiovascular system must be safe-
guarded against damage. Consequently all vertebrates store and circulate

316

substances in the blood that will stimulate clotting reactions to prevent blood loss if a cut or injury occurs.

The operational complexity and varied purposes of the cardiovascular transport functions require careful coordination and control of the specific transports. Such control is executed by mechanisms built into the structural components of the cardiovascular system itself and by the autonomic nervous system. We first need to understand the structural design of the various anatomically discrete segments of the cardiovascular system in the light of their functional importance. The vascular channels make up two separate but interrelated systems, the blood vascular system and the lymphatic system. Blood vessels are differentiated into arteries and arterioles carrying blood to the capillaries, and venules and veins bringing blood back to the heart. Finally, the blood itself constitutes a tissue vital to the transport operations.

The Heart: Source of Energy for Blood Movement

The vertebrate circulatory system is closed, that is, the blood that leaves the heart will return again to the heart by a continuous system of tubes. Vertebrate hearts are, in essence, two-stroke pumps with a filling phase and an emptying or ejection phase. Valves are located at appropriate places at the inflow and outflow ends of cardiac chambers to assure the unidirectional passage of blood. Valve actions are purely passive and depend only on the pressure changes at the two sides of a valve (Figure 8-27).

Vertebrate cardiac muscle, or myocardium, has an inherent ability to contract spontaneously in a rhythmic fashion. This autogenic excitation depends structurally on specialized cardiac tissue, referred to as a pacemaker or nodal tissue, discretely located at the venous inflow end of the heart (Figure 8-28). This tissue generates the waves of electrical excitation that result in subsequent contraction. The even spread of the excitation wave, which assures a coordinated contraction, is aided by a conducting system also derived from modified cardiac tissue, often referred to as Purkinje tissue or conducting tissue (Figure 8-28). Vertebrates without well developed conducting tissue depend on a remarkable property of cardiac cells to follow the contraction of neighboring cells in an orderly fashion. This sequence depends on particularly close contact between the cell membranes of neighboring cells and not, as was believed before cardiac tissue was studied with the aid of electron microscopy, on cytoplasmic continuity into a syncytial arrangement of the cardiac cells.

Myocardium has characteristics common with both skeletal muscle and visceral smooth muscle. In functional properties and control, it resembles smooth muscle but it is more akin to skeletal muscle in its red color, cross-striations, and the speed and vigor of contraction. The heart, unlike most other organs, must be on continuous duty and its high metabolic activity requires an effective supply of nourishment and an exchange of respiratory gases and metabolic waste products. The coronary vessels serve as transport channels for this important process. Figure 8-29 shows a coronary angiogram of a shark heart.

The Large Arteries:
Pressure Chambers
for Blood

The arteries leaving the heart are more than passive conduits for the blood on its way to the capillaries. Figure 8-30 summarizes the structural characteristics and the changing function of the arterial tree as we move from the heart to the capillaries. The large component of elastic tissue in the central arteries enables these vessels to serve a crucial function as pressure chambers, temporarily storing the kinetic energy released by the contracting heart as potential energy in their elastic walls. This, in effect, will assure that when

Figure 8-27. Valve action in the cardiovascular system. (a) Cardiac valves are passive structures. They are forced open or closed by pressure differences across their two sides. For example, when the right ventricle of a mammalian heart contracts, the intraventricular pressure exceeds both the right atrial and the pulmonary arterial pressure. Thus the inflow (atrioventricular) valve closes, and the outflow valve to the pulmonary artery opens. (b) Valves are located at strategic points in the veins of the extremities of mammals. Any activity involving the use of the skeletal muscles surrounding the veins will massage the blood in the direction of the heart. Venous valves are also present in the segmental veins of the fish. Use of the swimming muscle exerts a pumping action on the veins and promotes the return of venous blood to the heart.

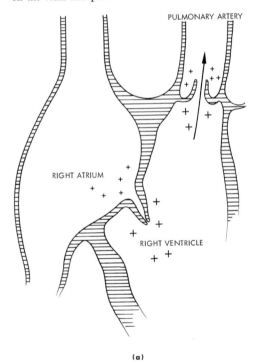

(a)

(b)

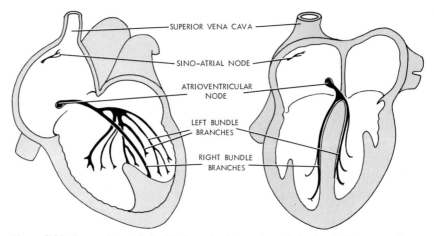

Figure 8-28. Pacemaker and electrical conduction system of the heart. The pacemaker and conduction system of the vertebrate heart generates and transmits the electrical impulses which cause contraction of the cardiac muscle. In lower vertebrates the pacemaker is in the sinus venosus, in higher vertebrates it is located at the superior inflow end to the right atrium and is called the sino-atrial node. The atria have no conduction system, but when the impulse reaches the atrioventricular node, the continued wave of exitation spreads along specialized conducting tissue (Purkinje fibers) in the ventricle. The electrical events of cardiac contraction can be recorded, and is referred to as an electrocardiogram which is of value in the study of cardiac physiology as well as clinical medicine.

the outflow of blood from the heart ceases between beats, the potential energy stored in the arterial walls will continue to drive the blood through the peripheral vessels; thus the intermittent flow of blood in the central arteries is converted to a more continuous flow in the peripheral arterioles and capillaries.

The Smaller Arteries and Arterioles: Resistance Vessels that Control Blood Flow

You will note from Figure 8-30 that the structure of the walls of arteries changes with increasing arborization and reduction in the caliber of the arteries. The elastic connective tissues are far less prominent, whereas the smooth muscle component becomes more conspicuous. This change reflects the change in the function of the arterial tree.

The demands that various organs and tissues make on the transport service of the cardiovascular system constantly change. Obviously the skeletal musculature needs more blood when it is exercising and the gastrointestinal system needs more blood right after a meal. The coordination of these varying requirements is largely handled by the nervous system, but the change in actual blood-flow distribution is executed by the smaller muscular arteries and arterioles. By actively changing their caliber, these vessels alter the resistance to blood flow in accordance with shifting requirements. An important safety and survival factor is built into this system. If simultaneous calls are raised for increased blood flow to many organs, the cardiovascular system may not be able to fill the requests. The autonomic nervous system responds by instructing the arterial smooth muscle to give priority to the more vital organs. This is why the blood flow to the central nervous system or to the heart muscle never drops below a minimal requirement, whereas

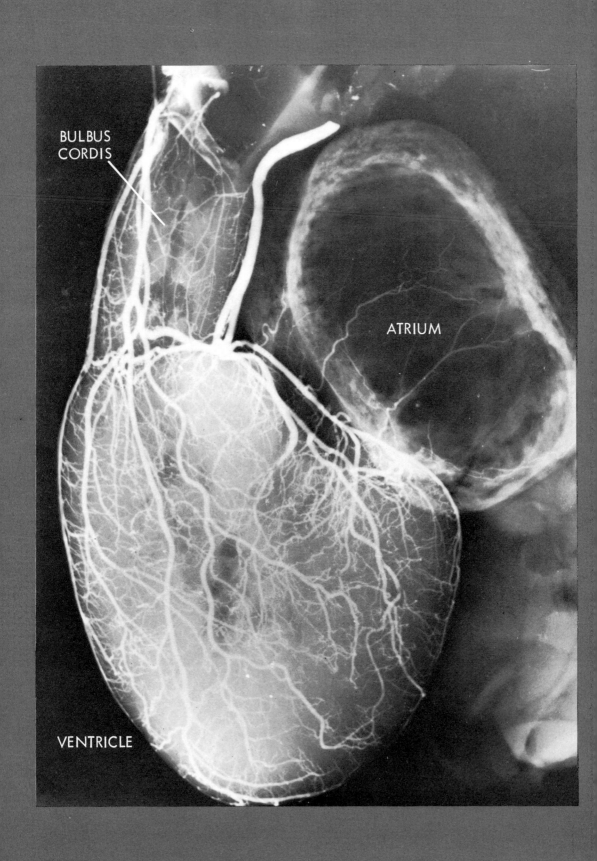

Figure 8-29 (opposite). The coronary arteries of the heart of *Selache maximus,* a large basking shark, have been injected with a radio-opaque medium for X-ray analysis. The coronary vessels bring a continuous supply of nourishment and oxygen to the heart muscle.

blood flow to skin and skeletal muscle can be reduced to very low levels in an emergency.

The Capillaries: Transport Terminals for Blood

When a blood vessel divides the combined cross-sectional area of the two branches is larger than that of the parent vessel [Figure 8-31(a)]. Repeated subdivisions of blood vessels will thus result in a greatly increased total cross-sectional area of the blood path [Figure 8-31(b)].

Figure 8-30. Structure of blood vessels in various parts of the vascular system. Diagram showing how the appearance, dimension, and composition of blood vessels change in accordance with their various functions. The entire vascular system is lined with a sheath of endothelial cells whereas the amount of smooth muscle and connective tissue varies.

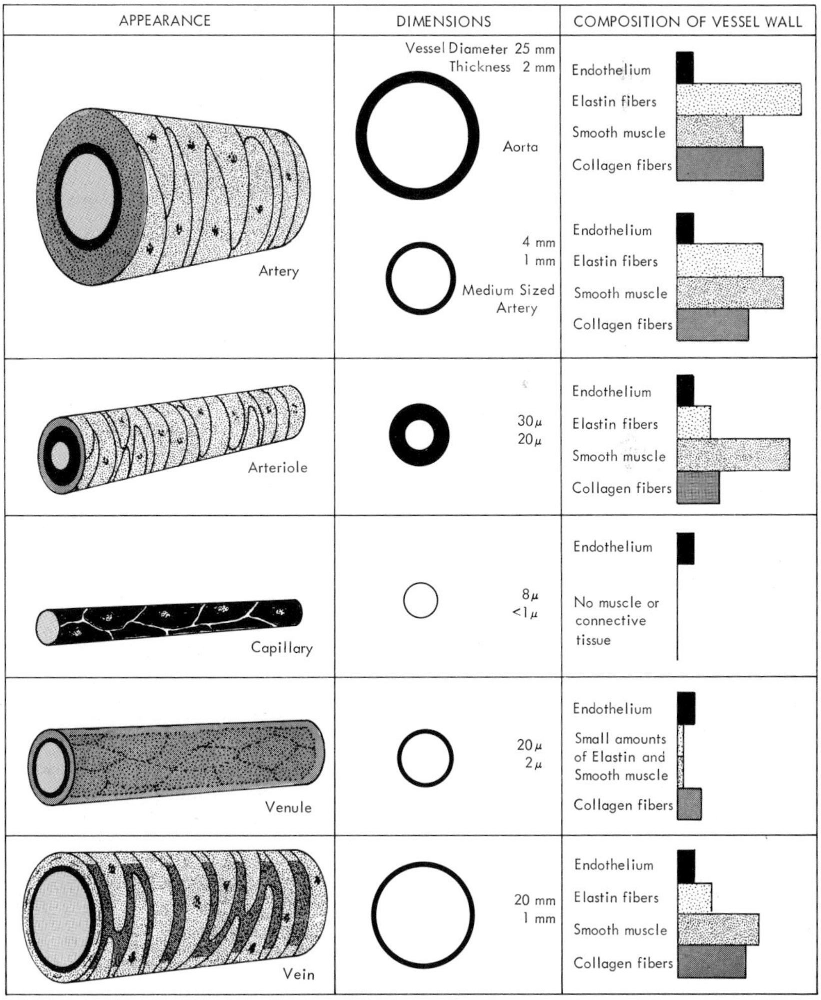

APPEARANCE	DIMENSIONS	COMPOSITION OF VESSEL WALL
Artery	Vessel Diameter 25 mm, Thickness 2 mm — Aorta	Endothelium / Elastin fibers / Smooth muscle / Collagen fibers
	4 mm, 1 mm — Medium Sized Artery	Endothelium / Elastin fibers / Smooth muscle / Collagen fibers
Arteriole	30μ, 20μ	Endothelium / Elastin fibers / Smooth muscle / Collagen fibers
Capillary	8μ, $<1\mu$	Endothelium / No muscle or connective tissue
Venule	20μ, 2μ	Endothelium / Small amounts of Elastin and Smooth muscle / Collagen fibers
Vein	20 mm, 1 mm	Endothelium / Elastin fibers / Smooth muscle / Collagen fibers

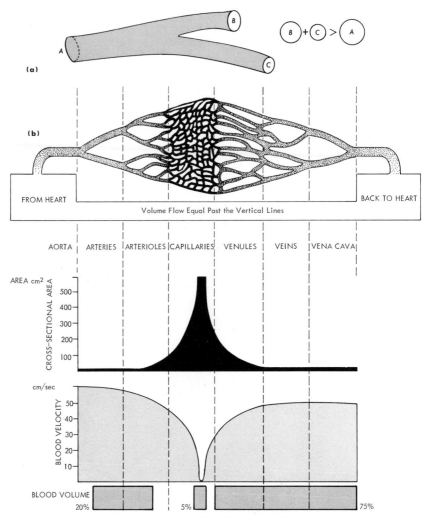

Figure 8-31. (a) When a blood vessel divides, the cross-sectional area of the branches is always greater than that of the parent vessel. $b + c > a$. (b) A schematic representation of the systemic vascular bed in a dog. The vascular system is a closed system of tubes. During any given period of time, the blood flow past any vertical section through the parallel arrangement of vessels must be equal to the volume of blood pumped from the heart or returning to the heart. For any given pressure, the velocity of a fluid is inversely proportional to the cross-sectional area of the tubes through which it flows. Therefore the enormous increase in cross-sectional area produced by the arborization of the arterial tree will cause the blood to slow down in the capillaries. The volume of blood held by the arteries is relatively fixed at about 20% of the total. The volume of blood held by the veins is variable, but under normal conditions they usually contain about 75% of the total.

If the cross-sectional area of the aorta in a mammal is one square centimeter, it can be calculated that the cross-sectional area of all the capillaries combined is more than 800 times larger. It has also been meticulously calculated that the aorta of a dog, by repeated subdivisions, makes up 1,200,000,000 capillaries in the mesenteric vascular bed alone (Table 8-3).

Where accurate counts and calculations are available for other mammals, it has been demonstrated that in skeletal musculature each capillary serves a volume of tissue only ten times larger than its own volume.

These simple geometrical relationships indicate some extremely important features in the design of the capillaries. Because the larger blood vessels as well as the many millions of interconnected capillaries represent a closed continuous system of fluid-filled tubes, some simple hydrodynamic principles apply. The law of continuity of flow in closed tubes states that a volume passing one end of the system per unit time must appear at the other end and must pass any cross-sectional segment of the system in the same time. Stated differently, the product of the total cross-sectional area and the mean velocity of the moving fluid must remain the same throughout the system. Figure 8-3(b) helps to visualize these important features of fundamental consequence to the transport function of the cardiovascular system.

Obviously, the large cross-sectional surface is correlated with a huge overall surface of the capillaries. This will present a large area for exchange diffusion. Moreover, the small size of individual capillaries will result in a remarkable slowing down of the blood, which in turn will promote the exchange of materials across the capillary walls. In a mammal (dog) the blood velocity in the aorta may be forty or fifty centimeters per second, which is reduced to less than 0.1 centimeter per second in the capillaries. The cross-sectional area of each individual capillary is reduced to an order where only one red blood cell at a time can squeeze through. This fantastic dimensional change is perhaps best expressed by the fact that it would take one milliliter of blood more than fourteen years to pass through a single capillary, yet in an adult human more than 5000 times that volume passes through all the capillaries each minute. The dimensional arrangements of capillaries give them a high surface-to-volume ratio, which again benefits exchange diffusion. Last, the thickness of the walls of capillaries is reduced to unbelievable thinness, and

Table 8-3. Geometry of the mesenteric vascular bed of a dog. [Reprinted from A. C. Burton, *Physiology and Biophysics of the Circulation* (Chicago: Yearbook Medical Publications, Inc., 1966), p. 217.]

Kind of Vessel	Diameter (mm)	Number	Total cross-sectional area (cm^2)	Length (cm)	Total volume (cm^3)
Aorta	10	1	0.8	40	30
Large arteries	3	40	3.0	20	60
Main artery branches	1	600	5.0	10	50
Terminal branches	0.6	1,800	5.0	1	25
Arterioles	0.02	40,000,000	125	0.2	25
Capillaries	0.008	1,200,000,000	600	0.1	60
Venules	0.03	80,000,000	570	0.2	110
Terminal veins	1.5	1,800	30	1	30
Main venous branches	2.4	600	27	10	270
Large veins	6.0	40	11	20	220
Vena cava	12.5	1	1.2	40	50

Capillaries through Vena cava: } 740

Total 930

this also ensures rapid and effective diffusion exchange.

The capillary wall consists of only one layer of flat endothelial cells. These cells are laced together by a substance called intercellular cement (Figure 8-30). The reason the ultra-thin endothelial capillary wall can support the substantial pressure needed to drive fluid through the thin tubes can be found in the physical law of La Place, which states the relationship between the pressure (P), the radius (R) and the internal tension (T) in a hollow tube or compartment (T = PR). In a mammal, a large central artery with a thick, elastic, and muscular wall supports a pressure of about 100 millimeters of mercury. In comparison, the capillaries support an average pressure of 30 millimeters of mercury with a wall so thin it can be seen only with a powerful microscope. Yet it does not break because the radius of the capillary is only four or five microns, whereas the central large artery has a radius of more than one centimeter. If you calculate the tension on the walls in the two examples you will see that the large artery must support a wall tension more than 10,000 times that in the capillary wall, in spite of the fact that the inside pressure is only about three times that inside the capillary.

The Venules and Veins: Reservoir for the Blood

The blood, after leaving the exchange vessels for the return to the heart, flows through a system of small tubes, the venules. These vessels show a structure not unlike that of the arterioles, although the vessel wall contains much less smooth muscle (Figure 8-30). The venules are important in controlling the lower end of the pressure gradient across the capillary bed, and hence the fluid balance in the exchange vessels.

Apart from their obvious role in returning blood to the heart, the veins are an important reservoir for blood. Their vessel wall is structured to give them a large and variable capacity [Figure 8-31(b)]. The veins in a higher vertebrate contain 75 percent or more of the total blood volume. Because their capacity is so large, only a small reduction in the caliber of veins will shift a large volume of blood toward the heart. When situations call for an increased outflow from the heart, the first important step in the regulatory mechanisms is an adjustment in the caliber of veins. The resistance to blood flow is low in veins because of their large caliber. Only a small pressure gradient normally suffices to drive the blood back to the heart.

Veins in extremities of most vertebrates have valves to prevent an engorgement of venous blood. Such valves allow the surrounding skeletal musculature to exert rhythmic pressure on the veins, with a squeezing effect on the blood in the direction of the heart. You will have noticed that long passive standing in an upright position will cause your feet to swell, because the fluid balance has been disturbed by inadequate return of the venous blood columns in the legs and feet. It was long thought that venous valves were present only in terrestrial animals, since they experience net gravitational forces. Recent studies have revealed, however, that fish have venous valves and some species even have valves in segmental arteries. In aquatic animals, which experience no net gravitational forces on their hydrostatic columns of blood, valves assist the unidirectional flow of blood. Swimming movements causing changing extra vascular compressive forces are very important to venous return in fish.

The Lymphatic Vessels: Balance Vessels
The lymphatic system is both anatomically and functionally closely associated with the veins. They share in the circulatory transport function by returning constituents of the capillary filtrate to the blood and removing foreign particles and abnormal fluid aggregations from interstitial tissue spaces. Figure 8-32 illustrates the close anatomical association between lymphatics and arteries and veins. Some of the lower vertebrates, notably amphibians but also fish, have lymph hearts that aid in the circulation of lymph.

The Blood: Transport Carrier
Blood is a highly functional tissue in regard both to its liquid part, the plasma, and to its cellular constituents. The percentage of the total volume

Figure 8-32. The lymphatic system is essentially a paravenous system since the lymphatic capillaries lie in close association with the capillaries and veins of the blood vascular system; the collecting lymphatics tend to accompany veins and arteries and drain into the central veins. Like the veins, the lymphatic system consists of both deep and superficial distributions of vessels and carries constitutents of the blood back to the region of the heart. (Redrawn from Rushmer.)

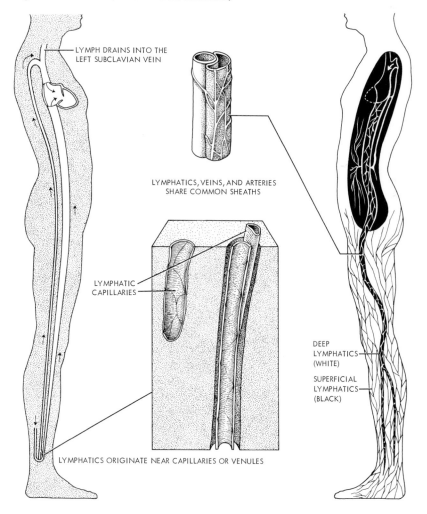

of blood occupied by the cells is called the hematocrit. Among the vertebrates it ranges from 10 percent in some fish to more than 60 percent in diving mammals. The specific gravity of cells is higher than that of plasma, a fact that makes it easy to separate the two fractions by centrifugation. The cell fraction is dominated by the red cells, the erythrocytes. In man there are normally about five million red cells per cubic millimeter. The normal number of white cells or leucocytes is only one six-hundredth of that, ranging from 5000 to 8000 per cubic millimeter (Table 8-4). The chief function of the various types of leucocytes is to defend the body against disease. They do not directly assist in the transport functions of the blood, but their mobility in the blood path makes their defense against pathogenic bacteria more efficient. The third cellular constituent, the thrombocyte (platelet in mammals), is more numerous than white cells but far fewer than red cells. Their role is in hemostasis, the formation of blood clots to prevent bleeding when blood vessels become severed or injured. The red cells or erythrocytes in contrast, are involved largely with the transport functions of the circula-

Table 8-4a. The average number of erythrocytes per lymphocyte in various vertebrate classes.

Class	Erythrocytes per Lymphocyte
Fish	5-12
Amphibians	20-70
Reptiles	100
Birds	70-200
Mammals	350-2000

Table 8-4b. Total erythrocyte count and size in various vertebrates.

	Number (per mm^3 of blood)	Long diameter × short diameter (microns)
Fish		
Lamprey	133,000	15 × 15
Ray	230,000	25 × 14
Flounder	2,000,000	12 × 9
Amphibians		
Salamander (Amphiuma)	95,000	78 × 46
Frog	400,000	22 × 15.5
Reptiles		
Turtle	630,000	21.2 × 12.4
Birds		
Hummingbird	6,500,000	
Ostrich	1,600,000	18 × 9
Mammals		
Man	4,500,000	7-8
	5,000,000	

tory system. In vertebrates the red cells gain their color from hemoglobin, a protein (globin) combined with four iron-containing groups (pyrrole groups). Hemoglobin possesses the ability to associate reversibly with oxygen and thus greatly increases the capacity of the blood to carry oxygen. Hemoglobin, also of utmost importance in carbon dioxide transport, combines directly with carbon dioxide and acts as an important buffer to neutralize acids. The oxygen-carrying capacity of vertebrate bloods ranges from 3 to 4 volume percent in some sluggish fish to more than 35 percent in very active or diving mammals and birds. In contrast to conditions in vertebrates, most invertebrates carry their respiratory pigments, like hemoglobin, in free solution in plasma, rather than enclosed in cells. Cellular hemoglobin makes possible optimal colloid osmotic pressure in the blood, the important force that balances filtration pressure in capillary exchange.

The size and shape of vertebrate red blood cells vary considerably (Figure 8-33). In all inframammalian vertebrates the red cells are nucleated and usually oval and flattened in shape. The mammalian red cell is generally a circular biconcave disc lacking a nucleus in its mature form. It shows an almost unbelievable efficiency in packing the important hemoglobin molecules. As much as 25 percent of the available volume is taken up by hemoglobin molecules, whereas water fills 70 percent and only 5 percent is taken up by other cellular constituents. In lower vertebrates these proportions are different. The nonnucleated type of red cell is one important reason why the oxygen-carrying capacity in mammals can attain such high values. The size of most mammalian red cells is about eight to ten microns in diameter, but in some species such as goats it may be as small as four microns. In contrast, the nucleated cells of fish and amphibians can attain diameters more than ten times, and volumes more than 100 times, greater than those common in mammals.

Blood cells in vertebrates have a limited existence, and new cells continue to develop and differentiate throughout the life of the organism. Like the rest of the tissues making up the circulatory system, the blood cells originate from mesoderm, and the tissues in which blood cells are formed later are called hemopoietic tissues. In vertebrate embryos hemopoietic tissues are very widespread, whereas they become more restricted in the adults. In teleost fish the kidneys show hemopoietic activity through the whole life cycle. In higher vertebrates the bone marrow is a most important site for blood cell production. Blood-forming tissues have also aggregated to form discrete hemopoietic organs like the spleen, for the formation, storage, and destruction of blood cells; and in mammals specialized lymph nodes produce lymphocytes.

Plasma, the other fraction of blood, is about 90 percent water by weight. Solid constituents (7 percent in mammals) are largely the plasma proteins which serve an important function in the fluid balance of the circulatory system. Since most of the protein molecules are too large to be filtered through the capillary walls, they remain inside the vessels where they create a colloid osmotic pressure greater than the osmotic pressure in the extravascular fluid. This resulting inward osmotic force is of crucial importance in maintaining the delicate balance between the fluid compartments of the body. The most important plasma proteins in vertebrates are the albumins and globulins. Besides maintaining the osmotic balance, the globulins, at least in higher vertebrates, function in antibody reactions to protect against disease. Fibrinogen is another protein that is crucial to the blood-clotting mechanism. Lipoproteins are important carriers of lipids to the various sites of synthesis in cells. All the plasma proteins are important agents that assist hemoglobin, carbonates, and other buffers to maintain the blood pH within narrow limits.

Phylogeny of the Vertebrate Circulatory System   The intimate functional connection between the respiratory and circulatory systems is also expressed in their phylogenetic development. In fact, changes in the mode of breathing have been the primary and most decisive factor in the evolutionary transformation of the cardiovascular system.

The branchial arches provide the structural basis for the respiratory organs in fish. Because the process of gas exchange with the environment is inseparably related to the transport function of the cardiovascular system, it is not surprising that the vascular channels, the blood vessels bringing blood to the

Figure 8-33. Morphology and size of various blood cells in vertebrates.

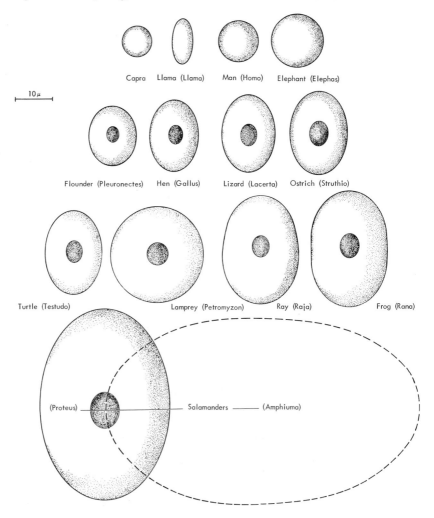

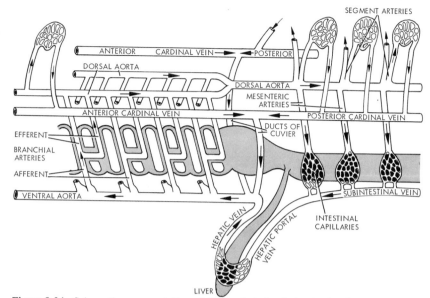

Figure 8-34. Schematic representation of the central circulation in *Amphioxus*.

branchial region, show a close spatial relationship to the branchial arches so that the paired vessels of the system, the aortic arches, match the number of branchial arches. After traversing the branchial region the vessels converge and connect to the dorsal aorta where the distributing arterial system originates. This fundamental plan is similar in the embryological development of all vertebrates. Subsequent changes in this vascular arrangement have occurred in response to a reduction or redistribution of the gas-exchanging surfaces of the gills or to the gradual development of aerial gas exchange and lungs in lungfish and tetrapods.

The vascular system in Amphioxus is often said to resemble that in ancestral vertebrates. Amphioxus lacks a discrete heart; blood is propelled forward in the ventral aorta by a peristaltic contraction of the vessel itself. The fifty or so pairs of gill arches receive paired afferent vessels (aortic arches). Where these branch off from the ventral aorta, contractile enlargements contribute to the further propulsion of blood (Figure 8-34). The branchial vessels converge to form the dorsal aorta which is paired in the branchial region. The forward extensions of the dorsal aortae correspond to the vertebrate internal carotids that supply much of the cranial circulation. Paired segmental arteries and unpaired arteries to the viscera branch off from the median dorsal aorta in its posterior course. The return of venous blood to the ventral aorta goes through posterior cardinals and subintestinal veins. The subintestinal veins resolve in the liver, where they recollect as hepatic veins. These, together with the postcardinals and the precardinals, unite to form the ducts of Cuvier which continue into the ventral aorta via the sinus venosus (Figure 8-34). Amphioxus does not show a renal portal system.

The fish heart, like that of all vertebrate embryos, develops from the ventral median blood vessel in the branchial region. During development the heart becomes oriented in a posterior direction in apparent correlation with the adult type of breathing. In gill-breathing aquatic species it remains in its anterior location, whereas in lung-breathing forms it has a more posterior position. The progressive development and differentiation of a distinct neck region in tetrapods contributes further to the posterior location of the heart.

The typical fish heart is often referred to as a venous heart because all the inflow is deoxygenated blood returning from the tissues. Similarly, it is called a single heart because it pumps blood of only one type and because the entire output from the heart is routed through the aortic arches perfusing the gills (Figure 8-35) where gas exchange takes place. The postbranchial circulation of blood leaving the gas exchange surfaces is called the systemic circulation. In the circulation of fish characteristically the gas exchange vessels are in direct series with the systemic vessels in one continuous circuit. After lung breathing became established in tetrapods the two types of vascular bed were still connected in series but in a double circuit in which the heart connected the two. In vertebrates that depend on bimodal gas exchange, such as lungfish, amphibians and in part in some reptiles, the respiratory vascular bed and the systemic vascular beds are coupled not in series but in parallel. During the evolution of air breathing, different vascular arrangements developed, some of which are still retained in air-breathing fish such as the bowfin and garpike, the bichir (*Polypterus*), the electric eel, and others (Figure 8-35).

Circulation in a Typical Fish
: Circulation in elasmobranchs (sharks and skates) is typical of fish where the heart consists of four chambers: the sinus venosus, the atrium, the ventricle, and the bulbus cordis (Figure 8-36). The whole organ is enclosed in a pericardial cavity surrounded by a lining, the pericardium, which in many fish, particularly the chondrichthyians and chondrosteans, is tough and makes a rigid casing around the heart. This pericardial cavity develops as an anterior portion of the primary coelom and becomes separated from the abdominal portion by the development of a septum transversum. In chondrichthyians (shark) and chondrosteans (sturgeon) the pericardial cavity retains a small communication with the abdominal cavity through a duct, the pericardio-peritoneal canal.

The receiving chamber of the fish heart, the sinus venosus, is thin walled and sparsely equipped with cardiac muscle fibers. Blood enters the sinus venosus through the paired ducts of Cuvier which in turn connect with

Figure 8-35 (opposite). Evolution of vascular circuits in vertebrates. (a) During the evolution of air-breathing mechanisms many fish were bimodal breathers, retaining functional gills while developing air-breathing organs. New vascular circuits developed to these organs. The arrangement in (a) is typical of the teleost *Symbranchus marmoratus*, which can use its gills and a vascular oral mucosa for air breathing.

(b) Only in the lungfish did the new air-breathing organ have a vascular circuit with direct connection back to the heart (a pulmonary vein). This condition was conducive to development of a partial separation of the two sides of the heart resulting in a partial separation of the well oxygenated (pulmonary venous) and poorly oxygenated (systemic venous) blood on their passage through the heart.

(c) In the homeotherm vertebrates, birds and mammals, the pulmonary and systemic vascular beds have attained complete separation in the heart. No admixture of the two types of blood occurs.

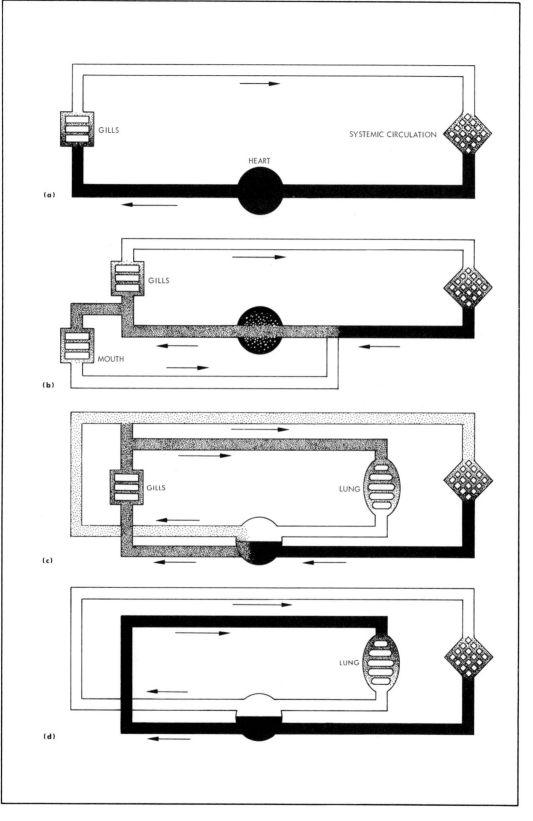

331

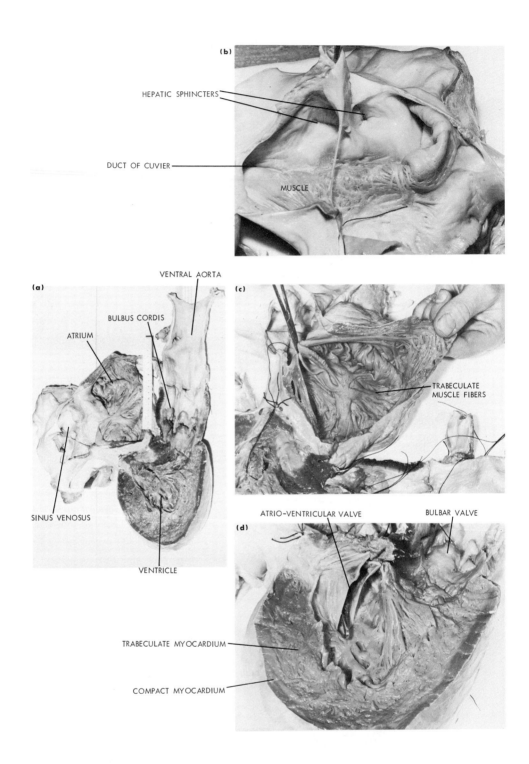

(b)

HEPATIC SPHINCTERS

DUCT OF CUVIER

MUSCLE

(a)

VENTRAL AORTA

BULBUS CORDIS

ATRIUM

(c)

TRABECULATE
MUSCLE FIBERS

SINUS VENOSUS

VENTRICLE

ATRIO-VENTRICULAR VALVE

BULBAR VALVE

(d)

TRABECULATE MYOCARDIUM

COMPACT MYOCARDIUM

anterior and posterior cardinal veins, the lateral veins, and the subclavian veins [Figure 8-37(a) and (b)]. In addition, the sinus venosus of elasmobranchs receives a substantial venous inflow through the hepatic veins entering directly through the septum transversum. This entrance is guarded by peculiar muscular sphincters acting as valves and controlling the large venous flow through the liver.

Effective propulsion of blood by a cardiac chamber requires valves that will prevent the regurgitation of blood when the chamber contracts. The sinus venosus lacks such valves at the inflow side, but X-ray studies have shown that it shortens considerably with each contraction, propelling blood into the atrium. A surprisingly small amount of blood is regurgitated posteriorly because the walls of the ducts of Cuvier have narrowed and the muscular sphincters guard the hepatic vein entrances to the sinus venosus.

The atrium is filled by the contraction of the sinus venosus and the pressure head building up in the great inflow veins to the heart. Unlike the sinus venosus the atrium is guarded by valves on both its inflow and outflow sides. This enables the chamber to have a more active part in pumping blood forward; the contractile force will close the inflow valves and propel blood in the anterior direction only. The presence of atrial valves is correlated with a more uniform distribution of cardiac muscle fibers in the atrial wall. This wall is still thin but numerous diverticulated extensions add to the overall volume of the chamber which, in fish, has the largest capacity of all the cardiac chambers. It functions as a distensible storage compartment and as a most important chamber for filling the main pump, the ventricle. It should be noted that when the sinus venosus is reduced and absorbed in the right atrium of higher tetrapods, the atrial inflow valves also disappear and the relative importance of the atria for filling the ventricles is much less than in fish.

The filling of the ventricle of all vertebrates is crucial for its performance as a pump. It has been shown that increased filling and distention of the ventricle increases the energy released by its subsequent contraction. Hence, it becomes important that the muscle fibers of the ventricle be arranged to offer minimal resistance to filling and distention, because filling occurs in response to very low pressure. Yet the ventricle must contain powerful muscle fibers that during contraction develop sufficient energy to overcome the arterial pressure on the outflow side and to eject a major portion of its volume. The architecture of the ventricular muscle differs markedly among the vertebrates. In fish the ventricular myocardium is spongy and fills almost

Figure 8-36. (a) The fish heart is typified by the large basking shark, *Selache maximus*. The four chambers of the heart, the sinus venosus, atrium, ventricle, and bulbus cordis, are invested in a tough semirigid pericardium. (b) The sinus venosus is a spacious chamber sparsely equipped with muscle fibers. Blood enters the sinus venosus from the ducts of Cuvier and through the sphincters marking the entrance from the hepatic veins. (c) The atrium has the largest capacity of all chambers in the fish heart. It is thin walled but well equipped with musculature. Valves prevent regurgitation to the sinus venosus during atrial contraction. Atrioventricular valves prevent backflow to the atrium during ventricular contraction. (d) The ventricle has a dense outer layer of compact myocardium. Most of the ventricle consists of a trabeculate sponge-like myocardium. A small central lumen shows the opening of the atrioventricular valve.

its entire cross-section. Instead of being held in a spacious central lumen, the blood fills up the thousands of smaller compartments between the trabeculated loosely arranged muscle fibers (Figure 8-36). This structural design of the ventricle may offer less tension on the individual fibers during their contraction. Efficient valves, the atrioventricular, guard the entrance from the atrium to the ventricle, and these close during the powerful ventricular contraction with its rapid development of high pressure.

Ventricular outflow is through the fourth chamber of the fish heart, the bulbus cordis. In elasmobranchs this chamber represents a direct forward continuation of the cardiac muscle. In higher fish such as the teleosts, the bulbus cordis is reduced and replaced by a bulbous swelling of the smooth muscle and elastic tissues of the ventral aorta. This latter structure, referred to as the bulbus arteriosus, belongs with the arterial system and not with the heart itself. The bulbus cordis of the elasmobranchs houses a variable number of outflow valves that prevent backflow of the cardiac ejectate. This heart chamber has three main functions. (1) Its musculature supplies the necessary support for the patency of the valves. The distention of the bulbous tube during ventricular contraction might otherwise interfere with the valve closure. (2) The bulbus cordis is an effective pressure chamber; it converts the abrupt ventricular pressure stroke to a more extended depulsated stroke which in effect prolongs the overall ejection time from the heart. (3) The bulbus cordis adds a small volume of blood to the ventricular ejectate passing through it with each contraction and thus functions as an auxiliary pump.

The single ventricular pump of the fish heart can be considered a pressure pump because it must develop a pressure in excess of the high arterial pressure to eject its stroke volume. The pumping action of the heart as it expells blood into the ventral aorta has an additional indirect effect that is particularly explicit in the chondrichthyians. In these forms, which have a rigid, tough pericardium, a sub-ambient pressure prevails in the pericardial space. The reduction in the size of the ventricle during its contraction will cause a transient further reduction of pressure in the pericardial fluid surrounding the heart. In turn this low pressure surrounding the heart will be transmitted into the thin-walled receiving chambers, as well as to the larger central veins. The resulting increase of the venous pressure gradient toward the heart will promote the venous return [Figure 8-37(b)]. In a sense the heart becomes a suction pump for venous blood returning to the heart while it has the opposite role of pressure pump for ejecting the blood on the outflow side of the heart. This double effect, possible only because of the rigid pericardium surrounding the heart, is also present to a lesser degree in teleost and dipnoan fish as well as in some amphibians. The pericardium also has an

Figure 8-37 (opposite). (a) Schematic representation of the elasmobranch heart showing the tough semirigid pericardium surrounding the cardiac chambers. (b) A subambient pressure always prevails inside the pericardium. This will steepen the pressure gradient toward the heart along the veins and promote venous return. When the ventricle contracts blood is ejected into the ventral aorta and intrapericardial pressure is reduced still further. This pressure transmits through the thin walls of the sinus venosus and atrium and causes a suctional attraction for venous blood. In this manner the heart functions both as a pressure pump and a suction pump.

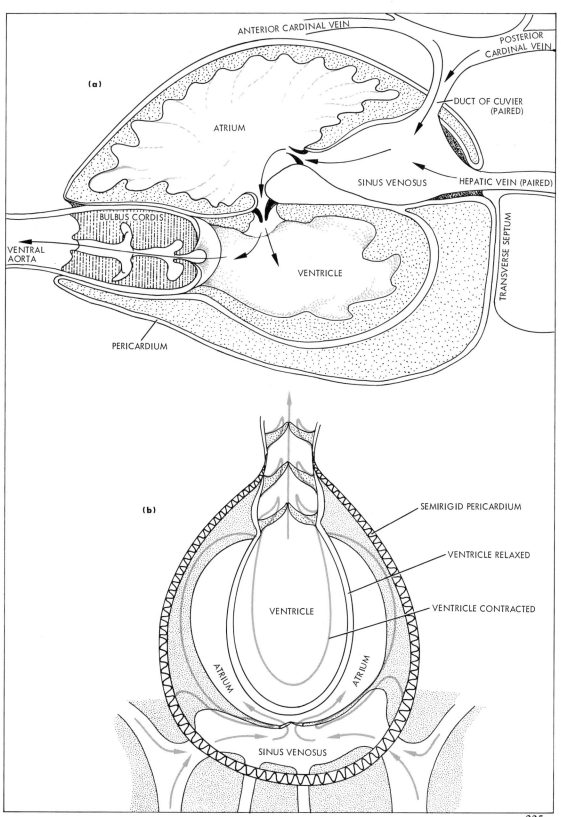

ANTERIOR CARDINAL VEIN

POSTERIOR CARDINAL VEIN

(a)

ATRIUM

DUCT OF CUVIER (PAIRED)

SINUS VENOSUS

HEPATIC VEIN (PAIRED)

BULBUS CORDIS

VENTRAL AORTA

VENTRICLE

TRANSVERSE SEPTUM

PERICARDIUM

(b)

SEMIRIGID PERICARDIUM

VENTRICLE RELAXED

VENTRICLE CONTRACTED

VENTRICLE

ATRIUM

ATRIUM

SINUS VENOSUS

335

important cushioning effect on the heart, suspended as it is in a fluid-filled compartment.

In all the gnathostome fish, six pairs of aortic arches develop embryologically, but among the adults there is great variation and modification in the number retained. No extant adult gnathostome has a first aortic arch. In some forms the anterior margin of the spiracle, which should be perfused by the first aortic arch, shows a small gill, but this is supplied by the efferent portion of the second aortic arch or by a vessel linked with the dorsal aorta. This small gill thus is not perfused with deoxygenated blood from the ventral aorta and consequently is called a pseudobranch. The efferent portion of the first aortic arch exists in some fish and is linked with arteries supplying the brain. The second aortic arch is typically present in chondrichthyians and perfuses a hemibranch between the spiracle and the first gill slit. In other fish the second aortic arch has a more inconsistent pattern. However, all fish as a rule show fully developed aortic arches III through VI.

In all fish the dorsal aorta continues forward into the internal carotid arteries (Figure 8-38), and in its posterior course is the distributing vessel for the entire arterial (systemic) circulation. Associated with the appearance of paired fins in chondrichthyians are the subclavian and iliac arteries branching from this vessel. Other branches include three arteries supplying the gastrointestinal tract, the coeliac and the anterior and posterior mesenterics. In addition there are renal arteries to the kidneys, intersegmental arteries to the body wall, and arteries to the gonads. Arteries break down into exchange vessels or capillaries in gills, lungs, and general metabolizing tissues; additional capillary beds are known as portal vascular beds.

The hepatic portal system, which is present in all vertebrates, receives its main blood supply from the veins draining the intestines, and empties

Figure 8-38. Schematic diagram of the central circulation in a fish (shark).

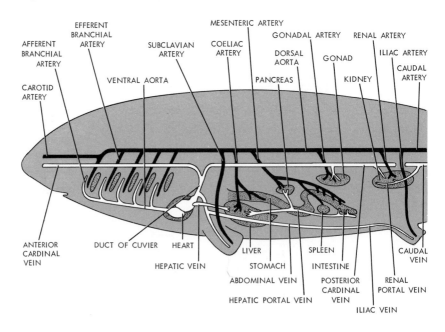

into a second capillary network in the liver. From there the blood collects
into larger veins that finally make up the hepatic veins draining into the
larger systemic veins or directly into the sinus venosus (elasmobranchs). The
functional significance of the hepatic portal system lies in its direct dispatch
of the nutriments absorbed by the intestines to the liver for further processing and storage (Figure 8-39).

Another type of portal circulation, the renal portal system, exists in fish
and lower tetrapods. This system develops as the result of a routing of the
entire caudal venous backflow, or a part of it, through capillaries in the
kidneys (Figure 8-39). When it leaves the kidneys, this blood flows in the
posterior cardinals or the posterior vena cava. The tissues perfused by a
portal system do not receive the needed oxygen from its portal afferent
supply because this blood is already deoxygenated. However, in addition to
the inflowing venous blood, these organs receive a supply of systemic arterial
blood via vessels branching off from the dorsal aorta (hepatic and renal
arteries).

Circulation in
Lungfish:
The Rise of
a Double
Circulation

The usefulness of any respiratory organ depends on how the vascular system
links the gas exchange surfaces in gills or lungs with the cells and tissues that
build the organism. Ideally, a respiratory organ should be supplied with the
most deoxygenated carbon dioxide-rich blood, while the discharge of
oxygen-rich blood from the respiratory organ to the metabolizing cells
should be as direct as possible. This scheme is fulfilled in fish (Figures 8-35,
8-38) and in birds and mammals, although in different ways, by a single
circulation in fish and by a completely separated double circulation in birds
and mammals (Figure 8-35). The gradual change from a single to a double
circulation is represented in lungfish, amphibians, and reptiles. This change
was probably the most profound adaptive change in the entire evolution of
vertebrates; it started with the adoption of air breathing.

It is essential to realize that the rise of air breathing started while vertebrates were still aquatic. Climatic conditions existing 350 million years ago
brought about very low oxygen concentrations in large tropical fresh-water
basins, and this created marginal and limiting conditions for vertebrate life.
The development of air breathing was thus originally the result of lack of
oxygen in water and the air-breathing organs were primarily organs for
oxygen absorption. However, the original respiratory organs, the gills, had
been long in the making and served important additional functions in carbon
dioxide elimination and other excretory processes. In addition, aquatic
organisms had arrived at solutions to fluid balance that depended on the
presence of gills. It was logical, then, and also typical of early air breathers,
that they kept the primary respiratory organs, the gills, and in fact, had a
bimodal breathing, extracting oxygen directly from the atmosphere but
retaining their gills for elimination of carbon dioxide and osmotic control
with the aquatic medium. In the preceding chapter the piscine swim bladder
and the tetrapod lung were described as homologous structures and available
evidence suggested that the original function of the swim bladder was respiratory.

A bimodal gas exchange called for major rearrangements of the cardiovascular system to increase the effectiveness of the new gas exchange organ.

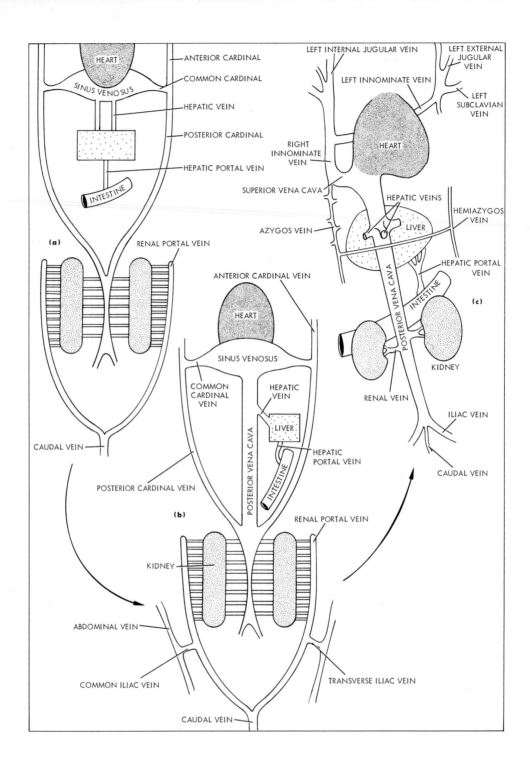

Figure 8-39. Diagrammatic outline of the transformation of the cardinal veins into the vena cava in representative vertebrates. The hepatic and renal portal systems and their transformation are also depicted. (a) Fish stage; (b) lungfish and lower tetrapod stage; (c) mammalian stage.

338

The first important steps in that direction are exemplified in the extant lung-fish. The most notable change is a separate routing of the blood from the aerial gas exchange organ, the lung, directly back to the heart. This is the first phylogenetic manifestation of the pulmonary vein, which in turn is the first structural vascular adaptation to minimize the mixing of oxygenated and deoxygenated blood. Many fresh-water fish have developed elaborate structural adaptations for air breathing but only in the lungfish is the vascular system modified to promote the efficiency of the air-breathing organ (Figures 8-34, 8-40).

While they retained their functional organs for aquatic respiration (gills) the air-breathing fish showed a gradual reduction of these as air breathing became more efficient and important (Figure 8-40).

The reduction in the distribution of gills on the primary branchial arches is correlated with corresponding changes in the aortic arches. The Australian lungfish is primarily a water breather and shows a typical piscine arrangement of the aortic arches, all of them diverging into branchial exchange vessels in the gills. In the African lungfish, air breathing has increased in importance and branchial arches 3 and 4 have become gill-less with the result that aortic arches 3 and 4 represent direct shunts to the dorsal aorta.

Figure 8-40. Central circulation in the African lungfish, *Protopterus*. Note that gills are absent on two branchial arches. A pulmonary artery branching off from the most posterior epibranchial artery and a pulmonary vein returning directly to the heart are features first seen among extant vertebrates in the lungfish.

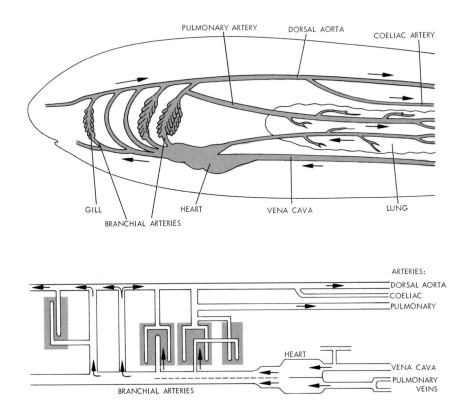

In lungfish and all tetrapods, as well as in some primitive fish showing a respiratory function of the swim bladder, the air-breathing organs are supplied with blood from specialized pulmonary arteries branching from the most posterior epibranchial arteries, derived from the sixth aortic arch (Figure 8-40).

Correlated with the development of separate specialized vessels conveying blood to the lung and back from the lung to the heart are structural changes in the heart itself which accommodate two blood streams of different quality. Thus the atrium in the lungfish has become partially divided by a septum. The sinus venosus connects the large systemic veins to the right portion of the partially divided atrium while the pulmonary vein carrying oxygenated blood empties to the left in the atrium. The partial atrial septum and the direction and dynamics of inflow prevent extensive mixing of the two types of blood in the atrium. Following atrial contraction this separation is maintained in the ventricle, which also shows a partial septum extending from the apex of the heart (Figure 8-41). Ventricular contraction expels the blood in a laminar streamlined flow pattern so that extensive mixing is also avoided in the anterior undivided part of the ventricle. In the bulbus cordis the separation of the two blood streams is largely maintained by the spiral folds that make a partial division of the bulbus in two channels. In the anterior end of the bulbus the two spiral folds fuse to form completely separated channels. A ventral channel dispatches the oxygen-enriched blood through the anterior aortic arches directly across to the dorsal aorta for direct distribution to the tissues, while most of the oxygen-depleted carbon dioxide systemic venous blood is conveyed via the dorsal bulbus channel to the posterior gill-bearing branchial arches. This blood will be subjected to gas exchange in the remaining gills where carbon dioxide will be eliminated. Subsequently, the greater portion of the blood traversing the sixth aortic arches will be diverted via the pulmonary arteries to the lungs where most of the oxygen absorption occurs.

Circulation in the lungfish (*Protopterus* and *Lepidosiren*) shows a high degree of selective passage through the heart. Blood rich in oxygen and low in carbon dioxide is conveyed predominantly to the anterior systemic aortic arches with little recirculation of blood to the lung. In turn, the most oxygen-depleted blood is channeled to the posterior arches. It is, however, important to realize that this arrangement can change depending on conditions in the external environment. These fish may experience aerated water in which most but not all of their respiratory needs can be supported by aquatic respiration. Conversely, they may experience very adverse oxygen-poor and carbon dioxide-rich water that compels their systems to rely more on aerial respiration. Finally, they may become air exposed during drought and thus be entirely at the mercy of their lungs for gas exchange.

Accordingly, the lungfish need the flexibility their vascular system offers in dispatching blood to the alternative organs for gas exchange. These animals are also first to show modifications in the typical piscine pattern of veins; the most notable change is the appearance of the large caval vein in replacement for the right cardinal vein in the more primitive fish (Figure 8-39).

Amphibian
Circulation

The circulatory system of amphibians shows little advance over that in lung-fish in regard to a complete separation of the systemic and respiratory vascular circuits. The differences reflect the diversity in modes of respiration seen in amphibians, such as external gills in neotenic salamanders, bucco-pharyngeal breathing, pulmonary breathing, and cutaneous breathing (see the previous section). This diversity is also reflected in the pattern of the aortic arches and their branches. In larval and neotenic urodeles (Figure 8-42), aortic arches 3, 4, and 5 usually branch into exchange vessels in the gills, whereas the sixth aortic arch functions as an afferent vessel to the lungs. However, a connection remains between the sixth aortic arch and the dorsal aorta (ductus arteriosus, ductus botalli) (Figure 8-42). In adult gill-less

Figure 8-41. Diagram showing the structure of the ventricle and the bulbus cordis seen from the dorsal side, and the course of the spiral fold and the shorter left fold in the conus arteriosus. The arrows indicate the course of the arterial and the venous blood flow. A, the anteriorly joined part of the folds; B, the short left fold; C, the spiral fold. Three cross-sections are shown at (a), (b), and (c).

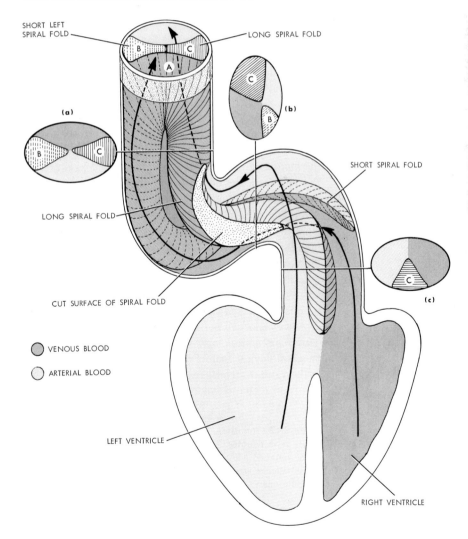

urodeles all aortic arches become direct, uninterrupted vessels. Arch 3 serves as parent vessel for the internal carotid system (Figure 8-42) and only in some species does this arch retain a connection with the dorsal aortic system through the ductus caroticus. Aortic arches 4 and 5 pass directly to the dorsal aorta. Arch 6 also retains a connection (ductus arteriosus), but this duct is functionally not very significant. The principal role of arch 6 is to serve as parent vessel for the pulmonary arteries. In adult anuran amphibians (Figure 8-42) further modifications include a loss of aortic arch 5 and the ductus aorticus. In addition to perfusing the lung, arch 6 gives rise to vessels perfusing the skin, which in many amphibians has a respiratory function, particularly in the elimination of carbon dioxide.

Turning to the venous backflow to the amphibian heart, the pulmonary vein of amphibians drains separately into the left atrial space. The systemic veins empty via the sinus venosus in the right atrial space. Blood returning from the skin is not routed to the left atrium but is mixed with systemic venous blood before entering the heart. The usefulness of the amphibian skin as a respiratory organ thus is limited to elevating the oxygen content of the systemic venous blood and has no direct part in providing oxygen-rich blood to tissues in need of it. It seems as though skin is too nonspecialized and too involved in other functions to have been selectively connected into a vascular circuit that joins the rest of the circulation only in the heart.

The heart itself shows a functional division of the atrial space into two compartments. The atrial septum in some salamanders is reported to be fenestrated, but little or no mixing of blood inside the atrium appears to result from this. Notably, the amphibian ventricle shows no ventricular septum. However, the densely trabeculated, sponge-like myocardium tends to arrest the blood inside the numerous small crypts and spaces and thus minimizes the mixing of the two types of atrial blood as they enter the ventricle. During ventricular contraction the blood is ejected in laminar streamlines. The bulbus cordis in amphibians is shorter than in the lungfish and the aortic arches have a separate origin closer to the base of the heart. As in the lungfish, the spiral fold maintains the separate outflow of the two types of blood confined to the left (oxygen-rich) and right (oxygen-depleted) sides of the ventricle.

Various studies based on indicator techniques such as radiological (X-ray) and dye dilution experiments as well as on analysis of blood gases in the various inflow and outflow vessels of the heart have documented an amazing degree of selective perfusion through the amphibian heart in spite of its only partial anatomical separation. The separation is, however, labile and depends on physiological factors such as blood pressure levels and vascular resistance in the various arterial trunks originating from the bulbus cordis. The selective perfusion tends to minimize recirculation to the lungs by channeling the

Figure 8-42 (opposite). Diagrammatic representation of the transformation of the aortic arches in vertebrates. Aortic arches are numbered with arabic numerals, gill slits with roman numerals. The dashed lines indicate extinct conditions. A, artery; AO, aorta; CA, cutaneous artery; COR A, coronary artery; DA, dorsal aorta; DC, ductus caroticus; PA, pulmonary artery; S, spiracle.

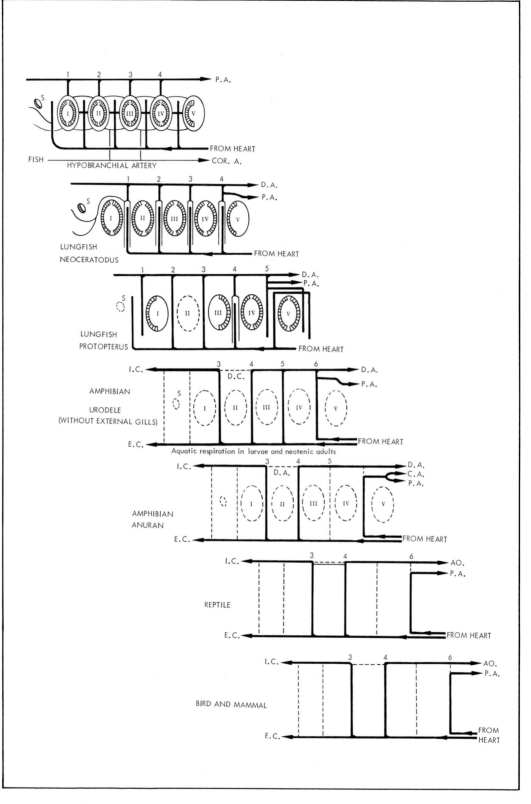

FISH

1 2 3 4 → P.A.

S

I II III IV V

FROM HEART

HYPOBRANCHIAL ARTERY → COR. A.

LUNGFISH
NEOCERATODUS

1 2 3 4 → D.A.
→ P.A.

S

I II III IV V

FROM HEART

LUNGFISH
PROTOPTERUS

1 2 3 4 5 → D.A.
→ P.A.

S

I II III IV V

FROM HEART

AMPHIBIAN

URODELE
(WITHOUT EXTERNAL GILLS)

I.C. ← 3 4 5 6 → D.A.
D.C. → P.A.

S

I II III IV V

E.C. ← FROM HEART

Aquatic respiration in larvae and neotenic adults

AMPHIBIAN
ANURAN

I.C. ← 3 4 5 → D.A.
D.A. → C.A.
→ P.A.

I II III IV V

E.C. ← FROM HEART

REPTILE

I.C. ← 3 4 6 → AO.
→ P.A.

E.C. ← FROM HEART

BIRD AND MAMMAL

I.C. ← 3 4 6 → AO.
→ P.A.

E.C. ← FROM HEART

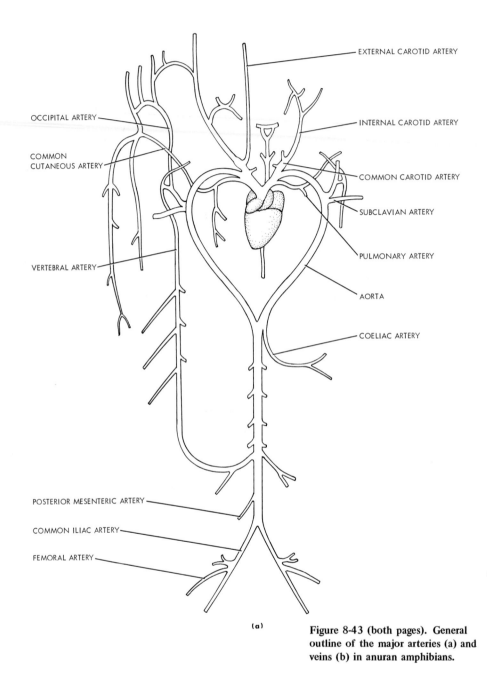

EXTERNAL CAROTID ARTERY

OCCIPITAL ARTERY

INTERNAL CAROTID ARTERY

COMMON
CUTANEOUS ARTERY

COMMON CAROTID ARTERY

SUBCLAVIAN ARTERY

PULMONARY ARTERY

VERTEBRAL ARTERY

AORTA

COELIAC ARTERY

POSTERIOR MESENTERIC ARTERY

COMMON ILIAC ARTERY

FEMORAL ARTERY

(a)

Figure 8-43 (both pages). General outline of the major arteries (a) and veins (b) in anuran amphibians.

344

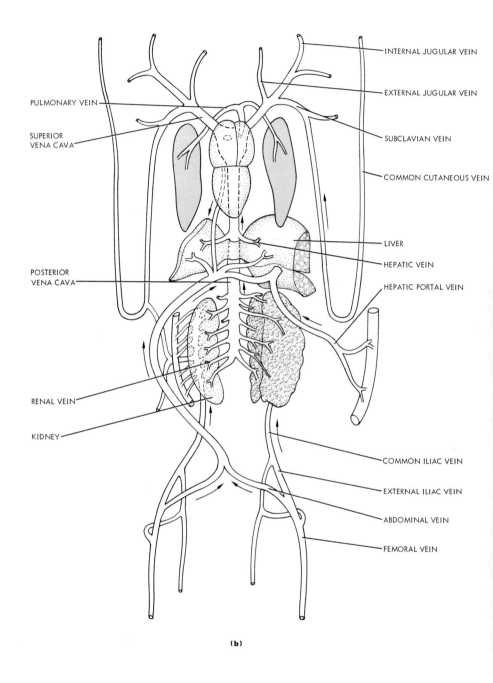

PULMONARY VEIN

SUPERIOR
VENA CAVA

POSTERIOR
VENA CAVA

RENAL VEIN

KIDNEY

INTERNAL JUGULAR VEIN

EXTERNAL JUGULAR VEIN

SUBCLAVIAN VEIN

COMMON CUTANEOUS VEIN

LIVER

HEPATIC VEIN

HEPATIC PORTAL VEIN

COMMON ILIAC VEIN

EXTERNAL ILIAC VEIN

ABDOMINAL VEIN

FEMORAL VEIN

(b)

oxygen-rich left atrial blood to the carotid and aortic arches, whereas the oxygen-poor blood reaching the heart from the systemic veins is selectively channeled to the sixth aortic arches where the pulmonary and skin circulations originate.

You will often see the argument that amphibians really do not gain from having a separated perfusion through the heart because the oxygen gained from gas exchange in the skin is admixed with venous blood before it reaches the heart. This statement has been proved presumptuous, inasmuch as the importance of skin respiration has been overestimated in most amphibians. Figure 8-43 delineates the general course of the larger blood vessels in amphibians.

Reptilian Circulation

When the stage of reptiles has been reached, several major modifications appear both in the arrangement of the larger blood vessels and in the heart itself. The changes clearly indicate that reptiles have reached the end of the transition from water breathing to air breathing. The lungs have now taken on the sole responsibility for respiratory exchange with the environment.

It is convenient to discuss the Chelonia (turtles, tortoises) and Squamata (snakes and lizards) separate from the crocodilians since the latter have attained a complete ventricular septum and, hence, distinct right and left ventricles. However, in all reptiles the large outflow arteries take origin directly from the heart and not from the bulbus cordis, which has regressed completely in the adult. Embryological development, however, shows the bulbus to be absorbed and to have an important part in the formation of the large arterial trunks and the outflow tracts from the heart. With the elimination of the bulbus segment a major advance was made toward a complete double circulation. Now, after the blood left the heart, it was confined to a certain direction. The aortic arches were no longer connected directly in parallel with each other.

However, as is apparent from Figure 8-44, the ventricular chambers of reptiles, except for the crocodilians, are in anatomical continuity. This fact and the lack of physiological experiments perhaps explain why it was thought that large mixing of oxygen-rich and oxygen-poor blood takes place inside the ventricles of reptiles. In recent experimental studies, including oxygen analysis of the blood in the various heart chambers and larger vessels, it has been discovered that such mixing is surprisingly small. The factors preventing mixing can best be explained by following the course of blood through the heart of a squamate reptile, as recently described by White (see the references at the end of this chapter). Figures 8-44 and 8-45 support this description. Figure 8-44 is highly schematic, the ventricular compartments are not drawn to size in order to emphasize the pattern of blood flow. The left and right atrial spaces are completely separated and the ventricle is subdivided into three compartments. A prominent muscular ridge MR divides the ventral ventricular compartment into two spaces, the cavum pulmonale to the left and the cavum venosum to the right. These spaces are oriented more or less horizontally and slightly to the right. The muscular ridge provides no permanent contact with the ventral ventricular wall and the two spaces are only partially separated. In particular, in the apical part of the heart (Figure 8-44) there is free communication around the edge of the muscular ridge. Dorsally to the left we find the third compartment, the cavum arteriosum. This communicates with the cavum venosum through an opening, the interventricular canal (IVC). The cavum arteriosum also communicates with the left atrium (LA), and the right atrium (RA) empties into the cavum venosum. The valves guarding the atrioventricular orifices take on special importance because when their large median flaps are open during atrial contraction they become adpressed against the apertures of the interventricular canal and thus temporarily close the canal and effect a complete septum. Left atrial blood will, hence, fill the cavum arteriosum and be confined there. Right atrial blood first fills the cavum venosum and continues past the free edge of the muscular ridge into the cavum

Figure 8-44. Schematic drawings of a squamate reptilian heart. (a) Ventral aspect showing the three incompletely separated chambers: CV, cavum venosum; CP, cavum pulmonale; CA, cavum arteriosum, RA and LA indicate the positions of the right and left atria, MR, longitudinal muscular ridge; IVC, intraventricular canal. The right and left aorta, RAA and LAA take origin from the cavum venosum, and the pulmonary artery is connected with the cavum pulmonale. (b) Frontal section through a squamate heart dorsal of the cavum pulmonale. (c) Cross-section of a squamate heart toward its base. AVV, atrioventricular junction, RAVJ, right atrioventricular junction. (After White 1959, 1968.)

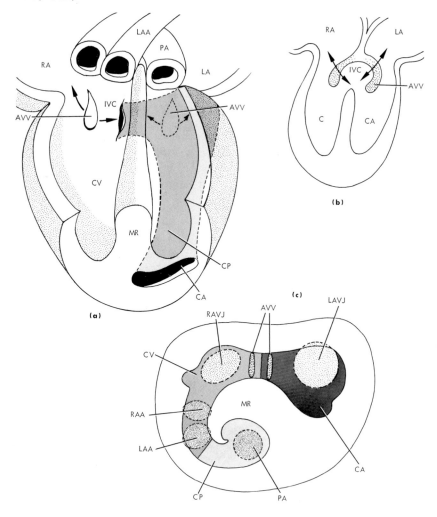

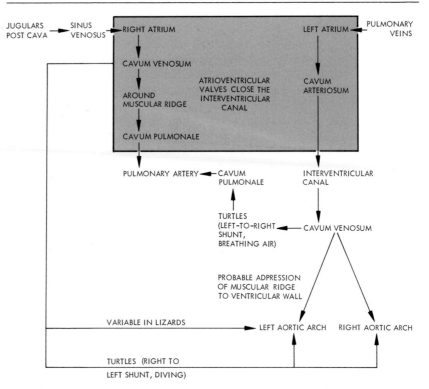

Figure 8-45. Schematic representation of the course of blood through the hearts of noncrocodilian reptiles. The events of ventricular diastole are within the solid rectangle, the systolic events are outside. (After White, 1968.)

pulmonale. When the ventricle contracts, ejection into the pulmonary circuit precedes that into the systemic trunks because the resistance to outflow is less in the pulmonary arteries. This in turn favors the displacement of the venous blood into the cavum pulmonale and its dispatch into the pulmonary arteries (Figure 8-46). It is also of great importance that as the shortening of the ventricle progresses during contraction, the muscular ridge will make

Figure 8-46 (opposite). Radio-opaque contrast medium has been injected into the right jugular vein of the large lizard, *Varanus niloticus*. (a)-(d) show successive stages of the passage of the contrast medium through the heart.

(a) Shows contrast medium in the sinus venosus with some reflux into the posterior vena cava. The right atrium is contracting and filling the cavum venosum of the ventricle. The pulmonary artery is visible from the previous ventricular contraction.

(b) The ventricle is now contracting and the cavum pulmonale is clearly delineated. Contrast medium is expelled into the pulmonary arteries with no admixture to the systemic aortic arches. Note the distinct demarcation between the right atrium and the ventricle indicating closure of the atrioventricular valves during ventricular contraction.

(c) Ventricular contraction almost completed and there is still no admixture to the systemic arteries. The sino-atrial valve is now open and the right atrium is being filled anew.

(d) In this frame the pulmonary veins are visible alongside the pulmonary arteries. The contrast medium has completed circulation through the lungs and has returned to the left atrium from where it has been expelled via the cavum arteriosum into the systemic arches which now have become visible.

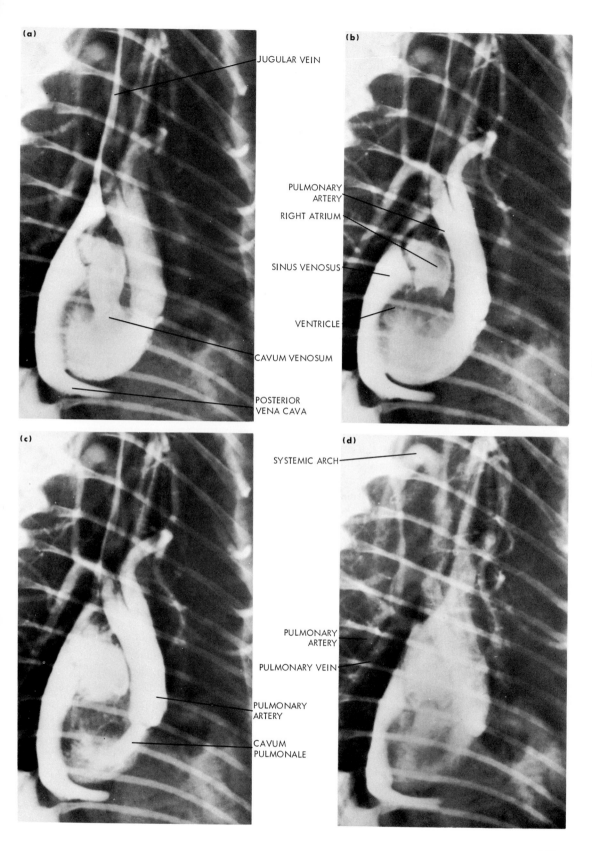

(a)

JUGULAR VEIN

(b)

PULMONARY
ARTERY

RIGHT ATRIUM

SINUS VENOSUS

VENTRICLE

CAVUM VENOSUM

POSTERIOR
VENA CAVA

(c)

(d)

SYSTEMIC ARCH

PULMONARY
ARTERY

PULMONARY VEIN

PULMONARY
ARTERY

CAVUM
PULMONALE

contact with the ventral ventricular wall and prevent a backflow from the cavum pulmonale to the cavum venosum. Meanwhile, as the ventricle contracts the atrioventricular valves swing back and close the atrioventricular openings, creating a free passage through the interventricular canal. Blood previously confined to the cavum arteriosum will thus flow through the canal and escape through the aortic orifices, filling both the right and the left aorta. This pattern of flow through the heart assures that oxygen-rich blood returning from the lungs to the left atrium is selectively dispatched to the systemic right and left aortae, whereas deoxygenated blood is predominantly channeled from the right atrium to the pulmonary arteries. However, some investigators have reported that under certain circumstances like diving, blood from the left aorta has a lower oxygen content than that from the right aorta, showing oxygen values between the right aorta and the pulmonary artery. Physiological studies have verified that this occurs in response to an increased resistance to blood flow in the pulmonary circuit during diving. This in effect will reduce the prevalence for blood in the cavum pulmonale to be ejected selectively into the pulmonary circuit, and some admixture back through the cavum venosum into the left systemic aorta will take place. Figure 8-45 summarizes the blood pathway through the reptilian heart as just described.

It seems to be a common characteristic of all respiratory organs that when the available oxygen decreases, their blood vessels will constrict and a reduced blood flow will result. In essence this response insures that the matching process between blood and respiratory gas is maintained at an optimal level. For instance, when a turtle has been submerged for a while, the oxygen in the lung has been largely depleted and nothing can be gained from sending blood through the lung until another air breath is taken. The energy cost of cardiac pumping is hence reserved mainly for the systemic circulation which continues to be important to the animal. Such shunting of blood would not have been possible had the systemic and pulmonary circuits been completely separated.

In the crocodiles, the cardiovascular system has advanced still further (Figure 8-47). A complete interventricular septum creates distinct left and right ventricles. However, conditions still differ from those in birds and mammals because of some peculiar relationships of the great vessels to the ventricles. The right aortic arch which gives rise to the entire circulation in the anterior direction originates from the left ventricle, and the left aortic arch arises from the right ventricle together with the pulmonary artery. Another unique crocodilian feature is a communication, the foramen Panizzae, between the right and left aortae at the base of the heart where they originate from the ventricles. This condition may at first sight seem to make it inevitable that deoxygenated blood from the right ventricle will escape through the left aorta, with the result that the descending dorsal aorta, made by the union of the right and left aortic arches, will carry blood of mixed oxygen content. Again physiological experiments have revealed a different story. First of all it has been shown that the oxygen content of blood in the right and left aortae under normal conditions corresponds with that in the left atrium. In contrast the much lower oxygen content in the pulmonary artery corresponds with that in the right atrium. This evidence leaves little doubt that both aortae are filled from the same ventricle, obviously the left. The left aortic arch must, therefore, receive its blood from the right arch through the foramen Panizzae.

But why does not blood from the right ventricle reach the left aorta? The answer can be found in the pressure relations inside the heart chambers and the great vessels. Already with the appearance of a functional lung in the lungfish, the vascular resistance of the pulmonary vascular bed is lower than that in the systemic circuit. This tendency grows stronger as the degree of anatomical separation between the two circuits increases. With complete sep-

Figure 8-47. (a) Sketch depicting the cardiac chambers and greater vessels of the crocodilian heart. During normal frequent breathing the pressures developed by the left ventricle and prevailing in vessels emanating from the left ventricle (in gray) exceed those on the right side. This will prevent the left aortic valves from opening and deoxygenated blood from being shunted from the right to the left side. (b) Schematic representation of the course of blood through the crocodilian heart. The events of ventricular diastole are within the solid rectangle, the systolic events are outside. (After White, 1968.)

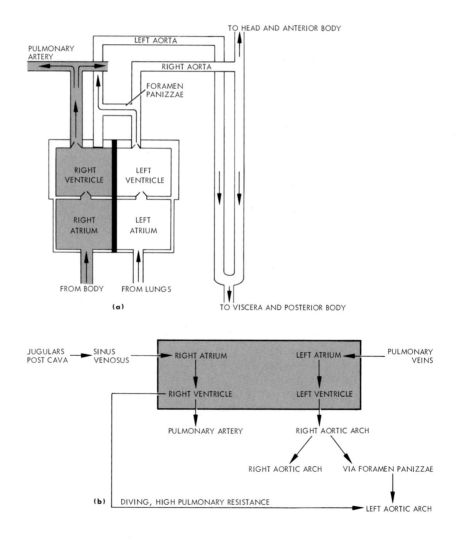

aration as in mammals and birds, the two circuits convey the same flow rate of blood but the driving pressure in the pulmonary circuit is less than one-fifth of that in the systemic. The crocodilians represent a crucial case in this progressive development. Under normal circumstances, when breathing is kept up the pressures prevailing in the right ventricle and pulmonary artery are lower than those in the left ventricle and right aorta. The higher pressure in the right aorta will transmit through the foramen Panizzae to the left aorta. Because cardiac valves open and close passively in response to the pressures acting on each side of them, this can only mean that the valves between the left aorta and right ventricle will not open (Figure 8-47). Functionally, the left aorta becomes connected to the left ventricle through the foramen Panizzae.

However, this system, as in other reptiles, allows for flexibility. Information on blood gases had revealed that during diving or lack of oxygen from reduced or arrested breathing, the oxygen content in the left aorta showed values between those in the right aorta and the pulmonary artery. Recent studies have resolved this problem by showing that when the available oxygen is reduced, the pulmonary outflow tract in the heart constricts, with a resulting increase in pulmonary vascular resistance. This, in turn, will change the pressure conditions inside the right ventricle so that the valves between the heart and the left aorta may open and blood may escape that

Figure 8-48. Components of ventricular contraction. (a) Blood is ejected from the right ventricle by shortening of the free wall. Compression of the right ventricular cavity may be supplemented by traction exerted on the free wall by left ventricular contraction (bellows action). (b) Left ventricular ejection is accomplished primarily by a reduction in the diameter of the chamber with some additional shortening of the longitudinal axis. (From R. F. Rushmer, *Cardiovascular Dynamics*, 2nd edition. Philadelphia: W. B. Saunders Co., 1961.)

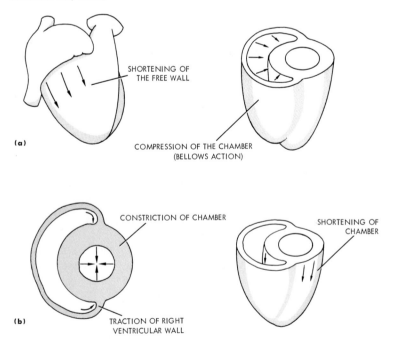

way, resulting in the mixture of deoxygenated blood from the right ventricle with oxygenated blood ejected from the left ventricle.

We see again how the seemingly imperfect vascular arrangement allows the animal a flexible perfusion pattern that makes possible a saving of oxygen and energy during the variable conditions of oxygen availability that often prevail in the normal behavior of lower vertebrates.

Birds and Mammals

Birds and mammals are the only vertebrates with completely separated pulmonary and systemic vascular circuits. Their four-chambered heart is a double pump connecting the two circuits in series. The two circuits differ markedly in their functional and structural characteristics and these differences are also reflected in the two pumps of the heart. The systemic circuit is a high-pressure circuit with arteriovenous pressure gradients many times steeper than in the pulmonary circuit. Yet, because the circuits are in functional continuity they must transport the same volume of blood per unit time. Figure 8-48 indicates how the structural design of the right and left ventricles reflects their functions as a volume pump and a pressure pump respectively. The right ventricular compartment is enclosed as a narrow space between two large surfaces. The chamber thus has a large surface-to-volume ratio. The thickness of the wall, the myocardium, is moderate and when the two curved sides of the chamber are pulled toward each other a large volume is displaced against the small resistance prevailing in the pulmonary arteries. The action of the ventricle resembles that of a bellows used to kindle fires. It is interesting to note that in mammals with a pathologically high resistance in their pulmonary circuit the right ventricular wall gradually thickens and becomes similar to the left ventricle. The left ventricular cavity resembles a cylinder with a conical end invested by a heavy layer of muscle (Figure 8-48). This shape gives the chamber a much smaller ratio between its surface area and volume than that of the right ventricle. The left ventricle develops a high pressure during its contraction. This is consistent with the higher energy release needed to overcome the high resistance of the systemic circulation. The normal left ventricle adapts poorly to ejecting changing large volumes, and if such loads are imposed on it under abnormal conditions of disease, the ventricle dilates and takes on a shape which gives it a larger ratio of surface area-to-volume; it then resembles more closely a typical right ventricle.

In lower vertebrate hearts, that have only one ventricular chamber, we see a better potential for adapting to a volume load than in the left ventricle of mammals. This may be the reason why lower vertebrates can adjust to a higher cardiac output by increasing their stroke volume, whereas higher vertebrate hearts predominantly increase their output by increasing the heart rate.

The arrangement of the arterial outflow trunks in birds and mammals has clearly developed from conditions in lower tetrapods. As in reptiles, the ventral aorta and the cardiac bulbus segment are replaced by arterial trunks arising directly from the heart. The external and internal carotids have the same associations with aortic arches 2 and 3 as outlined for lower vertebrates (Figure 8-35). Aortic arch 4 persists on the right side in birds as the main systemic aorta originating from the left ventricle. The fourth aortic arch on

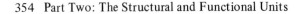

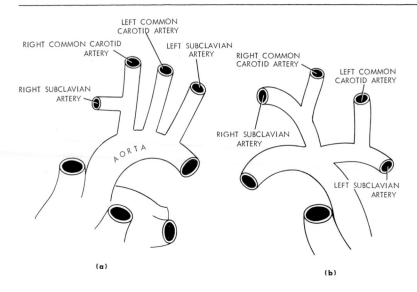

Figure 8-49. (a) Branching of major arteries from the mammalian aorta (human). (b) Branching of major arteries from the avian aorta (duck).

the left participates in the formation of the left subclavian artery.

You will often read that the theory of the origin of birds from an extinct group of sauropsid reptiles is supported by the loss of the left aorta, which assumes that this vessel carried oxygen-poor blood from the right ventricle and hence was detrimental to efficient oxygen transport. In light of the recent findings about circulation in reptiles, this view is no longer tenable.

The arterial system in mammals differs from that in birds by a persisting left aorta rather than a right one (Figure 8-49). The sixth aortic arch system constitutes the pulmonary arteries in both birds and mammals, which conveys blood from the right ventricle to the lungs. In embryological life the left sixth arch retains the primary connection with the dorsal aorta, the ductus arteriosus; this allows bypassing the lungs. Soon after birth the ductus arteriosus becomes progressively occluded and later atrophies, persisting only as a nonfunctional ligament.

In the venous system in birds and mammals the caval veins empty directly into the right atrium, the sinus venosus having been absorbed and incorporated in the right atrium. The venous channels show marked differences between species but, in general, birds show two precaval veins entering the heart against one in most mammals. Hence, the left subclavian and jugular veins of mammals connect with the right precaval system (Figure 8-42). Birds show some venous passage through the kidneys, but this is in all likelihood not functional as a renal portal system. Birds and mammals have functional hepatic portal systems; these systems, the hepatic portal veins and the hepatic veins are homologues with those in lower vertebrates.

The performance of the cardiovascular system in birds and mammals is strikingly superior to that of lower vertebrates. More than anything this is related to their acute homeostatic control, which maintains very stable internal conditions in temperature, osmolarity, blood composition, and other homeostatic functions. Their superior freedom from environmental stress is also manifest in a high mobility on land and in air and water. All these functions demand an efficient cardiovascular system.

A well trained man during hard exercise has, for instance, a cardiac output in excess of twenty-five liters per minute, which is more than twenty times the resting output from the heart. Similarly, in fast-flying birds the heart rates can promptly change several hundred percent in response to flight. Such sudden and profound adjustments in cardiovascular performance are entirely lacking in the lower vertebrates, whose activities are more at the mercy of environmental changes. The crucial role of a continued high blood supply to vital organs of mammals is perhaps best exemplified by the loss of consciousness and ensuing death if the blood flow to the central nervous system or to the heart muscle itself is interrupted for more than five or ten seconds.

References for Chapter 8

Bugge, J., "The Heart of the African Lungfish." *Vidensk, Medd. fra Dansk Naturhist Foren,* **123** (1961), 193-210.

Comroe, J. H., Jr., "The Lung." *Sci. Am.,* **217** (1966).

Goodrich, E. S., *Studies on the Structure and Development of Vertebrates,* "Vascular System and Heart," Vol. II, Chap. 10. New York: Dover, 1958, pp. 506-577.

Hughes, G. M., *Comparative Physiology of Vertebrate Respiration.* Cambridge: Harvard Univ. Press, 1963, p. 145.

———, "The Dimensions of Fish Gills in Relation to Their Function." *J. Exp. Biol.,* **45** (1966), 177-195.

———, and A. V. Grimstone, "The Fine Structure of the Secondary Lamellae of the Gills of *Gadus pollachius.*" *Quart. J. Micr. Sci.,* **106** (1965), 343-353.

Johansen, K., "Airbreathing Fishes." *Sci. Am.,* **219** (1968), 102-111.

———, and D. Hanson, "Functional Anatomy of the Hearts of Lungfishes and Amphibians." *Am. Zool.,* **8** (1968), 191-210.

———, and R. Strahan, "The Respiratory System of *Myxine glutinosa L.*" in *The Biology of Myxine,* A. Brodal, and R. Fänge (eds.). Oslo: Universitets-forlaget, 1963, pp. 353-371.

McCutcheon, F. H., "The Respiratory Mechanism in Turtles." *Physiol. Zool.,* **16** (1943), 255-269.

Poll, M., "Étude sur la structure adulte et la formation des sacs pulmonaires des Protoptères." *Annalen Reeks in 8° Zoologische,* Wetenschappen No. **108** (1962), 131-172.

Randall, J. D., "Functional Anatomy of the Fish Heart." *Am. Zool.,* **8** (1968), 190.

Robb, J. S., *Comparative Basic Cardiology.* New York: Grune and Stratton, 1965, p. 602.

Rushmer, R. F., *Cardiovascular Dynamics.* Philadelphia: W. B. Saunders, 1961, p. 503.

Satchell, G. H., "A Functional Appraisal of the Fish Heart." *Fed. Proc.,* (in press, 1970).

Schulz, H., "Some Remarks on the Submicroscopic Anatomy and Pathology of the Blood Air Pathway in the Lung" in *Pulmonary Structure and Function,* CIBA Foundation Symposium. Boston: Little, Brown, 1961.

Steen, J. B., *The Comparative Physiology of Respiratory Mechanisms.* New York: Academic Press (in press).

———, and A. Kruysse, "The Respiratory Function of Teleostean Gills." *Comp. Biochem. Physiol.,* **12** (1964), 127-142.

White, F. N., "Functional Anatomy of the Heart of Reptiles." *Am. Zool.,* **8** (1968), 211-219.

Wiggers, C. J., "The Heart." *Sci. Am.,* (May 1957).

Zweifach, B. W., "The Micro-Circulation of the Blood." *Sci. Am.,* (Jan. 1959).

9
Excretion and osmoregulation

Vertebrate cells carry out a vast range of activities in precisely regulated patterns. In view of the complexity of their functions, perhaps it is not surprising that these cells are often exceedingly sensitive to slight variations in their chemical organization and, reflecting this, to the composition of their immediate surroundings. Isolated from the vertebrate body, nerve, muscle, or gland tissues can carry out at least part of their normal activity with varying degrees of success. Thus, even under these circumstances nerve cells can conduct nerve impulses, muscles can contract, and glands can secrete characteristic fluids; but these lingering functions remain only while the tissues are maintained in solutions whose composition is controlled with respect to ions, nutritive supplies, oxygen, carbon dioxide and other metabolic products, pH, and osmotic pressure. There is evidence for the existence of intrinsic, self-regulating mechanisms operating to stabilize the chemical organization of individual cells, since slight variations in their immediate environments can occur while the tissues maintain a nearly constant composition. On the other hand, this intrinsic regulatory ability is quite limited even in the case of the sturdiest of vertebrate cells. Their capacity to survive depends on support by extracellular fluids which are, in turn, subject to continuing regulation (Figure 9-1). Thus, in the normal active vertebrate, the body fluids often show relatively little variation even under the drastically varying conditions of the external world. This is the result of the effective operation of the homeostatic mechanisms of the organ systems of the intact animal. The immediate environment of the cells—tissue (or interstitial) fluid—is maintained in rapid exchange with the mass of body fluids as a whole by the circulation of blood and lymph through the vascular systems of the body. The composition of blood and lymph in turn is maintained by controlled exchange with the external environment. Into the body come oxygen and other gases, water, nutrients, and salts, chiefly through the respiratory and gastrointestinal organs (also, in amphibians in particular, through the skin). Outward from the body go carbon dioxide (chiefly through the respiratory system), substances that have entered the body in excessive amounts, and waste products of metabolism. The chief route for ridding the body of these excessive or waste materials is through organs of excretion and osmoregulation.

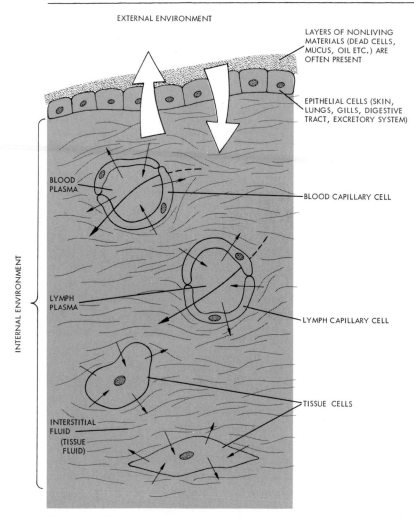

EXTERNAL ENVIRONMENT

LAYERS OF NONLIVING
MATERIALS (DEAD CELLS,
MUCUS, OIL ETC.) ARE
OFTEN PRESENT

EPITHELIAL CELLS (SKIN,
LUNGS, GILLS, DIGESTIVE
TRACT, EXCRETORY SYSTEM)

BLOOD
PLASMA

BLOOD CAPILLARY CELL

INTERNAL ENVIRONMENT

LYMPH
PLASMA

LYMPH CAPILLARY CELL

TISSUE CELLS

INTERSTITIAL
FLUID
(TISSUE
FLUID)

Figure 9-1. Diagram representing the relationship between vertebrate cells, tissue fluids, and the external environment. Exchange of chemical components between the organism and the external environment takes place at specialized epithelial layers of the skin, and in the respiratory, digestive, and excretory systems. Tissue fluids in every part of the body are maintained in physiological exchange with fluids in the body as a whole by circulation of the blood (all vertebrates) and lymph (bony fish and all tetrapods). All of the fluids of the body outside the boundaries of cells are grouped under the common name *extracellular fluids*, and represent the immediate *internal environment* of the cells. The extracellular fluids include not only the three types shown in the diagram, (blood plasma, lymph plasma, interstitial fluid), but also intraocular fluids (aqueous and vitreous humors), joint fluids, and fluids in the pericardial cavity and major body cavities (peritoneal, pleural fluids).

Vertebrate Mechanisms for Excretion and Osmoregulation

Among the structures of the excretory and osmoregulatory systems, the *kidneys* may be named first because they are so versatile and effective and occur throughout the range of vertebrate animals. Typically the kidneys form urine containing a relatively high concentration of nitrogenous wastes (chiefly ammonia, urea, and uric acid) and various other excessive or waste solutes (organic acids, phosphate and sulfate ions, and so on). Their function in ridding the body of such substances is supplemented in fish by the gills, for here ammonia can diffuse directly into the surrounding water of the environment. To a rather slight extent, too, the liver plays a part in excretion. This point has been touched on already in Chapter 7. Another major regulatory function of the kidneys is their important part in controlling the osmotic pressure of the body fluids. In most vertebrates the urine, as it leaves the kidney, is hypotonic to the blood plasma. Thus it can operate effectively to remove from the body an excess of water as compared with solutes. Such regulation toward increasing the osmotic pressure of the body fluids is of great value to animals living in fresh water or in any situation in which the surroundings are hypotonic to body fluids. Indeed, many biologists believe that this function of vertebrate kidneys gives strong support to the idea that vertebrates first evolved in fresh water. As yet we do not know enough to decide between this hypothesis and the concept that the sea was the first environment of primitive vertebrates. In any case, in the course of their evolution vertebrates have radiated into the full range of habitats available on earth, from fresh water through marine and terrestrial regions, including terrestrial deserts. Typically, their kidneys alone are not able to cope with the full impact of osmotic stress imposed by environmental conditions (deficiencies of water or solute, or excess of water or solute in the environment), and a variety of other osmoregulatory processes have a part in their survival. These will be considered briefly, before the more detailed account of the structure and function of vertebrate kidneys.

Fish show many structural-functional adaptations to the environmental osmotic stress that supplement kidney function. These include the following: (1) tolerance by the tissues of high osmotic pressure of body fluids, maintained slightly above the level of sea water by retention of salts (marine cyclostomes—hagfish) or urea (cyclostomes—lampreys, elasmobranchs, holocephalan and coelacanth fish); (2) transfer of ions by special cells in the buccal and pharyngeal gill regions *out* of the body (marine bony fish) or *into* the body (fresh-water fish); (3) formation of a strongly hypertonic secretion by gland cells, such as those of the *rectal gland* associated with the posterior gastrointestinal tract (elasmobranchs; see Figure 9-2); (4) structural adaptations of the skin, including the presence of mucus-secreting gland cells. These adaptations render the skin moderately impermeable (cyclostomes) or highly impermeable (gnathostome fish) to both water and solutes. In the cyclostome hagfish, mucus secretion is especially copious and tenacious, and so rich in salts that some biologists believe that it may be a route for salt excretion (and thus of osmoregulation).

The great majority of amphibians live in environments where fluids with which they come in contact are hypotonic to their own body fluids. Sodium ions (with chloride ions) are actively taken up by skin cells, and water moves readily in either direction through the relatively permeable skin. Adjustment of plasma composition is carried out effectively by kidneys, since the hypotonic urine which they form meets the major need for regulation (excretion of the net excess of water). Amphibians of a few species (*Rana cancrivora, Bufo viridis*) have adapted to life in salt water. These animals retain salt or urea and thus appear to have adjusted to the high osmotic pressure of the environment in a manner reminiscent of the cyclostomes and elasmobranchs. Amphibians living in dry terrestrial conditions (some frogs and toads) survive by systematic collection of water from external sources and by rigorous restriction of water loss from the body. They have no special ways of excreting solutes in excess of water.

In their highly successful adaptations to life on dry land and in the oceans, reptiles, birds, and mammals show a wide variety of mechanisms for osmotic regulation. (1) Reptiles and birds conserve water by excreting nitrogen waste in a nearly solid (nonosmotic) form such as uric acid and by absorbing water from the urinary bladder, lower digestive tract, and (or) cloaca. The structure of these organs will be discussed later in this chapter. (2) Reptiles and birds have special salt-secreting glands, located in the head, that form fluids of osmotic pressure well above that of blood plasma and thus remove salt from the body in excess of water (Figure 9-3). These glands have been studied most in marine reptiles and birds, where they are most conspicuous. (3) In all these forms the skin structure is highly impermeable, so neither water nor salts diffuse in significant amounts through the skin. In mammals, however, another type of skin adaptation mediates temperature regulation, but also affects osmotic regulation. This adaptation is the development of sweat glands that can actively secrete water and salts (chiefly sodium and chloride ions) when the skin or body temperature rises. In some cases sweat secretion represents a major threat to salt and water balance and must be compensated by other osmoregulatory mechanisms if the animal is to survive. (4) Birds and mammals have a specialized kidney structure that makes possible the formation of urine hypertonic to body fluids. This can be explained best in connection with the following more detailed description of vertebrate kidneys.

An understanding of the vertebrate kidney is furthered by comparisons among different forms, taking into account the variety of operations carried out by these organs in the range of vertebrate animals. Looking backward, as it were, in an evolutionary sense, the excretory structures of protochordates

Figure 9-2 (opposite). In elasmobranchs, specialized rectal gland tissue secretes a fluid of high sodium chloride concentration into the posterior digestive tract. This function was first discovered by J. W. Burger and W. N. Hess, in 1959. Subsequently, the structure of the gland has been revealed by careful studies of R. E. Bulger and others. The location of the rectal gland of the spiny dogfish, *Squalus acanthias*, is shown in (a). The gland drains into the intestine through a duct, which carries secretion from the gland's central canal. The secretion is formed in a dense mass of branching secretory tubules emptying into the central canal. There is a rich blood supply, with arteries bringing blood in from the external surface of the gland, and drainage through veins leading into the rectal vein lying in the central canal. (b) and (c) are low-power micrographs of the gland in longitudinal- and cross-section. In (d) the secretory tubules are seen at high-power magnification (light microscope). Each tubule has a wall consisting of a single layer of cells. Connective tissue, with blood vessels, surrounds the tubules. At yet higher magnification, in the electron micrograph in (e) the cells of the rectal gland may be seen to be filled with mitochondria and numerous membranes. The basal cell membranes are folded deeply into the cytoplasm to form a complex structure with extensive surface area. There are microvilli at the apical border where the cells open into the lumen of each tubule. These anatomical features of the cells, and of the gland as a whole, are correlated with the energy-demanding process of forming a secretion of high salt concentration. (All figures were kindly supplied by Dr. Ruth E. Bulger.)

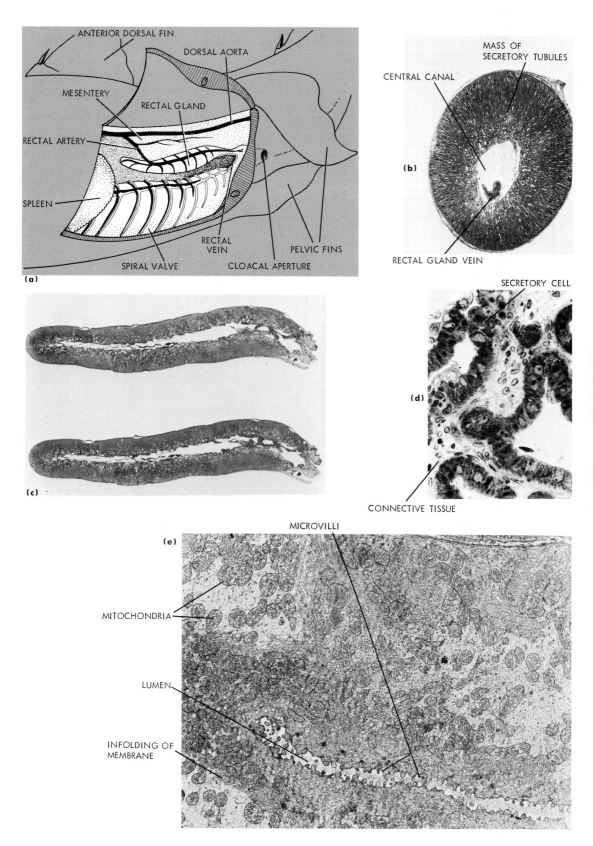

ANTERIOR DORSAL FIN

DORSAL AORTA

MESENTERY

RECTAL GLAND

RECTAL ARTERY

SPLEEN

RECTAL
VEIN

PELVIC FINS

SPIRAL VALVE

CLOACAL APERTURE

(a)

MASS OF
SECRETORY TUBULES

CENTRAL CANAL

(b)

RECTAL GLAND VEIN

SECRETORY CELL

(d)

(c)

CONNECTIVE TISSUE

MICROVILLI

(e)

MITOCHONDRIA

LUMEN

INFOLDING OF
MEMBRANE

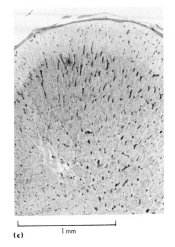

(a)

SG

(b)

5 cm

(c)

1 mm

(d)

I

II

SG   SG   SG   SG

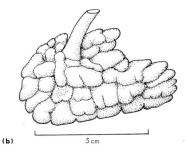

seem to have little in common with vertebrate kidneys (Figure 9-4) and so will not be discussed further here. On the other hand, kidneys throughout the entire range of vertebrate classes present striking common features—patterns of development and basic structures and functions. At the same time, of course, differences exist among the vertebrates, and often these are correlated with adaptive processes enabling the animal to exist in its particular environment.

Patterns of Development of Kidneys

In the development of vertebrate animals mesodermal tissue located on each side of the body gives rise to renal organs. Typically this tissue (variously called nephrogenic tissue, nephrotome) lies between the epimere (more dorsally and centrally located) and the lateral plate (more ventally located) mesoderm. In embryos the most anterior region of the nephrogenic tissue differentiates into one or a few tubules, the group of tubules on each side making up a pronephros. From each pronephros a cellular duct (variously called archinephric duct, pronephric duct) arises and grows backward to reach and open at the posterior end of the body. During the animal's further development, the functions of these primitive kidneys are gradually supplemented (some cyclostomes, and a few bony fish) or replaced altogether (all other vertebrates) by kidneys developed from more posterior regions of the nephrogenic tissue. Thus, in fish and amphibians there are two major stages of renal organization—the pronephros stage and the stage of functioning of the definitive kidney that operates throughout adult life (*holonephros* or *opisthonephros*—see Figure 9-5 and Table 9-1). Reptiles, birds, and mammals show a somewhat more complex pattern of kidney development, for here three stages of renal organization are recognizable: (1) anterior, nonfunc-

Figure 9-3 (opposite). Special salt-secreting glands (labelled SG in the drawings) are found in the region of the orbits of many reptiles [(a), the head of a turtle] and birds (d) adapted to life in or near salt water. The structure of these glands is richly tubular. (c) A photomicrograph of a salt gland of the turtle, *Caretta caretta,* shows many tubules cut in a variety of planes. Great numbers of these tubules may be built into rather conspicuous lobulated glands [(b), *Careta caretta*]. Ducts lead from the glands to orbital or nasal openings, and thence the secretion flows away from the body. In the late 1950's K. Schmidt-Nielsen and R. Fänge and their associates discovered the nature and important regulatory role of this secretion. It contains sodium and chloride ions at concentrations that are high relative to the plasma levels, and is formed in response to rising osmotic pressure of the body fluids. In a study of salt glands from twenty-one species of shore birds of the order Charadriiformes, H. Staaland found that the relative sizes and rates of secretion of the glands are correlated with the ecology of the birds. (d) The birds' skulls are represented in row II at half normal size, while above each bird's skull, in row I, is shown a cross-section of one of its salt glands, magnified five times. The birds are arranged from left to right in order of increasing adaptation to marine life; they are (left to right): the wood sandpiper, *Tringa glareola*; the common sandpiper, *Actitis hypoleucos*; the knot, *Calidris canutus*; and the little auk, *Plautus alle.* [Part (a) is from K. Schmidt-Nielsen, *Scientific American*, January, 1959, p. 114; part (b) is from K. Schmidt-Nielsen and R. Fänge, *Nature*, Vol. 182, p. 783 (1958); part (d) is from H. Staaland, *Comparative Biochemistry and Physiology*, Vol. 23, p. 936 (1967); all three parts are reproduced by permission of the authors and the journals. The photomicrograph (c) was prepared from histological material kindly supplied by Dr. K. Schmidt-Nielsen.]

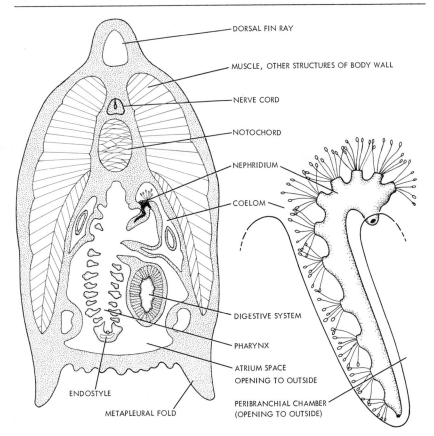

DORSAL FIN RAY

MUSCLE, OTHER STRUCTURES OF BODY WALL

NERVE CORD

NOTOCHORD

NEPHRIDIUM

COELOM

DIGESTIVE SYSTEM

PHARYNX

ATRIUM SPACE
OPENING TO OUTSIDE

ENDOSTYLE

METAPLEURAL FOLD

PERIBRANCHIAL CHAMBER
(OPENING TO OUTSIDE)

Figure 9-4. The excretory structures of protochordates are quite unlike the nephrons of even the most primitive vertebrates. The cephalochordate Amphioxus, *Branchiostoma lanceolatus,* has highly organized excretory structures, *nephridia,* situated segmentally and bilaterally near the pharynx at its dorsal surface. The nephridia provide communication between the coelom and the atrium. Since the atrial cavity communicates directly with the outside, the nephridia are strategically placed for transferring wastes from the coelom out of the body. In structure, they have little in common with vertebrate glomeruli and nephric tubules. It may be noted, too, that the exact mechanisms of excretion in urochordates are still not known in full detail, and perhaps are variable within the group. Special cells, nephrocytes, which wander among the body cells, may be major excretory structures in some species. Storage vesicles, with cellular walls, contain metabolic wastes in other forms. In the sea squirt, *Ciona intestinalis,* a branching tubular structure, the pyloric gland, meshes over the intestine, and this too has been suggested as having an excretory role. (Redrawn from classic illustrations of Boveri, Franz, and Goodrich.)

tional pronephroi arise first, then (2) functional *mesonephroi* form more posteriorly in the nephrotome. Each mesonephros is finally superseded in function by a (3) *metanephros*, which forms latest and most posteriorly from nephrogenic tissue. Even in the lower vertebrates in which they are transiently functional, the pronephroi generally degenerate sooner or later after the adult kidneys have become established. Similarly, in reptiles, birds, and mammals, excretory functions of the second-stage kidneys (mesonephroi) are taken over by the later developed metanephric kidneys. Typically, vertebrates have effective kidney function from a very early stage in development, and the "backward" shift of functional tissue allows the uninterrupted operation of the urgently important regulatory functions of the kidneys throughout all phases of the animal's active life. One might guess that the changing structure of the renal organs is correlated with changing demands for regulation, paralleling a progressively altered kidney function. So far, however, we know too little about the operation of embryonic kidneys either to confirm or disprove this hypothesis.

Just as consistent patterns of kidney structure in relation to development are observed, so also is there a striking consistency of structure correlated with function in vertebrate renal organs as a whole. They carry out their

Figure 9-5. The nephrogenic tissue of vertebrate embryos (roughly indicated in the diagram) gives rise to definitive kidneys in a variety of ways. In all vertebrate classes, the pronephric tubules appear in the most anterior segments. When nearly the entire mass of nephrogenic tissue gives rise to the adult kidney, this is termed a *holonephros* (as in cyclostomes. "Holo-" signifies "whole," whereas "nephros" is derived from the Greek word for kidney). In many fish and amphibians, the more posterior region of the nephrotome develops into the definitive kidney, or *opisthonephros* ("opistho-" signifies "behind"). In reptiles, birds, and mammals, there is a progressive developmental sequence from the nonfunctional pronephros, through the embryonic mesonephros, to the adult metanephros. The structures also form in the direction anterior-to-posterior. ("Pro-" signifies "before"; "meso-" is "middle"; "meta-" is "beyond.") The extent of the nephrogenic tissue giving rise to the various kinds of kidneys is indicated only roughly, for in fact there is both overlap and omission of segments where different kidneys of different vertebrates originate. Note, too, that the form of the "generalized vertebrate embryo" shown, as well as its nephrogenic tissue, are symbolic, rather than accurate. This figure may be reviewed in connection with Figure 9-15 as an aid to understanding the range of structures of excretory systems of adult vertebrates.

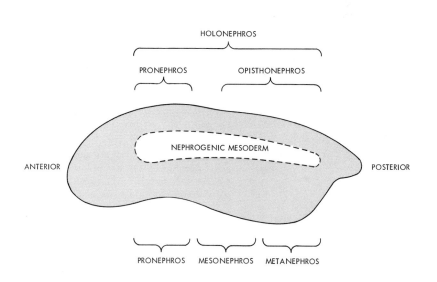

FISH, AMPHIBIANS

HOLONEPHROS

PRONEPHROS   OPISTHONEPHROS

ANTERIOR   NEPHROGENIC MESODERM   POSTERIOR

PRONEPHROS   MESONEPHROS   METANEPHROS

REPTILES, BIRDS, MAMMALS

unique activities chiefly by processing blood plasma, removing from it excess or injurious substances (water and solutes), and starting these on the way to discard from the body as the final excretory product, urine. It should be noted, however, that in most vertebrates (mammals excepted) urine, before it is finally voided, may be further modified by reprocessing in special organs such as the *urinary bladder*, the terminal end of the digestive tract, and the cloaca.

Kidney Structure and Function

Throughout the entire range of vertebrate classes and in all stages of development, the kidneys have three major types of basic functional structures: (1) *glomeruli*, (2) tubules, and (3) collecting ducts. The glomerulus is a tuft of capillaries fed by a small arterial branch. Typically, it lies in intimate contact with the end of a kidney tubule, and the details of this relationship between glomerulus and tubule are so important, from a functional standpoint, that they will be considered more fully later. Within the glomerular capillaries, blood pressure is relatively high, and some of the blood plasma is filtered off through the walls of the capillaries and collected in the adjacent tubule. In the most primitive vertebrates (cyclostome hagfish), the tubules are so rudimentary that the filtrate may be expelled from the body more or less

Table 9-1. A summary of vertebrate kidney types. Vertebrate kidneys differ not only in structure and function, but also in their mode of origin from mesodermal nephrogenic tissue. Types that are considered to differ significantly in ontogeny and in evolutionary history are listed in this table, which may be reviewed in connection with Figure 9-6. To simplify the description, each kidney type is listed as an individual, although, of course, almost all vertebrates have paired kidneys.

Kidney type	Brief description
Pronephros	Embryonic kidney developed from the most anterior region of the nephrogenic tissue, and often consisting of only a few tubules segmentally arranged. This is the functional kidney of embryos of many fish and amphibians. A pronephros arises and remains transiently in early development of amniotes, but apparently never functions as an excretory organ.
Holonephros	Kidney of the larvae of cyclostomes, some amphibians. The entire mass of nephrogenic tissue gives rise to this kidney, which is usually of simple form with a single tubule in each segment.
Opisthonephros	Kidney of many adult fish and amphibians, developed from the main mass of nephrogenic tissues exclusive of the part that gave rise to the pronephros. Except in cyclostome hagfish, in which the tubules of the opisthonephroi are paired and segmentally arranged, there are generally many tubules developed from each nephrogenic segment.
Mesonephros	Kidney of embryonic reptiles, birds, mammals, developed from a median region of nephrogenic tissue. There are great numbers of tubules without evidence of segmental arrangement.
Metanephros	Kidney of adult reptiles, birds, mammals, developed from the most posterior region of the nephrogenic tissue with great numbers of tubules and no evidence of segmental arrangement.

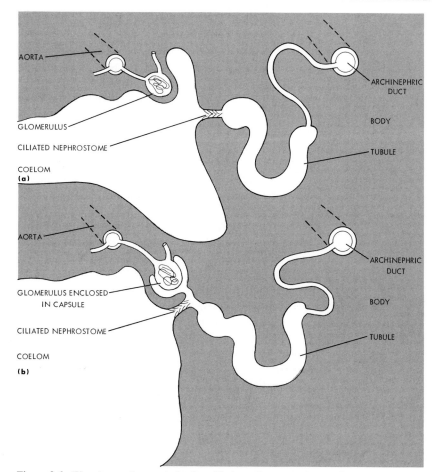

Figure 9-6. The glomerulus, or tuft of capillaries, of a pronephric duct may not (a) or may (b) be enveloped in the expanded end of the tubule. Fluid is filtered from the glomerulus into the coelom (passing from there into the tubule through the nephrostome) or directly into the tubule. In embryos with functional pronephroi, the individual pronephrons on each side drain into an archinephric duct, which connects all of them with the posterior of the body, usually through the cloaca; urine emerges from here to the outside.

unchanged. In most vertebrates, however, the composition of the filtrate is greatly modified as it flows along the tubules, which are channels formed of a single layer of cells surrounding a central space or lumen. The tubules are richly supplied with capillaries. Beyond the tubules and connecting with them are collecting ducts, channels of increasing diameter and wall thickness. They lead into the major urinary ducts (e.g., mesonephric ducts and *ureters*), and these in turn lead directly or through temporary storage chambers (bladder, cloaca) to the outside of the body. There is immense variation among vertebrates in the details of structure, assembly, and operation of these elements, in the number of each built into the functioning kidney organ, their relationships with the blood vessels that supply them, and the manner and degree to which they are controlled by the nervous and endocrine systems.

In the primitive kidneys (pronephroi) of cyclostome larvae and embryos of some other fish and amphibians, the glomeruli and tubules may not be directly connected (Figure 9-6). The glomeruli, arising from branches of the dorsal aorta, lie in the roof of the coelom, and fluid from plasma filters from them directly into the body cavity. Nearby pronephric tubules take up coelomic fluid continuously through ciliated openings, *nephrostomes*, communicating freely with the coelom. Once it has entered the tubules the coelomic fluid becomes the raw material that is converted into urine. A different and more integrated relationship between the glomeruli and tubules appears in the case of other pronephric tubules and in the adult-type kidneys of almost all forms. Here, typically, each glomerulus is enveloped in a delicate sheath formed by the closed end (*Bowman's capsule*) of the nephric duct (the end farthest from attachment to the collecting duct). Some of the components of the fluid flowing through the capillaries filter out between or across the capillary endothelial cells, and then through a differentially permeable *basement membrane*. This structure permits passage of low molecular weight substances (e.g., water, inorganic ions, simple sugars), but prevents the passage of large molecules (e.g., most of the blood proteins). Water and solutes then pass directly into the kidney tubule lumen between and across the delicate cells of Bowman's capsule, lying adjacent to the basement membrane. The process as a whole is termed *glomerular filtration*, and is the start of the kidney excretory process in the majority of vertebrates. The filtering unit, the glomerulus together with its intimately associated Bowman's capsule, is termed the *renal corpuscle*. The renal corpuscle and its attached tubule constitute the *nephron,* the basic functional unit of the kidney.

Ideas about the mechanism of operation of the renal corpuscle, as summarized in the preceding paragraph and in Figure 9-7, have been built up

Figure 9-7 (opposite). (a) The thin-walled, expanded end of the renal tubule (Bowman's capsule) completely covers the capillaries of the glomerulus with a delicate sheath, so that a complex structure, the renal corpuscle (a), is formed. Generally, the afferent arteriole, leading into the glomerulus, has a larger cross-sectional area than the efferent arteriole which drains the capillary tuft. This situation contributes to the maintenance of high blood pressure within the capillaries. At this high pressure, plasma components selectively filter out through the capillary wall (arrow marked ①). The movement is opposed by osmotic pressure of plasma proteins which are restrained from passing the glomerular membranes, and by fluid pressure built up with the capsular space (pressures opposing filtration pressure are suggested by the arrow marked ②). In the net, about one-fifth of the plasma traversing the mammal's glomeruli is filtered off into the capsules to flow away through the proximal convoluted tubules. (b) Some details of the filtration membrane (magnified about 30,000×) are shown, summarizing data obtained with the electron microscope and by study of chemical and filtration characteristics of renal corpuscles. The capillary endothelial cells lie closely adjacent to the *basement membrane*. This is a thin, continuous layer consisting of protein (collagen), glycoprotein, and lipid, probably secreted by both the capillary and capsular cells. It appears to be a major filtration barrier, so its chemical organization must participate in limiting the size and form of molecules which can traverse the filtration barrier as a whole. On the side opposite the capillary cells, the basement membrane is in close contact with many fine projections sometimes called "feet", of the capsular epithelial cells (podocytes). In the diagram, the capsular cells are shown in a single plane of section, so the projections appear, in some cases, as isolated masses although, of course, in the real three-dimensional structure they are continuous with the rest of the cells' cytoplasm. (c) Photograph of a renal corpuscle and adjacent cut segments of tubules from the kidney of a rat (magnified 442×). (Histological material prepared by Mrs. Deborah Christensen.)

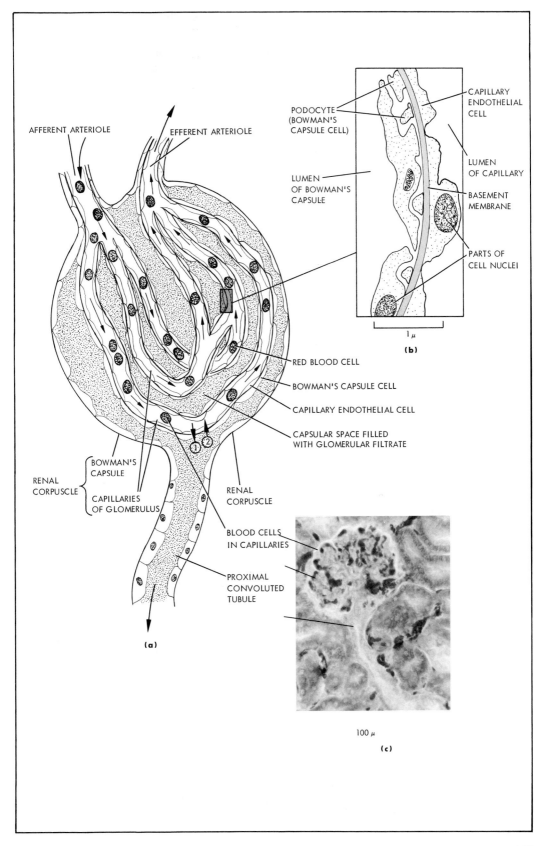

AFFERENT ARTERIOLE

EFFERENT ARTERIOLE

PODOCYTE
(BOWMAN'S
CAPSULE CELL)

CAPILLARY
ENDOTHELIAL
CELL

LUMEN
OF BOWMAN'S
CAPSULE

LUMEN
OF CAPILLARY

BASEMENT
MEMBRANE

PARTS OF
CELL NUCLEI

1 μ

(b)

RED BLOOD CELL

BOWMAN'S CAPSULE CELL

CAPILLARY ENDOTHELIAL CELL

CAPSULAR SPACE FILLED
WITH GLOMERULAR FILTRATE

BOWMAN'S
CAPSULE

RENAL
CORPUSCLE

CAPILLARIES
OF GLOMERULUS

RENAL
CORPUSCLE

BLOOD CELLS
IN CAPILLARIES

PROXIMAL
CONVOLUTED
TUBULE

(a)

100 μ

(c)

369

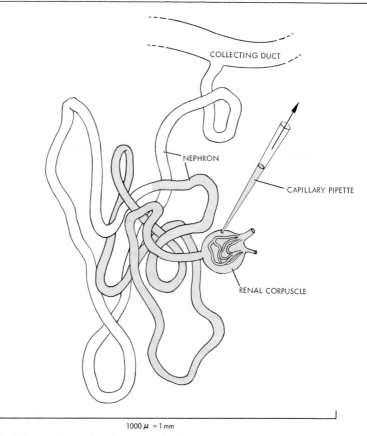

1000 μ = 1 mm

Figure 9-8. Diagram illustrating the approach taken by A. N. Richards and his associates to collect fluid from amphibian renal corpuscles. This pioneering work was of great importance in establishing filtration as a main mechanism for the formation of glomerular filtrate. The experiments were begun in the 1920's, and by now have been carried far by many physiologists. Fluid has been collected also from different parts of the nephron and collecting ducts in many species, including a variety of mammals. The extremely small size of the nephron and the experimental tools make this work most taxing and difficult.

gradually over the course of a century or so through the use of many observational techniques. Even the general form of the renal corpuscle offered certain clues to its function. By the middle of the nineteenth century the great German physiologist, Carl Ludwig, had suggested, on the basis of this form, that urine must originate by filtration of fluid from the capillaries, through the flat cells of Bowman's capsule, into the nephric tubule. Later this hypothesis was supported by a growing mass of experimental evidence. It was shown, for instance, that if other factors are kept constant urine formation is dependent on the arterial pressure (necessary for filtration), and it ceases altogether when this pressure falls too low. Fluid has been collected directly from Bowman's capsule by aspiration through fine capillary pipettes inserted through the capsular wall (Figure 9-8). Microchemical analyses then confirmed the hypothesis that the fluid arises by filtration through the capillary and capsule walls, for the composition of capsular fluid is essentially the same as the composition of plasma, though plasma proteins and other large molecules are generally absent from (or present at only low concentration in) the capsular fluid. Many physiological studies and intensive examinations with electron microscopy have rounded out our current knowledge of the renal corpuscles of vertebrates.

Though each renal corpuscle is exceedingly small (for instance, about 0.1-0.3 millimeter in diameter in mammals), the total filtration surface of capsule-sheathed capillaries is relatively immense. In man it has been estimated as about equal to the entire body surface area. Correspondingly, indirect estimates show that large volumes of fluid are filtered across the membranes into the beginning of the renal tubule. The values listed in Table 9-2 are especially striking in the case of birds and mammals, with their relatively high arterial pressures and consequently high filtration pressures in the glomerular capillaries.

Fluid entering the capsule flows away from the glomerulus through the tubular lumen. In its path it is surrounded by tubular cells, and these have most significant and varied functions in modifying the composition of the fluid; gradually that process converts it into urine. In almost all vertebrates (cyclostome hagfish appear to be the exception) the tubular cells carry out energy-requiring processes that transfer substances filtered into the luminal fluid back through the tubular cells toward the blood stream. Such reabsorptive processes "save" useful substances, including glucose, amino acids, and ions such as potassium and sodium from the possibility of discard from the

Table 9-2. A comparison of urine flow and glomerular filtration rate as measured under experimental conditions in a variety of vertebrates. These figures may be thought of as representative, but they do not give an adequate picture of the variation among members of a class or between individuals within a species, or of changes in a single individual over a period of time. Yet an animal's renal function changes with the character of the environment, with health, activity, age, and many other variables. Note that in birds and mammals the glomerular filtration rate is so high that a volume equivalent to several times the entire mass of fluid in the body is filtered into the tubules during each twenty-four-hour period.

	Urine flow (ml/kg in 24 hr)	Glomerular filtration rate (ml/kg in 24 hr)	(per cent of body fluid volume formed in 24 hr)
Some fresh-water and terrestrial vertebrates:			
Elasmobranch (Pristis microdon)	150-450	450	56
Teleost (Ameiurus nebulosus)	154	225	28
Amphibian (Rana clamitans)	317	822	100
Bird (Gallus domesticus)	15-32	3170	490
Mammal (Canis familiaris)	15-100	6190	890
Some marine vertebrates:			
Cyclostome (Myxine glutinosa)	5.4	. . .	. . .
Elasmobranch (Squalus acanthias)	1.5	50	7
Teleost (Lophius piscatorius)	27	0	0
Mammal (Seal)	12	3600	525

body. Urea, phosphate, sulfate, ascorbic acid, and other solutes can also be reabsorbed actively in some vertebrates. Further, the tubule walls act as selectively permeable barriers between tubular fluid and body fluids (blood plasma), so that water, urea, and a variety of other substances may diffuse passively across the cells back into the blood stream. In addition, certain tubule cells are capable of transferring solutes actively in the direction plasma-to-tubule lumen. This process is often termed *renal secretion*. The capabilities of tubules to secrete vary widely from one region to another and from one organism to another. Generally, the proximal tubule, the region lying nearest to the renal corpuscle, shows most cellular activity. In some cases metabolic wastes such as urea and phenolic compounds may be secreted into the tubules, as may certain ions (phosphate, sulfate in some marine fish). Abnormal compounds, such as some organic dyes and the antibiotic penicillin, may be secreted as well. Many vertebrate nephrons show another region of marked secretory activity. This is the distal tubule, the portion that joins directly with the collecting duct.

In some instances tubular cells can form new compounds by virtue of their metabolic activities. These compounds are generally produced in relation to

Figure 9-9. Nephron structure in a mammal. (a) Simplied diagram of a complete nephron with its blood supply. The richness of the capillary network around the tubule is suggested. These capillaries intermesh, receiving blood from several different arterioles besides the particular arteriole which drains the tubule's own renal corpuscle. (b) Diagram suggesting some important features of a proximal convoluted tubule cell (shown as if magnified ca 30,000X), as indicated by electron micrography. The luminal surface of the cell is covered with fine projections, microvilli, each about 1 mμ long. Together, the microvilli greatly increase the surface area bounding the tubular lumen (by as much as forty-fold, according to calculations of J. A. C. Rhodin, who has estimated that a single cell may have as many as 6500 microvilli). The microvilli form a mass visible in the light microscope and termed the *brush border* of the proximal tubular cells. The nucleus lies toward the base of the cell next to the basal layer where deep infoldings of the cell membrane surround numerous mitochondria aligned with the long axis of the cell. Surrounding the entire tubule is a relatively thick, continuous *basal lamina* (basement membrane). The microvilli of the brush border are important features of proximal tubules of almost all vertebrates. They are generally believed to participate in the major transport roles of these cells, which secrete some substances into the urine, and reabsorb back into the blood many components of the glomerular filtrate. Likewise, functionally important characteristics of the cells are the basal arrays of numerous mitochondria arranged in folds of the basal membranes (seen in the light microscope, these arrays of mitochondria and membranes are termed *basal striations*). These appear to be correlated with the major transport activities of the tubular cells in mammals (and in the few teleosts and amphibians so far studied). According to recent work of B. Schmidt-Nielsen and others, in reptiles and birds the lateral boundaries, rather than the basal region, show specialized folding, and mitochondria are more uniformly distributed rather than being concentrated in the basal region of the cells. Somewhat similar basal arrays of infolded membranes and mitochondria (or lateral in-foldings) occur in distal tubules of vertebrate kidneys, as well as in salt glands of reptiles and birds. (c) Micrograph showing a region of the outer zone of the kidney (cortex) of a rat (magnification 96X). Many renal corpuscles are visible, packed among segments of complexly coiled tubules. The structure of the renal tubule, as diagrammed in (a) has been established by a study of serial sections such as this, as well as by microdissection, delicate maceration of the tissue, and other techniques to reveal the continuity of individual tubules. (Histological material prepared by Mrs. Deborah Christensen.)

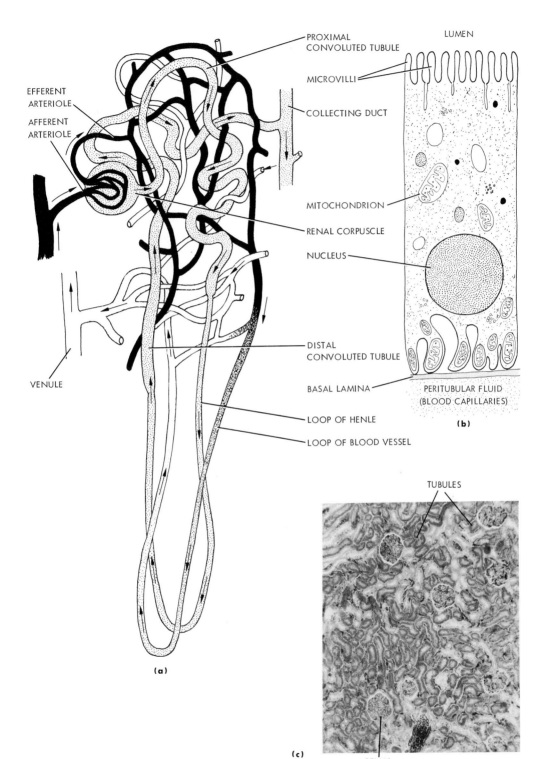

PROXIMAL
CONVOLUTED TUBULE

LUMEN

MICROVILLI

EFFERENT
ARTERIOLE

COLLECTING DUCT

AFFERENT
ARTERIOLE

MITOCHONDRION

RENAL CORPUSCLE

NUCLEUS

DISTAL
CONVOLUTED TUBULE

VENULE

BASAL LAMINA

PERITUBULAR FLUID
(BLOOD CAPILLARIES)

LOOP OF HENLE

LOOP OF BLOOD VESSEL

(b)

(a)

TUBULES

(c)

RENAL
CORPUSCLE

373

special regulatory functions of the kidney. For instance, many vertebrates excrete large amounts of ammonium ions in the urine as part of the overall mechanism for regulating body acid-base balance. The highly toxic ammonium ions are not present in great enough concentration in plasma to account for the amounts excreted in the urine, and this observation led to the discovery that ammonium ions are actually synthesized in kidney tubule cells. Kidney cells also form enzymes and hormones that aid in the control of the circulation as a whole (renin, erythropoietin). Thus, the cells that make up the walls of the tubules assist in a wide variety of ways in regulating body-fluid composition. They modify the glomerular filtrate in fine detail, extracting from it some components, adding others to it. These functions depend on special characteristics of renal cells, which vary distinctively from one region of the tubule to another (Figure 9-9).

Renal Corpuscles   The account so far has summarized typical common features of nephrons among a wide range of vertebrate animals. When we consider in greater detail the kidneys of different vertebrates, important variations in nephron structure are noticeable at once (Figure 9-10). In cyclostomes, elasmobranchs, and bony fish permanently inhabiting fresh water, the renal corpuscles tend to be large and to contain numerous capillaries. For all these animals the environment is hypotonic (very hypotonic in the case of fish living in fresh water; moderately to slightly hypotonic in marine cyclostomes and elasmobranchs whose body fluids are highly concentrated). In correlation with this, filtration occurs quite briskly, aiding the animal to eliminate excess water entering the body from the surrounding fluid (Table 9-2). Where the environment is hypertonic and water conservation is a major problem a contrasting situation is seen in marine fish. The renal corpuscles tend to be far smaller in size and fewer in number than in elasmobranchs and fresh-water bony fish. (See Table 9-2 for some evidence of the effects of this trend on filtration rate.) Indeed, kidneys of some forms, such as the toad fish *Opsanus tau*, may be essentially devoid of renal corpuscles. Consisting chiefly of compact masses of tubules with their associated blood vessels, such kidneys are termed aglomerular. Amphibians tend to have large renal corpuscles with many capillaries, though here, as in the case of the bony fish, there is a clear correlation between kidney structure and the stress imposed on the animal by its environment. Thus, salamanders and frogs living in fresh water have large renal corpuscles and quite high rates of filtration as compared with amphibians adapted to arid conditions. Frogs living in desert areas (two *Cyclorana* species of Australia) show such reduction of their renal corpuscles that they are sometimes described as aglomerular. In reptiles and birds, as compared with other vertebrates, there is a consistent trend towards reduction of renal corpuscles, paralleling the successful adaptation of these forms to life on land. Reptiles tend to have few renal corpuscles, and in birds the renal corpuscles, though very numerous, are of small size. In both these classes the glomeruli have few capillaries and the capsule is partly filled with connective tissue. Mammals are, of course, as successful at land dwelling as are the other amniotes, but mammalian renal corpuscles do not show a trend towards reduction. They are generally large, well vascularized, and numerous.

Marked changes in the patterns of tubular function have enabled the kidneys of mammals to adjust to terrestrial life. These adaptations will be described in more detail in the next paragraph.

Renal Tubules

At least as varied as the structure of the renal corpuscle is the structure of tubules in the range of the vertebrates. In the pronephros, and even in the adult kidneys of some fish and amphibians, individual tubules may have a ciliated funnel, or nephrostome, opening from the body cavity directly into the tubular lumen (or tubular blood supply). This permits direct adjustment of the coelomic fluid, supplementing the regulation of plasma composition. Such nephrostomes are absent from the nephric tubules of many fish, and from all metanephric tubules. In other ways, too, tubular form as well as the shape of individual tubular cells vary greatly from vertebrate to vertebrate. Nephrons tend to be simpler and shorter in fish and amphibians, longer and more complex in the amniotes (Figure 9-11).

Some limited groups of vertebrates show special tubular regions. In prone-

Figure 9-10. Diagrams of representative nephrons from members of the various vertebrate classes. Note the variation in relative sizes of glomeruli, and the trend towards increased complexity of tubular structure.

1. Cyclostome *Bdellostoma stouti*
2. Elasmobranch *Raja stabulaforis (R. laevis)*
3. Teleost *Myxocephalus octodecimspinosus*
4. Teleost *Ameirus nebulosus*
5. Teleost *Opsanus tau*
6. Amphibian *Rana catesbiana*
7. Reptile *Chrysemys marginata*
8. Bird *Gallus domesticus*
9. *Gallus domesticus*
10. Mammal *Lepus cuniculus*
11. *Lepus cuniculus*

[From C. L. Prosser and F. A. Brown, *Comparative Animal Physiology*. (Philadelphia: W. B. Saunders Co., 1961.)]

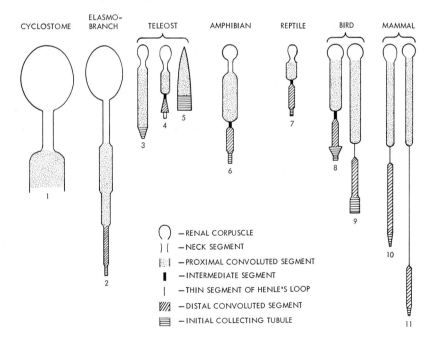

phric tubules and in parts of the tubules of adult amphibians and reptiles areas of ciliated cells are commonly found. These are thought to aid the flow of fluid along the tubular path. In birds and mammals a unique and important tubular section is inserted between the proximal and distal tubules. It is of narrow diameter, built up chiefly of thin cells. This tubular region is bent back upon itself to form a hair-pin loop. The presence of such loops (loops of Henle) is correlated with a special capacity of bird and

Figure 9-11. Diagram of a section through a human kidney, suggesting the compact organization of nephrons, draining-collecting ducts, and blood vessels in the mammalian kidney. The renal corpuscles, proximal convoluted tubules, and distal convoluted tubules of about one million nephrons are packed into the *cortex*, or outer layer of the kidney. Many of the thin loops and collecting ducts pack into parallel arrays in the *medula*, giving the medullary *pyramids* a readily observed appearance of striation. The collecting ducts of the pyramids empty into a few large channels, *minor calyces*, each minor calyx then merging with others to form *major calyces*. These, in turn, open into the great common chamber, or *pelvis*, leading to the ureter. The pelvis is the site of entry into the kidney of the renal artery and vein, which feed and drain the vast branching system of blood vessels culminating in the glomerular and tubular capillaries.

In the diagram, the part of the kidney shown above the line AB is highly schematized to indicate the relative positions of glomeruli, thin loops, collecting ducts, and other structures within the mass of the kidney. Many of the structures are magnified and simplified to assist the comprehension of their relationship to one another. Below the line AB, the structures shown are represented more realistically, appearing much as they would if you were to view an actual human kidney in section. [Modified from H. W. Smith, *Principles of Renal Physiology* (New York: Oxford University Press, 1956).]

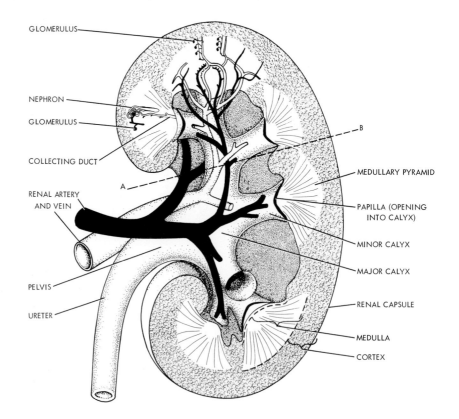

mammal kidneys to form urine hypertonic to blood plasma. As a result of this capability, these animals can conserve water in urine excretion by a process that is not available to any other vertebrate. At this point it may be well to refer again to Table 9-2 for comparison of the rates of glomerular filtration and urine flow in various vertebrates. The difference between these figures represents tubular conservation of fluid.

Because the structure and function are most elaborate and have been studied most fully in mammals, the tubular loops will be discussed here in relation to the mammalian kidney. In this organ most of the renal corpuscles and proximal and distal tubules are packed into the surface layer or *cortex*. The loops of Henle, collecting ducts, and associated blood vessels occupy the more central volume (or *medulla*) of the kidney (Figure 9-12). Thus, after passing through the proximal tubule the glomerular filtrate formed in the cortex plunges down into the medulla along the tubular loop, turns back along this same loop to re-enter the cortex in the distal tubule, and finally flows back into the medulla as it traverses the collecting duct on its way to the ureter and the urinary bladder. The hair-pin loops of Henle, which are paralleled by blood vessels of comparable hair-pin form (vasa recta), have long been known to exist. Only in the last decades, however, has it become clear that they have special functions that allow the formation of urine which differs from blood plasma in osmotic pressure so that, in the net, water may either be conserved (formation of hypertonic urine) or excreted in excess (formation of hypotonic urine). This functional import-ance of kidney tubular architecture is so interesting that further discussion is profitable (Figure 9-13). Along the tubule, cellular transport processes remove sodium ions from the fluid in the lumen and transfer these ions into the interstitial fluids. Generally, sodium ions are accompanied by chloride ions (or other anions). It has been established experimentally that the result of this ion transfer is a build-up of a gradient of osmotic pressure in the fluid in the tubules and in the interstitial spaces. Thus, although these fluids are essentially isosmotic with circulating systemic blood in the cortex, they become progressively more hypertonic to blood plasma in the medulla where the loops of Henle lie. This phenomenon is symbolized in Figure 9-12 by the large stipled arrow, representing the gradient of tonicity with increasing values occurring in regions more distal to the cortex (approaching the entry to the ureter).

The exact mechanism whereby this build-up of tonicity occurs is not fully established. One important theory is that it depends on a counter-current multiplier effect directly attributable to the shape, cellular activities, and permeability characteristics of the tubular loops. According to this theory, the cells in the descending limb of each loop reabsorb sodium ions actively, and anions and water move with these into the interstitial fluids. In at least parts of the ascending limbs of the loops, the cells continue to transfer ions out of the lumina, but here water and ions do not move by passive diffusion easily through the relatively impermeable walls of the tubules, so the fluid outside the tubule becomes enriched in ions whereas the fluid inside the tubule becomes more dilute. One major net effect of the cell activity of the ascending limb is to increase the tonicity of the fluids surrounding the descending limb. This, in turn, may increase the tonicity of the tubular fluid

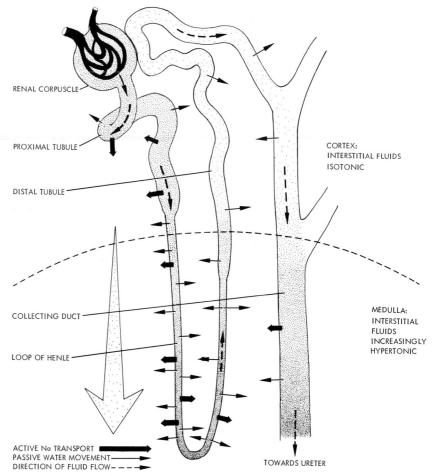

RENAL CORPUSCLE

PROXIMAL TUBULE

DISTAL TUBULE

COLLECTING DUCT

LOOP OF HENLE

ACTIVE Na TRANSPORT
PASSIVE WATER MOVEMENT
DIRECTION OF FLUID FLOW

CORTEX:
INTERSTITIAL FLUIDS
ISOTONIC

MEDULLA:
INTERSTITIAL
FLUIDS
INCREASINGLY
HYPERTONIC

TOWARDS URETER

Figure 9-12. Diagram representing processes occurring in the mammalian nephron, resulting in formation of urine of variable tonicity (varying degrees of water conservation or excretion). Sodium ions and accompanying anions are transferred out of the tubule along its entire length (dark arrows). As fluid flows along the tubule (dashed arrows) in the medullary region, it encounters a progressively solute-enriched, hypertonic environment of extracellular fluids (direction of osmotic gradient indicated by a large stippled arrow). Water traverses the walls of the tubule by passive diffusion (thin arrows) in the proximal tubule and the first part of the loop, but in the ascending limb the tubular walls must become less permeable because the tonicity of the fluid in the tubule begins to drop while sodium transport continues. Fluid entering the collecting duct may be quite hypotonic, and if it reaches the ureters unchanged, the urine excreted from the body is hypotonic (i.e., excess body water is excreted). If, however, as suggested in this diagram, the walls of the collecting ducts are in a state of high water permeability (resulting from high level of antidiuretic hormone in the blood), water flows from the collecting ducts back into the medullary interstitial fluids. Thus, the final urine is *hypertonic* (i.e., body water is conserved).

delivered by the descending limb to the ascending limb. The reader may recognize that the overall picture represents a classical situation for counter-current build-up of a concentration gradient—in this case of sodium ions and anions. According to the general hypothesis presented here, the progressive build-up of tissue-fluid tonicity in the medulla is favored by the fact that the blood vessels also form hair-pin loops parallel to the tubules. If, as current experimental evidence suggests, the walls of the blood vessels are quite freely permeable to water, blood can flow through them with continuous adjustment of the osmotic pressure of the plasma to conform with the pattern of interstitial tonicity. Thus, the retrieval of water, lost from the blood as it flows through the descending part of the loop, occurs as the blood traverses the ascending part of the vascular loop. In net effect, the loop shape of the blood vessels protects the osmotic gradient dependent on activity of the

Figure 9-13. (a) As shown in this figure, based on work of I. Sperber, the form of the medulla of the mammalian kidney may be modified in animals inhabiting dry environments, as well as in those that live on diets rich in salts and other solutes. The medullary countercurrent system is expanded and protrudes into the ureter as an asymmetrical, though more or less conical structure, the *papilla* (some animals have several papillae; see Figure 9-11). The length and mass of the papillae are approximately correlated with the power of the kidney to form hypotonic urine. Thus, the more effective water conservation in mammals adapted to relative water deficient environments is based on characteristic structural modifications of the metanephroi. (Courtesy of Dr. B. Schmidt-Nielsen; slightly modified from *Physiological Review,* **38:** 139, 1958.)
 (b) Shows typical anatomical divisions of the mammalian kidney; it is in fact an enlargement of the kidney diagram given for Macroscelides under the column heading "Dry habitat" in part (a).

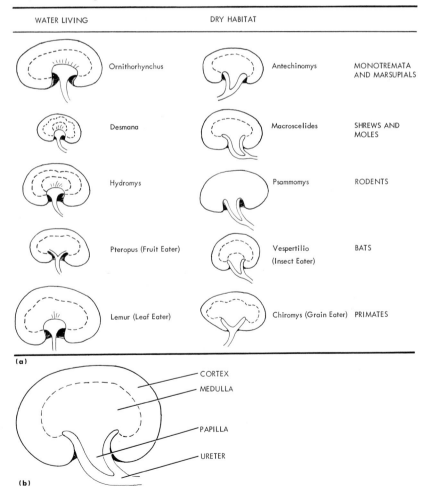

tubular loops of Henle, rather than allowing the gradient to be dissipated by the flow of blood through the tissues.

To complete this interpretation of the function of the tubular loops in enabling the kidney to form hypertonic urine, it is necessary to take into account the special role of the collecting ducts. These lie parallel to the tubular loops and thus traverse an area where the interstitial fluid is hypertonic to blood plasma. They have the important physiological property that the cells making up their walls have variable permeability to water. This variability is controlled by the supply of a posterior pituitary hormone (antidiuretic hormone) in the blood reaching the collecting-duct cells. When the collecting ducts are relatively *permeable* to water (as in dehydrated animals, with a high rate of release of antidiuretic hormone from the posterior pituitary) water is reabsorbed from the fluid traversing the collecting ducts and a *hypertonic* urine is formed. If, on the other hand, the collecting ducts are in a phase of relative *impermeability* to water (as in hydrated animals, with suppression of the secretion of antidiuretic hormone by the posterior pituitary), the dilute, sodium- and chloride-depleted urine, flows through the collecting ducts and on toward the outside of the body.

Finally, looking at the entire mechanism, we can see that the varying capability of the mammalian kidney to form urine more concentrated, equally concentrated, or less concentrated than the blood plasma results from an interplay of the structural organization of the tubules, collecting ducts, and their blood supply on the one hand, and on the other hand of the functional capacity of tubular cells to transport ions actively and the controlled and varying permeability of the collecting ducts. Other factors, such as the transport of urea, may play a part as well. Even though the exact details of the concentrating mechanism of the kidney are not as yet agreed upon by physiologists, the general situation should prove, in the long run, to be similar to this account. In any case, it accords with interesting findings about structural variations among mammalian kidneys. Thus, mammals that can form highly concentrated urines (such as some species adapted to life in the desert) have extra long tubular loops organized together in an elongated *renal papilla* (Figure 9-13). Similarly, mammals that must form large volumes of hypertonic urine have great numbers of tubular loops and a thick renal papilla. On the other hand, some mammals have adapted to life in a water-rich environment (*Hydromys*, the Australian water rat, is an example), and in these the tubular loops and renal papillae may be poorly developed. Such differences in this aspect of kidney structure are indicated in Figure 9-13.

Without going into detail, it may be noted that the kidneys of birds also have tubular loops, although the lobulated form of the avian kidney is correlated with a somewhat different patterning of tubule form and tonicity gradient development. In general, bird kidneys also show correlation of structure with adaptation to environmental osmotic stress. Tubular conservation of water tends to be less effective in birds than in mammals. As will be noted later, however, birds have some interesting accessory devices to facilitate the conservation of water.

Kidney Circulation and Innervation

Intimately bound up with the structure of the nephrons are the blood vessels which supply them. The process of filtration of blood plasma in the renal corpuscle to form glomerular filtrate is dependent on the exceptionally high pressure of the blood in the glomerular capillaries, as well as on the thinness and permeability of the capillary-capsular membranes. Blood flow to the tubules is of prime importance in nourishing the cells, in supplying solutes for excretion, and as a route for return to the body as a whole of valuable substances reabsorbed from the tubular lumina. The general architecture of the blood supply is fairly consistent throughout the vertebrate series. Each kidney is supplied by one (or more) great arterial branch from the dorsal aorta, which breaks up into finer and finer divisions, at last giving rise to the tufts of glomerular capillaries. As noted earlier in this chapter, these may be absent or much reduced in kidneys with suppressed glomerular function such as those of marine fish and desert amphibians. The glomerular capillaries generally drain into still smaller arterioles (efferent arterioles) which lead in turn into capillaries meshing about the nephric tubules. In cyclostomes and mammals these arteriole-fed capillaries furnish the only blood supply to the tubules, but in members of all the other vertebrate classes blood is supplied to the tubules entirely or in significant part by renal portal veins, branches of the great veins draining the posterior part of the body. Of prime importance in amphibians, the renal portal system also participates, to a varying extent as compared with arteries, in supplying blood to the renal tubules of reptiles and birds. In birds, venous valves may control the flow of blood from the posterior part of the body to, or bypassing, the kidneys. There is no renal portal system in mammals. Blood that has traversed the capillaries around the tubules drains into venules. These join larger vessels which in turn give rise to the renal veins leaving the kidney along courses that generally parallel those of the renal arteries and nerves.

The nerves to the kidney appear to function chiefly in the regulation of blood supply. In amphibians, for instance, the pressure and flow of blood in the glomeruli and, therefore, the rate of glomerular filtration, is under nervous as well as hormonal control. Thus blood supply is acutely sensitive, varying from moment to moment, and it also responds to changing external conditions. In contrast to the knowledge of nerve regulation of kidney function in amphibians, little is known about this particular role of nerves in most vertebrates.

Overview of Kidney Structure

Among vertebrates variation exists in the degree of compactness of the organization of the kidneys (Figure 9-14). In fish and some amphibians the renal tissue is rather loosely bound together by connective tissue, whereas the kidneys are quite compact in anuran amphibians (frogs, toads) and in reptiles, birds, and mammals. Generally these compact kidneys show a high degree of organization of tubule, collecting duct, and blood vessel systems, as in reptiles, birds, and some mammals with their lobulated kidneys, and in the clear distinction of cortex and medulla in birds and mammals. In vertebrates with compact kidneys, a connective tissue capsule invests each

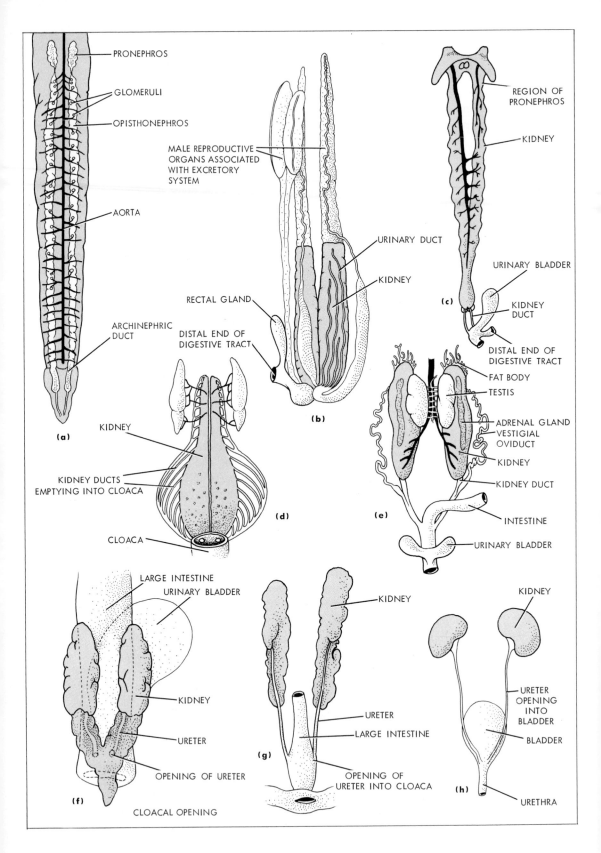

PRONEPHROS

GLOMERULI

OPISTHONEPHROS

MALE REPRODUCTIVE
ORGANS ASSOCIATED
WITH EXCRETORY
SYSTEM

AORTA

ARCHINEPHRIC
DUCT

RECTAL GLAND

DISTAL END OF
DIGESTIVE TRACT

URINARY DUCT

KIDNEY

REGION OF
PRONEPHROS

KIDNEY

URINARY BLADDER

KIDNEY
DUCT

DISTAL END OF
DIGESTIVE TRACT

FAT BODY

TESTIS

ADRENAL GLAND
VESTIGIAL
OVIDUCT

KIDNEY

KIDNEY DUCT

INTESTINE

URINARY BLADDER

(a)

(b)

(c)

KIDNEY

KIDNEY DUCTS
EMPTYING INTO CLOACA

CLOACA

(d)

(e)

LARGE INTESTINE

URINARY BLADDER

KIDNEY

URETER

OPENING OF URETER

CLOACAL OPENING

(f)

KIDNEY

URETER

LARGE INTESTINE

OPENING OF
URETER INTO CLOACA

(g)

KIDNEY

URETER
OPENING
INTO
BLADDER

BLADDER

URETHRA

(h)

organ. The capsule may protect the kidneys from mechanical stress and may limit the variations of blood and tissue fluid pressures within the organ. Connective tissue, lymphoid and blood-forming tissue, and reproductive tissue may be incorporated into the overall structure of the kidneys in various animals belonging to different vertebrate classes.

The Participation of Ducts, Urinary Bladders, and Cloacae in Excretion

When urine leaves the nephrons and collecting ducts, it traverses a longer or shorter path before being voided from the body. It passes first through urinary ducts (archinephric ducts in vertebrate embryos, many adult fish, and some amphibians; opisthonephric ducts in other fish and amphibians; metanephric ducts or ureters in amniotes). Then it may be voided directly from the body through a special opening behind the anus (bony fish), or it may enter a storage chamber. This may be a urinary bladder or urogenital sinus, an expanded region of the ureters, and thus, as in the case of some fish, of mesodermal origin. In tetrapods the urinary bladder is of endodermal origin. In amphibians it arises as an outpocketing of the ventral wall of the cloaca, and urine must traverse the cloaca on its way to storage there. Reptiles and mammals have urinary bladders that are derived embryologically from the allantois and so also are of endodermal origin. Most birds as well as some reptiles (snakes, crocodiles) are devoid of such a bladder, and their urine flows directly from the ureters into the cloaca. From its storage site the urine finally emerges from the body through the cloacal orifice (amphibians, reptiles, birds, monotremes) or through a *urethra* leading to the outside (higher mammals). The function of urine-storage structures appears to vary from one vertebrate form to another, but probably they generally allow a final reprocessing of the urine formed by the kidneys. Ions such as sodium and chloride may be actively reabsorbed into the body fluids through the walls of the large intestine, cloaca, or bladder (amphibians, fresh water dwelling reptiles, birds), and water may also be reabsorbed. In some cases the bladder wall is known to be sensitive to hormone (posterior pituitary) control, with increasing water retention when blood levels of the hormone

Figure 9-14 (opposite). Great variety exists in the form of the kidneys, their associated ducts and bladders, and their relationships to the cloaca (if this is present), and to the reproductive system. Most varied are excretory systems of fish, ranging from cyclostomes through bony fish. The kidneys may be of holonephric type, stretching almost the entire length of the body cavity; or may be, as in the case of some opisthonephroi, condensed into much smaller and more compact masses. Usually the kidneys are located dorsally in the body cavity, but even here variety exists among different fish species. The two kidneys of some fish may fuse into a single organ. One of the most unusual situations is seen in the coelocanth *Latimeria chalumnae*, where there is a single kidney located posteriorly and ventrally in the body cavity. In the case of male anamniote vertebrates the excretory and reproductive organs are intimately interconnected in structure. In amniotes, on the other hand, the kidneys are fully separated from male reproductive structures; thus, in (f)-(h) reproductive structures have been omitted from the diagrams. Throughout this figure, the excretory systems have been represented as if seen from the ventral aspect of the body. (a) Cyclostome, *Bdellostoma stouti*; (b) elasmobranch, *Galeus canis*, ♂; (c) teleost, *Salmo*; (d) amphibian, urodele salamander; (e) amphibian, anuran *Rana*; (f) reptile, lizard *Iguana*; (g) bird, *Coturnix coturnix japonica*; (h) mammal, *Rattus norvegicus*. (a)-(c) have been redrawn from classic illustrations by Conel, Borcea, and Haller.

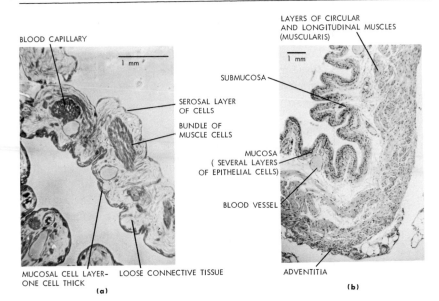

Figure 9-15. The structure of the urinary bladder ranges widely from vertebrate class to class . The amphibian bladder wall is thin, with a single layer of absorptive (mucosal) cells lining the bladder cavity. Loose connective tissue, a few muscle cell bundles, and a thin layer of serosal cells make up the rest of the wall. Fluid is readily absorbed through the delicate wall, especially when the bladder is filled and the wall has become thin as a result of stretching. (a) Is a photomicrograph (270X) of a small part of the unstretched bladder wall of the large toad, *Bufo marinus.* The micrograph was taken from an unstained epoxy section with phase contrast microscopy. (Courtesy of Dr. Alexander Leaf.)

  In the mammal, the bladder wall is relatively thick and muscular. The many-layered epithelium lining the bladder cavity changes in thickness as the bladder fills and empties (transitional epithelium), and the inner layers of the wall can be thrown into deep folds, or stretched, depending on the degree of bladder filling. The heavy muscular layer plays a major part in controlling bladder volume. (b) is a photomicrograph (100X) of a small part of the unstretched bladder of the laboratory mouse, *Mus musculus,* stained and shown at about one-third the magnification used for the toad bladder micrograph (Courtesy of Dr. Katharine P. Hummel.)

rise. This adjustment parallels the effects of the hormone on kidney tubules. Bladder- and cloacal-water conservation is of urgent importance in desert-dwelling amphibians and in reptiles and birds. Indeed, in reptiles and birds so much water may be reabsorbed in the cloaca that the final urinary product emerges as a semisolid paste consisting of uric acid, salts, and other excretory materials, with only a minimal amount of water. Such reabsorptive functions are not found in the urinary bladders of higher mammals, but even here the bladder may have important functions (Figure 9-15). It retains the urine until a time suitable for its ejection from the body (by a complicated process, mediated by nerves and muscles of the bladder wall, urinary tract, and body as a whole, termed *micturition*). Urine voided at appropriate times serves as a behavioral cue in many mammals, and the intermittency of urine flow may protect tissues lying near the urinary orifice from constant dampness and excessive threat of bacterial invasion.

  A variety of vertebrate animals use the urinary passages as channels for releasing reproductive cells from the ovaries and testes. Thus, in some fish and amphibians the oviduct arises by longitudinal division of the archinephric duct. The male reproductive tract in most vertebrates includes ducts originating from the archinephric ducts. In some fish and amphibians the sperm and urine traverse common pathways, but in most other vertebrates special tubes for the transfer of urine arise after incorporation of the archinephric ducts into the reproductive system. Some nephric tubules develop into sperm transit routes in many vertebrates. Where this structure is present, sperm generally emerge into the cloaca, but in higher mammals sperm travel through the urethra on their way to the outside. The final form of the excretory apparatus is more or less dependent on its interaction with the reproductive system. These points will be discussed more fully in Chapter 13.

Perspective on Excretion and Osmoregulation

As was suggested at the beginning of this chapter, the kidneys, despite their highly effective organization for homeostatic regulation, never operate alone. In all vertebrates they are supported by extrarenal excretory mechanisms ranging, for instance, from the liver's excretion of organic compounds to the secretion of sodium and chloride ions by fish gills and rectal glands, and by reptile and bird nasal glands. To understand excretory and osmoregulatory functions completely, the interplay between these various regulatory structures must be taken into account. Perhaps a specific illustration will clarify this point. As was noted earlier in this chapter, various marine fish have essentially aglomerular kidneys. This condition is reasonable because of the highly concentrated (i.e., relatively salt-rich and water-deficient) environment in which they live. Rather surprisingly, however, fresh-water fish of a few species, such as the pipefish *Microphis boaja*, also have aglomerular kidneys. Further, some fish, including the eel *Anguilla rostrata*, can adapt to life both at sea and in fresh water without corresponding changes in the structure of their renal corpuscles. In all these exceptional cases compensatory adjustments must be sought in the tubular regions of the kidneys and in extrarenal mechanisms. In most instances the details of these adjusting mechanisms are unknown.

The functions of the extrarenal salt-secreting structures and of the kidneys are at least partly controlled by endocrine secretions (chiefly from the pituitary and adrenal glands). As might be expected, the regulatory mechanisms in general are highly sensitive to conditions of the external and internal environments. For instance, the tubules of the nasal salt glands of marine reptiles and birds enlarge as the animals adapt to increasingly hypertonic environments. In mammals healthy kidney tubules enlarge when the diet is excessively rich in protein (which creates an increased demand for excretion of nitrogenous waste) or when part of the kidney tissue is damaged or destroyed. As in every other phase of the life of vertebrates, the intimate interplay between structure and function is clearly reflected in the details of the intricate, varied, and labile organization of the excretory and osmoregulatory systems.

Figure 9-16 is a simplified illustration of one type of man-made "kidney" used by physicians to substitute for the urgently important excretory functions of patients with impaired renal operation. Comparing and contrast-

Figure 9-16 (opposite). Artificial "kidneys" have been designed to substitute for the impaired kidneys of people suffering from certain kinds of kidney disease, poisoning, and circulatory shock. (a) Is a photograph of a patient with an artificial kidney in operation. The blood (rendered incoagulable) is led from an artery, such as one in the lower arm or leg, into a dialyzing system. Here the blood comes in contact with a porous membrane (e.g., cellophane) of large surface area (e.g., about 400 cm²). Waste materials, as well as other components of plasma, filter through the membrane into a mass of balanced salt solution containing glucose, and with pH and osmotic pressure at levels characteristic of the normal person. Plasma proteins and other very large molecules cannot penetrate through the membrane, and so are retained in the circulating blood plasma. Normal plasma constituents, such as sodium and chloride ions and glucose, even though they may be lost through the dialysis membrane, are restored to the blood by diffusion from the balanced solution of the bathing medium which contains these substances at normal blood concentrations. Waste materials of low molecular weight, such as urea and uric acid, pass through the dialysis membrane and are distributed through the bathing medium. Thus, they are effectively removed from the blood before it returns to the body through the vein. Note the countercurrent arrangement of flow of blood and dialysis fluid through the system. The rates of flow of dialysis fluid are high (e.g., 400-500 ml/min).

(b) Schema indicating components of an artificial kidney. The artificial kidney is quite selective in removing harmful wastes from the body, while retaining valuable components of the blood plasma. In its functioning, it can be compared with a vertebrate kidney operating with effective glomerular filtration, and with blood flow to the tubules intact, but without any active cellular processes (reabsorption, secretion) of the tubular cells. In this analogy, the dialysis fluid may be compared with the urine of intact vertebrates. The analogy is not exact, however, and the reader is invited to analyze it further, considering for instance, the relative efficiency, demands for water supply, and other aspects of the operation of a normal kidney as contrasted with the artificial kidney.

ing real and artificial kidneys may serve to bring into clear focus some basic aspects of vertebrate renal structure and function.

References for Chapter 9

Bentley, P. J., "Adaptations of Amphibia to Arid Environments." *Sci.* **152** (1966), 619-623.

Brodal, A., and R. Fänge, *The Biology of Myxine.* Oslo: Universitetsforlaget, 1963.

Bulger, R. E., "Fine Structure of the Rectal (Salt-Secreting) Gland of the Spiny Dogfish, *Squalus acanthias.*" *Anat. Rec.,* **147** (1963), 95-107.

Chan, D. K. O., and J. G. Phillips, "The Anatomy, Histology and Histochemistry of the Rectal Gland in the Lip-Shark *Hemiscyllium plagriosum.*" (Bennett), *J. Anat.,* **101** (1967), 137-159.

Chase, S. W., "The Mesonephros and Urogenital Ducts of *Necturus maculosus Rafinesque.*" *J. Morph.,* **37** (1923), 457-532.

Doyle, W. L., "The Principal Cells of the Salt-Gland of Marine Birds." *Exp. Cell Res.,* **21** (1960), 386.

Dunson, W. A., and A. M. Taub, "Extrarenal Salt Excretion in Sea Snakes (Laticauda)." *Am. J. Physiol.,* **213** (1967), 975-982.

Fox, H., "The Amphibian Pronephros." *Quart. Rev. Biol.,* **38** (1963), 1-25.

Fraser, E. A., "The Development of the Vertebrate Excretory System." *Biol. Rev.,* **25** (1950), 159-187.

Philpott, C. W., "Halide Localization in the Teleost Chloride Cell and Its

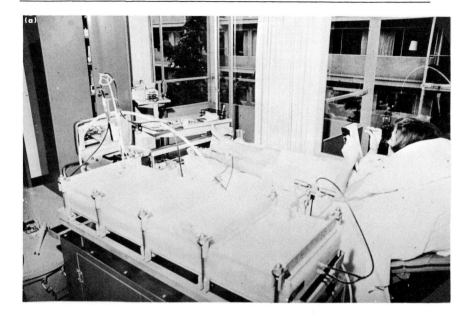

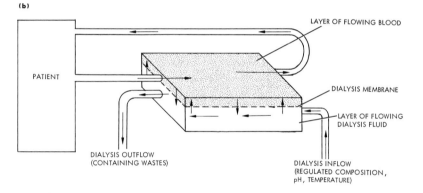

Identification by Selected Area Electron Diffraction." *Protoplasma,* **60** (1965), 7-23.

——, and D. E. Copeland, "Fine Structure of Chloride Cells from Three Species of Fundulus." *J. Cell. Biol.,* **18** (1963), 389-404.

Schmidt-Nielsen, K., "Organ Systems in Adaptation: The Excretory System," in *Adaptation to the Environment* by D. B. Dill, E. F. Adolph, and C. G. Wilber, *Handbook of Physiology,* Section IV. Washington: American Physiological Society, 1964.

——, C. Barker Jorgensen, and H. Osaki, "Extrarenal Salt Excretion in Birds." *Am J. Physiol.,* **193** (1958), 101-107.

——, A. Borut, P. Lee, and E. Crawford, "Nasal Salt Excretion and the Possible Function of the Cloaca in Water Conservation." *Sci.,* **142** (1963), 1300-1301.

Staaland, H., "Anatomical and Physiological Adaptation of the Nasal Glands in Charadriiformes Birds." *Comp. Physiol. Biochem.,* **23** (1967), 933-944.

10
The sensory receptors

The Role of the Nervous System

The *nervous system* and the *endocrine system* are the integrating systems of the vertebrates. In its role as a coordinator, the nervous system evokes actions and reactions to the myriad of environmental stimuli that are continually bombarding the organism. These responses are directed primarily (1) to the survival of the organism (e.g., movements, protection against enemies, drive for the acquisition of food, maintenance of body temperature in warm-blooded animals) and (2) to the survival of the species (e.g., reproduction: mating, nesting, and care of offspring). The nervous system is organized (1) to sense and to test the environment and to project the resulting influences as *input* to the central nervous system; (2) to process and to store this input within the *central nervous system* for the immediate and future use by the organism: (3) to transmit *output*, which regulates the organism's activities by stimulating or inhibiting the actions of the muscles and glands of the body, and (4) to interact with the endocrine system.

Input (Sensory or Afferent Information) to the Central Nervous System

The nervous system is continually monitoring the environment, both external and internal to the organism, through many sensors (sensory endings). Through these sensors pertinent environmental energies are selected and coded into nerve impulses that are transmitted as *input* by the peripheral nerves to the central nervous system. This input may be perceived at conscious levels or utilized at unconscious levels. Conscious sensations are the organism's unique interpretation of the environmental stimuli; they are not precise copies of the environment. For example, pain is felt, yet environmental pain as such is nonexistent; a sound is heard, yet a sound is actually not a sound, but rather a wavelength frequency (vibration).

Processing and Storage of Information within the Central Nervous System

The input from the periphery is projected to central nervous system processing stations, which are organized groups of neurons called *nuclei, ganglia,* centers, *neuronal pools*, and cortical areas. These stations act as complex analytic computers and intricate control systems. The new input, acting upon the reactive matrix of the nervous system, may influence and activate the expression of the organism's actions. These influences may have an *immediate effect* (e.g., from a simple knee jerk to the reactions exhibited by a hungry predator at sensing prey) or a *delayed effect* (e.g., reactions after the recall of an event that occurred in the distant past). The input may be "held in storage" and later utilized in behavioral patterns, emotional responses, learned skills, memories, and abstractions.

388

Output (Motor or Efferent Actions)

The actions and reactions of the nervous system are overtly expressed exclusively through muscular activity, glandular secretion, *neurosecretion,* electric discharges in certain fish, and luminescent discharge of a photogenic organ in some deep-sea fish. The output from the central nervous system to the effectors is mediated largely through the peripheral nervous system and, in part, through the endocrine system.

The nervous system and the endocrine system are interacting feedback systems. In fact, the endocrine system is primarily controlled by and integrated with the nervous system. Because of this interaction, the endocrine system is often called the neuroendocrine system.

Classification of Sensory (Afferent) Input

The varieties of information received by the body as input from environmental stimuli are sensed, appreciated, and interpreted by the organism in many ways. To codify the product of these afferent stimuli, several classifications have been proposed. Although none is wholly satisfactory, each makes significant points concerning sensory receptors (nerve endings), sensors, or sensations.

Viewed subjectively, afferent stimuli have roles in the conscious or in the unconscious. Because sensations are basically the organism's subjective interpretations, it is difficult for man to conceive of the manner in which each vertebrate perceives conscious sensations. The unconscious sensations are integrated into activities such as muscular coordination, respiration, cardiovascular tone, alimentary canal motility, and secretory activities. The senses and the sensors may be named according to the organ system with which they are associated; somatic and visceral. *Somatic* refers to the extremities, body wall, and portions of the head; *visceral* refers to the vital organs of the digestive, circulatory, excretory, respiratory, and endocrine systems. Senses with a wide distribution in the body are called *general senses,* those limited to a restricted region are called *special senses.* The general senses (and their receptors) include pain, temperature appreciation, touch, visceral sense, body sense, position sense, and unconscious senses associated with reflex activities. Those of special sense include hearing, balance sense by vestibular receptors, appreciation of water currents (monitored by the inner ear and lateral line), sight (monitored by eye), smell (monitored by olfactory and vomeronasal mucosa), and taste (monitored by *taste buds*). General senses (and their receptors) are further classified as general somatic senses and general visceral senses; for example, pain in the skin and joints is a general somatic sensation, whereas pain in the stomach is a general visceral sensation. The special senses are either somatic senses (appreciation of water currents, hearing, balance, and sight) or visceral senses (smell and taste).

The General Senses

The general senses may be classified as *exteroceptive senses, proprioceptive senses*, and *interoceptive senses*. Exteroceptive cutaneous senses are the product of many external environmental energies that stimulate receptors located in the skin (Figure 10-1), and include the general sensations of pain,

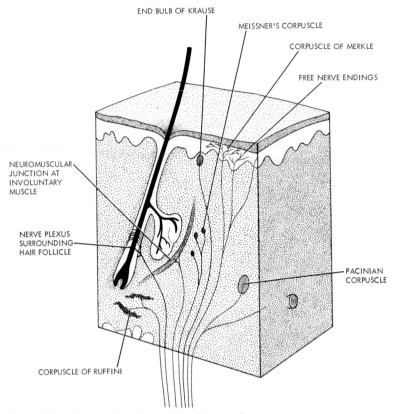

Figure 10-1. Nerve endings in the skin of mammals.

warmth, cold, and light touch. The movement of hairs and vibrissi and the contact on the skin without deforming it produce light touch. The proprioceptive senses (kinesthetic and deep sensibility) result from the stimulation of receptors by energies generated within the somatic structures (Figure 10-2); these include both conscious and unconscious sensations. Conscious senses include those of position and movements of body parts (joint sense), vibratory sense (base of vibrating tuning fork on bone), appreciation of the weight, shape, and form of an object, pressure sense (touch resulting in deformation of skin), and deep pain. Unconscious senses provide the information essential for the maintenance of muscle tone and muscular reflex activity. The interoceptive visceral senses that result from the stimulation of receptors within the viscera, include the conscious visceral sensations of pain, temperature, distention, fullness, cramps, hunger, thirst, and satiety. Unconscious influences result in the numerous activities of the visceral organ systems (digestive, cardiovascular, respiratory, and urinary).

The general senses, especially those of exteroception and proprioception, are most highly evolved in birds and mammals, but are relatively poorly developed in fish and amphibians. In the various vertebrates the presence or absence of the ability to perceive certain senses is apparently correlated with the survival value of each sense. An animal living constantly in water is subject to equal pressure over its body and to only gradual changes in environmental temperature, hence fish have probably not evolved a variety of elaborate general senses (e.g., two-point discrimination and temperature). In contrast, terrestrial vertebrates receive a variety of continuously changing stimuli from both exteroceptors and proprioceptors about external and internal environments. The exteroceptors sense temperature changes and touch from the differential contact of objects on the body surface (for example, contact of feet on ground); the proprioceptors monitor for data from the muscles and joints as they constantly readjust to the alteration in the tension of muscles and the movement of joints. In general, fish and amphibians have many free nerve-ending receptors. Relatively simple proprio-ceptors (neuromuscular spindles) are found in the muscles of amphibians. In addition to simple free nerve endings, birds and mammals have a wide variety of specialized sensory receptors (Figures 10-1 and 10-2). These include Meissner's corpuscle (touch), Paccinian corpuscle (pressure), Merkel's corpuscle (touch), corpuscle of Ruffini (warmth), end-bulb of Krause (cold), neuromuscular spindle (tension within muscles), neurotendinous endings of Golgi (tension within tendons), and others. Transitional forms exist as well.

Free nerve endings are the primary pain receptors; they are located in many regions including the skin, pulp of a tooth, cornea of an eye, and the intestinal tract. Each of these receptors may be excited by thermal, mechani-

Figure 10-2. Nerve endings terminating in the voluntary muscles, tendons and joints. (Adapted from Noback and Demarest.)

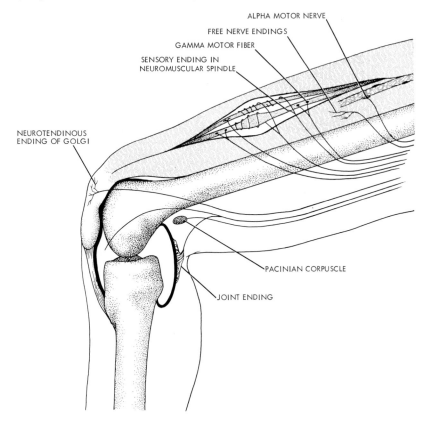

ALPHA MOTOR NERVE

FREE NERVE ENDINGS

GAMMA MOTOR FIBER

SENSORY ENDING IN
NEUROMUSCULAR SPINDLE

NEUROTENDINOUS
ENDING OF GOLGI

PACINIAN CORPUSCLE

JOINT ENDING

cal, and chemical stimuli. Tissue damage may evoke pain sensations; the traumatized tissue releases chemicals, such as histamine, that stimulate the pain receptors. The thermal modalities are sensed by heat and cold receptors located mainly in the skin. Besides the capsulated endings, the corpuscle of Ruffini and end-bulb of Krause noted before, free nerve endings also are thermal receptors. Heat may elicit sensations of both pain and temperature. Within the skin of man, cold receptors are said to be more abundant and more superficially located than warmth receptors. Following stimulation of the cold receptors, reflexes can be evoked that tend to conserve heat; hair and feathers are erected to create a dead air space around the animal; cutaneous blood vessels constrict to reduce the radiation of heat into the air; and the muscle contractions of shivering produce heat. Following the stimulation of heat receptors, reflexes are evoked that tend to dissipate heat, cutaneous blood vessels dilate to increase radiation of heat from the body, and the evaporation of water from the body surface is increased following panting and sweating.

The concept that each nerve ending is exclusively the receptor associated with a specific sense (modality) is known as the law of specific nerve energies. This has been implied before in associating a modality with a receptor (e.g., touch with Meissner's corpuscle). A modern concept is the pattern theory of sensation which relates a group of nerve endings with each modality. In this concept a small complex of endings is associated with a *spot*, called warm spot, cold spot, or touch spot. The differential stimulation of the receptors within each spot in different combinations results in various nuances associated with a sensation (e.g., sharp, burning, and dull pain).

A specialized heat receptor, called the pit organ or facial pit, is present in a depression in front of the eye in certain snakes called pit vipers (rattlesnakes). With this receptor, the pit viper can detect the presence, even in the dark, of a warm-blooded prey such as a mouse.

Special Senses

The receptors of the senses are innervated by branches of the cranial nerves (Figure 10-3): smell by the *olfactory nerve* (I) from the olfactory mucosa and by the terminal nerve from the vomeronasal organ; vision by the *optic nerve* (II) from the eye; sound, head position, and appreciation of water currents by the *vestibulo-acoustic nerve* (VIII) from the inner ear and the lateral line organ; and taste by some fibers in the *facial nerve* (VII), *glossopharyngeal nerve* (IX), and *vagus nerve* (X) from the taste buds. The receptors of smell and taste are the chemists; they are chemoreceptors or special visceral afferent receptors reacting to chemical stimuli. (They are visceral because of their association with sensing for food.) The receptors of the optic system and the vestibulocochlear systems are the physicists or special somatic afferent receptors reacting to physical stimuli. The eye is a photoreceptor and the inner ear and lateral line organ are mechanoreceptors; the former react to light, the latter to vibration.

The Chemical Senses

Vertebrates sense a wide variety of chemical constituents from simple inorganic compounds (e.g., salt and acids) to complex organic compounds.

The chemical senses are commonly divided into three categories: common (general) chemical sense, olfaction (smell), and *gustation* (taste). These three chemical senses are arbitrary and overlap. The role of these sensory systems is more than just to identify chemical entities; they are the activators and the sensitizers of the nervous system, evoking many complex behavioral patterns associated with such activities as the search for food, the sexual responses of animals during the mating season, the *agonistic* actions in the presence of an enemy, the preservation of an animal's status within a social group (pecking order), and the identification of offspring, parents, or friendly species.

The olfactory sensors are "distance chemical receptors" stimulated by ultraminute concentrations of odors conveyed through the water to the nasal mucosa of aquatic animals and through the air to the nasal mucosa of terrestrial animals. The gustatory sensors are contact receptors stimulated by the direct contact of the chemical substances, which are dissolved in the secre-

Figure 10-3. Brain and cranial nerves of the shark *Carcharius littoralis.* Cranial nerves, I through X. (Adapted from Kingsley.)

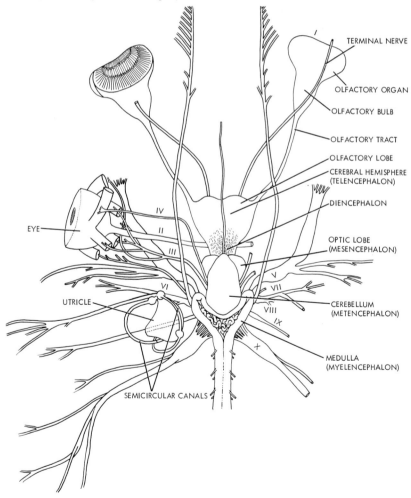

tions surrounding such sensor cells as the taste and olfactory neurons (Figures 10-4 and 10-5). In general, the olfactory system is more sensitive than the gustatory system; quantitative estimates indicate that it is from 10 to 20,000 times more sensitive (10,000 in man). This explains why we smell food more than we taste it, and why food tastes flat when we have a cold.

The Common (General) Chemical Sense

The common chemical senses are nondiscriminative senses which often produce irritating sensations and evoke protective responses. In fish and amphibians, nerve endings in the skin are sensitive to some chemical changes in the water. Terrestrial mammals have nerve endings that monitor the chemical sense located within the mucous membranes of the respiratory and digestive systems. Stimulation of these endings results in the protective secretion of mucous and serous substances. Smoke and chlorine act as suffocants on the respiratory tract and evoke mucous secretions and choking responses. Irritants such as ammonia, acids, and astringent food such as persimmon stimulate the common chemical sensory endings. Tear gas irritates the eyes and stimulates the secretion of tears.

Chemical receptors have a significant role in the regulation of the internal environment of an organism. The carotid body, located at the bifurcation of the common carotid artery in the neck of birds and mammals, is a chemoreceptor that monitors the carbon dioxide and oxygen concentration of the blood. Through reflexes initiated in the carotid body the appropriate cardiovascular responses of increasing or decreasing blood pressure and blood flow follow.

Taste

Taste is a complex, subjective sensation that is difficult to define objectively; there is no truly objective classification of taste. The so-called "elementary

Figure 10-4. Microscopic section through a taste bud.

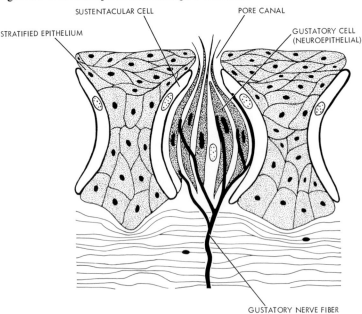

SUSTENTACULAR CELL

PORE CANAL

STRATIFIED EPITHELIUM

GUSTATORY CELL (NEUROEPITHELIAL)

GUSTATORY NERVE FIBER

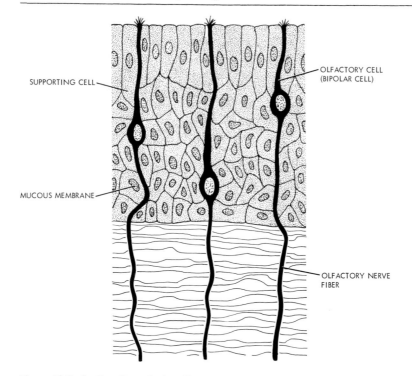

SUPPORTING CELL

OLFACTORY CELL
(BIPOLAR CELL)

MUCOUS MEMBRANE

OLFACTORY NERVE
FIBER

Figure 10-5. Section through the olfactory mucosa.

taste sensations" of sweet, sour, salt, and bitter are incorporated into a subjective classification that is used for want of a better substitute. In all probability there are no primary taste qualities comparable to sounds defined in frequencies of cycles per second.

The peripheral receptor for taste is the brandy-snifter-shaped taste bud (Figure 10-4). Each bud is a "contact chemical receptor" comprised of up to twenty-five neuroepithelial taste cells and a number of so-called *sustentacular cells*; the latter are actually immature taste cells which replace the aged taste cells. The distal tip of each taste cell has a surface specialization of microvilli that interact with sapid substances, either as whole molecules or as ions. Structural differences among the various taste buds do not seem to exist. Current theory suggests that each taste cell reacts to several taste qualities and that the nuances of taste are transmitted by a variety of patterns of sensory impulses from each taste bud.

In fish and amphibians the taste buds are found not only in membranes lining the mouth, but may be widely distributed in the body skin. In all vertebrates these taste buds are innervated by the three cranial nerves, VII, IX, and X. Taste buds on the rostrum of the sturgeon, a bottom feeder, enable it to sense food by tasting the water before reaching the food. A catfish, which has taste buds scattered over its body surface, tail, and barbels, can immediately be attracted to swim to that side on which a barbel has been stimulated with a drop of meat juice. By tasting the water, many fish maintain contact with their school. After detecting by taste the presence of a predator fish, certain fish are alarmed into an escape reaction.

Mammals, whose taste buds are primarily concentrated in the surface epithelium of the tongue, also have taste buds in the palate, mouth, and pharynx. Birds have a few taste buds on the back of the tongue and the palate.

Smell   The olfactory sensors, including the olfactory mucosa and the vomeronasal mucosa, are fundamentally similar in living vertebrates (Figure 10-5). The main difference among the various animals is not in this relatively stable sensory apparatus but rather in the degree of complexity of the chambers housing these receptor membranes. Vertebrates with a well-developed sense of smell are called *macrosmatic animals*; most mammals, including carnivores, ungulates, and rodents, are macrosmatic. Those vertebrates with a poorly developed sense of smell are *microsmatic animals*; these include birds, primates, and the baleen whales. The toothed whales are anosmatic mammals with no sense of smell.

In fish the olfactory mucosa, which comes into direct contact with water, is restricted to a single area. In elasmobranch and teleost fish the sensors are located in the blind olfactory pit (nasal sac); water flows in and out of this chamber without passing into the mouth. In lungfish the mucosa lines a nasal cavity that extends from the exterior to the mouth; as in many higher vertebrates the medium containing the odors passes over the olfactory sensors before entering the mouth. The olfactory nerve projects to the olfactory bulb (Figure 10-3). Unlike the condition in higher vertebrates, there is no separation into a main olfactory bulb and an accessory olfactory bulb. The nerve fibers from the olfactory bulb project via the olfactory tract to the olfactory cortex of the brain.

In most tetrapods two sensory areas are associated with the olfactory apparatus: an olfactory mucosa with nerve fibers projecting to the main olfactory bulb via the olfactory nerve, and a vomeronasal (Jacobson's) mucosa with nerve fibers projecting to the accessory olfactory bulb via the terminal nerve (Figure 10-3). Whereas the olfactory mucosa is always located within the nasal cavity, the vomeronasal mucosa, which is always separated from the olfactory epithelium, is located either in the ventral medial aspect of the nasal cavity or in an outpocket of the oral cavity. The precise function of the vomeronasal organ is still vague. The organ is well developed in amphibians, lizards, snakes, monotremes, marsupials, insectivores, bats, prosimians, and New World monkeys. It is absent or rudimentary in crocodiles, birds, most aquatic mammals, Old World monkeys, and man. The well-developed vomeronasal organs in lizards and snakes are used to sense chemicals picked up from the air by the protruded tongue. After testing the air the snake's forked tongue is retracted and inserted into the two vomeronasal pockets; the dissolved chemical particles on the tongue stimulate the sensors of the organ.

The olfactory mucosa is composed of bipolar neurons and supporting cells (Figure 10-5). Its bipolar neurons are unique; they are the only nerve cells that perform the dual roles as sensors in direct contact with the external environment and as transmitters of the codes directly to the olfactory bulb of the central nervous system (Figure 10-3). A peripheral process of each bipolar cell terminates in a swelling called an olfactory vesicle (rod) comprised of a tuft of one to fifteen cilia (olfactory "hairs" or streamers) depending upon the species. These hairs form a feltwork embedded in the odor-absorbing secretion coating the olfactory mucosa. The ultrasensitive odorant-receptor interaction is presumed to occur at the olfactory hairs. Associated with the olfactory mucosa of many tetrapods are special glands of Bowman, which have an obscure function. These glands are not found in the olfactory mucosa of fish or in the vomeronasal mucosa.

The relative significance of olfaction in the behavioral patterns of any animal is not really known. Many fish utilize olfactory cues (1) to maintain contact with their territory or their school, (2) to sense enemies and to trigger appropriate escape reactions, (3) to detect food and prey, and (4) to recognize the dominant and submissive members (pecking order) of the social community to which they belong. This last use is vital to the maintenance of the social structure of the fish community. Olfactory cues may be used by migrating fish such as salmon to identify their home and spawning grounds. Apparently the young salmon is imprinted (a permanent change in an animal's behavior as the result of the impact of a sensory cue at a critical time in its life), probably during the first weeks of life, by the odors of the tributary stream of its youth. Later, as a migratory adult, the innate drive to return to the spawning grounds is guided primarily by swimming against a current (*rheotaxis*). The selection of the correct tributary at each fork in the stream is thought to be a function, in part, of the olfactory system; the fish makes a positive response to the key odor cues and a negative response to their absence. Upon entering a tributary lacking the key odor cues, the fish retreats and tests other tributaries until the key cues are sensed. Key odors need not be consciously recognized.

Although most birds are microsmatic, some have a keen sense of smell; these include the nocturnal New Zealand kiwi, vulture, condor, albatross, petrel, and others. The macrosmatic "nose-mammals" probably have the most elaborate, acute and evolved olfactory discriminatory sense of all vertebrates. Elephants, deer, antelopes, sheep, and dogs are in this category. The stalker, to avoid detection, must approach the "nose-species" from a downwind position. By smelling her newborn infant immediately after birth, the mother seal registers a scent imprint; with this imprint she is able, by the sense of smell, to recognize and to identify her pup from the others in the rookery. Each of these species has extensive and elaborate scrolls of bone (turbinals, conchae) to increase the surface area of the nasal cavity in order to accommodate the enlarged olfactory epithelial mucosa.

The Eye: The Photoreceptor

Paired lateral eyes are present in the vertebrates. They have secondarily degenerated into vestigial and near-functionless organs in species such as the hagfish, cave-dwelling and abyssal fish, and underground-living amphibians, reptiles, and mammals (e.g., moles). Median eyes, known as pineal and parietal eyes, are found in lampreys and some lizards.

The eyes are the sensitive detectors of light waves. The photoreceptor cells in the eyes of all vertebrates are stimulated by approximately the same range of the radiomagnetic spectrum from 760 to 390 millimicrons. In a general way this spectral sensitivity corresponds to the transmission spectrum of water; this suggests that the vertebrate eye was initially evolved to function in the milieu of the primordial vertebrates, the shallow water.

The eyes of vertebrates are constructed with similar structural features. Within this basic pattern, a vast array of adaptive variations have evolved to enable the eye to function in many ecological niches. The complete structure of the eye comprises the eye proper (eyeball) and accessory parts such as the eyelids, several types of glands and their ducts, and the extraocular muscles. The optic nerve is made up of fibers projecting from the sensory retina of the eye to optic centers in the brain.

Size and
Shape of
the Eye

There is no correlation between eye size and body size; in some birds each eye may occupy one-third the volume of the head. The size of the eyeball is related to the image size and has adapted to the light-gathering demands of the animal. A large eye, with its proportionately large image-producing retina, can register a large copy of the environmental field. *Nocturnal* animals have large eyes with which to capture more light out of the dark; their eyes are efficient visual receptors for night vision.

The eyes of vertebrates have three basic shapes: spherical, ovoid, and tubular. Many vertebrates and all mammals have roughly spherical eyes (Figure 10-6), varying from a slightly elongated eye (cat) to a slightly oblate eye (horse). Many *diurnal* birds have flattened ovoid eyes. Some birds (owls, eagles, and hawks) and some abyssal fish have tubular eyes (Figure 10-6). Eyes have evolved to gather and to focus light (called *accommodation*) upon the photoreceptive membrane, the *retina*. To accomplish this the eyeball has two segments: the accommodation segment formed by the cornea and lens and the photoreceptive segment formed by the *retina*, *choroid*, and *sclera* (Figures 10-6 and 10-7). In each eye the proximity of these two segments is such that the accommodation segment focuses the environmental field of vision upon the retina of the photoreceptive segment. The shape of the eye is largely maintained by the forces exerted by the internal intraocular pressure from within the eye upon the soft tissues of the coats of the eyeball. The natural shape of the eye is generally a sphere. The tubular eye is an adaptation to meet the functional demands of a large eye in a relatively small skull by constricting (hourglass effect) the eye at the junction of the accommodation segment (cornea) and the receptor segment (sclera, choroid, and retina). In effect, the advantages of the large spherical eye are retained in the tubular eye, with only a slight, if any, change in the size and curvature of the cornea and of the retina because of this constriction. By such adaptation the volume of the eye is definitely reduced. This is accomplished, in part, with the aid of a constricting continuous ring of bones or cartilages, called scleral ossicles (Figure 10-6), located adjacent to the sclero-corneal junction; by this means the intraocular pressure maintains a tubular eye instead of a spherical one. This is analogous to placing a constricting circular band around an inflated balloon.

Figure 10-6 (opposite). Diagrams of sections through the eyes of (a) lamprey, (b) teleost, (c) frog, (d) snake, (e) eagle-owl, and (f) placental mammal. The cornea may be derived from dermal connective tissue (dermal cornea) and the scleral connective tissue (scleral cornea). (After Duke-Elder and after Marshall.)

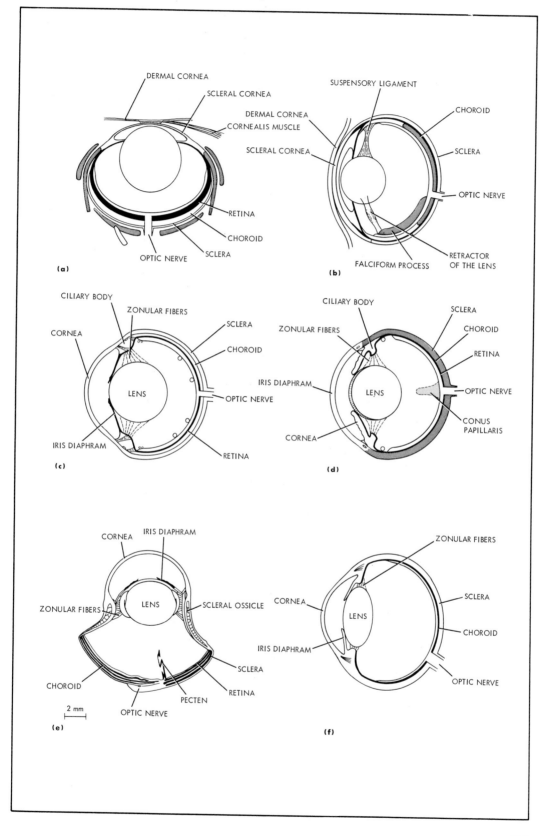

(a) DERMAL CORNEA, SCLERAL CORNEA, DERMAL CORNEA, CORNEALIS MUSCLE, SCLERAL CORNEA, RETINA, CHOROID, OPTIC NERVE, SCLERA

(b) SUSPENSORY LIGAMENT, DERMAL CORNEA, SCLERAL CORNEA, CHOROID, SCLERA, OPTIC NERVE, RETRACTOR OF THE LENS, FALCIFORM PROCESS

(c) CILIARY BODY, ZONULAR FIBERS, CORNEA, SCLERA, CHOROID, LENS, OPTIC NERVE, IRIS DIAPHRAM, RETINA

(d) CILIARY BODY, ZONULAR FIBERS, SCLERA, CHOROID, RETINA, IRIS DIAPHRAM, LENS, OPTIC NERVE, CONUS PAPILLARIS, CORNEA

(e) CORNEA, IRIS DIAPHRAM, ZONULAR FIBERS, LENS, SCLERAL OSSICLE, SCLERA, RETINA, CHOROID, PECTEN, OPTIC NERVE, 2 mm

(f) ZONULAR FIBERS, CORNEA, SCLERA, CHOROID, LENS, IRIS DIAPHRAM, OPTIC NERVE

Basic
Structure of
the Eye

The eye is composed of three tunics: (1) an outer fibrous tunic, the cornea and sclera, (2) intermediate tunic, the *uvea*, and (3) an internal tunic, the retina (Figures 10-6 and 10-7). The outer tunic, a thick lamina of dense connective tissue, consists of the opaque sclera (the white of the human eye) and the transparent *cornea*. This tunic acts as the skeleton of the eye and resists the intraocular pressure. The uvea consists of the vascular and pigmented choroid layer, the ciliary body (with muscles essential in accommodation), and the *iris diaphragm* surrounding the pupil. The internal tunic is the retina, which is made up of the light-sensitive receptors (rods and cones) and many nerve cells arranged in layers. The *lens*, located behind the cornea and the iris, is suspended by fine, taut zonula fibrils that extend from the circumference of the equator of the lens to the ciliary body. The region between the lens, ciliary body, and iris is the posterior chamber and that between the iris and the cornea is the anterior chamber. These two chambers are filled with a fluid called the aqueous humor, which is largely formed by the *ciliary body*. From the ciliary body, the aqueous humor passes successively through the posterior chamber, pupil, anterior chamber, and the meshwork of the filtration angle; from here the humor diffuses into Schlemm's canal and the venous drainage (Figure 10-8). The large region between the lens and the retina is filled with a gelatinous matrix called the vitreous humor, which consists of mucoproteins.

To perform its functional role efficiently the eyeball must fulfill several criteria. (1) Light must reach the photoreceptors in the retina. (2) Stray and unwanted light must be prevented from exciting the receptors. (3) The size and shape of the eye must permit light from the visual field to focus an image upon the retina. The curvatures and location of the cornea, lens, and retina must be precise within narrow limits. (4) The eye should be adapted to see objects in focus at different distances; the process of making these

Figure 10-7. Diagram of horizontal section through the right human eye.

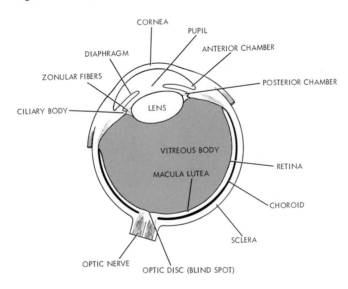

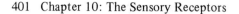

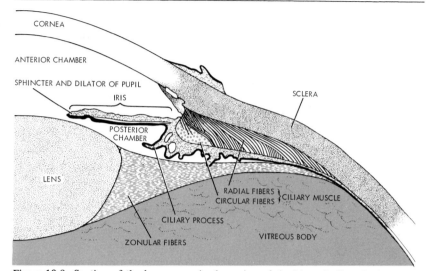

Figure 10-8. Section of the human eye in the region of the iris and ciliary body.

adjustments is known as accommodation. (5) The eye must be able to increase and decrease the amount of light entering it.

Cornea

The cornea is the transparent window that permits light to enter the eye (Figures 10-6 to 10-8); in terrestrial animals it is the site of the refraction of light. In aquatic animals the refracting capacity of the cornea is largely neutralized by its immediate contact with water. In land animals the refraction of the light at the cornea and the lens is collectively integrated to focus the environmental image on the retina. In true nocturnal vertebrates and abyssal fish, the cornea is large, permitting the eye to trap as much available light as possible.

Pupil and Iris

The pupil is the aperture surrounded by the iris diaphragm, through which the light enters the eye before reaching the lens (Figure 10-9). Muscles within the iris can alter the size of the pupil; muscles which constrict the pupil are sphincters and those which enlarge the pupil are dilators. In many vertebrates iridic sphincter muscles are present, whereas iridic dilators are absent. Except for the reptiles and birds in which the iridic muscles are striated and voluntary all other vertebrates have smooth involuntary iridic muscles. In general the pupil assumes the shape of either a slit (cat, horse) or of a circle (man and other primates). The slit pupil is the more efficient because both maximum dilation and constriction can be attained; a narrow slit can be almost completely constricted. The circular pupil cannot contract to a pinpoint because in the fully contracted iris the tissues at the edge of the pupil bunch up to prevent complete constriction. The "color of the eye" is largely determined by pigments within the iris. An albino animal has pink eyes because the color of the blood is not obscured in the pigmentless iris.

Accommodation

Accommodation is the mechanism by which the light entering the eye, after being refracted by the cornea, is focused upon the retina by the lens with

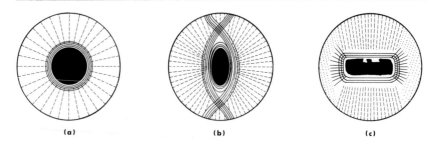

Figure 10-9. Diagrams of musculature of mammalian iris. (a) Round pupil of diurnal
and noctural mammals. Note the sphincter muscle (solid lines) and symmetrical dilater
muscle (broken lines). (b) Vertical slit pupil (cat) of nocturnal mammals that live in
daylight. The scissor-like action of the two bundles of sphincter muscle (solid lines)
compresses the pupil. Note the symmetrical dilater muscle (broken lines). (c) Horizontal
pupil of ungulates, some whales and other mammals. The sphincter muscle (solid lines)
is anchored to connective tissue (dotted lines). Note the dilator muscle (broken lines).
The dilated pupil outlines a circle; the contracted pupil outlines a horizontal slit. (After
Walls.)

such fidelity that the field is "in focus." Lenses vary in size and shape in
each of the classes of vertebrates. In general, aquatic vertebrates are "short-
sighted." This condition is probably associated with the fact that distant
vision is not possible or useful in water; these animals have spherical lenses in
order to obtain a great degree of refraction from the increased curvature and
thereby compensate for the lack of refraction at the cornea (Figures 10-6
and 10-7). Nocturnal terrestrial animals have large spherical lenses that are
usually close to the retina. Such lenses serve two functions: they permit a
maximum amount of light to enter the eye and also a maximum refraction
to focus the image on the retina. Other terrestrial animals have lenses ranging
from ovoid (carnivores and herbivores) to flattened shapes (diurnal primates
including man). In the four-eyed fish *Anableps*, the upper half of each eye
(the air half) has an ovoid lens with a short axis from the cornea to the
lower half of the retina, and the lower half of each eye (the water half) has
a spherical lens with a long axis from the lens to the upper half of the
retina. In this fish the water line cuts through the middle of the cornea, and
it can see both above and below the water at the same time.

    Fine adjustments in accommodation are effected by changing the curva-
tures of the cornea or the lens or by adjusting the relative position of the
lens to the cornea. The focusing of objects close to the eye (near-sighted
vision) may be accomplished by one or more of the following ways: increasing the curvature of the cornea, increasing the curvature of the lens, or by
decreasing the distance between the cornea and the lens. By each of these
means the image is focused on the retina instead of behind the retina. In the
lamprey, the curvature of the cornea can be flattened by the contraction of
a muscle attached to it; thus, the near-sighted lamprey accommodates for
distant vision (Figure 10-6). In birds, reptiles (except snakes), and mammals,
the lens is an elastic resilient structure; its curvature can be altered by
muscles located in the ciliary body (Figure 10-6). In these animals the ciliary
muscles are relaxed during distant vision and are contracted to accommodate
during near vision. In birds and reptiles the effective ciliary muscle com-

presses the lens in its equatorial plane; the result is a rounder lens (Figure 10-6). After the muscle relaxes the lens returns to its former shape. In mammals, in the normal relaxed eye adjusted for distant vision, the ciliary muscles are relaxed; in this state the normal tension exerted through the taut zonula fibers on the lens maintains a flattened lens. In near-sight vision in mammals, the ciliary muscles contract to bring the ciliary body closer to the lens. This reduces the tension exerted by the zonula fibers on the lens (the muscle acts as a sphincter) and because of its intrinsic elasticity the lens rounds up. In lampreys and teleost fish a special muscle contracts to retract the lens backward; thus these normally near-sighted animals retract their lenses for distant vision (Figure 10-6). In sharks, amphibians, and snakes, a special muscle contracts to protract the lens forward; thus these normally far-sighted vertebrates protract their lenses closer to the cornea for near-sight vision (Figure 10-6).

Retina   The retina is the photoreceptor and neural processing organelle. It comprises four layers of cells: pigment epithelial cells, *rods* and *cones,* bipolar neurons, and ganglionic neurons (Figure 10-10). The organization of the retina can be outlined by following the path of a light ray and the resulting neural activity. After reaching the retina, light rays pass through all layers of the retina to the outer segments of the rods and cones (Figure 10-10). The interaction of the light waves with the photopigments results in the transduction of the physical energy of the light waves into chemical activity. Light has performed its function. In a sequence as yet unknown, this chemical activity is converted into neural influences that stimulate the bipolar neurons (cells) and outer horizontal neurons (Figure 10-10). Unused light is absorbed by the pigmented epithelium of the vascular choroid layer. The photopigments are special proteins (retinine) plus a carotenoid pigment derived from vitamin A localized within the outer segments which are modified cilia. The rods, each with a long cylindrical outer segment, are the sensors for black and white

Figure 10-10. Schematic diagram of the primate retina.

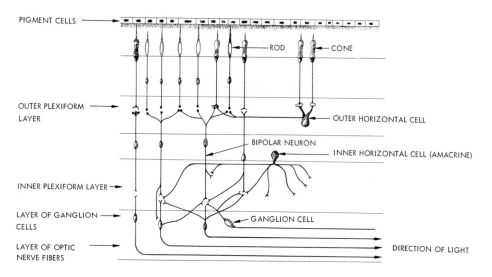

PIGMENT CELLS

ROD   CONE

OUTER PLEXIFORM LAYER

OUTER HORIZONTAL CELL

BIPOLAR NEURON

INNER HORIZONTAL CELL (AMACRINE)

INNER PLEXIFORM LAYER

LAYER OF GANGLION CELLS

GANGLION CELL

LAYER OF OPTIC NERVE FIBERS

DIRECTION OF LIGHT

vision; the photopigments within different rods are rhodopsin (visual purple) and porphyropsin (visual red). The cones, each with a short cylindrical outer segment, are the sensors for color vision. Three types of cones are present in primates with color vision, with each cone sensitive to one of three photopigments. These include blue-, green- and red-sensitive color-vision pigments, which absorb at maximum wavelengths of about 435, 540, and 565 millimicrons respectively. In general the rods have a low threshold to light stimulation and are effective in dim light (twilight vision), whereas the cones have a high threshold to light stimulation and require good illumination to be properly stimulated. The bipolar neurons, which are stimulated by the rods and cones and outer horizontal cells within the outer plexiform layer, have synaptic connections with the ganglion neurons (cells) and inner horizontal neurons (also known as *amacrine* cells—each a neuron with dendrites but without an axon) in the inner plexiform layer (Figure 10-10). In brief, the intricate connections among the neurons of the retina are essential to the complex neural processing that occurs within the eye before neural influences are projected via the ganglion cells to the brain. The ganglion cells are influenced by light in the environment—called the visual field. In turn, the delineated region in the visual field which influences a specific ganglion cell is the receptive field of that ganglion cell—that cell's eye view of the world. The visual image of the retina is actually a mosaic of the fields of the ganglion cells. The retina is also a remarkable photographic plate, analogous to a composite black and white film and a color film. The black and white film has the fast emulsion (rods) effective in twilight, and the color film has the slow emulsion (cones) most effective in broad daylight.

To make efficient use of light, some fish, reptiles, and mammals have a *tapetum*, which is a light reflector located within the deep retina (some teleosts, crocodiles, some bats, and the Virginian opossum) or choroid (chondrostean fish, carnivores, ungulates, nocturnal lemurs, and some Australian marsupials). Light that has passed beyond the rods and cones is reflected by the tapetum back to the layer of rods and cones where it can stimulate these receptors again. In the dark, the reflection of light by the tapetum produces eye shine in many mammals.

Visual Acuity
Visual acuity (resolving power) is a measure of the sharpness with which details can be distinguished by vision. In general, vertebrates with superior visual acuity (birds, primates, certain lizards, squirrels, some carnivores and ungulates) have a small area known as the *fovea*. The fovea, often located within a depression called the *macula*, is composed of a high concentration of cones, bipolar cells, and ganglion neurons organized to relay more discrete details to the brain than the rest of the retina (Figure 10-7). Some sharp-eyed hawks have as many as 1,000,000 cones in one square millimeter of fovea. Those mammals that have a fovea have only one of these structures, whereas some birds have two. Because visual acuity is associated with high threshold cones, good illumination is essential to discriminate visual detail.

Certain vertebrates have a vascularized pigmented protuberance extending into the *vitreous body*. This structure, which is thought to increase the ability of the eye to sense moving objects by casting a shadow on the retina, is known as the *pecten* in birds, the conus papillaris in snakes and lizards, and the falciform process in fish (Figure 10-6).

Dim-Light Vision

Animals that lead primarily nocturnal and crepuscular lives view the environment in shades of gray from black to white. These animals usually have large eyes, each with an all-rod retina (Figure 10-11), a large cornea, and possibly a tapetum. The light sensibility is enhanced further by a retina in which each ganglion cell (receptive field) may receive input through bipolar neurons from up to many thousands of rods (Figure 10-10). Each group of rods converges on one ganglion cell which senses one receptor field. Because each receptor field of a ganglion neuron in nocturnal animals is large, these animals do not have high visual acuity.

Animals with all-cone eyes are diurnal (Figure 10-11). This is one reason why many birds are active only by day. Many diurnal animals, like man, have retinas with both rods and cones.

Color Vision

The ability to perceive color (hue discrimination) is a rare phenomenon among vertebrates; it is well developed in highly visually oriented diurnal animals with a cone-rich retina possessing a fovea. Because it is present in unrelated vertebrates color vision probably evolved independently a number of times in the course of vertebrate phylogeny. These vertebrates include some teleosts, urodeles, lizards, turtles, birds, certain ground squirrels, Tupaia (classified either as an insectivore or a primate), and many primates. Color

Figure 10-11. Retinas of diurnal and nocturnal animals. In general, the retina of a diurnal vertebrate contains many cones, which summate but slightly to bipolar cells and these in turn summate but slightly to ganglion cells. In general, the retina of a nocturnal vertebrate contains many rods; these summate extensively to bipolar cells which in turn summate extensively to ganglion cells. (Adapted from Walls.)

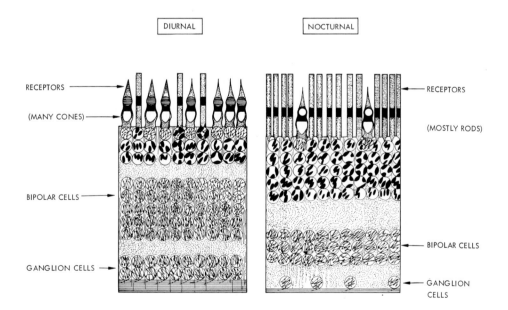

is best perceived when there is good illumination in order to adequately stimulate the high threshold cones.

Protection of the Eye

The eye is protected from injurious irritants and environmental obstacles by several adaptations that include the eye socket (orbit), true eyelids, *nictitating eyelid membrane, spectacle (brille)*, and a variety of glands. True movable eyelids are present only in terrestrial animals. They help to prevent the cornea from drying out by lubricating it with tear secretions and they also protect the eye from bright light. The nictitating membrane, a transparent third eyelid, is present in most land animals. When closed during flight this lid permits the bird to see and, at the same time, it prevents the cornea from drying. In grazing animals such as sheep it protects the cornea from abrasion by rough vegetation. The membrane is small to vestigial in man as well as in many arboreal and nocturnal animals. The spectacle (brille) is a tough transparent membrane located permanently over the eye, and the eye moves beneath it (Figure 10-12). It protects the cornea from being scratched. The brille is a modified skin in lampreys and aquatic amphibians, but is the fused upper and lower eyelids in snakes and certain lizards.

Numerous glands are associated with the eye and its eyelids in many terrestrial vertebrates. The prominent lacrimal gland secretes a watery fluid. The Harderian gland, absent in man and other primates, secretes an oily substance that lubricates the nictitating membrane. One secretory ingredient is lysozyme, a powerful enzyme capable of destroying bacteria. Only in man are tears secreted under emotional stress.

Extraocular Muscles

In general most vertebrates have the same complement of *extraocular muscles* as man—four recti and two oblique muscles. Few vertebrates use these muscles extensively. Their basic function is to suspend the eye and to make the necessary compensatory eye movements in response to irregular motions or shifting of the head during erratic movements on land, air, or water. In a few vertebrates, including lizards, man, and primates, the

Figure 10-12. Spectacles. (a) Primary spectacle of cyclostomes and aquatic amphibians. A mucoid tissue is located between the skin spectacle (dermal cornea) and the cornea (scleral cornea). (b) Secondary spectacle (transparent fused eyelids) as seen in reptiles. (Adapted from Duke-Elder.)

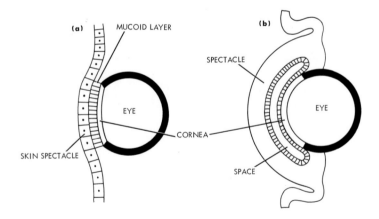

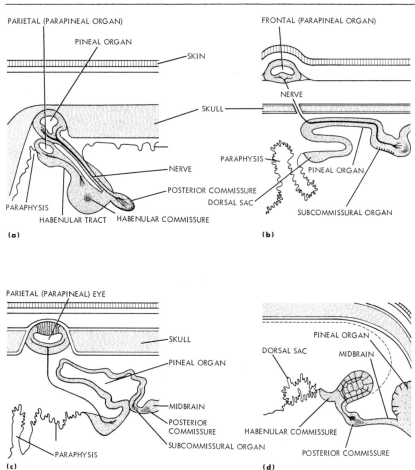

Figure 10-13. Sketches of median sagittal views of the roof of the diencephalon: (a) lamprey; (b) frog; (c) lizard; and (d) mammal. (Adapted from Studnicka.)

movements are integrated into head and body motion patterns. In birds the muscles are so small as to be essentially useless; these animals make their compensatory movements by moving the head and neck. Many amphibians, reptiles, and mammals, excluding man and other primates, have a retractor bulbi muscle that can pull the eye deep into the socket.

Median Eyes
(Pineal Organs)
Median eyes or their derivatives are present in vertebrates on the middorsal aspect of the head and brain (Figure 10-13). The "pineal complex of organs" includes the pineal organ (gland, epiphysis cerebri), the parapineal (*parietal* or *frontal*) organ, and some associated structures including the *paraphysis*, dorsal sac, and subcommissural organ. All are located in the roof of the diencephalon. The pineal and parietal organs may have once been paired structures, the pineal organ being the right member and the parietal organ the left. The lampreys have both organs, with the pineal organ located superficial to the parietal. Some lizards have a highly evolved parietal or third eye, complete with lens and retina. Many frogs have a less specialized frontal

organ located just beneath a transparent fleck in the skin on top of the head. The pineal organ is present in virtually all mammals, birds, fish, and tailed amphibians.

The paraphysis and the dorsal sac are secretory structures. The subcommissural organ, present in all vertebrates, produces a mucoid material which, in all but higher vertebrates, is secreted into the cerebrospinal fluid of the third ventricle. The functional significance of these various secretions is not known.

The parietal organ has cells that are cytologically similar to retinal photoreceptors with proven visual capabilities. These cells are also found in the deeper-lying parapineal organ of lampreys, amphibians, and lizards. The stimulation of these structures by light does not result in the perception of visual images; rather the light influences the diencephalic roof structures to secrete substances that have systemic effects such as changing the color of skin. When the pineal apparatus is excised or shielded in aquatic vertebrates, the coloration of the skin changes. Influences from the visual pathways may stimulate the pineal gland of mammals and possibly other vertebrates to synthesize and secrete specific compounds. In this respect it is presumed to act as a kind of neuroendocrine transducer following the indirect stimulation by environmental light. Melatonin, a substance found in the mammalian pineal gland, can produce blanching of the skin of the frog by contraction of the melanophores, and mammalian pineal extracts have some functional role in the seasonal activity of the gonads (photoperiodic regulation of gonadal activity).

The Mechanoreceptors

Special *mechanoreceptors* are located in the lateral line system, the vestibular system and the auditory system. The lateral line system (Figure 10-14) is found in fish and tailed amphibians; the vestibular and auditory systems are found in some form in all vertebrates. All these systems belong to a common

Figure 10-14. Side of the head of a shark illustrating lateral line canals (parallel lines) and cranial nerves (solid lines). These lateral line nerve fibers are actually fibers of the eighth (VIII) cranial nerve which are distributed with the branches of cranial nerves VII, IX, and X. (Adapted from Norris and Hughes.)

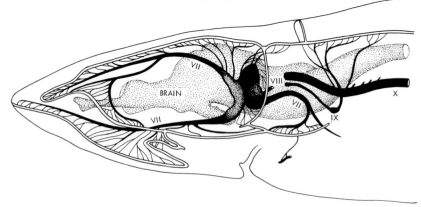

══════ LATERAL LINE CANALS
───────── CRANIAL NERVES

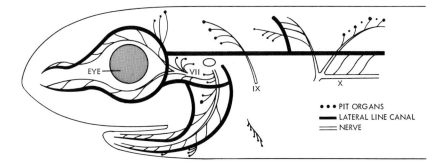

Figure 10-15. Side of the head of a fish illustrating the general distribution of the lateral line canals (solid lines), pit organs (large dots), and the nerve supply (fine lines). (Adapted from Goodrich.)

overall sensory complex called the acousticolateralis system innervated by the vestibulocochlear (VIII, stato-acoustic) cranial nerve. The common statement that the lateral line is innervated by the facial (VII), glossopharyngeal (IX), and vagus (X) cranial nerves is technically erroneous; the receptors of the lateral line are innervated by nerve fibers originating from the same complex of nuclei in the medulla that innervate the receptors of the vestibular and cochlear labyrinth. These systems are embryologically derived from a common anlage, called the *otic* (lateral, auditory) *placode*. Many of the fibers of this nerve secondarily join the VII, IX, and X cranial nerves before innervating the receptors of the lateral line (Figure 10-15).

The sensors of these mechanoreceptors are ciliated neuroepithelial cells. The cilia extend into a gelatinous capsule (cupula) as in the neuromast (Figure 10-16) or into a gelatinous capsule containing small sand-like concretions called otoliths or statoliths as in the macula of the utriculus (Figure 10-17) or they extend into a noncalcareous stiffened membrane (the

Figure 10-16. Schematic illustration of a section through a free neuromast.

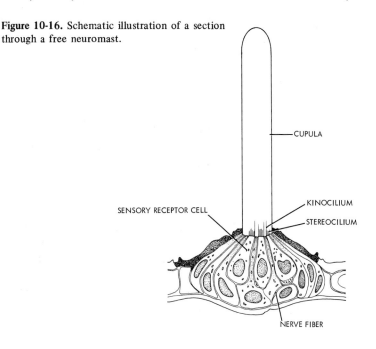

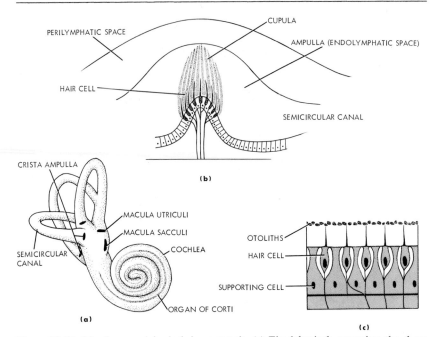

Figure 10-17. Membranous labyrinth in mammals. (a) The labyrinth comprises the three semicircular canals and the cochlea. (b) A crista ampulla is the nerve ending located in the ampulla of each semicircular canal. (c) A macula is the nerve ending located in the utricle and the saccule. The organ of Corti is the nerve ending in the cochlea. (Adapted from Noback and Demarest.)

tectorial membrane) as in the amphibian papilla or organ of Corti (Figure 10-18). The mechanical bending of these cilia is the key transduction action triggering the sequence leading to the generation of nerve impulses in these sensors. Most of the details of this sequence are unknown.

The Lateral Line System   The receptor organelles of the lateral line system are the neuromasts (Figure 10-16) which are either free in the skin or located in open grooves on the body surface or in recessed canals with little or no direct access to the body surface (Figures 10-19 and 10-20).

Free Neuromasts. Free *neuromasts* (sensory hillocks) are apparently present in the skin of all fish and tailed amphibians. A neuromast is composed of hair cells supported by sustentacular cells and covered by the gelatinous cupula enclosing the sensory hairs, or cilia (Figure 10-16). The hair bundle of each hair cell comprises up to sixty *stereocilia* and one thick *kinocilium* (Figure 10-21). A hair cell responds maximally when the cilia are bent in the direction of its axis of sensitivity from the shortest stereocilia toward the side of the kinocilium. These cilia are directionally polarized. Some hair cells of each neuromast have the kinocilium on the cephalic side of the stereocilia and others have it on the caudal side. The current flowing over the fish swimming upstream will activate only the hair cells with the kinocilium on the caudal side of a neuromast. Isolated groups of free neuromasts, called pit organs, are located on the head of some fish.

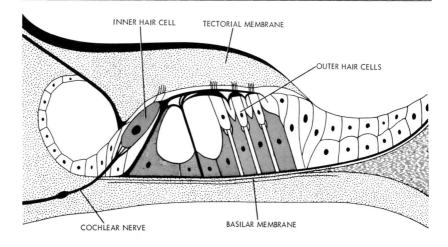

INNER HAIR CELL   TECTORIAL MEMBRANE

OUTER HAIR CELLS

COCHLEAR NERVE

BASILAR MEMBRANE

Figure 10-18. Organ of Corti.

Figure 10-19. (a) Diagram of neuromast within a lateral line canal. (b) Ampulla of Lorenzini of a shark (see Figure 11-12). (Adapted from van Bergeijk and Alexander and from Peabody.)

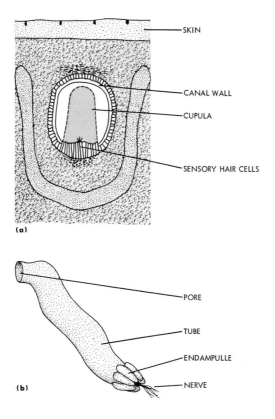

SKIN

CANAL WALL

CUPULA

SENSORY HAIR CELLS

(a)

PORE

TUBE

ENDAMPULLE

NERVE

(b)

Lateral Line Organ. The lateral line system is a special sense organ that includes a long canal on either flank of the body (often with secondary canals) plus a complex of canals on the head in fish, tadpoles, and adult tailed amphibians. In a few elasmobranchs and bony fish the neuromasts lie in open grooves with direct access to surface currents, while in cyclostomes some occur in isolated pits arranged in a linear pattern. In most fish the neuromasts are present within canals that may be in contact with the external environment through small openings (Figure 10-20); these canals may be buried within or below the body scales or within the bones of the head. Such neuromasts are stimulated by slight currents generated within the canals. The lateral line is a displacement detector which is extremely sensitive to minute vibrations and movements of water. The axis of sensitivity of half of the hair cells is oriented in one direction and the other half in the opposite direction.

Fish of fast-flowing streams such as trout have most of their neuromasts within canals whereas fish of still waters such as cyprinids, have many free neuromasts and relatively few within the canals. Apparently the canal reduces the impact upon the neuromasts of the constant contact with fast currents. Functionally the neuromasts are the receptors sensing the hydrodynamic motions. Fish and aquatic amphibians also are sensitive through the

Figure 10-20. (a) Free neuromast and lateral line canal neuromast in the fish *Gadus lota*. (b) Lateral line canal with external openings, adjacent to surface scales, on the trunk of a bony fish. (Adapted from Goodrich.)

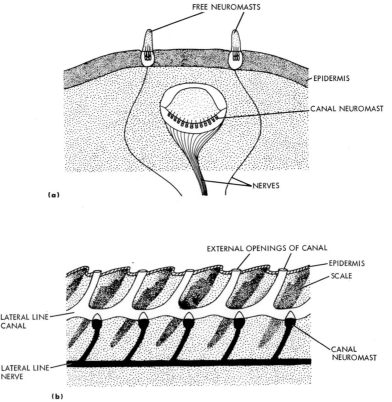

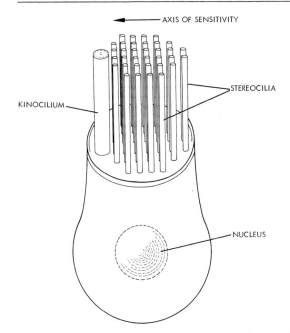

Figure 10-21. Schematized hair cell of the acoustico-lateralis system. Note that the location of the kinocilium with respect to the stereocilia is significant in determining the axis of sensitivity. (Adapted from Van Bergeijk.)

lateral line organ to water displacements caused by objects or animals. Prey, enemies, and sexual partners are detected and localized with this sensor on the basis of water vibrations.

Specialized Lateral Line Receptors. The *ampullae* of Lorenzini located in the heads of elasmobranchs and some bony fish (mormyrids, gymnotids, and silurid fish) are nonciliated receptors (probably a modified neuromast with receptor cells that lost their cilia) located at the end of a tube filled with a gelatinous substance (Figure 10-22). These flask-shaped organs, which

Figure 10-22. Location and innervation of the ampullae of Lorenzini in the dogfish shark (see Figure 11-19). The ampullae are innervated by fibers from the eighth cranial nerve distributed via the seventh cranial nerve. (Adapted from Dotterweich.)

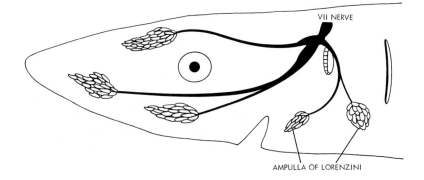

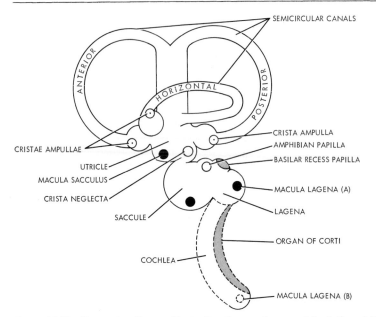

SEMICIRCULAR CANALS

ANTERIOR

HORIZONTAL

POSTERIOR

CRISTA AMPULLA
AMPHIBIAN PAPILLA
BASILAR RECESS PAPILLA

CRISTAE AMPULLAE
UTRICLE
MACULA SACCULUS
CRISTA NEGLECTA

MACULA LAGENA (A)
LAGENA

SACCULE

ORGAN OF CORTI

COCHLEA

MACULA LAGENA (B)

Figure 10-23. Composite diagram illustrating the membranous labyrinth and its sensory receptors in most vertebrate classes. Macula lagena A is found in fish and amphibians and macula lagena B in reptiles and birds. (Adapted from Lowenstein.)

contain a sensory epithelium not covered by a cupula, may be temperature sensors, pressure receptors, *chemoreceptors* detecting the salinity (NaCl) of the water or, more likely, *electroreceptors* monitoring the electric charges in the environment. Mormyromasts are modified lateral line receptors in the mormyrid fish which emit low voltage electric pulses and utilize these sensors as electroreceptors to detect the reflected electric pulses. The vesicles of Savi are specialized canal receptors in the *Torpedo*, an elasmobranch. Specialized ampullary receptors have evolved independently several times during phylogeny in various unrelated groups. Even the lateral line may be electrosensitive in some fish. Sharks and rays are capable of detecting at short distances the electrical potentials produced by muscular activity. Actually the electric organs of electric eels and some other fish are derived from muscle tissue which is specialized to produce electric discharges.

Inner Ear   A membranous labyrinth and a bony or cartilaginous labyrinth comprise the inner ear. The membranous labyrinth is a continuous series of inter-connected tubes (*semicircular canals*), vesicles (*saccule* and *utricle*), and a duct (cochlear duct) enclosing a cavity filled with endolymphatic fluid (end-olymph) (Figures 10-17 and 10-23). A slender endolymphatic duct usually extends upward and inward to terminate in an endolymphatic sac within the brain case. All the specialized receptors of the inner ear face into the fluid-filled cavity. Surrounding the membranous *labyrinth* is another cavity filled with perilymphatic fluid (perilymph), and the entire complex is encapsulated by cartilage or bone (cartilaginous or bony labyrinth). The semicircular canals, with the saccule and utricle, constitute the vestibular labyrinth, and the *cochlea* forms the cochlear labyrinth. The cochlear duct filled with

endolymph, the vestibular duct, and the tympanic duct filled with
perilymph are components of the cochlea.

Within the labyrinth the specialized neuromast receptors are called *crista,*
macula and *papilla*. A crista has hair cells with cilia that extend into a gelatinous cupula (Figure 10-17). The cristae include the crista ampullaris of
each semicircular canal and the crista neglecta of the utricle (Figure 10-17).
A macula has essentially the same structure as a crista except that within the
cupula are mineralized concretions (ear stones, otoliths, otoconia). There are
three maculae: macula utriculus, macula sacculus, and macula *lagena* of the
saccule (Figure 10-17). A papilla has hair cells with the tips of the cilia
embedded within a noncalcareous membrane called the *tectorial membrane;*
the various kinds of papillae include the amphibian papilla, basilar recess
papilla (both found in the saccule), and the organ of Corti (Figures 10-18,
10-23, and 10-24).

Vestibular Labyrinth. Basically similar in all vertebrates the vestibular
labyrinth is an enlarged and elaborate cephalic portion of the lateral canal

Figure 10-24. Membranous labyrinth in several vertebrates: (a) fish; (b) turtle; (c) bird;
and (d) mammal. (Adapted from Retzius and from von Frisch.)

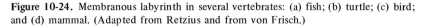
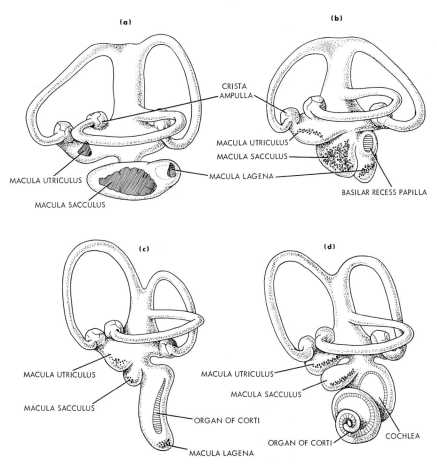

which has sunk beneath the surface of the skin. Three semicircular canals are present in each ear in all vertebrates except cyclostomes. The horizontal (lateral) canal is oriented in a plane parallel to the ground or water surface and the two vertical canals (anterior and posterior) are perpendicular to the plane of the horizontal canal and at right angles to each other (Figures 10-17, 10-23 and 10-24). In the cyclostomes the hagfish have one semicircular canal and the lampreys have two. Within each canal there is one enlarged bulb-like ampulla enclosing a crista ampullaris; the cupula of the crista is in direct contact with the wall of the ampulla. Acting as a swinging door, the cupula may gently pivot back and forth in response to the pressures exerted by the motion of the fluid endolymph. In each crista the hair cells are oriented so the transduction of motion to neural activity results in movements in only one direction. The shearing forces bend the cilia and initiate the sequence of events producing neural activity. The crista neglecta of the utricle is a receptor found in some fish, amphibians, reptiles, birds, and mammals (Figure 10-23).

Present in most vertebrates are the macula of the utricle and the macula of the saccule whereas the macula lagena, located in an outpocket of the saccule called the lagena, is found in teleosts, reptiles, birds, and monotreme mammals (Figure 10-24). Each hair cell of the macula utriculus has an axis of sensitivity in one of two directions; in some cells the axis is in the direction parallel to ground or water surface and in other cells the axis is in the direction of gravitational pull. The shearing forces exerted by the concretions upon the cilia are induced by acceleration forces of the animal in straight-line motion and by gravitational forces.

The basic function of the membranous labyrinth is to monitor the position of the body in space and to generate neural influences that will stimulate coordinated muscular activity to right the body and to maintain normal postural attitudes and balance. Labyrinths are organs of equilibrium that analyze rotational or angular motion (semicircular canals) and accelerational gravitational forces (utricle and saccule). The maculae of the saccule and of the lagena may function as receptors for sensing vibrations, which is perhaps a form of hearing. The role of the crista neglecta is unknown.

Cochlear Labyrinth. All vertebrates are probably capable of hearing (phonoreception), if hearing is thought of as both a conscious and an unconscious sense that an observer can recognize from the animal's behavior. Does the animal behave as if it were hearing? In this context "the primitive function of hearing is the location of objects not in contact with the animal. . .an animal hears when it behaves as if it has located a moving object (a sound source) not in contact with it. And sound can be defined as any mechanical disturbance whatever which is potentially referable to an external and localized source". [10]

Fish   Behavior studies of fish and amphibians indicate that the lateral line system is a hydrodynamic receptor of water-borne vibrations (near-field hearing organ). Phonoreception has also been attributed to the macula of the saccule and to the crista neglecta and papilla of fish (Figure 10-24). The lateral line system has been called both a near-field hearing organ and a "distant touch" receptor detecting vibrations up to several hundred per second. It is not important in orienting the organism to water currents (rheotaxis). The swim bladder of bony fish functions as an accessory vibratory (sound) resonator; the vibrations of the bladder pass in turn through the body to the hair cells of receptors of the membranous labyrinth. In the herring the swim bladder comes into direct contact with the utricle. Certain fish, the Ostariophysii (cyprinid, silurid, characinids, and gymnotids), are able to transfer the vibrations of the swim bladder to the saccules of the two labyrinths via a paired chain of four bones called Weberian ossicles, which extend from the bladder to a sinus containing perilymph and a canal with endolymph with direct access to the saccule (Figure 10-25). In this Weberian apparatus the swim bladder is analogous to the eardrum and the ossicles to the ear ossicles of mammals. Many fish have an excellent sense of hearing, and can be conditioned experimentally to discriminate among different tones. Several species of fish can produce sounds by which they communicate with other fish, for example during the mating season. Various mechanisms for sound production have been reported.

Terrestrial Vertebrates   The terrestrial vertebrates have evolved (1) a number of modifications for the transfer of the vibratory energy from the compressible atmospheric air (low impedence) to the incompressible perilymphatic fluid (high impedence)

Figure 10-25. The organization of the "hydroacoustic" receptor of the Ostariophysii, a group of teleosts. Note the swim bladder, Weberian ossicles. perilymphatic sac, and endolymphatic sac. Vibrations are transmitted via this sequence of structures. (Adapted from von Frisch.)

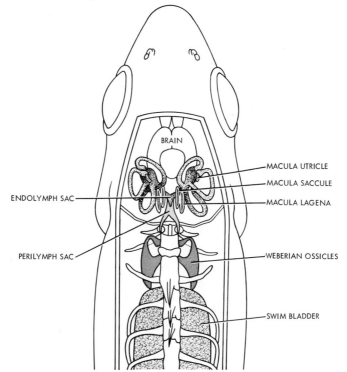

and (2) some elaborate *phonoreceptors*. Because the threshold for hearing is low, a near-perfect impedence matching device for the efficient energy transfer has evolved. In general it includes the sequence of an eardrum (tympanic membrane) and one to three ear bones that act as levers between the drum and the oval window at the junction of the ear bone with the perilymph (Figure 10-26). In effect, mechanisms have evolved that amplify and transfer vibrations from the air to the perilymph, endolymph, and phonoreceptors. The phonoreceptors are the papillae, noted before, with their tectorial membranes.

In the terrestrial vertebrates the generalized ear has three parts: outer, middle, and inner ears. The outer ear includes an ear lobe (pinna) and the external auditory canal, a tube extending from the exterior to the eardrum (Figure 10-26). The eardrum (*tympanum*) is located at the junction of the outer and middle ears. Many amphibians, reptiles, and birds have one bony ear ossicle within the cavity of the inner ear, called the stapes or *columella*; it extends from the eardrum or its equivalent to the oval window. An exception among air breathers are the mammals with three such bones known as the *malleus* (hammer), *incus* (anvil) and *stapes* (stirrup) that form a sequence of levers between the malleus at the eardrum to the stapes at the oval window. Extending from the middle ear chamber to the pharynx is the tympanic (Eustachian) tube. During the act of swallowing, the tube may be opened to permit the pressure within the middle ear to equal the atmo-

Figure 10-26. Schema illustrating the evolution of the middle ear and ear ossicles. All diagrams are cross-sections through the otic region of the heads of (a) fish, (b) primitive amphibian, (c) primitive reptile, and (d) mammal. (Adapted from Romer.)

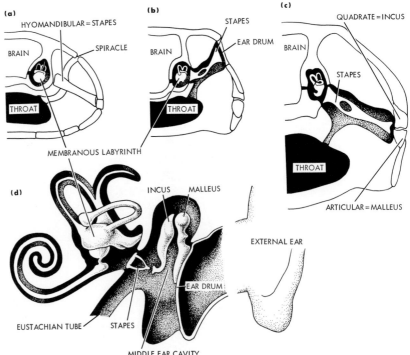

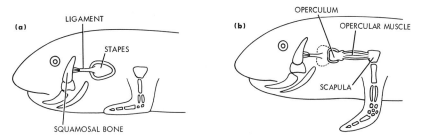

Figure 10-27. Diagrams illustrating the mechanisms for transmitting vibrations from the environment to the inner ear in urodeles. (a) In this aquatic urodele, vibrations picked up by the skull are transmitted from the squamosal bone via a ligament to the stapes (columella). (b) Vibrations picked up by the upper extremity are transmitted from the scapula through a muscle connected to the operculum. (Adapted from Kingsbury and Reed.)

spheric pressure being exerted on the eardrum through the external canal. The external canal arises as an inpushing of the embryonic body ectoderm in the vicinity of the first gill pouch that in turn is the origin of the middle ear chamber and tympanic tube. The ears of tetrapods are modifications of this general piscine organization.

Various amphibians respond to sounds of from 50 to 10,000 cycles per second. In most frogs and toads the stapes extends from the eardrum, located on the surface of the head, to the oval window. Salamanders, which have neither an eardrum nor a middle ear, pick up vibrations with their skulls or their upper extremities (Figure 10-27). Vibrations are transmitted from the skull to the oval window in aquatic forms; in other amphibians ground vibrations picked up by the forelimbs are transmitted from the shoulder blade via a contracted voluntary muscle to an ossicle called the *operculum* which articulates at the oval window. Two receptors in the saccule are the phonoreceptors; in frogs the basilar papilla (Figure 10-24) responds to sounds with frequencies of 1000 to 2000 cycles per second and the amphibian papilla to sounds with frequencies of 100 to 1000 cycles per second.

Reptiles hear in a variety of ways. All snakes, which pick up earth-borne vibrations through their skulls, lack an eardrum and a middle ear; they are deaf to air-borne sounds. The vibrations are transmitted from the skull via the stapes to the oval window. Tortoises, which lack an eardrum, transmit vibrations from a thick patch of skin on the head via the stapes to the oval window. Crocodiles and some lizards have a short external auditory tube; the stapes is composed of an outer cartilaginous segment and an inner bony segment. The phonoreceptors in the reptile are probably the basilar papilla and macula lagena of the saccule. Reptiles respond to frequencies as low as 80 cycles per second in tortoises and as high as 10,000 cycles in some lizards.

The phonoreceptive apparatus is most highly evolved in birds and mammals. In birds the eardrum is located within a short external auditory tube whose external opening is covered with feathers. As in the lizards the stapes is in two segments. The receptive efficiency of the three ear ossicles in mammals can be dampened or enhanced by changes in the tension of the two muscles inserted on the ossicles, the tensor tympani muscle to the malleus and the stapedius muscle to the stapes. Phonoreceptors in birds and mammals constitute the organ of Corti (Figures 10-18 and 10-24), located in an extension of the saccule called the cochlear duct. Like all papillae, it comprises sustentacular cells and hair cells whose cilia are embedded in a tectorial membrane. The cochlear duct (filled with endolymph) and the vestibular duct and tympanic duct (both filled with perilymph) form the cochlea. In birds, as in reptiles, the cochlea is short and straight whereas in mammals it is coiled, e.g., one-quarter turn in the duckbill platypus, two turns in the horse, three and one-half in man, and four in the guinea pig. Sound waves are conducted from the oval window successively through the perilymphatic fluid of the vestibular duct and the tympanic duct to the membrane of the round window; this membrane "absorbs" and dampens the vibrations. The sound waves produce vibrations of the organ of Corti, its basilar membrane, and the tectorial membrane; the resulting movements of the cilia of the organ of Corti will eventually result in nerve impulses that are projected to the brain.

Two structural adaptations of significance to the role of the cochlea in hearing include (1) the hair cells of the organ of Corti (attached to the basilar membrane), with the distal tips of cilia embedded within the tectorial membrane and (2) the basilar membrane, which becomes wider and stiffer in the progression from the base to the apex of the cochlear coil (the basilar membrane is not tense). Vibrations within the fluids of the cochlear coil (vestibular, tympanic, and cochlear ducts) produce vibrations of both the tectorial membrane and the basilar membrane with the attached organ of Corti. The vibrations of these two membranes produce shearing motions in the cilia of the hair cells, that trigger a sequence of events as yet not fully understood. The ciliary movements stimulate the nerve fibers of the auditory nerve to fire neural signals in the form of action potentials to the brain. Differential disturbances within the length of the basilar membrane are important to the analytic function of the cochlea in hearing.

The organ of Corti analyzes sound for (1) loudness, (2) pitch, and (3) tones and overtones. The lowest notes are "sensed" at the base of the coil near the oval window and the highest notes at the apex of the coil. The upper limit of pitch for birds and most mammals is roughly 20,000 cycles per second, rodents and shrews up to 30,000 cycles per second and bats, whales, and dolphins over 100,000. Birds seem to have as efficient a pitch discrimination as man. Owls have an exceptional ability to localize a sound; in total darkness an owl can strike a squeaking mouse with a margin of error of less than one degree in both horizontal and vertical planes.

Echolocation   Bats, whales, porpoises, and certain birds have evolved elaborate and efficient systems of emitting pulses (squeaks) of sonic and ultrasonic vibrations up to 150,000 cycles per second from their vocal cords, and after hearing the reflections they are able to *echolocate* the objects reflecting the pulses. Varying with the animal, the squeaks may be emitted at the rate of 5 to 200 pulses per second. The reflected squeaks are recognized, for example, by the bats, which have a large basal portion (low tone receptive portion) of the cochlea and a highly developed auditory system in the brain.

Many bats utilize echolocation to avoid obstacles such as fine wires strung across a totally dark room and to catch flying insects upon which they feed. Bats are strong expert flyers and their seemingly erratic flight does not result from being buffeted by air currents; rather the echolocating and the subsequent catching of flying insects, one at a time every few seconds, produce the constant maneuvering. The precision and speed by which a porpoise echolocates a fish are aided by the water environment which conducts sound waves more than four times as fast as air. Two cave birds, the Venezuelan Oilbird, *Steatornis*, and the Asian Swift, *Collocalia*, echolate their way about caves by emitting and echolocating sonic vibrations.

References for Chapter 10

See also the bibliography at the end of Chapter 11.

[1] van Bergeijk, W. A., "The Evolution of Vertebrate Hearing" in *Contributions to Sensory Physiology,* Vol. 2, W. Neff (ed.). New York: Academic Press, 1967. A modern account of hearing in the vertebrates.

[2] von Buddenbrock, W., *The Senses.* Ann Arbor, Mich.: The University of Michigan Press, 1958. Compact survey of sensation in animals.

[3] Cahn, P. H. (ed.), *Lateral Line Detectors.* Bloomington, Ind.: Indiana University Press, 1967. Articles by outstanding authorities on many aspects of lateral line detectors.

[4] Case, J., *Sensory Mechanisms.* New York: The Macmillan Company, 1966. A clear, readable discussion. Paperback.

[5] Detweiler, S. R., *Vertebrate Photoreceptors.* New York: The Macmillan Company, 1943. An outstanding, classic review.

[6] Griffin, D. R., *Listening in the Dark.* New Haven, Conn.: Yale University Press, 1958. A superb and fascinating account of acoustic orientation of bats and men.

[7] Matthews, L. H., and M. Knight, *The Senses of Animals.* London: Museum Press, 1963. A review of many expressions of the senses of animals.

[8] Milne, L. J., and M. Milne, *The Senses of Animals.* New York: Atheneum, 1962. Another review of many expressions of the senses of animals.

[9] Prince, J. H., *Comparative Anatomy of the Eye.* Springfield, Ill.: Thomas, 1956. An excellent account of the structure of the eye in vertebrates.

[10] Pumphrey, R. J., *Hearing. Symposium of the Society of Experimental Biology,* **4** (1950), 1-18. A classic account of structural and functional aspects of hearing.

[11] Rochon-Duvigneaud, A., *Les Yeux et la vision des vertèbres.* Paris: Masson et Cie., 1943. A comprehensive review of the eyes of vertebrates.

[12] Walls, G. L., *The Vertebrate Eye and Its Adaptive Radiation.* Bloomfield Hills, Mich.: Cranbrook Institute of Science, 1942. An outstanding volume on the comparative anatomy and function of the eye.

[13] Wersäll, Jan, and A. Flock, "Functional Anatomy of the Vestibular and Lateral Line Organs" in *Contributions to Sensory Physiology,* Vol. 1, W. Neff (ed.). New York: Academic Press, 1965. Modern analyses of the functional anatomy of the lateral line system.

11

The nervous system

The cells of living organisms are excitable; they possess the ability to respond to stimuli. This excitability is expressed in a variety of ways: muscles contract, nerve cells conduct impulses, gland cells secrete, cells of electric organs discharge electric pulses, and white cells ingest micro-organisms. A positive response to a stimulus is known as *excitation* (gland cell secretes) and a negative response as *inhibition* (gland cell ceases to secrete). The nerve cells (neurons) of the nervous system and the gland cells of the endocrine system are the basic structural and functional units of these two major integrating systems of the body. These specialized cells are adapted to receive and to process stimuli, and then to respond to the stimuli by releasing chemical secretions that can influence other cells. The secretion of a neuron is a *neurosecretion*, which may stimulate an adjacent cell; the secretion of a cell of the endocrine system is a *hormone*, which stimulates distant target cells. Neurosecretions may influence endocrine cells and hormones may influence neurons, and in this way the two systems interact. The nervous system is the high-speed coordinator, usually operating with a fast time course in fractions of a second whereas the endocrine system is the slow-speed coordinator, operating with a slow time course of hours and days.

The nervous system is conventionally divided into a central nervous system and a peripheral nervous system. The central nervous system is comprised of the brain and the spinal cord surrounded by connective tissue membranes called *meninges*. The peripheral nervous system includes the spinal nerves emerging from the spinal cord and the cranial nerves from the brain; each nerve and its branches are enclosed by connective tissue. The peripheral nerves that are distributed through the body are composed primarily of the processes (fibers) of neurons. These nerve fibers of the peripheral nerves convey neural influences from the receptors in the body as input to the central nervous system and from the nervous system as output to effectors (e.g., muscles and glands). Associated with the neurons are the Schwann (neurolemma) cells of the peripheral system and the neuroglia (*oligoden-droglia* and astroglia) of the central nervous system.

Of all the phyla of the animal kingdom, only the vertebrates have a vascu-larized central nervous system. This innovation in early vertebrate phylogeny was an essential prerequisite to ensure the adequate nourishment of a delicate yet bulky brain and spinal cord.

422

Neuron
The diversity of shapes and forms of neurons is probably greater than for any other cell type. However, each neuron may be subdivided into four structural segments: *dendrites,* cell body (*soma*), *axon,* and *telodendria* (Figure 11-1), and into four functional segments: receptive, *trophic,* conductile, and transmissive segments (Figure 11-2).

The Generalized Neuron as a Structural Unit
The cell body is that portion of the neuron containing the nucleus, Nissl substance, and other organelles essential to the maintenance of a functional unit (Figure 11-1). The Nissl substance is a concentration of ribonucleoproteins (RNP), which synthesize proteins, including the neurosecretory

Figure 11-1. (a) Diagram of a peripheral motor neuron (alpha motor neuron). (b) Diagram of a synapse between an axon and a cell body (axosomatic synapse), between an axon and a dendrite (axodendritic synapse) and between an axon and an axon (axoaxonic synapse). (c) Diagram of a motor end plate (synapse between nerve terminal and muscle cell).

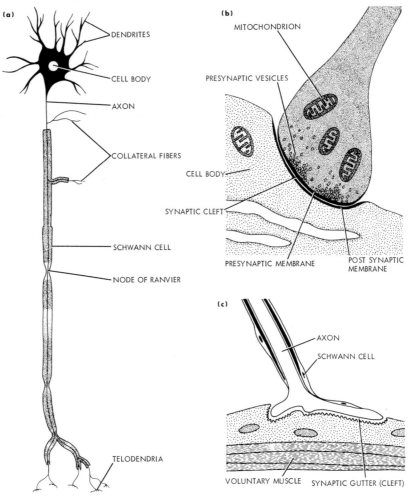

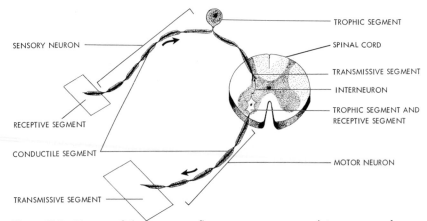

SENSORY NEURON

RECEPTIVE SEGMENT

CONDUCTILE SEGMENT

TRANSMISSIVE SEGMENT

TROPHIC SEGMENT

SPINAL CORD

TRANSMISSIVE SEGMENT

INTERNEURON

TROPHIC SEGMENT AND
RECEPTIVE SEGMENT

MOTOR NEURON

Figure 11-2. Diagram of three-neuron reflex arc: sensory neuron, interneuron, and motor neuron. Each neuron may be subdivided into a receptive segment, trophic segment, conductile segment, and transmissive segment.

(neurotransmitter) chemicals. Short processes extending from the cell body are the dendrites that generally convey neural information toward the cell body. Nerve impulses from the cell body are conducted by the *axon* toward the *telodendria*, which are short terminal branches of the axon (Figure 11-1), and they come into close proximity with another cell and form a synapse. The synapse (Figure 11-1) is the structural complex comprising the telodendritic ending of one neuron (*presynaptic* neuron), the space of approximately 200 Angstrom units wide called the *synaptic* cleft, and the dendrites or soma of another neuron (*postsynaptic* neuron). The presence of the synaptic cleft indicates that the presynaptic neuron is in contiguity but not in continuity with the postsynaptic neuron. Several morphologic types of synapses are found, for example, an axodendritic synapse between axon and dendrite, an axosomatic synapse between axon and soma, and a motor end plate between an axon and a voluntary muscle fiber.

The Generalized Neuron as a Functional Unit

The *trophic segment* (Figure 11-2) is the metabolic center of the neuron where the synthesis of proteins, neurosecretory chemicals, and other products essential to the neuron occur. This segment is the soma of the neuron. The *receptor segment* (Figure 11-2) is adapted to receive a continuous input of both excitatory and inhibitory stimuli; this input is processed, sorted, and integrated in this segment, which is usually located in both the dendrites and the soma. Excitatory synapses and inhibitory synapses transmitting input upon this segment in one neuron may number as many as 30,000. The specialized *conductile segment* (Figure 11-2), called the axon, has evolved an all-or-none nerve impulse to perform at least two roles: (1) to conduct impulses a long distance from the receptive segment to the transmissive segment, and (2) to conduct neural information in the form of coded messages. The all-or-none impulse is an expression of a physiological process by which information can be conveyed at full strength over the entire distance along a nerve fiber; there is either a completely developed

impulse or none at all. Coded messages may be (1) binary in the form of an
ON (impulse) or an OFF (no impulse) activity or (2) expressed in the
number of impulses per unit time. The speed of conduction varies from a
fraction of a meter per second to 120 meters per second, and the conduction velocity increases as the temperature rises. Conduction by the axons of
a cold-blooded animal takes place at slower speeds when the animal is cold
than when it is warm. The larger the diameter of the axon, the faster will
be its conduction velocity. In many vertebrates the speed of conduction is
increased in many axons by the presence of a lipid and protein coat called
the myelin sheath (Figure 11-1); fibers with this layer are called myelinated
fibers. The fastest conducting fibers are the heavily myelinated fibers in
mammals.

The *transmissive segment* (Figure 11-2) includes the short terminal
branches of the axon, or telodendria, each of which forms the presynaptic
portion of the synapse. Within the transmissive segment are small vesicles,
the neurosecretory granules or presynaptic vesicles (Figure 11-1), which
contain the precursor of the neurosecretory transmitter chemicals. The nerve
impulse of the conductile segment activates the transmissive segment to
secrete the transmitter chemicals (e.g., acetylcholine or noradrenalin) into
the synaptic cleft where they can stimulate the postsynaptic neurons,
muscles, or gland cells. Although each nerve fiber may conduct an impulse in
either direction within the neuron, conduction in a sequence of neurons
proceeds in only one direction. This unidirectional conduction is determined
at the synapse, which acts as a one-way valve with the transmission of neural
influences across the synapse occurring only from the presynaptic neuron to
the postsynaptic neuron.

The sensory neuron of the spinal nerves and of many cranial nerves has
these functional segments organized as follows: the receptive segment is a
short terminus within the nerve endings in the periphery of the body, the
conductile segment extends from the receptive segment to the short transmissive segment located within the central nervous system where the
synaptic contacts are made. The trophic center (soma) is located within the
conductile segment in the dorsal (sensory) root ganglion (Figure 11-1).

**Other Cells
of the Nervous
System**

Except at their receptive endings, nerve fibers of the peripheral nervous
system are surrounded by cells called Schwann (neurolemma) cells (Figure
11-1); these cells are responsible for the formation of the myelin sheath.
Fibers surrounded only by Schwann cells are called unmyelinated fibers;
those having both Schwann cells and myelin are said to be myelinated. The
myelin sheath is segmented at intervals by indentations known as nodes of
Ranvier (Figure 11-1); the nerve impulse in myelinated nerve hops from
node to node by *saltatory* (leaping) conduction. The speed of conduction is
faster in the thicker myelinated fibers with the greater distance between two
successive nodes. Nerve fibers are organized into fascicles which are encapsulated by connective tissues.

Within the central nervous system are nonneural cells called neuroglial cells
(Figure 11-3). Oligodendroglia are characterized by processes that encapsu-

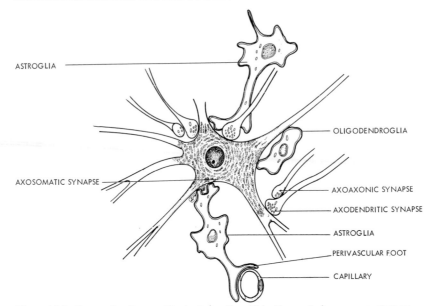

ASTROGLIA

OLIGODENDROGLIA

AXOSOMATIC SYNAPSE

AXOAXONIC SYNAPSE

AXODENDRITIC SYNAPSE

ASTROGLIA

PERIVASCULAR FOOT

CAPILLARY

Figure 11-3. Composite diagram illustrating cells within the central nervous system as visualized at an ultramicroscopic level. (Adapted from Noback and Demarest.)

late portions of the cell body and nerve fibers; the cells elaborate the myelin sheaths of the myelinated fibers of the central system. The astrocytes have processes that extend from the blood capillaries to the cell bodies of the neurons; these cells are presumed to act as intermediaries between the blood and the neurons and thus maintain a constant extraneuronal milieu for the neurons and protect them from changes in the internal environment. Some investigators claim these cells have a role in memory storage.

Meninges

The meninges are the connective tissue membranes surrounding the central nervous system (Figure 11-4). In most fish the meninx is a single vascularized connective tissue sheet located between the central nervous system and the axial skeleton (skull and vertebral column). In amphibians and reptiles two meninges are present: the vascularized *pia mater* attached to the central nervous system, and the outer tough *dura mater* adjacent to the skeleton. Mammals and birds have three membranes; a delicate vascularized membrane called the *arachnoid* is located between the pia mater and the dura mater [Figure 11-4(a)]. In a sense, these meninges may be thought of as a pial sac within an arachnoid sac within a dural sac. The interval between the pia mater and the arachnoid, called the subarachnoid space, is filled with cerebrospinal fluid. This fluid is also present within the spinal and ventricular cavities that are in communication with the subarachnoid space through foramina in the choroid plexus in the roof of the medulla.

Spinal Nerves and Spinal Cord

The spinal cord is enclosed within the vertebral canal in the cartilaginous or bony vertebral column. The length of the generally cylindrical spinal cord varies (Figure 11-5). In most fish, tailed amphibians, reptiles, and birds, the cord extends throughout the entire length of the vertebral canal. A few fish, tailless amphibians, and mammals have a cord that is shorter than the vertebral column, and in most mammals it extends into the lumbar region.

The spinal cord is subdivided into segments called spinal segments; a bilateral pair of dorsal (sensory) nerve roots and of ventral (motor) nerve roots emerge from each segment (Figure 11-6). In all vertebrates except the cyclostomes (Figure 11-7) the dorsal root and the ventral root on each side of a segment unite to form a spinal nerve. The segment and the nerve are named from the vertebral column segment adjacent to which the nerve emerges through the vertebral column (e.g., the fifth thoracic nerve emerges from one thoracic segment of the spinal cord and caudal to the fifth thoracic vertebra). Thus, there are cervical, thoracic, lumbar, sacral, and coccygeal (caudal) nerves, each emerging from its respective segment of the spinal cord. In the cyclostomes the roots remain distinct and do not unite to form a spinal nerve (Figure 11-6). The number of spinal nerves varies from ten pairs in the tailless amphibians to over 500 pairs in some snakes. In general, each spinal nerve branches into several primary divisions (rami): the dorsal ramus to the

Figure 11-4. Diagrams of cross-sections of the spinal cord in (a) mammal and (b) dogfish shark (*acanthias*) to illustrate its relations to the meninges.

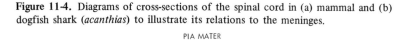

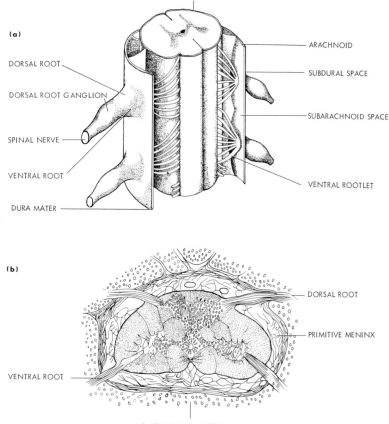

back region, the ventral ramus to the ventral region including the extremities, and the rami communicantes to the visceral organs (Figure 11-6).

The term sensory, although usually applied to consciously perceived input,
is used in its broadest sense here to include all input from nerves to the
central nervous system whether consciously appreciated or not. This avoids,
among other problems, deciding whether the animal is consciously aware of
a stimulus. The sensory (afferent) input to the spinal cord is conveyed via
neurons with fibers that pass through the peripheral nerves and dorsal roots;
the cell bodies of these sensory neurons are located in the dorsal root ganglia
(Figure 11-6). In certain lower vertebrates the afferent neurons, called
Rohon-Beard cells, have fibers in the dorsal roots and cell bodies within the
spinal cord (Figure 11-8). A sensory segment of the adult body, where limbs
or fins are innervated by fibers from one dorsal root is called a dermatome,
and each is derived from a dermatome of a somite in the embryo. Afferent
fibers conveying sensory input from the body to the cord are known as
general somatic afferent fibers, and those conveying input from the visceral
organs to the cord are general visceral afferent fibers. Many peripheral nerves
are composed exclusively of fibers derived from one spinal nerve (e.g., most
thoracic nerves). Many spinal nerves form *plexuses* (Figure 11-9), which are
the result of the mingling and regrouping of nerve fibers of several segments
of the spinal cord. Thus the brachial plexus is an organized meshwork of

Figure 11-5. Diagrammatic representation of the spinal cord and the proximal portion of
spinal nerves in (a) turtle, (b) man, (c) seal, and (d) toad. In the turtle, the cord
extends throughout the vertebral canal. The spinal cords are drawn relative to the
vertebral column length, which is standardized to the same length in all the figures.
(Adapted from Nieuhenhuys.)

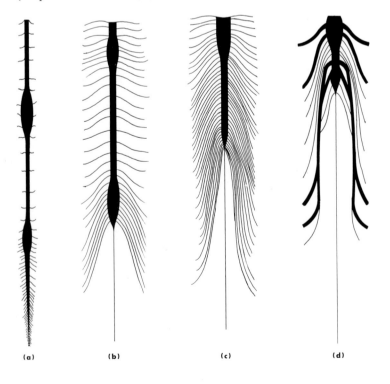

(a)　　　　　(b)　　　　　(c)　　　　　(d)

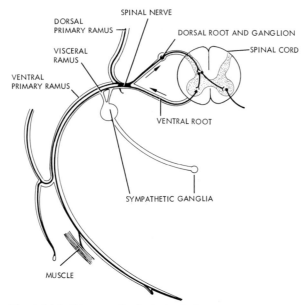

Figure 11-6. Diagram of a typical spinal nerve.

fibers innervating the pectoral fin or the forelimb, as the lumbosacral plexus innervates the pelvic fin or the hindlimb.

The motor (efferent) output from the spinal cord to the muscle and gland cells (effectors) is conveyed via fibers passing through the ventral roots and the peripheral nerves to the effectors. The efferent fibers projecting output to the voluntary (striated) muscles are the general somatic efferent fibers and those projecting output to the involuntary (smooth) muscles, heart muscle, and glands are the general visceral efferent fibers of the autonomic nervous system, noted later.

The spinal cord consists of a small central canal surrounded by an inner column of gray matter and an outer column of white matter. Within the gray column three horns or zones are visible: dorsal (sensory, afferent), inter-mediate, and ventral (motor, efferent) (Figure 11-10). The gray matter is made up mainly of cell bodies, their dendrites, and some axons organized into groups of these cell bodies and their dentrites called nuclei (neuron pools or centers). A nucleus in the nervous system is an anatomically identi-fiable group of cell bodies, whereas a neuron pool or center is a physiolog-

Figure 11-7. Diagram of the spinal cord and spinal nerves of the lamprey. Note that the separate dorsal roots (nerves) and ventral roots (nerves) alternate. Each dorsal spinal nerve passes through the intermyotomic space, whereas each ventral spinal nerve termi-nates in the myotome. The visceral fibers (autonomic nervous system) are located in the dorsal root (nerve).

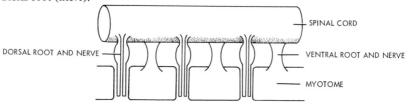

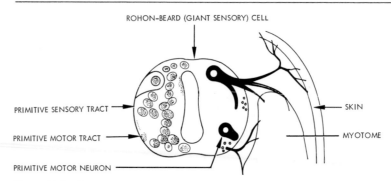

Figure 11-8. Cross-section through the spinal cord of a larval *Ambystoma*. The Rohon-Beard cell is an afferent (sensory) neuron with its cell body in the central nervous system and its dendrite extending peripherally in the dorsal root to the skin. (Adapted from Nieuhenhuys.)

ically defined group with a similar functional role. Within the white matter are myelinated and unmyelinated axons that ascend to or descend from one to many spinal segments, or to and from the brain. In tetrapods the gray matter is enlarged at those spinal levels that innervate the extremities.

The numerous *interneurons* in the gray matter interact with other neurons of the central nervous system. In this context, most neurons are interneurons. Those projecting to nuclei in the same spinal segment are intrasegmental interneurons; those projecting to the other spinal segments are intersegmentals, and the interneurons to the opposite (contralateral) side of the spinal cord are known as *commissurals* (Figure 11-11). Of the fibers which ascend from the spinal cord to the brain stem nuclei, cerebellum, and thalamus, many cross over (decussate) and ascend in the contralateral white matter; in addition many ascend in the white matter on the same side. Motor fibers from the brain descend in the white matter before synapsing in the nuclei of the gray matter of the spinal cord (Figure 11-11).

The activities of the neuronal circuits of the spinal cord regulate the coordinated undulating movements of the segmental body wall muscles of

Figure 11-9. (a) Nerve plexus of the pelvic fin of a chimaera (elasmobranch), and (b) branchial plexus of the forelimb of a mammal. Both illustrate the regrouping of nerve fibers and nerve bundles to form an organized meshwork of nerves. The proximal aspects of the plexuses are in the upper part of the figures. (Adapted from Romer.)

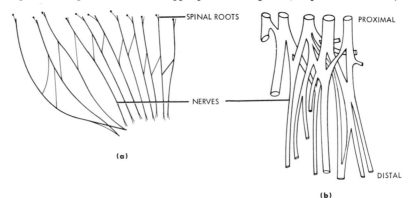

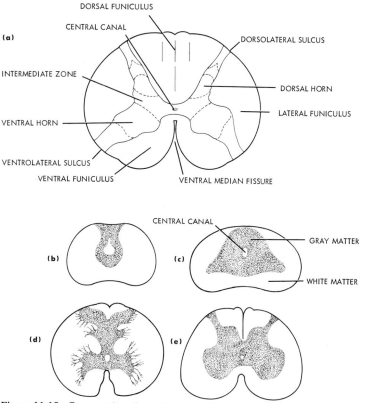

Figure 11-10. Cross-section through the spinal cord of (a) man, (b) Amphioxus, (c) cyclostome, (d) teleost fish; and (e) amphibian. Note the configuration of the gray matter and the white matter. The ventrolateral sulcus is shown in (a). (Adapted from Nieuhenhuys.)

swimming fish and other vertebrates and the more complex integrated actions of tetrapod limbs. Segmental spinal reflex arcs form the basic circuits integrated through intersegmental circuits; in turn these spinal circuits are modulated by neural influences descending from nuclei in the brain. Two basic spinal segmental reflex arcs are the two-neuron arc and the three-neuron arc. The two-neuron reflex arc includes the sequence of (1) an afferent neuron of the dorsal root that terminates and synapses in the gray matter of the spinal cord with (2) the motor neuron with its axon which emerges in the ventral root. The three-neuron reflex arc includes the sequence of (1) an afferent neuron of the dorsal root that terminates and synapses with (2) an interneuron of the gray matter which, in turn, synapses with (3) the motor neuron. The motor neurons terminate by synapsing at the motor end plates on voluntary muscle fibers (Figures 11-1, 11-11). Acetylcholine is the neurotransmitter at this synapse. In a coordinated action, the two-neuron reflex excites muscle groups to contract; the three-neuron reflex may either excite or inhibit various muscle groups to contract.

Spinal reflex arcs containing interneurons are numerous, with the intrasegmental, intersegmental, and commissural interneurons integrated in circuits of different levels of complexity. Some excite and others inhibit the post-

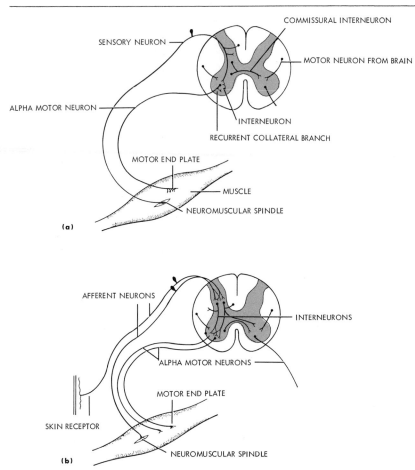

Figure 11-11. (a) The two-neuron monosynaptic reflex arc is composed of the sequence: neuromuscular spindle, sensory neuron, alpha motor neuron, and muscle cell. (b) The three-neuron, disynaptic reflex arc is composed of the sequence: receptor, sensory neuron, interneuron within central nervous system, motor neuron, and muscle cell.

synaptic neurons. In a spinal reflex the sensory neuron from the periphery excites a complex of interneurons in the spinal neuronal pools; some of these interneurons excite the motor neurons which in turn stimulate the agonistic muscle groups to contract, and others inhibit the antagonistic muscle groups. In other words, the neuron pools are geared to produce integrated movements; in the simple act of flexion of the joints of an extremity, the flexor muscle (agonist) groups are stimulated to contract in harmony with the inhibition of the extensor muscle (antagonist) groups. In turn, other interneurons cross over to excite and to inhibit other neuron pools involved in the coordinated movements on the opposite side; these are synchronized with the movements on the original side (as in a swimming fish or a walking tetrapod). The neuron pools of the spinal cord and brain are organized to integrate and to synchronize precisely the timing of gross movements through inhibitory circuits and excitatory circuits. These produce the postural adjustments (*tonic* contractions) and the active movements (*phasic* contractions).

The role of the neuromuscular spindle, a sensory receptor with a motor innervation, in a spinal reflex will be briefly outlined. The neuromuscular spindle is an elongated spindle-shaped sensory ending surrounded by and oriented parallel to the voluntary muscle (*extrafusal*) fibers of the gross muscle of which it is a part. It is an encapsulated structure composed of nerve endings terminating upon small voluntary (*intrafusal*) fibers in parallel to the extrafusal fibers. The spindles are stretch receptors (acting as strain gauges) monitoring the tension within the muscle. When the muscle is relaxed and elongated, the spindles within the muscle are now passively stretched along with the muscle. In this stretched posture, sensory nerve fibers innervating the spindle are stimulated to fire numerous impulses to the spinal cord to excite the alpha motor neurons. These innervate and stimulate the extrafusal fibers of the voluntary muscle, which contains the stretched spindles, to contract. In summary, the stretched spindles evoke a simple reflex in which the extrafusal muscle fibers of the muscles containing the stretched spindles contract and shorten. In the contracted muscle the spindle, now passively shortened, excites its sensory endings to fire at a lower rate; as a consequence the extrafusal fibers tend to relax. How can a contraction be sustained, such as occurs when a heavy object is held? Another neural system is utilized. The central nervous system evokes stimuli (e.g., volitional stimuli) to excite the gamma motor neurons which innervate and excite the intrafusal muscle fibers of the spindle to contract. This stretches a region in the spindle to increase the firing rate of the sensory nerve fibers to the spinal cord which excite the alpha motor neurons to sustain the contraction of the extrafusal muscle fibers. Thus the spindle-firing rate can be increased by (1) stretching the spindles passively and (2) exciting its intrafusal muscle fibers to contract. The delicate and subtle balance of these two mechanisms as well as of others is continually operating in the control of the nuances of muscle activity.

The innervation pattern of the spinal motor neurons is different in the amphibians from that in mammals. In the amphibians this type of neuron innervates both voluntary muscle cells and neuromuscular spindles. In mammals the innervation pattern is fractionated; the alpha motor neurons innervate voluntary muscle cells and the gamma motor neurons innervate the neuromuscular spindles.

In general the comparative functional aspects of the spinal cord may be summarized in the following manner. This complex organ is the simplest of the organized regions of the central nervous system. The higher vertebrates have evolved more complex circuits within the spinal cord; in turn these circuits interact with circuits within the brain. The interactions between the brain and spinal cord and the dependence of the cord upon the brain also increase in these organisms. Animals with the spinal cord transected (a spinal-animal) exhibit varying degrees of dependence upon the brain. Most spinal fish have well-coordinated rhythmic movement during swimming. Spinal-amphibians assume normal postural poses (e.g., frog ready to jump) and if stimulated, will jump with integrated movements. A spinal-mammal cannot stand (*paraplegia*). Immediately after transection mammals exhibit no reflexes (spinal shock); the spinal reflexes return in dogs and cats after a few days but only after weeks and months in man. The sensory spinal neurons have numerous and longer branches within the gray matter of higher vertebrates, whereas the dendrites of the motor neurons are longer in the lower vertebrates (fish) than in higher forms (mammals).

Autonomic Nervous System

The autonomic nervous system (general visceral efferent system) influences the organs of the visceral systems by modifying the activity of heart muscle, involuntary (smooth) muscle, and secretory cells. This system does not innervate voluntary (striated) muscle. The visceral systems include the cardiovascular system, digestive, respiratory, urinary, and endocrine systems, the sweat glands, and the pupillary and accommodation (focusing) muscles of the eye. The autonomic nervous system is represented in the central nervous system by a number of centers and pathways in many regions of which the *hypothalamus* is the highest regulatory complex (Figure 11-12). In mammals this visceral motor system is subdivided into the *parasympathetic* or craniosacral system and the *sympathetic* or thoracolumbar system. Parasympathetic fibers emerge from the central nervous system with cranial nerves III, VII, IX, and X and with several sacral nerves; thus it is called the craniosacral system. Sympathetic fibers have exit with the thoracic and lumbar nerves, and constitute the thoracolumbar system.

In the autonomic nervous system, a sequence of two sets of neurons make up the pathway from the central nervous system to the muscle and gland-cell effectors (Figures 11-12 and 11-13). This is in contrast to the course of motor impulses, which are carried by a neuron projecting directly from the central nervous system to a voluntary muscle. The first set of neurons (preganglionic neurons or fibers) with their cell bodies located in the gray matter of the central nervous system have axons which, after emerging from the nervous system via nerve trunks, terminate by a synapse with other neurons in nearby ganglia. Ganglia are collections of cell bodies, dendrites and synapses occurring outside the central nervous system. A second set of neurons, with cell bodies in ganglia, have axons that in turn innervate the effectors. This second set consists of postganglionic neurons (fibers). The chemical, acetylcholine, is the neurotransmitter released at all synapses between preganglionic and postganglionic neurons of the autonomic nervous system. The neurotransmitter released at the synaptic junction of the sympathetic postganglionic neuron and the effector (smooth muscle or gland) is noradrenalin (norepinephrine), hence the sympathetic system is called the adrenergic system and the postganglionic sympathetic neurons are called adrenergic neurons (fibers). Noradrenalin is inactivated by catecholomethyl transferase and monamine oxidase. The neurotransmitter released at the synaptic junction of the parasympathetic postganglionic neuron and its effector is *acetylcholine*, hence the parasympathetic system is called the

Figure 11-12 (opposite). Schematic representation of the autonomic nervous system in mammals. The parasympathetic system is indicated on the left side and the sympathetic system on the right side. Roman numerals refer to the cranial nerves. The sympathetic innervation of the blood vessels, sweat glands, and muscles erecting hair is not shown. Sympathetic and parasympathetic ganglia (G) are named.

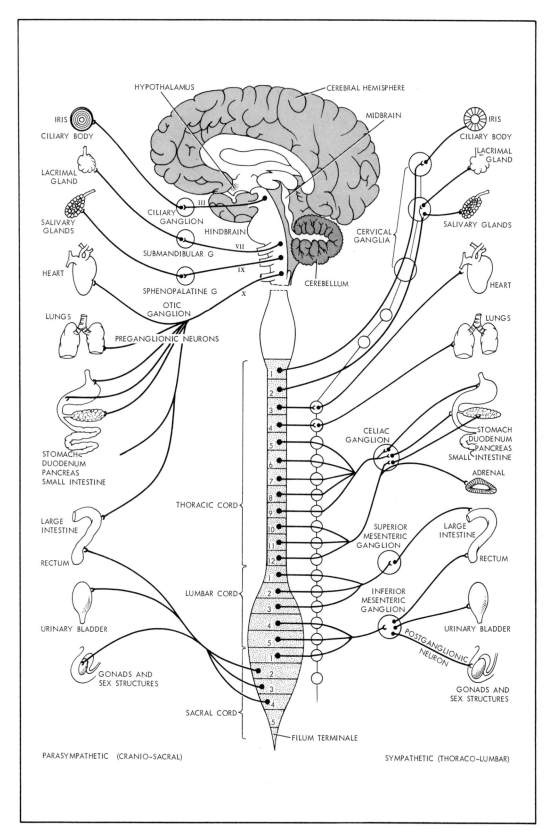

HYPOTHALAMUS

CEREBRAL HEMISPHERE

IRIS
CILIARY BODY

MIDBRAIN

IRIS
CILIARY BODY

LACRIMAL
GLAND

LACRIMAL
GLAND

SALIVARY
GLANDS

CILIARY
GANGLION

III

HINDBRAIN

SUBMANDIBULAR G

VII

CERVICAL
GANGLIA

SALIVARY GLANDS

HEART

SPHENOPALATINE G

IX

X

CEREBELLUM

HEART

OTIC
GANGLION

LUNGS

LUNGS

PREGANGLIONIC NEURONS

1
2
3

STOMACH
DUODENUM
PANCREAS
SMALL INTESTINE

4
5
6

CELIAC
GANGLION

STOMACH
DUODENUM
PANCREAS
SMALL INTESTINE

7

ADRENAL

THORACIC CORD

8
9
10

LARGE
INTESTINE

11
12

SUPERIOR
MESENTERIC
GANGLION

LARGE
INTESTINE

RECTUM

1
2

LUMBAR CORD

3

INFERIOR
MESENTERIC
GANGLION

RECTUM

URINARY BLADDER

4
5
1

POSTGANGLIONIC
NEURON

URINARY BLADDER

GONADS AND
SEX STRUCTURES

2
3

GONADS AND
SEX STRUCTURES

SACRAL CORD

4
5

FILUM TERMINALE

PARASYMPATHETIC (CRANIO-SACRAL)

SYMPATHETIC (THORACO-LUMBAR)

435

cholinergic system and its postganglionic neurons are called cholinergic
neurons (fibers). *Cholinesterase* is the enzyme that inactivates the acetylcholine. Many drugs may chemically enhance or suppress the actions of the
neurosecretions.

The sympathetic system intensifies those activities which are most dramatically expressed during emergencies and stress, called the "fight, fright, and
flight" situations. These reactions are accompanied by activities associated
with the expenditure of energy: acceleration of the rate and force of the
heart beat, increase in blood pressure, elevation of the concentration of sugar
in the blood, and increase in blood flow directed to voluntary muscles at the
expense of the skin and visceral organs. In contrast, the parasympathetic
system stimulates those activities which are associated with the conservation

Figure 11-13. Schematic representation of the autonomic nervous system in the shark.
The sympathetic and parasympathetic systems are not sorted out by regions.
Autonomic ganglia are present. The preganglionic fibers are indicated by solid lines and
the postganglionic fibers by dotted lines. (Adapted from J. Z. Young.)

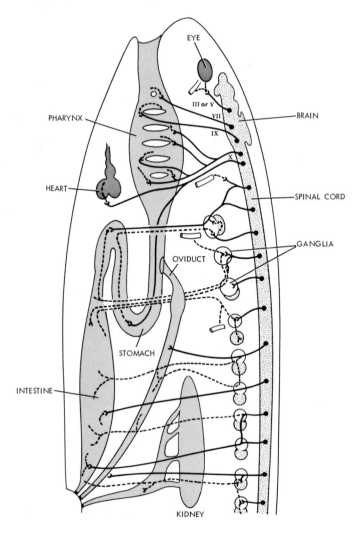

and restoration of the energy stores of the body: decrease in the rate and force of the heart beat, decrease in blood pressure, increase in digestion through stimulation of the gastrointestinal tract (greater secretion of enzymes and motility of wall of tract), stimulation of actions resulting in elimination of fluids (urination) and solids (defecation). The actions of the two systems are integrated; they are not basically antagonistic. In the body economy they act synergistically, although at times some activities are executed independently. The autonomic nervous system functions to regulate the internal activities of the organism at a level commensurate with the intensity of the stress situation and with the emotional state (anger, fear) of the individual. The medulla of the adrenal gland, which is innervated by preganglionic cholinergic neurons, secretes noradrenalin and adrenalin into the blood stream; this gland augments the activity of the sympathetic system, hence the term sympathoadrenal system.

The viscera are not totally dependent upon the autonomic nervous system; the heart beats, blood flows, digestion and other vital visceral processes proceed without neural influences. An animal can live without a sympathetic nervous system and an adrenal medulla; however, it cannot adjust to changes in the environment and it must be kept in a sheltered place.

The autonomic nervous system is a most highly evolved and delicately synchronized system of higher warm-blooded vertebrates. In birds and mammals, it functions by providing the feedback circuitry by which the organism can (1) adjust to the stresses made by the environment upon it and (2) make the necessary corrections to maintain a constant body temperature. In general, terrestrial animals are able to meet the demands of such environmental fluctuations as temperature and humidity changes. On the other hand, aquatic cold-blooded animals whose body temperature varies, live in, or are required for their survival to live in, a more stable environment where sudden temperature change is minimal.

The comparative anatomy, physiology, and functional activity of the autonomic system are as yet incompletely known in the submammalian vertebrates, in part because of the difficulty of analyzing the details of its structure and function. In cyclostomes and elasmobranchs the anatomical and functional distinctions between the sympathetic and parasympathetic systems are not clear. They have not been sorted out regionally, the ganglia are scattered in the body, and apparently no autonomic fibers innervate the skin. The regional distribution of the cranial outflow and the spinal cord outflow are fairly distinct. Only a slight amount of anatomical overlap has been demonstrated, and organs do not have dual innervation from both cranial and spinal nerves. In teleosts the anatomical and functional distinctions between the two systems are clearly indicated. The overlap in the peripheral distribution of the cranial parasympathetic outflow and a spinal cord sympathetic outflow results in a dual innervation of many organs. In some amphibians (frogs and toads) the sacral parasympathetic outflow is present for the first time. The separation into anatomic subdivisions along with the functional "antagonism" between the sympathetic and parasympathetic systems are considered to be basically similar but simpler in pattern than in the mammals. Among birds and mammals the anatomical and functional duality between the two systems is well differentiated.

The Structural and Functional Organization of the Brain

The brain is conventionally subdivided into five major regions: telencephalon, diencephalon, mesencephalon, metencephalon, and myelencephalon (Figure 11-14, Table 11-1). From the embryonic prosencephalon develop the telencephalon and diencephalon, while the rhombencephalon gives rise to the metencephalon and the myelencephalon. The embryonic mesencephalon remains undivided. A major character, unique to vertebrates, is the presence of cavities in the central nervous system. Within the brain this "hollow" includes the ventricular system, a continuous series of cavities (ventricles) filled with cerebrospinal fluid.

The cerebral cortex (gray matter on the surface of the cerebrum) of the brain of mammals is the complex portion consisting of the archicortex, paleocortex, and neocortex. In the submammalian vertebrates the cerebral cortex consists of the archicortex and paleocortex; in reptiles a primitive neocortex has been added and an equivalent structure in birds is probably the hyperstriatum. The paleocortex and the archicortex are often called the limbic lobe or allocortex. In many mammals, particularly the large-brained species (elephants, cetaceans, primates, carnivores and ungulates such as pigs, cows, and horses), the large cortex is convoluted into raised ridges called *gyri* and narrow indentations called *sulci*. The presence of gyri and sulci is related to the fact that the volume of the cerebral cortex is relatively larger in proportion to the underlying subcortical structures in large-brained *gyrencephalic* (convoluted) brains than in the small-brained *lissencephalic* (nonconvoluted) brains. With the thickness of the cortex varying between narrow limits among mammals, the larger cortical volume in the large brains is provided by a two-dimensional increase of the cortex with the concomitant formation of gyri and sulci. The olfactory bulb and the olfactory portion of the paleocortex form the *rhinencephalon* or the "smell brain." The cerebrum includes the telencephalon and the diencephalon. A decerebrate animal refers to an animal with its brain transected through the midbrain below the cerebrum, that isolates the dominant association center, seat of the highest mental faculties, from the remainder of the brain. Interconnecting the mammalian neocortex of one side with that of the other side is the corpus callosum, a commissure made up of many fibers. The corpus striatum and the ventral thalamus are complexes of nuclei which are integrated into the motor pathways.

The thalamus, a complex collection of nuclei, is the major processing station in the ascending sensory pathways. Except for the olfactory pathway, all sensory pathways in mammals, reptiles, and birds have connections in the thalamus before projecting to the sensory cortex. The hypothalamus is the

Figure 11-14 (opposite). Diagrams illustrating the major brain subdivisions and structures. (a) The three major subdivisions of the brain and the special senses projecting to these structures in the lower vertebrates. (b) The ventricles of the vertebrate brain. (c) Lateral view of a generalized vertebrate brain: (1) prosencephalon; (2) rhombencephalon; (3) telencephalon; (4) diencephalon; (5) mesencephalon; (6) metencephalon; (7) myelencephalon. (d) Median section of a generalized vertebrate brain. (e) Dorsal view of a generalized brain. V, ventricle. The iter is the aqueduct of Sylvius. (Adapted from Neal and Rand and from Romer.)

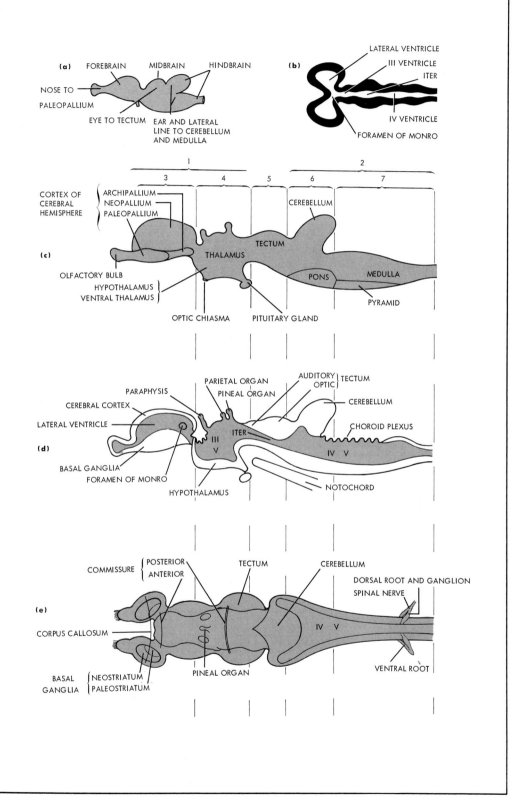

Figure 11-15 (opposite). Median aspect of the brain of (a) an opossum and (b) man. (Adapted from Romer.)

highest integrative center and projects influences to the autonomic nervous system and the endocrine system via the pituitary gland.

The brain stem is comprised of the medulla, pons, and midbrain. The core of this region of the brain, the tegmentum, is present in all vertebrates. Within it are the ascending (afferent) *reticular* pathways, the descending (efferent) reticular pathways, the ascending pathways of the sensory systems associated with the conscious sensations of pain, temperature, touch, taste, and audition (lemniscal systems), and the pathways associated with the vestibulolateral line system, and others. The superior colliculus (optic tectum) and the inferior colliculus (torus semicircularis, auditory tectum) are nuclei associated with the optic and auditory pathways respectively. The cerebral peduncles, *pons* proper, and pyramids, all present in mammals exclusively,

Table 11-1. The major subdivisions of the brain. The neocortex, cerebral peduncle, pons proper, and pyramid are found exclusively in mammals. The other structures listed, each of which is present to some degree in all vertebrates, exhibit many structural alterations associated with modified functional correlates; these are expressions of the vast potential inherent in the central nervous system for both morphologic and physiologic changes during phylogeny (Figures 11-15 through 11-18).

Telencephalon	cerebral cortex	neocortex	limbic lobe
		(paleocortex)	allocortex
		(archicortex)	paleostriatum
	corpus striatum	(basal ganglia)	(globus pallidus)
			neostriatum
			(caudate nucleus and putamen)
	olfactory bulb		
	corpus callosum		
	lateral ventricles, foramina of Monro, and choroid plexus		
	hyperstriatum (of birds)		
Diencephalon (between brain)	thalamus		
	hypothalamus and pituitary gland		
	ventral thalamus		
	third ventricle and choroid plexus		
Mesencephalon (midbrain)	superior colliculus (optic tectum)		
	inferior colliculus (torus semicircularis, auditory tectum)		
	tegmentum		
	cerebral peduncle		
	aqueduct of Sylvius (iter)		
Metencephalon (afterbrain)	cerebellum		
	tegmentum ⎫ pons proper ⎬ pons		
	fourth ventricle		
Myelencephalon (spinal brain) (medulla)	tegmentum		
	pyramid		
	fourth ventricle and choroid plexus		

Brain Stem { ... }

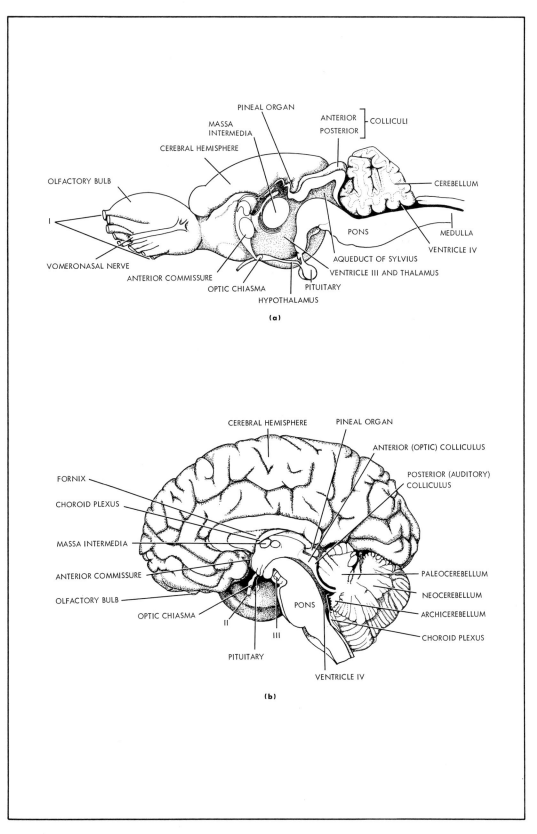

(a)

(b)

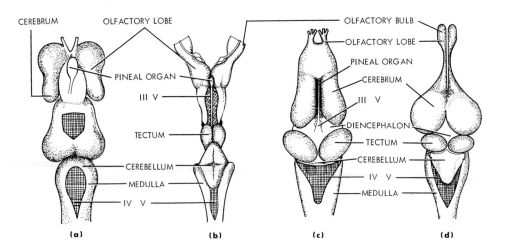

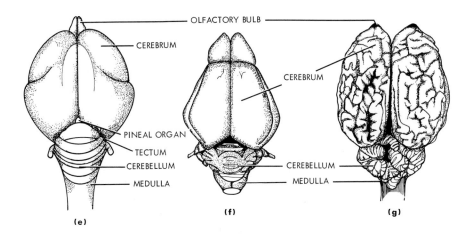

Figure 11-16 (above). Dorsal views of the brains of a representative series of vertebrates: (a) lamprey, *Petromyzon;* (b) shark, *Scymnus;* (c) frog, *Rana;* (d) alligator, *Alligator;* (e) goose, *Anser;* (f) insectivore, *Gymnura;* and (g) horse, *Equus.* An insectivore is representative of the primitive mammals and the horse of the higher mammals. (Adapted from Duke-Elder.)

Figure 11-17 (opposite). Lateral views of the brains of a representative series of vertebrates: (a) the lamprey, *Petromyzon;* (b) shark, *Scymnus;* (c) codfish, *Gadus;* (d) frog, *Rana;* (e) alligator, *Alligator;* and (f) insectivore, *Gymnura.* (Adapted from Romer.)

442

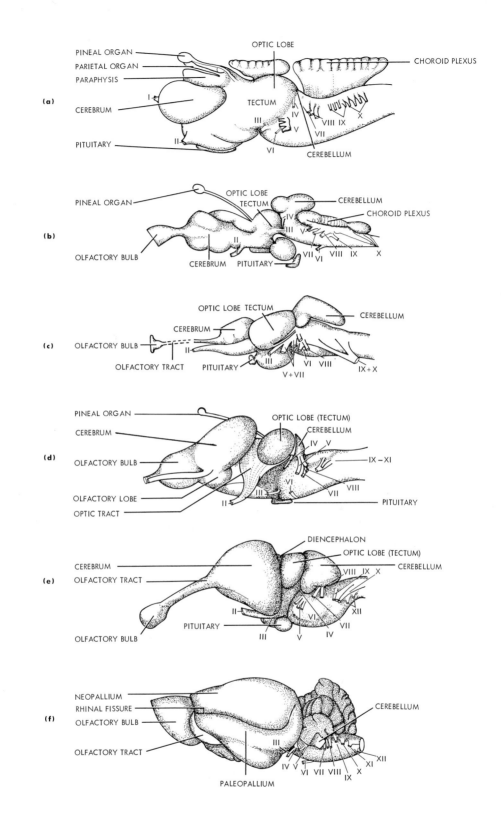

(a)

PINEAL ORGAN
PARIETAL ORGAN
PARAPHYSIS

CEREBRUM

PITUITARY

OPTIC LOBE

CHOROID PLEXUS

TECTUM

I

III

II

IV

V

VI

VII

VIII IX

X

CEREBELLUM

(b)

PINEAL ORGAN

OPTIC LOBE
TECTUM

CEREBELLUM

CHOROID PLEXUS

OLFACTORY BULB

II

III

IV

V

VII VI

VIII IX

X

CEREBRUM

PITUITARY

(c)

OPTIC LOBE TECTUM

CEREBRUM

OLFACTORY BULB

II

CEREBELLUM

OLFACTORY TRACT

PITUITARY

III

V + VII

VI VIII

IX + X

(d)

PINEAL ORGAN

CEREBRUM

OLFACTORY BULB

OLFACTORY LOBE

OPTIC TRACT

OPTIC LOBE (TECTUM)

CEREBELLUM

IV V

IX – XI

II

III

VI

VIII

VII

PITUITARY

(e)

CEREBRUM

OLFACTORY TRACT

DIENCEPHALON

OPTIC LOBE (TECTUM)

CEREBELLUM

VIII IX X

II

VI

XII

OLFACTORY BULB

PITUITARY

III

V

VII

IV

(f)

NEOPALLIUM
RHINAL FISSURE
OLFACTORY BULB

OLFACTORY TRACT

CEREBELLUM

III

IV V

VI VII VIII

X

XII

XI

IX

PALEOPALLIUM

443

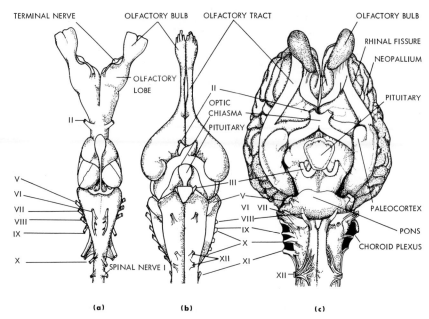

Figure 11-18. Ventral views of the brains of a representative series of vertebrates: (a) the shark, *Scymnus*; (b) alligator, *Alligator*; and (c) horse, *Equus*. (Adapted from Romer.)

are bundles of descending motor fibers from the cerebral cortex terminating either in the pons (corticopontine fibers) or spinal cord (corticospinal tract); from the pons, fibers are projected to the neocerebellum.

The cerebellum is subdivided into the archicerebellum, paleocerebellum, and neocerebellum. The archicerebellum is integrated with the lateral line vestibular system. The paleocerebellum receives, processes, and utilizes in coordinating movements the unconscious polysensory input from tactile, proprioceptive, auditory, and visual sources. The neocerebellum, found exclusively in mammals, is integrated with feedback connections with the motor neocortex of the cerebrum. The cerebellum functions to prevent oscillations (tremor) during motion and thereby maintains stability in movements; it smooths out the actions of muscle groups by delicately regulating and grading muscle tensions and muscle tone. The neocortex and neocerebellum evolved in parallel.

Cranial Nerves

The cranial nerves are the peripheral nerves of the brain. Their names, numbers, and functional components are essentially similar in all the vertebrates. They were originally named in man, which explains why the names of their branches and components are not always obvious in some animals. The sensory and motor components and the nerve fibers of the cranial nerves are characterized as: (1) somatic, for those of the head, body wall, and limbs; (2) visceral, for those having to do with the viscera of the body; (3) general, for the components widely distributed in the head and body; (4) special, for the components located in restricted regions of the head and body; (5) afferent, for the sensory components or nerve fibers transmitting input to the central nervous system; and (6) efferent, for the motor components transmitting output from the central nervous system.

The following list includes the number (roman numeral) and name of the cranial nerve, the main distribution segment of the brain from which it emerges, and its main functional components.

I   Olfactory nerve
Sensory nerve of smell, from olfactory mucosa in nose to olfactory bulb of the telencephalon (special afferent nerve).

Terminal nerve
Sensory nerve associated with chemical reception, from the vomeronasal organ to accessory olfactory bulb of the telencephalon (special afferent nerve).

II   Optic nerve
Sensory nerve of sight, from the eye through the optic chiasma to the midbrain (optic tectum) and to the thalamus of the diencephalon (special afferent nerve).

III Oculomotor nerve
Motor nerve to eye, from the midbrain to four or more extraocular muscles (general somatic efferent nerve) and pupillary and accommodation (focusing) muscles (general visceral efferent nerve).

IV   Trochlear nerve
Motor nerve to eye, from the midbrain to an extraocular muscle, the superior oblique muscle (general somatic efferent nerve).

V   Trigeminal nerve
Sensory nerve from the head to the pons, with three branches: ophthalmic, maxillary, and mandibular (general somatic afferent nerve); motor nerve from the pons to the jaw muscles (special visceral efferent nerve).

VI   Abducens nerve
Motor nerve to an eye muscle, from the pons to an extraocular muscle, the lateral rectus muscle (general somatic efferent nerve).

VII Facial nerve
Sensory nerve from the taste receptors (special afferent nerve) and other visceral receptors (general visceral afferent nerve) to the pons; and motor nerve from the pons to the muscles of the face and muscles of the hyoid arch (special visceral efferent nerve) and to the glands and smooth muscles of the head (general visceral efferent nerve, parasympathetic component).

VIII Vestibulocochlear nerve (stato-acoustic nerve)
Sensory nerve from the lateral line, vestibular labyrinth, and cochlear labyrinth to the pons (special afferent nerve).

IX   Glossopharyngeal nerve
Sensory nerve from the taste receptors (special afferent nerve) and other visceral receptors (general visceral afferent nerve) to the medulla; motor nerve from the medulla to the muscles of the third gill arch (special visceral efferent nerve) and to the glands and smooth muscles of the head (general visceral efferent nerve, parasympathetic component).

X   Vagus nerve
Sensory nerve from the taste receptors (special afferent nerve) and other visceral receptors (general visceral afferent nerve) of the head and visceral organs of the thorax and abdomen to the medulla; motor nerve from the medulla to the muscles of the fourth gill arch (special visceral efferent nerve, e.g., laryngeal muscles) and to the glands and smooth muscles of the viscera of the thorax and abdomen (general visceral efferent nerve, parasympathetic component).

XI   Spinal accessory nerve
Motor nerve (accessory to the vagus nerve) from the medulla to the sternomastoid muscle and trapezius muscle (special visceral efferent nerve).

XII Hypoglossal nerve

Motor nerve to the muscles of the tongue, from the medulla to the tongue (general somatic efferent nerve).

All twelve cranial nerves are found in living reptiles, birds and mammals (Figure 11-20) and the first ten in living fish and amphibians (Figure 11-19). Although there are functional differences, the cranial nerves XI and XII have their equivalent in fish and amphibians as occipital and spinal cord nerves which innervate "neck" muscles.

Certain functional aspects of the cranial nerves can be summarized by grouping the nerves and their functional components into several categories. Several modalities are conveyed by special nerves; these include the special afferent (sensory) cranial nerves I, II, and VIII. A modality is a term customarily used to mean a "kind of sensation," such as pain, sound, and odor. Taste is a special afferent component of cranial nerves VII, IX, and X. The modalities of smell and taste are often classified as visceral senses (associated with the visceral activity of sensing food). The optic and vestibulocochlear nerves are called somatic nerves because the modalities they convey are derived from somatic afferent sensory receptors.

Figure 11-19. Dorsal view of the brain and cranial nerves of the dogfish shark.

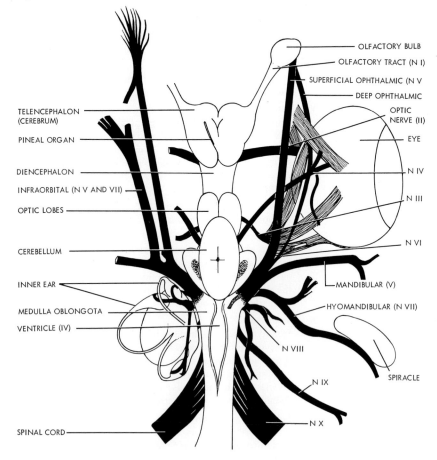

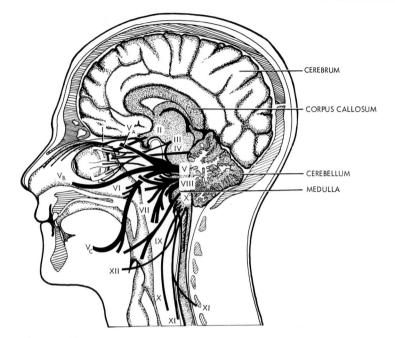

Figure 11-20. Median view of the brain and head of man illustrating the twelve cranial nerves. The cranial nerves include the olfactory nerve (I), optic nerve (II), oculomotor nerve (III), trochlear nerve (IV), ophthalmic division of the trigeminal nerve (V_1), maxillary division of the trigeminal (V_2), mandibular division of the trigeminal (V_3), abducens nerve (VI), facial nerve (VII), vestibulocochlear nerve (VIII), glossopharyngeal nerve (IX) vagal nerve (X), spinal accessory nerve (XI), and the hypoglossal nerve (XII).

A number of cranial nerves innervate voluntary muscles derived from the embryonic somites; these include the general somatic efferent (motor) cranial nerves III, IV, VI, and XII. They innervate the extraocular muscles (move the eyes and elevate the eyelids) and the tongue muscles (move the tongue).

Several cranial nerves innervate the branchiomeric (gill) arches of fish (Figure 11-21) and their derivatives among the tetrapods; these include nerves V (first arch, the jaws), VII (second arch, hyoid arch), IX (third arch), and X and XI (other arches). The many functional components of these complex nerves may be summarized in the following way. Essentially all the general senses (pain, temperature, touch, position, sense, and unconscious proprioception) are transmitted via cranial nerve V. The taste fibers are located in cranial nerves VII, IX, and X. Many general visceral afferent fibers are integrated into vital reflex arcs that influence the heart and respiration through their connections with the cardiac and respiratory centers in the tegmentum of the pons and medulla. The sensory fibers from the lateral line organ are located in many branchiomeric nerves; however, these fibers terminate in the brain stem nuclei associated with the vestibulocochlear nerve (see Chapter 10). The special visceral efferent fibers to the voluntary muscles of the gill arches of fish and amphibians and their phylogenetic successors in tetrapods (visceral because they are associated with the visceral activities of the digestive and the respiratory systems) innervate the muscles of mastication (cranial nerve V), muscles of facial expression (VII).

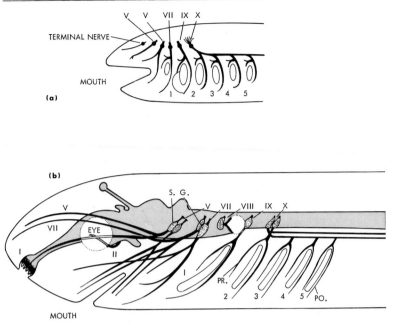

Figure 11-21. Diagrams illustrating the distribution of the branchial cranial nerves. (a) The relation of the nerves to the mouth and the gill slits. (b) Branchiomeric nerves in a lower vertebrate. The nerves include the terminal nerve, trigeminal (V), facial (VII), glossopharyngeal (IX), and vagal (X). The nerve branch that passes in front of each gill slit is the pretrematic branch (pr), and that behind the gill slit the posttrematic branch (po). Each branchiomeric nerve has a sensory ganglion (G). The Roman numerals represent the cranial nerves; S, spiracle. The arabic numerals are gill slits. (Adapted from Kingsley.)

pharyngeal muscles of swallowing, laryngeal muscles of the vocal cords (IX and X), and the trapezius and sternomastoid muscles of the neck (XI). Several of these branchiomeric nerves have general visceral efferent (para-sympathetic) components. The cranial nerves with parasympathetic compon-ents include III, VII, IX, and X. The fibers of the third nerve influence the muscles of accommodation (focusing) and the pupillary constrictor muscles of the eye. The fibers of the branchiomeric nerves (V, VII, IX, X, and XI) supply the parasympathetic motor innervation to the visceral structures of the head, neck, thorax, and abdomen, including the heart and digestive system.

Comparison of the Functional Components of the Cranial Nerves and the Roots of the Spinal Nerves

Several similarities and differences are found between the functional components of the nerve fibers in the cranial nerves and those in the roots of the spinal nerves. General somatic efferent (motor) fibers in the III, IV, VI, and XII cranial nerves and in the ventral roots of the spinal nerves innervate the voluntary muscles derived from the somites of the embryo. General somatic afferent (sensory) fibers occur in the trigeminal cranial nerve and the dorsal roots of the spinal nerves. General visceral efferent fibers (fibers of the autonomic nervous system) are present in the III, VII, IX, and X cranial nerves and in the ventral roots of the thoracolumbar and sacral spinal nerves. General visceral afferent fibers in the VII, IX, and X cranial nerves and in the dorsal roots of the spinal nerves convey afferent input from the viscera of the head and body to the central nervous system.

Several special components are restricted to the cranial nerves. Special visceral efferent fibers are present in the V, VII, IX, X, and XI cranial nerves; these fibers innervate the voluntary muscles associated with the gill arches and their derivatives. Special afferent fibers are found in the I, II, VII, VIII, IX, and X cranial nerves.

Origin of the Nervous System

The most primitive known vertebrates, the agnatha fish of the Ordovician, already had a highly organized nervous system with a topographic anatomy basically similar to that of lower living fish. Hence, the steps leading to the origin of the vertebrate nervous system can only be reconstructed in theory. The first cells with some characteristics of neurons were probably types of receptor-effector (neuro-effector) cells; such cells are present in living sponges [Figure 11-22(a)]. These combine the capacity to be stimulated (receptor) and to react by contracting as a muscle cell or by secreting as a glandular cell. In a subsequent stage, separate receptors and effectors evolved; in this condition the receptor cell (combined receptor and neuron) receives the stimuli and, in turn, influences the effector cell (muscle or gland) to contract and secrete [Figure 11-22(b)]. Examples of this stage in evolution are found in the modern sea anemones. In a more highly evolved stage a nerve cell became intercalated between the receptor cell and the effector cell; hence the sequence of receptor cell, neuron, and effector cell

Figure 11-22. Evolution of the receptor-neuro-effector apparatus in the animal kingdom according to Parker. (a) The primitive type is the combined receptor-effector cell of sponges. (b) The sequence of receptor (R) and effector muscle (M) is present in the sea anemone. (c) The sequence of receptor (R), interneuron (I), and muscle effector is also present in the sea anemone. (d) The development of a central nervous system, as present in the earthworm, includes the sequence of receptor (R) in the skin with an axon (A) terminating in the ventral nerve cord neuronal networks (SC), motor neuron (MN) to muscle (M). (e) The vertebrate reflex arc is schematically represented with the sensory neuron (S), spinal cord, motor neuron (MN), and muscle (M).

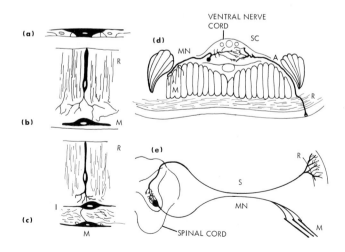

[Figure 11-22(c)]. In the subsequent complex phylogenetic changes the intercalated neurons (interneuron) increased in numbers and connectivity. These stages evolved into the central nervous system.

In the evolution of the nervous system of vertebrates, which occurred in concert with the evolution of other organ systems, several directions and expressions were developed. The nervous system is a bilaterally symmetrical and craniocaudally segmented (e.g., spinal segments) organ system with the cephalic end differentiated into the brain with its many adaptations. In the head and neck the brain and its special sensors evolved as the monitor of the environment through sight, smell, taste, and vibrations. Concomitantly there developed in the digestive system oral structures for the intake of food and in the pharyngeal region the organs of the respiratory system (gills) that functioned initially to obtain oxygen from the water.

Some indications of early evolutionary states may be found among living vertebrates. An early stage is represented by the bipolar cells in the olfactory mucosa; each cell acts both as a receptor cell in direct contact with the external surface to sense chemical molecules in the water or air and as a neuron to transmit information directly to the olfactory lobe of the central nervous system [Figure 11-23(a)]. Another stage is represented by neurons that do not have connections with the external surface but rather arborize in the epidermis; this neuron transmits to the central nervous system [Figure 11-23(b)]. In the most advanced stage a special receptor cell is intercalated between the environment and the neurons; such a cell is excited by environmental stimuli which, in turn, are passed on to a neuron projecting to the central nervous system [Figure 11-23(c)]. The special receptor cells include the rods and cones of the visual system, the taste cells of the taste bud, and

Figure 11-23. Postulated evolution of sensory neurons in vertebrates. (a) First stage, represented by an olfactory neuron, is a combination of receptor cell-sensory neuron in direct contact with the external environment. (b) Second stage, represented by some neurons with cell bodies in the dorsal root ganglion or its equivalent, is a combination of receptor cell-sensory neuron not associated with cells in direct contact with the external environment. (c) Third stage, represented by neuron (e.g. taste neuron) with cell body in dorsal root ganglion or its equivalent, is a sensory neuron in direct contact with a specialized neuroepithelial cell (e.g. taste bud). (Adapted from Neal and Rand.)

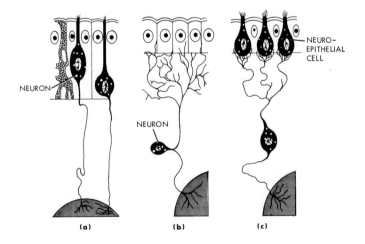

the hair cells of the lateral line vestibulo-acoustic system. During the phylogeny of the metazoa along with the specialization that resulted in the differentiation of the three cell types—receptor cells, neurons (nerve cells), and effector cells (muscle and gland cells)—certain similarities in these cells were retained. Each still preserves its activity both as receptor and effector. These specialized cells are capable of being stimulated (a function of a receptor) and are also effectors that produce a secretion (neurons produce a neurosecretion) or contract as a muscle.

The Structural and Functional Organization of the Vertebrate Brain

The central nervous system is organized as complex networks of pathways generally oriented parallel to the longitudinal axis of the spinal cord and brain. Each pathway system is comprised basically of sequences of neurons with long axons terminating at other neurons in one or more nuclei (centers, neuronal pools) of the main pathway (Figure 11-24). Within each nucleus are small interneurons, which, through interconnections with other neurons, process the input before relaying the output of the nucleus to other nuclei of the pathway. The ascending pathways associated with both unconscious and conscious senses (input) are the afferent (sensory) systems of neurons conveying neural information from the peripheral sensors to several centers in the brain. For example, the stimuli, felt as pain, excite nerve endings of the cranial nerves or peripheral nerves; the resulting excitation is channeled in the "pain" pathways that ascend to terminate in a number of centers at various levels of the spinal cord and brain. The descending pathways are the efferent (motor) systems of neurons conveying neural influences from many centers in the brain to the nuclei of the cranial and spinal motor nerves.

In general the pathways of the nervous system may be divided into two major subgroups: (1) the ascending (afferent) reticular system with its pathways and the descending (efferent) reticular system and its pathways; and (2) the ascending (afferent) lemniscal system and its pathways and the descending (efferent) corticospinal tract (Figures 11-24 and 11-25). The reticular systems are the phylogenetically older systems present in all vertebrates, cyclostomes through mammals. The lemniscal systems are phylogenetically new systems that are well developed in mammals; these systems are only slightly represented in amphibians and reptiles and are moderately present in birds. Both the reticular and the lemniscal systems show evidence of continued evolution even in the highest vertebrates. The corticospinal tract is present only in mammals.

The reticular pathways are comprised of intricately organized neural networks (Figure 11-24) with each neuron receiving synaptic input from many other neurons (convergence) and also making synaptic contacts with many other neurons (divergence). The reticular formation (and its pathway) refers to an anatomical entity; it comprises the neuron networks which are structural substrates of the functional and physiologically defined reticular system. Reticular pathways are present in the spinal cord, in the tegmentum of the brain stem, hypothalamus, thalamus, and the cerebral cortex. The ascending reticular system is involved with modulating states of awareness and alertness from deep sleep to the most active levels of attentiveness and responsiveness. It is often called the ascending reticular activating system and

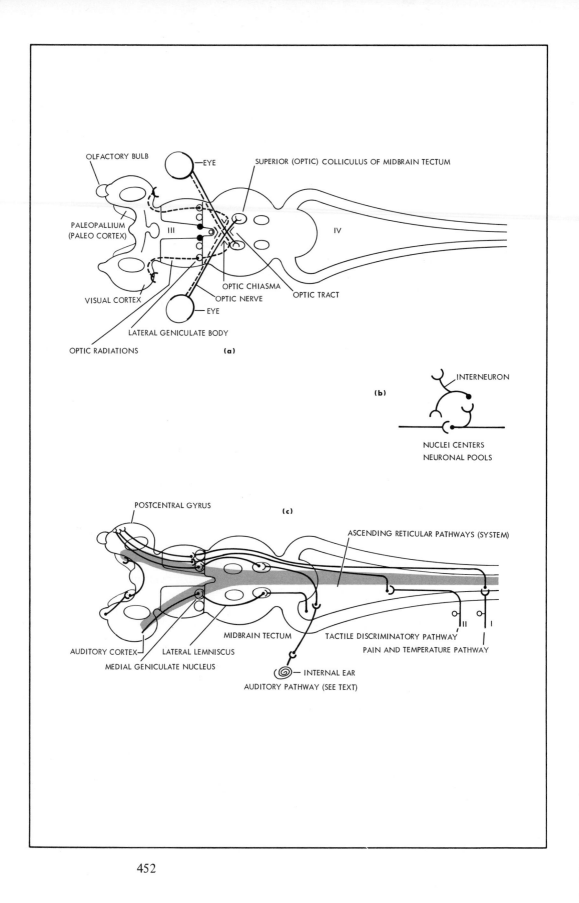

OLFACTORY BULB

EYE

SUPERIOR (OPTIC) COLLICULUS OF MIDBRAIN TECTUM

PALEOPALLIUM
(PALEO CORTEX)

III

IV

VISUAL CORTEX

OPTIC CHIASMA

OPTIC NERVE

OPTIC TRACT

EYE

LATERAL GENICULATE BODY

OPTIC RADIATIONS

(a)

(b)

INTERNEURON

NUCLEI CENTERS
NEURONAL POOLS

POSTCENTRAL GYRUS

(c)

ASCENDING RETICULAR PATHWAYS (SYSTEM)

MIDBRAIN TECTUM

TACTILE DISCRIMINATORY PATHWAY

PAIN AND TEMPERATURE PATHWAY

II

I

AUDITORY CORTEX

LATERAL LEMNISCUS

MEDIAL GENICULATE NUCLEUS

INTERNAL EAR

AUDITORY PATHWAY (SEE TEXT)

452

Figure 11-24 (opposite). Schematic representation of the sensory pathways. See the text for explanations. (a) the "pain and temperature" pathway, the "tactile discriminatory" pathway, the auditory pathway, and the ascending reticular pathways. (See figure 11-14 for major structures.) (b) The synaptic complexes of interneurons are located within each nucleus, center and neuronal pool where neuronal processing takes place. (c) The visual pathway and the olfactory pathway. The shaded regions represent the ascending reticular pathways in (a).

functions in such complex activities as the nuances of the organism's emotional state, perception, drive, wakefulness, and sleep. The descending reticular system is a complex of motor fibers and nuclei that mainly influence nuclei in the lower brain stem (medulla) tegmentum; from these nuclei excitatory and inhibitory stimuli are relayed via the reticulospinal tracts to the motor neuronal pools of the spinal cord (see under the next heading for further discussion).

Sensory Pathways of the Central Nervous System

Lemniscal systems comprise those pathways which transmit neural information through precise "point-to-point" relays successively from a peripheral spot (point) to a small group (point) of neurons in each nucleus and cerebral cortex of the pathway. The lemniscal pathways in mammals include pain and temperature, tactile discriminatory, taste, auditory, and visual pathways. For example, stimulation of a touch spot on the fingertip is projected by a relay generally composed of a sequence of three sets of neurons (Figure 11-24), each neuron with a long axon: the first set extends from the sensory receptors in the finger to neurons in a nucleus in the medulla; the second set with cell bodies and dendrites in the medullary nucleus extends by long axons to a nucleus in the thalamus; the third set of neurons with cell bodies and dendrites in the thalamus extends by long axons to a small group of cells in the postcentral gyrus of the cerebral cortex. Each nucleus in the pathway processes the data. The processing within each nucleus tends to suppress (by inhibition) the accessory unimportant information (suppression of the background noise) and tends to enhance the significant and pertinent information (enhances the signal). The lemniscal system conveys details of

Figure 11-25. Schematic representation of the descending motor pathways in the vertebrates. See the text for an explanation. The shaded regions represent the descending reticular pathways.

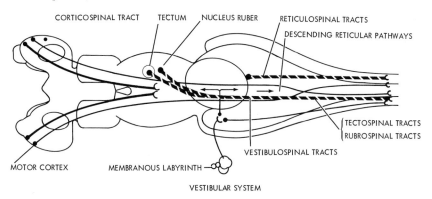

CORTICOSPINAL TRACT TECTUM NUCLEUS RUBER RETICULOSPINAL TRACTS

DESCENDING RETICULAR PATHWAYS

TECTOSPINAL TRACTS
RUBROSPINAL TRACTS

VESTIBULOSPINAL TRACTS

MOTOR CORTEX   MEMBRANOUS LABYRINTH

VESTIBULAR SYSTEM

varying degrees of precision; there are more point-to-point relays for example, conveying information of touch from the fingers and lips than from the small of the back, and, similarly, visual details from the macula lutea of the eye than from the nonmacular portions of the retina.

Comparative Functional Anatomy of the Nervous System: General Principles

The diversity exhibited by the nervous system is succinctly expressed by Herrick's classic statement: "The nervous system shows a wider range of adaptive structural modifications than is exhibited by any other organ system of the body." Some general principles within the complexity of comparative functional anatomy of the vertebrate nervous system may be epitomized as follows: (1) The nervous system in all vertebrates is based upon the same general plan (Figure 11-14). (2) The afferent input systems are hierarchically organized with the phylogenetically older centers in the lower forms functionally and structurally integrated with the phylogenetically newer centers in the higher forms. Even the older centers may become modified during phylogeny. (3) The efferent output systems are organized with the phylogenetically older reflex circuits that regulate the generalized patterned movements. The phylogenetically newer pathway systems, especially from the higher levels of the brain, influence and modify the phylogenetically older circuits and patterned movements.

Afferent Systems

The basic role of the afferent system is to sense the environment, to evaluate this input and to influence the efferent systems. In the lower forms there evolved the functionally efficient olfactory system, optic system, vestibulolateral line system, gustatory system, and general sensory systems. In many of these lower forms, specializations and refined elaborations took place, for example, in fish which echolocate by emitting electric pulses and detecting the reflected pulses. In the lower forms the senses were relayed to centers primarily located in either the brain stem or the paleocortex of the central nervous system; the visual system in fish, amphibians, and reptiles, for example, is mainly processed at the midbrain level, whereas in the higher forms processing also occurs in the cerebral cortex in mammals and the hyperstriatum in birds. Put simply, the lower vertebrates have evolved the senses and the basic processing centers. Higher forms retain these basic centers, often in a further evolved state, and develop new centers that also process the input information. For example, in vertebrates, including mammals, responses to "sound" vibrations evoke reflexes (without the conscious awareness of the vibrations); the awareness of sound may be appreciated in the tectum at the midbrain level. In higher vertebrates the distinctions among tones are evaluated at the primary cortical level (mammals) and hyperstriature (birds). The subtle appreciation of sounds as words (symbolism of sounds) requires the association areas of the neocortex. In this hierarchy of stations, each has its function, with the highest centers performing the most sophisticated roles. A major obstacle that confronts any investigator in this area is the difficulty of determining the level of conscious perception of any input to the animal.

Efferent Systems

The basic role of the motor systems is to evoke motor responses which have survival value for the organism. In all vertebrates there are many stereotyped patterned movements. These basic movements are regulated by a hierarchy of circuits and processing centers in the spinal cord and brain stem. Within the spinal cord are the integrative intrinsic circuits; the activity of these circuits evokes the basic postural movements of the body, including the undulating rhythm of swimming fish and the trunk and generalized limb movements of the terrestrial vertebrates. The various influences from the centers of the brain stem act almost exclusively upon the intrinsic circuits of the spinal cord. In all vertebrates the descending pathways from the brain stem include vestibulospinal pathways from the lateral line vestibular receptors, tectospinal pathway from the visual centers in the tectum, and the reticulospinal pathways from the reticular formation of the brain stem. Influences of the higher centers upon the brain stem come from the paleo-striatum, archicortex, and paleocortex of the telencephalon, the ventral thalamus of the diencephalon, and the archicerebellum and paleocerebellum. These centers influence the brain stem centers and, in large measure through the reticulospinal pathways, interact with the intrinsic circuits of the spinal cord. In the higher vertebrates, additional influences are derived from further differentiated older centers and newly evolved centers, such as the neo-cortex, neostriatum, and neocerebellum. All vertebrates utilize the basic stereotyped movements to a greater or lesser degree. The modified older centers and the newly evolved centers in the higher forms project neural influences upon the coordinated muscle groups involved with the stereotyped movements. Many of these patterned movements are modified in the higher forms by being fractionated. A fractionated movement is one that is released in some degree from the patterned sequence; for example, in primates and such mammals as racoons, the independent movements of the fingers or the delicate adjustments of wings of birds and bats during flight.

Sensory Pathways of the Central Nervous System

The ascending sensory pathways concerned with the general senses (pain, temperature, tactile and related modalities) in nonmammals are conveyed via neurons of the reticular pathways; even in mammals the cruder aspects utilize the ascending reticular pathways. The precise preceptive nature of these and other modalities is always difficult for the human observer to ascertain in any animal because of their subjective qualities. In nonmammals some incipient lemniscal pathways for the general senses may be present. Two major sensory lemniscal pathways from the spinal cord are present in mammals. The pain and temperature pathway (Figure 11-24) includes the first-order neurons which extend from the sensory receptors in the body to relay nuclei in the spinal cord; the second-order neurons which extend from the spinal relay nucleus to the lateral column of the opposite side (decussates) of the spinal cord and ascend to the thalamus as the *spino-thalamic tract*; and the third-order neurons which extend from the thalamus to the postcentral gyrus of the cerebral cortex. In the tactile discriminatory pathway, the first-order neurons extend from the sensory receptors in the

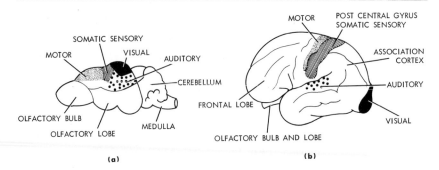

Figure 11-26. Lateral view of (a) the brain of the shrew, an insectivore, and (b) the cerebrum of man. The primary sensory projection areas and the primary motor areas are indicated. Note that the association cortex is relatively larger in man than in lower placental mammals such as the shrew.

body to the spinal cord and ascend in the dorsal column of the same side to relay nuclei in the medulla; the second-order neurons extend from the relay medullary nuclei to the opposite side and ascend as the *medial lemniscus* to the thalamus; the third-order neurons extend from the thalamic nucleus to the postcentral gyrus (somatic sensory) of the cerebral cortex (Figures 11-24 and 11-26). Note that both pathways convey information from the sensory receptors of one side of the body to the cerebral cortex of the opposite side. The elaboration of these inputs from the general sensory pathways into the appreciation and recognition of shape, form, and texture occurs in the association cortex of the parietal lobe.

Taste is conveyed from the taste bud receptors via several cranial nerves (VII, IX, and X) to a brain stem nucleus from which fibers project to the thalamus. The thalamic nucleus projects fibers to a portion of the *postcentral* gyrus (Figure 11-26). Odors are conveyed from the olfactory mucosa via the olfactory nerve to the olfactory bulb, where considerable neural processing takes place. From the bulb, neurons project fibers via the olfactory tract to the olfactory cortex of the paleocortex (Figure 11-18).

The auditory pathways (Figure 11-24) begin as neurons extending from the organ of Corti of the internal ear to several relay nuclei in the brain stem. Neurons from these nuclei project via the *lateral lemniscus* to the inferior colliculus of the midbrain tectum and medial geniculate nucleus of the thalamus. The lateral lemniscus is composed mainly but not exclusively of fibers from the opposite side. The medial geniculate nucleus projects to the auditory cortex of the temporal lobe of the cerebrum (Figure 11-26). Other aspects of the auditory system, will be discussed later.

The visual pathways are well organized in the vertebrates. In fish, amphibians, reptiles, and birds, the visual images processed in each eye are projected to the optic tectum on the opposite side of the midbrain (Figure 11-24). All the nerve fibers projecting from an eye pass through the optic nerve, cross to the opposite side through the *optic chiasma*, and continue through the *optic tract* to the optic tectum. In these lower vertebrates the tectum acts both as (1) a reflex center involved with the accommodation and pupillary light reflexes and (2) the highest integration center of conscious vision. In birds the hyperstriatum of the cerebrum may have a significant role in conscious vision. In mammals many of the nerve fibers from the retina of each eye terminate not only in the optic tectum (superior colliculus) but also in the lateral geniculate nuclei of the thalamus of both sides. These bifurcate and terminate as two terminal branches. From the geniculate nuclei, the optic radiations project to the visual cortex of the occipital lobe of the cerebrum (Figure 11-26).

The superior colliculus of the mammalian tectum is an optic center integrated into the accommodation reflex and the pupillary light reflex (Figure 11-24). Both the tectum and the visual cortex have a significant role in conscious visual discrimination. In many mammals, including rats, cats, and dogs, the ability to distinguish various patterns by sight and to discriminate between light and dark is retained after the entire visual cortex has been removed; such animals have lost some ability, however, to make fine visual discriminations. These observations indicate that in these animals vision is primarily a subcortical sense, with only some higher visual discriminations occurring at the cortical level. In primates, including man, conscious visual discriminations are made in the cerebral cortex; this functional aspect of vision is almost completely corticalized. In these forms the superior colliculus is almost exclusively a reflex center. A man, without the visual cortex, is blind; he cannot distinguish light from dark, or colors and patterns.

**Motor Pathways
of the Central
Nervous System**

For descriptive purposes, the structural organization of the motor circuits, nuclei, and pathways may be subdivided into (1) the suprasegmental level of circuits (Figure 11-27), (2) the major descending tracts (Figure 11-25), and (3) the intrasegmental and intersegmental circuits and neuronal pools of the spinal cord. The third category has been discussed before, in the section on the spinal cord. The suprasegmental level of interacting circuits comprises many centers and pathways within the brain that have a significant function in influencing motor activity. The resolution of the activities among these

Figure 11-27. Three of the major feedback circuits influencing motor activities in the mammals: (1) circuit of cerebral cortex to basal ganglia to thalamus to cerebral cortex (2) circuit of cerebral cortex to pons to neocerebellum to nucleus ruber and thalamus to cerebral cortex; and (3) circuit of vestibular nuclei to archicerebellum to vestibular nuclei. In the circuits with connections in the cerebellum, there are synaptic connections within the cerebellar cortex and the deep cerebellar nuclei.

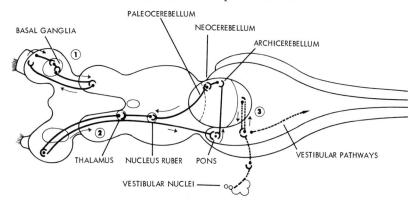

centers is finally relayed to the brain stem and spinal cord via several major tracts (Figure 11-25). Among the major pathways from the brain to the brain stem and spinal cord are (1) the *corticospinal* (pyramidal) *tract* and corticoreticular tracts from the cerebral cortex to the spinal cord and brain stem reticular formation; (2) the vestibulospinal tracts and the *medial longitudinal fasciculus* from the vestibular nuclei of the pons and medulla to the brain stem and the spinal cord; (3) the *tectospinal tract* from the midbrain tectum (optic) to the spinal cord; (4) the *rubrospinal tract* from the nucleus ruber of the midbrain reticular formation to the spinal cord; and (5) the *reticulospinal tracts* from the reticular formation of the pons and medulla to the spinal cord. Except for the corticospinal tract (a mammalian tract), the other motor tracts are found in varying degrees of specialization in most groups of vertebrates. The corticospinal (pyramidal) tract of mammals projects influences from the cerebral cortex directly to the spinal cord; this pathway is presumed to have a role in influencing "skilled voluntary" movements. It is well developed in primates and carnivores. In general, the pathways from the cerebral cortex and midbrain decussate and project to the opposite side of the spinal cord; the tracts from the lower brain stem project mainly to the same side of the cord. In a broad conceptual sense, the corticospinal tract is a descending lemniscal pathway and the reticulospinal and rubrospinal tracts are descending reticular pathways.

Within the vertebrates the phylogeny of the major motor pathways from the brain to the spinal cord may be schematized as follows. The reticulospinal pathways and vestibulospinal pathways are present in all classes of vertebrates; the tectospinal tract is well developed in amphibians, reptiles, birds, and placental mammals; the rubrospinal tract is definitely found in birds and mammals, and the corticospinal tract is present only in mammals. The degree of complexity and size to which a tract or pathway may evolve in any group of vertebrates is correlated with the functional requirements of the organisms. In the cyclostomes the reticulospinal pathways are the basic final common pathway for projecting influences from the brain; in fish the *vestibulospinal pathways* are as significant as the reticulospinal pathways; in the amphibians and the reptiles a tectospinal tract is also found; in the birds the tectospinal tract is well developed and a small rubrospinal tract is present; in the placental mammals the rubrospinal tract and the corticospinal pathways are well differentiated.

In their totality the suprasegmental circuits are integrated complexes of excitatory neuron pools and tracts and of inhibitory neuron pools and tracts which finally interact with other neuron pools resulting in the integrated and coordinated muscular movements. In effect, within the circuitry of the brain each neuron pool gives rise to fibers that stimulate other neuron pools; each neuron pool is, in turn, stimulated by other neuron pools and feedback circuits. In this complexity, a nucleus may excite an excitatory pool and thus facilitate neuronal activity; a nucleus may inhibit an excitatory pool and suppress activity; a nucleus may excite an inhibitory pool and suppress activity; or a nucleus may inhibit an inhibitory pool and thus enhance activity by suppressing inhibition (this is called *disinhibition*). Included in the suprasegmental system are several complex feedback circuits, to be noted in the section on encephalization. Two such feedback circuits are (1) the circuit, from cerebral cortex to cerebellar cortex and back to cerebral cortex via several intermediary connections (Figure 11-27) and (2) the general circuit, from cerebral cortex to corpus striatum, to the thalamus and back to cerebral cortex. These suprasegmental circuits have an important influence through excitation and inhibition on the activities of the descending motor pathways. The intricately organized interactions are integrated to produce the numerous nuances of the coordinated muscular activities in the vertebrates. Malfunctioning of some of the *suprasegmental* circuits is expressed in such diseases as paralysis agitans (Parkinson's disease).

Encephalization The evolutionary expression by which the higher neural centers assume greater significance in the functions of the nervous system is known as encephalization. In this concept the nervous system is organized in sequences of various levels of hierarchy. The basic principles of encephalization are demonstrated in the evolution of the auditory system. On the premise that a lower vertebrate hears when it behaves as if it has located a moving object by sensing vibrations (Chapter 10), it is believed that fish do hear. Their auditory pathways are probably restricted to certain nuclei of the reticular system and of the tectum of the midbrain. In amphibians and reptiles the auditory pathways are indicated with a more fully differentiated nucleus, the torus semicircularis in the tectum of the midbrain. In nonmammalian tetrapods the appreciation of the auditory stimuli is resolved at the brain stem level, with the highest integration center located in the midbrain. In birds and placental mammals the auditory pathways are more fully evolved with the elaboration of the inferior colliculus of the midbrain tectum, the medial geniculate nuclei of the thalamus, and the primary auditory cortex. In birds the equivalent of the cerebral cortex is the hyperstriatum. In these higher vertebrates, an appreciation of auditory stimuli results from the neural activity of the brain stem and of the thalamus and cerebral cortex; assumption of this function by the cerebral cortex (mammals) and the hyperstriatum (birds) is an expression of encephalization (specifically corticalization). In mammals an association auditory neocortex evolves in conjunction with the primary auditory cortex (Figures 11-24 and 11-26).

The awareness of crude sounds is an expression of subcortical activity, probably at the midbrain level. With encephalization, the elencephalic centers are related to the more discriminatory perceptions of the auditory sense; the thalamic and cortical levels are involved in the appreciation of more elaborate auditory perception. The primary auditory cortex receives its input from the medial geniculate body of the thalamus. The auditory association cortex has complex neuronal interconnections; these include input from the primary auditory cortex and reciprocal interconnections with neothalamic nuclei (other than the medial geniculate nucleus) and with the association auditory cortex of the other cerebral hemisphere through the corpus callosum. In man, the association cortex has a crucial role in the recognition of sounds and the spoken language.

The concept of encephalization is exhibited by each major subdivision of the nervous system. Stated another way, each division is made up of structures with phylogenetic histories of different lengths. This principle is illustrated by the cerebral cortex and the cerebellar cortex. The archicortex and the paleocortex of both the cerebrum and the cerebellum have a long phylogenetic history. Present in all vertebrates, these structures have evolved in the various classes in connection with different functional demands. In the cerebellum, the *archicerebellum* is functionally integrated with the vestibular and lateral line systems, whereas the *paleocerebellum* is primarily associated with integrating the input from the general sensors of the body. In the cerebrum the paleocortex has a primary function in the sense of smell. The archicortex is integrated with neural mechanisms associated with the behavioral expressions of animals; these include the degree of aggressiveness and emotional tone (lethargy to alertness) which they exhibit. The so-called "pleasure centers" and "punishing centers" are located in the paleocortex and archicortex; the stimulation of the pleasure centers evokes favorable activity by the animal (the animal likes the stimulation) and the stimulation of the punishing centers evokes avoidance responses (the animal dislikes the stimulation).

The neocortex of the cerebrum is basically a mammalian structure, with primordial elements in the reptiles and an independently evolved counterpart in the birds called the hyperstriatum. It is functionally associated with the highest levels of sensory perceptions of the auditory, visual, gustatory, and general senses (the latter include appreciation of weight, shape, texture, and form of objects from input from the general body senses), and also with thought, intelligence, and certain regulatory aspects of motor activity. The *neocerebellum*, a mammalian structure, evolved in concert with the neocortex of the cerebrum; the cerebral cortex projects through neopathways to the neocerebellum and paleocerebellum (Figure 11-27), which in turn course through other neopathways back to the neocortex. The entire feedback circuit follows the sequence of cerebral cortex to pons, pons to neocerebellum and paleocerebellum of the opposite side (neocerebellar circuits), cerebellum to thalamus of the original side, and thalamus to the neocortex. In brief, part of the neocortex of the cerebrum is integrated in a feedback circuit with the neocortex of the opposite cerebellar hemisphere and the neocerebellar hemisphere of one side with the neocortex of the opposite cerebral hemisphere (Figure 11-27). The function of this circuit is expressed in movements induced by cerebral cortical activity (e.g., skilled movements). The motor centers of the cerebral cortex project influences to motor centers in the brain stem and spinal cord as well as to the cerebellum; the stream of influences to the cerebellum are fed back to the cerebral cortex for integration into the on-going motor activities. In cerebellar injury the cortically induced movements can be executed, but with the absence of cerebellar control. The movements are performed with poor timing (tremor); actually the precisely coordinated timing between the agonist and antagonist muscles of a movement is no longer perfectly synchronized and thus the movement is not smooth. The degree of encephalization can be seen in the greater malfunction shown in animals with an *ablated* cerebellum. Decerebellate vertebrates reveal various results: sharks have no impairment in their ability to swim, teleost fish (goldfish) have side-to-side rolling movements while swimming, frogs can jump and swim but have some muscular rigidity, birds can eat and drink but walk, stand, and fly with extreme difficulty, and mammals can perform the crude aspects of an intended movement but do so with tremor.

Another complex feedback circuit evolved in conjunction with the motor centers of the neocortex of mammals. The path of this circuit is from neurons of the neocortex to the corpus striatum (corticostriate fibers), intrastriatal connections, neurons from the corpus striatum to the thalamus (striatothalamic fibers), and thalamic projections to the neocortex (Figure 11-27). This circuit remains within the same cerebral hemisphere, its fibers do not project to the contralateral side. Malfunctioning of this circuitry in man may result in Parkinson's disease, as noted before. The archicerebellum is integrated into a feedback circuit with the vestibular pathways (Figure 11-27).

Ventricular System

The ventricular system is a series of fluid-filled cavities within the brain. This cerebrospinal fluid is formed, in part, at the choroid plexuses of the lateral, third, and fourth ventricles (Figure 11-14). It flows slowly from the paired lateral ventricles of the cerebral hemispheres, through the foramina of Monro, third ventricle of the diencephalon, aqueduct of Sylvius (iter) of the midbrain, and the fourth ventricle of the metencephalon and myelencephalon; the fluid leaks through several foramina in the roof of the fourth ventricle into the subarachnoid space surrounding the central nervous system. In birds and mammals it circulates slowly until absorbed by the venous vessels.

References for Chapter 11

Bass, A. D. (ed.), *Evolution of Nervous Control from Primitive Organisms to Man.* Washington, D.C.: American Association for the Advancement of Science, 1959. The impact of the evolutionary process upon the nervous system, presented by many authorities representing a variety of disciplines.

Gardner, E., *Fundamentals of Neurology.* Philadelphia: W. B. Saunders, 1968. A brief account of the neuroanatomy and neurophysiology of man.

Herrick, C. J., *Neurological Foundations of Animal Behavior.* New York: Hafner Publishing Co., Inc., 1927, 1952. Reprinted in 1962. This classic is an account of the nervous system written from an evolutionary point of view by the father of the American school of neurology.

———, *The Brain of the Tiger Salamander, Ambystoma trigrinum.* Chicago: The University of Chicago Press, 1948. Probably the most penetrating account of the nervous system of any species. A classic.

Johnston, J. B., *The Nervous System of Vertebrates.* Philadelphia: Blakiston, 1906. This classic can still be read with profit.

Ariëns Kappers, C. U., G. C. Huber, and E. C. Crosby, *Comparative Anatomy of the Nervous System of Vertebrates, Including Man,* 2nd ed. 3 vols., New York: Hafner Publishing Company, 1960. A detailed work which is useful for special information.

Noback, C. R., *The Human Nervous System.* New York: McGraw-Hill Book Company, 1967. A brief account of the neuroanatomy and neurophysiology of man.

Papez, J. W., *Comparative Neurology.* New York: T. Y. Crowell Co., 1929.

Reprinted in 1962 by Hafner Publishing Company. A short, useful account
of the comparative neuroanatomy of the vertebrates.

Parker, G. H., *The Elementary Nervous System*. Philadelphia: J. B. Lippin-
cott Company, 1919. An excellent presentation of the early evolution of
the nervous system.

Zeman, W. J., and R. M. Innes, *Craigie's Neuroanatomy of the Rat*. New
York: Academic Press, 1963. An excellent account of modern concepts of
the organization of the nervous system as well as of the neuroanatomy of
the rat.

Bibliography:
Sensory Receptors
and the Nervous
System

van Bergeijk, W. A., J. R. Pierce, and E. E. David, Jr., *Waves and the Ear*.
Garden City, New York: Anchor Books, 1960. A lucid account of the
structural and functional aspects of sound and the ear. Paperback.

Brown, M. W. (ed.), *The Physiology of Fishes*, Vol. 2. New York: Academic
Press, 1957. Excellent chapters by leading authorities: "The Nervous
System" by E. G. Healey; "The Eye" by J. R. Breet; "The Acoustico-
lateralis System" by O. Lowenstein; and "Electric Organs" by R. D.
Keynes.

Duke-Elder, S., "The Eye in Evolution" in *System of Ophthalmology*, Vol. 1.
London: Henry Limpton, 1958. A detailed and comprehensive account
of the eye and visual pathways of the vertebrates.

Florey, E., *General and Comparative Animal Physiology*. Philadelphia: W. B.
Saunders, 1966. An excellent account of comparative neurophysiology.

Gilbert, P. W. (ed.), *Sharks and Survival*. Boston: D. C. Heath, 1963. Excellent chapters by leading authorities: "The Central Nervous System of
Sharks and Bony Fishes" by L. R. Aronson; "Hearing in Elasmobranchs"
by R. H. Backus; "Olfaction, Gustation, and the Common Chemical Sense
in Sharks" by A. L. Tester; and "The Visual Apparatus of Sharks" by
P. W. Gilbert.

Hoar, W. S., *General and Comparative Physiology*. Englewood Cliffs, N. J.:
Prentice-Hall, Inc., 1966. An excellent account of comparative physiology.

Marshall, A. J. (ed.), *Biology and Comparative Physiology of Birds*, Vol. 2.
New York: Academic Press, 1961. Excellent chapters by leading author-
ities: "The Central Nervous System" by A. Portmann and W. Stingelin;
"Sensory Organs" by A. Portmann and R. J. Pumphrey.

Polyak, S., *The Vertebrate Visual System*. Chicago: The University of
Chicago Press, 1958. A comprehensive and detailed analysis of the vertebrate visual system. A monumental book.

Prosser, C. L., and F. A. Brown, Jr., *Comparative Animal Physiology*, 2nd
ed. Philadelphia: W. B. Saunders, 1961. An excellent presentation of vertebrate comparative physiology.

Romer, A. S., *The Vertebrate Body*, 3rd ed. Philadelphia: W. B. Saunders,
1962. A good account of classical comparative anatomy of the sense
organs and the nervous system of the vertebrates.

Sturkie, P. D., *Avian Physiology*, 2nd ed. Ithaca, New York: Cornell University Press, 1965. A good presentation of the physiology of the nervous
system and sensory systems of birds by M. R. Kare and J. ten Cate.

12

The endocrine system

Introduction   The endocrine system of vertebrates consists of a diverse assemblage of glands and glandular tissues which secrete minute amounts of hormones into the blood or other body fluids. When they have been distributed throughout the body by the circulation, these substances are taken up by various tissues in which they elicit responses. Specificity of control by the endocrine system depends upon the facts that each particular hormone is chemically distinct and recognizable by particular target tissues and that each is secreted in response to specific stimuli. In a general way, then, the functional strategy of the endocrine system is like that of the nervous system; it produces specific control signals in response to sensory information about conditions in the external and the internal environments, and these signals in turn are interpreted by specific effector systems to command adaptive responses to the sensory input. But there are marked differences in the ways in which the two systems are structured to carry out their control functions.

Compared with the complex architecture of the nervous system, the endocrine system is relatively unstructured anatomically. Some fifteen or twenty different glands constitute the endocrine system of vertebrates, and these appear to be scattered almost randomly throughout the body (Figure 12-1). This impression of unrelatedness among the endocrine glands is supported by the diverse and unrelated embryonic origins of many of them. Superficially, the principal justification for considering the endocrine glands together as a system is the gross similarity of the manner in which the hormones function as blood-borne secretions. In addition, however, there are complex interactions among the endocrine glands which weld them into a functionally unified system.

Functional Organization of the Endocrine System   The most elementary control system possible consists of a minimum of two functional components: (1) a means for receiving relevant sensory input and (2) a means for generating a suitable command signal to the motor unit or effector. Most biological control systems, including the nervous system and most of the endocrine system, are more sophisticated than this and usually contain in addition (3) an integration center (brain) where the total sensory input may be integrated and evaluated relative to the prospective response, (4) one or more feedback loops from the effector (or generated by the response itself) to the control circuit, and (5) one or more amplifying steps

463

(Figure 12-2). If we analyze the endocrine system within this scheme, we find that three principal organizational patterns, with variations, have been utilized:

1. Simple negative feedback loops. Certain hormones are primarily concerned with the homeostasis of various substances such as salts, glucose, and amino acids, contained in the body fluids. In some instances the entire informational input used in regulating the rate of hormone secretion is derived by monitoring—by the endocrine gland itself—deviations in the concentration of the regulated substance from some preset norm. Deviation in one direction from the norm activates secretion of the hormone, which in turn activates mechanisms for restoring the normal concentration of the substance. Deviation in the opposite direction suppresses secretion of the hormone, and mechanisms are activated which again push the level of the regulated substance toward normal. Such negative feedback loops are usually paired, involving one hormone which corrects for deviation in one direction and a second hormone which corrects for deviation in the opposite direction. This

Figure 12-1. Location and comparison of the principal endocrine glands of man and trout. Note that the parathyroids are lacking in the fish; Stannius corpuscles and the caudal neurosecretory system are lacking in man and all other tetrapods; the functions of these structures are still incompletely defined.

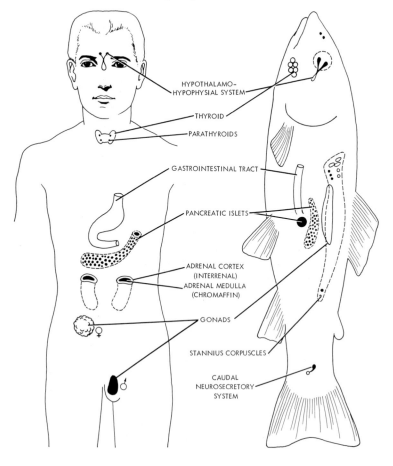

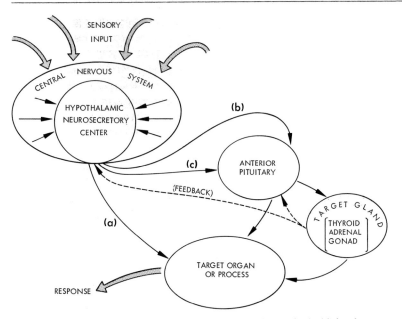

Figure 12-2. Diagram of (a) first-order, (b) second-order, and (c) third-order neuro-endocrine processes. The broken arrows indicate feedback from the target endocrine glands to the pituitary-hypothalamus complex. Feedback may be to the hypothalamic control centers, to the pituitary gland directly, or both. (From B. Frye, *Hormonal Control in Vertebrates*. New York: Macmillan, 1967.)

type of endocrine control mechanism is well illustrated by the homeostasis of blood calcium levels (Figure 12-3). In a similar way blood glucose is regulated through the opposing actions of the pancreatic hormones, insulin and glucagon.

2. Neuroendocrine circuits involving secretory-motor innervation. Most of the sensory information relevant to endocrine function is transduced by sensory organs into afferent neural input into the central nervous system. But at some point in the efferent limb of the neuroendocrine stimulus-response arc a hormone is secreted that acts as the control signal. Such circuits involving both neural and hormonal components are known as neuroendocrine reflexes.† In at least one endocrine gland, the adrenal medulla, the transposition from neural to hormonal signals within the efferent pathway takes the form of direct secretory-motor innervation of the gland. The adrenal nerve, a branch from the sympathetic system, richly innervates the medulla, making direct synapses with the gland cells. Stimulation of the nerve results in secretion of adrenalin and noradrenalin, the medullary hormones, and blockage of the nerve inhibits secretion of these hormones.

Most neuroendocrine reflex circuits are not completed by means of direct secretory-motor innervation, however. Indeed, the majority of vertebrate

---

†The use of the term "reflex" in this sense may be at variance with the original meaning of the term, because considerable central nervous integration may be involved in so-called neuroendocrine reflexes. The term has, however, come into common use.

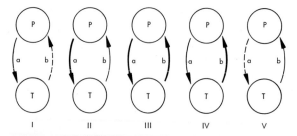

Figure 12-3. Feedback interaction between the pituitary and the target endocrine glands. I to V represent different stages of the interaction. (From B. Frye, *Hormonal Control in Vertebrates*. New York: Macmillan, 1967. After E. and B. Scharrer, *Neuroendocrinology*. New York: Columbia Univer. Press, 1963.)

endocrine glands continue to function in an essentially normal manner even when totally denervated. The nerves that enter most endocrine glands in relative abundance are apparently strictly vasomotor and have no direct part in the control functions with which the glands are involved.

3. Neurosecretory circuits. In the majority of neuroendocrine circuits transition from afferent neural input to hormonal output is achieved by special *neurosecretory* cells located within the central nervous system. In many respects these cells look like typical nerve cells, but they are also glandular in certain features, most notably in the large numbers of secretory granules which they contain (Figure 12-4). At the dendritic end the neurosecretory cell makes synaptic connections with nerve fibers that relay integrated sensory information to it from elsewhere in the central nervous system. The axonal end takes the form of a swollen axonal bulb that is replete with secretory granules as well as typical synaptic vesicles. The axon typically terminates in a *haemal organ,* a structure consisting mainly of a dense bed of capillaries and supporting connective tissue. The neurosecretory product is produced in the region of the cell body and packaged into the granules which are transported down the axon to the haemal organ. There it accumulates until the sensory information received by the neurosecretory cell dictates that it shall be secreted into the blood stream. The products secreted are neurosecretory hormones which either act directly upon the peripheral tissues or control the activities of other endocrine glands. The widespread occurrence of neurosecretory mechanisms, not only in vertebrates but in most phyla of multicellular invertebrates as well, suggests that the neurosecretory cell is in a unique position to make the transition from neural to hormonal pathways. Because of its key position in the nervous system and its nerve cell characteristics, the neurosecretory cell can receive many kinds of sensory information as relayed to it by neurons elsewhere in the central nervous system. Because of its gland cell properties, it can translate this information into a specific hormonal message and so become the final common pathway by which many kinds of external and internal stimuli can influence a particular hormone-controlled response.

The hypothalamus is the principal neurosecretory center of vertebrates. As the chief integrative center of the autonomic nervous system, the hypothalamus has control over a great variety of visceral functions. This includes control over a large segment of the endocrine system, which it governs through neurosecretory connections between the hypothalamus and the pituitary gland. The major structural features of the hypothalamus related to its neuroendocrine functions include the following:

1. An extensive array of afferent connections with the major sensory pathways and integrative centers of the brain. These connections include the median forebrain bundle, the fornix, the mammillary peduncle, and diffuse thalamihypothalamic and pallidohypothalamic fiber tracts. Through these pathways sensory input of virtually every modality is relayed directly or indirectly to the hypothalamus.

2. Neurosecretory nuclei. In birds and mammals the two largest neuro-secretory nuclei of the hypothalamus are the supra-optic and the paraventric-ular nuclei. In lower vertebrates these two pairs of nuclei are represented by a single homologous pair of pre-optic nuclei. They produce mainly the hormones of the posterior pituitary gland and will be discussed later. In addition, the anterior hypothalamus contains a number of other smaller neurosecretory nuclei whose secretions have to do primarily with the regula-tion of the activities of the anterior lobe of the pituitary gland. There appear to be at least six of these functional "areas" (not all have been precisely identified with specific morphological nuclei) associated with a corresponding number of anterior pituitary functions. The specific functional nature of these will be discussed in connection with the pituitary gland.

3. The neurohypophysis. The floor of the hypothalamus, known as the infundibulum, is differentiated into a more or less complex neurohaemal

Figure 12-4. Diagram of neurosecretory cells. (From B. Frye, *Hormonal Control in Ver-tebrates.* New York: Macmillan, 1967. After E. and B. Scharrer, *Neuroendocrinology.* New York: Columbia Univer. Press, 1963.)

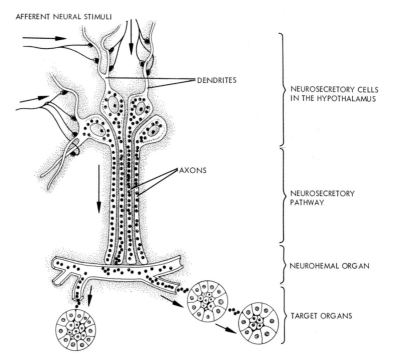

organ known as the neurohypophysis. The axons of the neurosecretory cells located in the neurosecretory nuclei pass downward through the walls of the hypothalamus to terminate adjacent to the rich plexus of capillaries that penetrate the outer surface of the neurohypophysis. Most of the neurosecretory axons are collected into a number of bundles known as hypothalamohypophysial tracts. The largest of these are the supra-opticohypophysial tracts from the large supra-optic and paraventricular nuclei, but a number of other minor tracts are present also from the smaller neurosecretory nuclei. Except for the cyclostomes, in which the neurohypophysis may be relatively undifferentiated, the neurohypophysis of vertebrates is differentiated into two distinct haemal organs. These are the *neural lobe of the pituitary gland,* and the *median eminence.* Most of the fibers of the supra-opticohypophysial or pre-optic fiber tracts terminate in the neural lobe, whereas the remainder of the hypothalamic neurosecretory fibers, including some from the supra-optic and pre-optic tracts, terminate in the median eminence. This anatomical subdivision of the neurohypophysis is the basis for a functional subdivision, in that different neurosecretory hormones are secreted at different sites. In the tetrapods the circulatory drainage of these two sites is distinct; blood leaving the plexus of the neural lobe enters the systemic circulation via branches of the anterior cardinal or internal jugular vessels, and so these hormones are carried to their peripheral targets. Blood leaving the median eminence, on the other hand, is collected into a group of minute *hypophysial portal vessels* which transport the blood directly into a secondary capillary plexus within the anterior pituitary gland. In fish a portal circulation between the neurohypophysis and the pituitary exists which is functionally equivalent to that of tetrapods; but this generally takes the form of a capillary plexus which begins in proximity with the neurosecretory fibers in the surface of the median eminence and neural lobe and continues on into the anterior pituitary without anastomosing into distinct portal veins. The direct vascular connection between the hypothalamus and the anterior pituitary is highly significant because the neurosecretory hormones which regulate the anterior pituitary gland are secreted in exceedingly minute amounts and are ineffective when diluted in the general circulation. For example, if the portal vessels are blocked, or if the anterior pituitary is transplanted to another site within the body, it no longer responds to the afferent input normally relayed to it by the hypothalamus and subsides into a very low state of functional activity. The anatomical relationships between the hypothalamus and the pituitary are summarized in Figure 12-4.

With respect to the number of relays between the neurosecretory process in the hypothalamus and the final regulated function, neuroendocrine reflexes show several levels of complexity. The neurosecretory hormone may itself be the final command signal to the target tissue. This is a *first-order* neurosecretory function, and is well illustrated by the functions of the posterior pituitary hormones. Or, the neurosecretory hormone may act upon another endocrine gland (the pituitary) to stimulate the release of another hormone. If this hormone then acts as the final command signal to the motor unit, the circuit is known as a *second-order* neuroendocrine process. But, if the hormone produced by the second member of the relay acts upon yet another gland which then produces the hormone controlling the motor unit, it is termed a *third-order* neuroendocrine process. These functional relationships between the hypothalamus and the endocrine system are shown in Figure 12-2.

The functional organization of third-order neuroendocrine systems is complicated by the fact that negative feedback occurs between the target gland and the pituitary-hypothalamus complex (Figure 12-2). The chief advantage of this relationship, in which the target gland hormone tends to suppress the output of the corresponding pituitary hormone, appears to be that it acts as a mechanism by which some autonomy from external sensory input can be obtained. This has two effects: on one hand, the feedback circuit may set the maximum level of the endocrine response to environmental stimulation; on the other hand, given the fact that the pituitary-hypothalamus is able to sustain some low level of function independently of specific stimulatory input, the feedback circuit provides the necessary information to keep the system functioning at some stable minimal (but perhaps adjustable) level. In mammals, at least, it is well established that basal levels of secretion of many hormones are required to sustain a basal state of morphological organization and metabolic activity within the target tissues. Such hormones may be regarded as having supportive or permissive functions in addition to commanding responses to specific afferent input via the neuroendocrine circuit. Which of these roles is the most primitive is impossible to say, since very little data on the hormone dependence of tissues for minimal metabolic capabilities exist on animals below the mammals.†

The significance of the organization of neuroendocrine circuits into multiple relays is not altogether clear. A mechanism for intrinsic feedback control is one of the properties of the system, as discussed in the previous paragraph. Other possible functions of the relay organization are *amplification* and *modulation*. Amplification occurs because each gland in the relay emits a "stronger" signal than it receives. Modulation of the frequency of the signal can occur because the time course of endocrine secretory processes is intrinsically much slower than neuronal signals. Thus, the efferent output reflects overall trends in the sensory input, but not the minute fluctuations or "static" that are registered in the neuronal input. For example, gonadal activity in photoperiodically regulated annual reproductive cycles reflects progressive changes in daylength, but not daily fluctuations in light intensity, nor even sporadic discrepancies in the photoperiod within the general trend of lengthening or shortening days.

Evolution proceeds historically, however, and not with the mechanistic objective of solving a current problem the "best" way. There is no a priori reason why the advantages of feedback, amplification, and modulation cannot be achieved within the limits of the organization of first-order neuro-

†A perplexing problem that arises here is why limitations on the basal metabolic capabilities of cells have been given over to some extent to systemic control by hormones rather than being retained intrinsic to the cells themselves. The probable answer is that the "minimal" or "basal" level required for functional viability changes with the seasons as activity states change. Consequently, a fixed limit would be adaptively inappropriate, and systemic control that can make use of sensory information about the seasons provides a mechanism for the adaptive resetting of the metabolic state throughout the body.

secretory processes, and indeed they are. Consequently, these functional considerations do not, of themselves, account for the evolution of the particular patterns of endocrine organization that we have been discussing. Equally important is the question, "What came first?" It is very likely that the last members in the relay—adrenals, thyroid, gonads—initially evolved as autonomous glands with regulatory effects upon adjacent, ontogenetically related tissues and that they only secondarily came under neuroendocrine control. For example, gonadal steroids have important direct effects upon the gametogenic functions of the gonad which could have favored the differentiation of gametogenic and steroidogenic components of the gonad independently of the existence of systemic control by gonadotropic hormones.

The evolution of the hypothalamic-pituitary-neurosecretory complex is an enigma. The association between these two glands is already present in the most primitive living vertebrates. But, inasmuch as the evolutionary history of the association between the pituitary and the hypothalamus is completely obscure, it is possible that (1) this association is indeed primitive or (2) an earlier stage saw the development of a functional association between the pituitary and its target glands and the neurosecretory unit was the final link to be connected.

The Endocrine Glands of Vertebrates

Most groups of multicellular animals are known to produce hormones that regulate metabolism in ways analogous to the functions of the endocrine system of vertebrates. However, the complement of endocrine glands possessed by the vertebrates is unique and appears to have had its evolutionary development almost entirely within the vertebrates. Most of the hormones produced by these glands are also characteristic of the vertebrates. It is true that certain hormones of simpler chemical structure, notably adrenalin and iodine-containing amino acids, found in the thyroid, are known to occur in some invertebrates; and steroids very similar to those produced by the adrenal and the gonads are found among the invertebrates as well as in flowering plants. These coincidences, however, are probably cases of evolution of parallel biosynthetic pathways rather than homology.

The Pituitary Gland

A pituitary gland is present in all vertebrates. Its unique relationship to the nervous system, already discussed, makes it a central figure in the vertebrate endocrine system. The pituitary is actually a complex of glandular tissues. It consists of three principal subdivisions, usually referred to as the anterior, intermediate, and posterior lobes (Figure 12-5). On the basis of embryonic origin, the pituitary may more accurately be said to consist of two major anatomic divisions: (1) the adenohypophysis, derived from Rathke's pouch, an ectodermal invagination from the stomodeum; and (2) the neurohypophysis, derived from the infundibulum of the diencephalon of the embryonic brain (Figure 12-6). The adenohypophysial rudiment grows posteriorly from its origin along the floor of the brain until its posterior margin contacts the infundibulum. That portion of the rudiment which contacts the infundibulum gives rise to the intermediate lobe, or *pars intermedia,* of the pituitary, and the remainder of the rudiment forms the anterior lobe, or *pars distalis.* In addition, in most vertebrates lateral outgrowths from the body of the adenohypophysial rudiment grow upward and anteriorly around the stalk

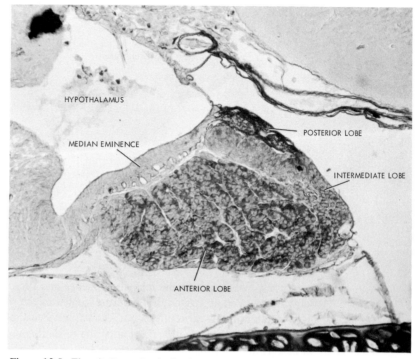

Figure 12-5. The pituitary gland of a frog tadpole. (From B. Frye, *Hormonal Control in Vertebrates.* New York: Macmillan, 1967.)

of the pituitary to form a minor but anatomically distinct component known as the *pars tuberalis.*

The neurohypophysis is derived primarily from the ependymal layer of the infundibular evagination, but by the time its development is complete it has become heavily invaded by capillaries and by the axonal endings of the neurosecretory cells of the hypothalamus. As has already been noted, the neurohypophysis becomes differentiated in most vertebrates into two subdivisions, the neural or posterior lobe of the pituitary (*pars nervosa*) and the median eminence. In those species in which the infundibulum evaginates far enough for the neural lobe to become dependent from the brain (as in man), the connecting portion is known as the pituitary stalk. The stalk is traversed by the nerve fibers and some of the blood vessels which enter the posterior lobe.

In addition to these more or less universal features, certain exceptional features of the pituitary of some groups of vertebrates should be noted:

1. In cyclostomes the neurohypophysis is neither distinctly evaginated from the floor of the brain nor clearly differentiated into a median eminence and a neural lobe of the pituitary. It consists of a thickened area in the floor of the diencephalon behind the optic chiasma. However, because of its position and because it receives neurosecretory fibers from the hypothalamus and is closely associated with the adenohypophysis, there is no doubt of the general homology of this region with the neurohypophysis of higher vertebrates.

2. In all fish classes above the cyclostomes, the neurohypophysis

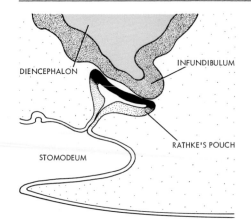

Figure 12-6. Embryonic origin of the pituitary. Neurohypophysial rudiment stippled; pars intermedia solid; pars distalis open. Later in development the epithelial stalk formed during evagination of Rathke's pouch from the stomodeum will disappear.

comprises, in addition to the median eminence and the posterior lobe, a large, thin-walled, nonglandular structure known as the saccus vasculosus. The function of this structure is not known, but because it is derived embryologically from the posterior portion of the infundibulum it may be regarded in part as homologous with the pars nervosa.

3. In elasmobranchs there extends downward from the main body of the pituitary gland a large lobe known as the ventral lobe. This lobe is formed from bilateral outgrowth of the adenohypophysial rudiment, and it may be homologous to the pars tuberalis. The ventral lobe secretes gonadotropic hormones, and so is functionally equivalent to the gonadotropin-secreting cells of the pars distalis of other vertebrates. The significance of the anatomical separation of this tissue from the main body of the pituitary in elasmobranchs is not known.

4. In birds and a few species of mammals (whales, elephants) the intermediate lobe of the pituitary is absent. In these forms the posterior margin of the adenohypophysial rudiment fails to make intimate contact with the infundibulum during development, and a layer of connective tissue usually forms between the pars nervosa and the pars distalis. In amphibians, formation of the pars intermedia from the posterior margin of the adenohypophysial rudiment has been shown to result from an inductive interaction with the infundibulum, so we assume that the absence of this lobe in birds and some mammals is related to the failure of contact between these two rudiments during development.

Pars distalis. Six hormones have so far been isolated from the pars distalis of mammals. On the basis of the biological activities of pituitary extracts and the consequences of hypophysectomy, the same six hormones seem to be present in the anterior pituitary of all classes of vertebrates. But the actual chemical identities and homologies of these hormones cannot be claimed until the molecules have been completely purified and their amino acid sequences compared.

Four of the six anterior pituitary hormones are primarily concerned with the regulation of other endocrine glands through third-order neuroendocrine circuits. These include a thyroid-stimulating hormone (TSH or thyrotropin), an adrenocortical-stimulating hormone (ACTH or corticotropin), and two gonadotropins, the follicle-stimulating hormone (FSH) and the luteinizing hormone (LH, also called interstitial cell-stimulating hormone or ICSH). Each of these hormones is highly specific for its effect upon the corresponding target gland, where the overall effect is to stimulate secretion of the target gland hormones. This includes not only a stimulation of the discharge of the target gland hormone, but stimulation of the entire functional apparatus of the gland cells in such a way as to support continued or increasing rates of hormone secretion. Morphologically, strong stimulation by trophic hormones is expressed as enlargement of the target glands. Hypophysectomy, conversely, results in deterioration of the intracellular secretory apparatus and atrophy of the target glands. The target gland hormones in turn may suppress the secretion of the corresponding trophic hormones by the pituitary. Administration of an excess of any given target gland hormone suppresses the pituitary cell type responsible for secreting the corresponding trophic hormone, and elimination of the target gland hormone (as by surgical removal of the thyroid, adrenals, or gonads) results in enlargement and proliferation of the corresponding pituitary cell. Although this negative feedback relationship is a very important factor in the regulation of the functional state of the endocrine system, it can be superseded by neurosecretory control from the hypothalamus in response to appropriate afferent input.

The remaining two hormones of the anterior pituitary are prolactin and somatotropin. Prolactin (mammotropic hormone; luteotropic hormone or LTH) has a remarkable spectrum of effects throughout the vertebrates. In mammals it promotes milk secretion by the mammary glands and also stimulates lipid synthesis in adipose tissue. In a few species of mammals prolactin stimulates the secretion of steroid hormones by the corpus luteum of the ovary, and it is for this reason that it has been called luteotropic hormone and is sometimes regarded as a third gonadotropin. Prolactin stimulates lipid synthesis in certain birds and it may be involved in regulating premigratory fattening of migratory birds. In columbid birds it stimulates the secretion of epithelial "milk" by the crop glands, and in certain other birds it stimulates brooding and the formation of the brood patch (a highly vascularized, de-feathered area of the skin used in incubating the eggs). In reptiles and in larval amphibians prolactin promotes growth and regeneration. In newts it stimulates the so-called water-drive response, a behavioral response involved in the transformation of the terrestrial "red eft" stage to the aquatic adult state of the life cycle. Finally, in teleosts prolactin has a role in osmoregulation, and in one species, the discus fish, stimulates the proliferation of the epidermal discus gland upon which the young feed. Even from this incomplete list (over forty effects of prolactin can be tabulated among the vertebrates) it is obvious that many seemingly unrelated actions of this hormone have evolved.

The most dramatic effect of somatotropin is, as the alternative name, growth hormone, suggests, to promote growth. This effect is best demonstrated in mammals. In the absence of this hormone, dwarfism results, and with an excess, as may occur with certain types of pituitary tumors, either giantism or acromegaly results. If the excess occurs in a growing individual, nearly proportionate acceleration of bodily growth results, and the condition is known as giantism. In the adult in which growth has ceased normally, the response to excess STH is uneven; joints enlarge, bones grow in width but not length, the jaw, nose, ears, and viscera enlarge, and the resulting distorted condition is known as acromegaly. The anterior pituitary produces a growth-promoting hormone in other vertebrates, but whether this is always a molecule homologous with the mammalian growth hormone is not known. As was mentioned before, prolactin may be an important growth hormone in some lower vertebrates. Somatotropin also has important metabolic effects, and these occur in adult as well as growing individuals. It promotes the release of fat from adipose tissue and at the same time interferes with the utilization of glucose and stimulates protein synthesis. Through these effects STH interacts in a complementary way with insulin to regulate the balanced use of foodstuffs. Somatotropin secretion in the adult is promoted by the same circumstances (notably, a fall in blood glucose) which cause a decline in insulin secretion.

Pars intermedia.   The intermediate lobe of the pituitary secretes a hormone known as intermedin, or melanophore-stimulating hormone (MSH). This is a peptide hormone, generally consisting of nineteen amino acids, but with some variation in exact structure among the various species in which it has been chemically identified. In the poikilotherms, MSH has an important function in environmental adaptation by regulating physiological color change in response to the degree of lightness or darkness of the background. The primary target of MSH is the melanophore, a black pigment-containing cell in the skin. Intermedin stimulates darkening of the skin by causing dispersal of the melanin pigment granules into the arms of these highly branched cells. In the absence of intermedin the pigment becomes tightly clumped in the center of the cell, and the animal becomes lighter. The melanophore response to MSH is relatively slow, requiring several minutes, and occurs more or less uniformly throughout the skin. The very rapid and mosaic patterns of color change which some fish and reptiles exhibit are controlled by direct innervation of the pigment cells.

Pigmentation of the skin of birds and mammals is entirely structural, resulting from the deposition of pigment in the skin, feathers, or hair by pigment-secreting melanocytes and to the physical defraction of light by feathers or hair. Thus, rapid physiological color change cannot occur. MSH probably affects the degree of pigmentation of the skin of mammals by affecting the amount of pigment produced by the melanocytes. There is some evidence that the hormone in this way is involved in the seasonal color change which may occur during spring and fall moulting. Birds do not have MSH—we have already noted the absence of the pars intermedia in this group—but the thyroid and sex hormones have been shown to effect the pigmentation of the feathers.

Pars nervosa.   As has been indicated, the hormones of the posterior lobe of the pituitary are actually neurosecretory products that originate in the supra-optic and paraventricular nuclei of the hypothalamus or in lower vertebrates, the equivalent of these nuclei. The hormones of the posterior

1. LYSINE VASOPRESSIN (SUINA)

CyS—Tyr —Phe — Glu(NH$_2$)—Asp(NH$_2$)—CyS—Pro—Lys—Gly(NH$_2$)

2. ARGININE VASOPRESSIN (ALL MAMMALS)

CyS—Tyr —Phe — Glu(NH$_2$) — Asp(NH$_2$)—CyS—Pro—Arg—Gly(NH$_2$)

3. ARGININE VASOTOCIN (ALL VERTEBRATES EXCEPT MAMMALS)

CyS—Tyr —Ileu — Glu(NH$_2$) — Asp(NH$_2$)—CyS—Pro—Arg—Gly(NH$_2$)

4. OXYTOCIN (LUNGFISH AND ALL TETRAPODS)

CyS—Tyr — Ileu — Glu(NH$_2$) — Asp(NH$_2$)—CyS—Pro— Leu—Gly(NH$_2$)

5. TELEOST OXYTOCIN-LIKE PRINCIPLE

CyS— Tyr —Ileu — Ser — Asp(NH$_2$) — CyS — Pro —Ileu —Gly(NH$_2$)

Figure 12-7. Posterior pituitary hormones of various vertebrates.

pituitary are nonapeptides (i.e., they consist of nine amino acids).†

The posterior pituitary hormones that have been extracted from among the various classes of vertebrates can be arranged into a phyletic series of closely related peptides (Figure 12-7). These all appear to have evolved from a single ancestral molecule, possibly arginine vasotocin (since it is found in all vertebrates from the cyclostomes up) by substitutions of different amino acids at one or more positions. The significance of this evolutionary series is not completely known because the functions of the molecules in the lower vertebrates, and therefore the selective pressures that may have directed their evolution, are largely unknown. The close anatomical and vascular association of the pars nervosa with the pars distalis in fish suggests that the original function of the posterior lobe peptides may have been the regulation of the pars distalis. Subsequently this function may have been given over completely to the median eminence, whereas the pars nervosa and its hormones evolved in the direction of independent effects upon peripheral tissues. Ascending the vertebrate line, the first *known* case of a physiological function of the pars nervosa independent of the pars distalis is seen in the amphibians, and it may be significant that this is also the class in which clear anatomical and vascular independence of the pars nervosa from the pars distalis is first seen.

In mammals the two important posterior pituitary hormones are oxytocin and vasopressin (arginine vasopressin in most mammals, but both arginine and lysine vasopressin in the Suina; so far as is known arginine and lysine

†Because two of the amino acids are cysteine molecules that are joined in a disulfide bond to form a single molecule of cystine, the posterior lobe hormones have often been regarded as octapeptides, which consist of eight amino acids.

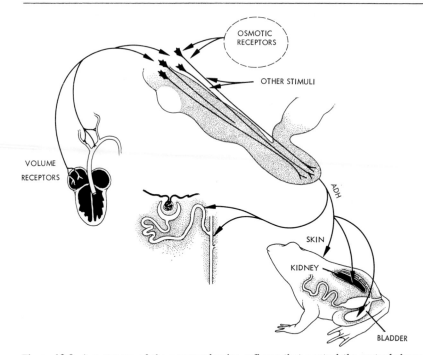

Figure 12-8. A summary of the neuroendocrine reflexes that control the water-balance response. This figure depicts the amphibian response mechanism, which differs from that of mammals in the absence of a loop of Henle and in the effects of ADH on the skin and bladder (see the text). (From B. Frye, *Hormonal Control in Vertebrates.* New York: Macmillan, 1967.)

vasopressin are functionally equivalent), which have the following major functions: oxytocin increases the intensity of contraction of the myometrium of the uterus and thus promotes labor. Exactly how oxytocin secretion is stimulated at the time of labor is unknown, however, so this neuroendocrine reflex remains to be completely described. Oxytocin also stimulates the ejection of milk from the lactating mammary gland by stimulating the contraction of smooth muscle fibers around the secretory alveoli. This reflex is initiated by stimulation of the nipples and, in the case of humans, by the sound or sight of the crying infant.

Vasopressin promotes the reabsorption of water from the forming urine in the kidneys, and is thus aptly called the *antidiuretic hormone.* The effect of vasopressin is to increase the permeability of the renal collecting ducts to water so that water is withdrawn from the urine by osmosis as the urine passes through the hyperosmotic medullary zone of the collecting ducts (see Chapter 9). In the absence of vasopressin these ducts are relatively impermeable to water so the urine passes through them unaltered and the surplus water is voided. The secretion of vasopressin is stimulated by either a drop in blood volume or by a rise in the concentration of solutes in the blood, either of which can reflect dehydration and appropriately activate this neurosecretory reflex which promotes water conservation (Figure 12-8). Historically, the first effect of vasopressin to be discovered was that it elevates blood pressure, and for this reason the name vasopressin was given to the hormone.

We now know that vasopressin has little effect on the blood pressure except when administered in abnormally large doses, and it is believed that anti-diuresis is the major physiological function of the hormone.

In birds, reptiles, and amphibians, vasotocin is the antidiuretic hormone. In amphibians, in addition to reducing the rate of urine excretion in the kidney, vasotocin elicits two other responses that are related to the mainte-nance of water balance: (1) it makes the wall of the bladder permeable to water so that the very dilute urine stored here can be redrawn osmotically into the body fluids, and (2) it increases the permeability of the skin to liquid water so that any available moisture is rapidly absorbed (again osmot-ically) into the body. In birds vasotocin has an additional role in reproduc-tion. It stimulates contraction of the muscles of the "uterus," causing egg expulsion. Vasotocin is present in the pituitaries of fish but, as mentioned before, its function in these classes is unknown. If vasotocin is injected into mammals it causes both oxytocic and antidiuretic effects. The evolutionary "replacement" of vasotocin by vasopressin in mammals would appear to have been favored because it achieved a more distinct separation between oxytocic and antidiuretic functions than had previously existed.

The Thyroid Gland

In all vertebrates the thyroid originates as an outgrowth from the floor of the pharynx at the level of the first and second gill pouches (Figure 12-9). The position and gross form of the gland in adult animals vary considerably. Generally the thyroid is located posterior to the pharyngeal area, adjacent to the carotid arteries or their major branches. Cyclostomes and most teleost

Figure 12-9. Embryonic origin of the thyroid and other pharyngeal derivatives. (After A. Gorbman and H. Bern, *Textbook of Comparative Endocrinology*. New York: Wiley, 1962.)

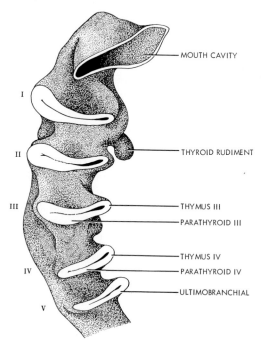

fish are exceptional in that the thyroid, being unencapsulated by connective tissue, tends to subdivide into tissue fragments which become scattered widely through the central pharyngeal region of the animal. In all other vertebrates including parrot fish and elasmobranchs, however, the thyroid consists of either a single median lobe or paired lobes located anterior to the heart.

The position and form of the thyroid are apparently without particular functional significance since thyroid tissue transplanted to other sites in the body functions normally and regulates the physiology of thyroidectomized animals perfectly well so long as the transplants have a good blood supply. The anatomical location of the thyroid is better explained by its apparent homology with the endostyle of protochordates. This structure, an exocrine mucous gland running as a groove along the floor of the pharynx in animals such as *Amphioxus* and *Ciona,* contains groups of cells that bind large quantities of iodine—a characteristic property of the thyroid—and also synthesize certain iodine-rich compounds which are found in the thyroid. Apparently in these protochordates iodine-rich substances are secreted into the endostylar groove where they are swept into the mucosal food stream and on into the gut, from which they are absorbed into the circulation. Whether the iodinated compounds secreted by the endostyle have any biological function in the protochordates is unknown. Possibly the significance of the thyroid-like activities of the endostyle is in the iodine-trapping and conserving mechanism, and the hormonal activities of the products may be an acquisition within the vertebrates. The homology of the thyroid gland with the iodine-accumulating cells of the endostyle is strongly supported by the developmental origin of the thyroid in cyclostomes. In the ammocoetes, the larval stage of lampreys, there lies in the floor of the pharynx an endostyle (or subpharyngeal gland) equivalent to that of protochordates, though more complex. Like the protochordate endostyle, certain nonglandular cells in this organ accumulate iodine and synthesize "thyroid" compounds. At the time of metamorphosis into the adult lamprey, the mucus-secreting portion of the endostyle degenerates, but the iodine-accumulating cells become transformed into typical vertebrate thyroid tissue.

The microscopic anatomy of the thyroid gland is remarkably similar in all vertebrates: its cells are arranged into hollow vesicles known as follicles, the cavities of which, in most vertebrates, are filled with a viscous secretion known as colloid (Figure 12-10). An exception is the hagfish. The follicular organization of the thyroid is functionally related to the storage of iodinated compounds and to certain aspects of synthesis and secretion of hormones. The colloid consists of a semi-gel, mainly of the protein, thyroglobulin. The latter, upon hydrolysis, yields a mixture of amino acids which includes particularly large proportions of iodinated amino acids—iodotyrosines which are precursors of the thyroid hormones, and iodothyronines, including thyroxine, which are the hormonally active substances (Figure 12-11).

The primary selective force in the evolution of a follicular organization of thyroid cells may have been the relative scarcity of iodine in some environ-

Figure 12-10 (opposite). Thyroid follicles. (From B. Frye, *Hormonal Control in Vertebrates.* New York: Macmillan, 1967.)

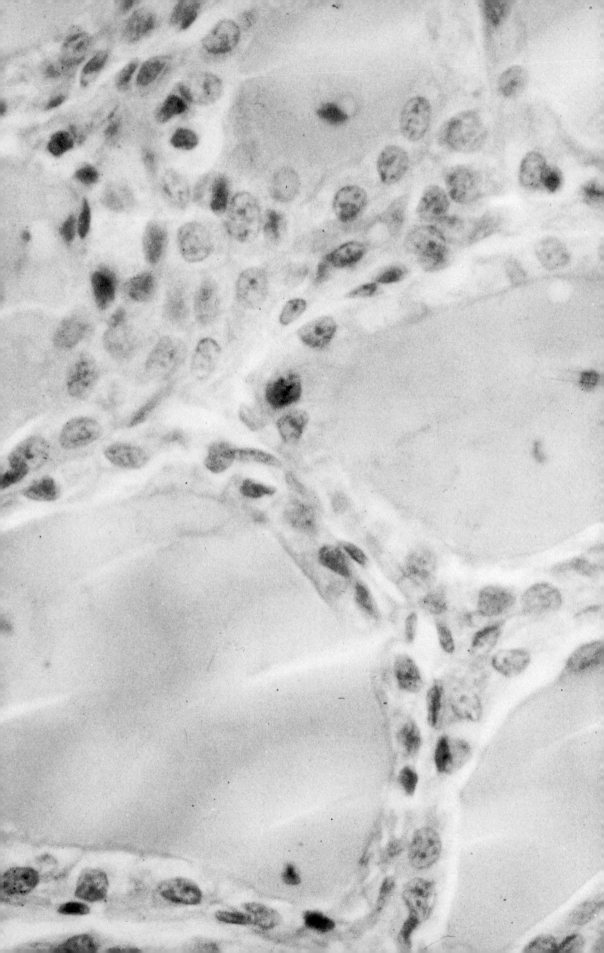

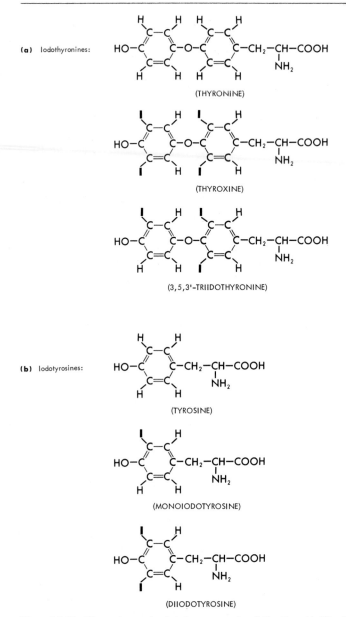

Figure 12-11. Thyroxine and related compounds of the thyroid. The iodothyronines, thyroxine and 3,5,3'-triiodothyronine, are the major hormonally active substances. Monoiodotyrosine and diiodotyrosine function as precursors in the biosynthesis of thyroxine and triiodothyronine, and are not normally secreted by the gland. (From B. Frye, *Hormonal Control in Vertebrates*. New York: Macmillan, 1967.)

ments. This would place value upon an organization of cells in a gland which not only avidly accumulates iodine from the environment but also stores its essential hormonal products in a form readily accessible during periods of iodine shortage. Alternatively, one can argue that the follicular organization is one way whereby a gland already specialized for exocrine secretion can be "turned into" an endocrine gland. Thus, we have already seen that the endostyle of protochordates and ammocoetes synthesizes thyroid substances, but liberates these into the gut. In the vertebrate thyroid gland the products are likewise secreted in an exocrine manner, but into the blind cavities of the follicles, and are only secondarily reabsorbed from these cavities across the thyroid cells into the capillaries which surround each follicle. In a sense, then, exocrine secretory mechanisms pre-existing in the endostyle have been retained in the organization of the thyroid, and endocrine function has been acquired by adding additional steps by which the products can be transferred from the lumen of the gland into the circulation.

The synthesis and secretion of thyroid hormones involves several steps: (1) active uptake of inorganic iodide salts from the blood by the thyroid; (2) oxidation of the iodide to an active elemental form—possibly iodine itself; (3) synthesis of thyroglobulin and secretion of this protein into the follicle lumen; (4) combination of the active iodine with the tyrosine residues of thyroglobulin; (5) coupling of two molecules of iodotyrosine to form the various hormonally active iodothyronines shown in Figure 12-11; (6) hydrolysis of thyroglobulin by proteolytic enzymes to liberate its component amino acids, including the hormonally active amino acids. These then enter the blood stream, presumably by diffusion.

In a general way the size of the thyroid cells reflects the state of activity of the thyroid. In the inactive state the cells regress to a low squamous state, whereas in stimulated glands the cells enlarge to a cuboidal or columnar state. In warm-blooded animals the normal condition of the thyroid epithelium is cuboidal. However, under certain circumstances, such as dietary iodine deficiency, the cells and the entire gland may undergo enlargement to form a goiter. In cold-blooded vertebrates the thyroid generally is most highly developed during the warm seasons and regresses to a low squamous state during winter. However, both positive and negative correlations between thyroid activity and certain phases of the life cycle, such as migrations or reproduction, make the pattern of thyroidal activity more complex than mere seasonal waxing and waning.

The physiological effects of the thyroid hormones cannot be summarized accurately for the vertebrates as a group because the effects are so diverse. In birds and mammals, at least, three principal classes of effects are well established:

1. Effects on oxidative metabolism. In warm-blooded animals the thyroid hormone stimulates oxygen consumption and heat production in the tissues. The basal rate of metabolism may be elevated 50 or 100 percent over normal by injections of the thyroid hormones and falls as low as 40 percent below normal after thyroidectomy or thyroid inhibition. This effect has been shown to result from the action of the hormones upon the mitochondria, but there are several as yet unreconciled opinions as to the nature of this effect. Many functions have been shown to be dependent upon normal levels of thyroid hormone. A partial list includes nervous function, muscle contractility, reproduction, glandular secretion, and growth and development. It is possible that all these effects are consequences of the basic role of the thyroid hormones in supporting normal capabilities for energy metabolism. Most attempts to demonstrate an effect of the thyroid hormones upon

energy metabolism in cold-blooded vertebrates have failed, although there are sporadic claims of stimulation of oxygen consumption in fish, amphibians, and reptiles. It must be remembered that cold-blooded animals do not exhibit a "basal" rate of metabolism and do not liberate a surplus of metabolic energy as heat. Possibly in these organisms, therefore, hormonal effects on energy production can be demonstrated only under test conditions which allow the energy produced to be utilized in various forms of metabolic work, such as movement, growth, or synthesis. If this is so, then failure to demonstrate consistently an effect of thyroid hormones on mitochondrial energy metabolism in cold-blooded vertebrates may be due to inadequate experimental designs rather than to a real lack of this effect.

2. Effects on growth and development. In birds and mammals normal development is dependent upon the thyroid hormones. In the absence of these hormones growth is drastically retarded, and maturation of the skeletal and nervous systems is particularly delayed. The result is a condition of infantile physiognomy and mental retardation known as *cretinism*. Severe, untreated human cretins may reach an age of fifteen or twenty years but a stage of physical and mental development equivalent only to an infant of one or two years. Although not many reptiles have been studied, their development seems to depend similarly on the thyroid. In fish, a role of the thyroid in supporting growth has been reported for several species, but the failure to demonstrate such a role has been reported even more often.

The most dramatic effect of thyroid hormones upon vertebrate development is the effect upon amphibian metamorphosis. Precocious metamorphosis of amphibian larvae can be induced by administering the thyroid hormones, and metamorphosis can be altogether prevented by thyroidectomy. This key control mechanism over metamorphosis is activated by the maturation of hypothalamic neurosecretory centers which regulate the secretion of TSH. The thyroid hormones act upon the larval tissues directly to activate metamorphic changes. A unified, synchronous pattern of metamorphosis of the whole animal is brought about by the fact that the level of circulating thyroid hormone rises progressively during metamorphosis, and the sensitive tissues each have different inherent sensitivities and rates of response to the hormone.

3. Effects on the integument. The thyroid hormones are necessary for normal skin proliferation and pigmentation in all vertebrates. In birds and mammals hair or feather growth is inhibited by a deficiency of thyroid hormone, and melanin pigment deposition is reduced. The skin becomes thinner, and normal moulting is interferred with. Moulting is also blocked by thyroid deficiency in amphibians and reptiles. In fish thyroid hormone promotes the thickening of the epidermis and the deposition of silvery guanine pigments in the skin. The physiological significance of these integumentary effects is not clear in all cases, but because they are universally observed they must be recognized as one of the more generalized classes of effects of the thyroid hormone.

In recent years the thyroid gland of mammals has been shown to secrete a hormone concerned with the regulation of calcium, called calcitonin (or thyrocalcitonin). This hormone suppresses blood calcium when calcium rises above the normal level and is therefore complementary to the action of para-thyroid hormone.

The Adrenal
Glands

The adrenals are bilaterally paired glands located along the dorsal wall of the abdominal cavity, generally in the vicinity of the kidneys. The name adrenal (or suprarenal as the glands are called in man) was given to these organs because of their location in mammals—on or immediately adjacent to the anterior surfaces of the kidneys. Considerable variation in the exact distribution and organization of the adrenals is found among the various classes of vertebrates but homologous tissues are found in all classes.

The adrenals consist of two distinct glandular components, one secreting the catecholamines adrenalin and noradrenalin, and one secreting steroid hormones. The catecholamine-secreting tissue stains avidly with chromium salts and is therefore usually referred to as the chromaffin tissue. The steroid-secreting component is usually called the interrenal tissue, or in mammals, the adrenal cortex. As the latter name implies, in mammals the chromaffin and interrenal tissues are organized into a histologically double-layered gland in which the chromaffin tissue constitutes an inner medulla in each adrenal and the interrenal tissue forms an outer cortex around this (Figure 12-12). Below the mammals the interrenal and chromaffin tissues tend to be intermingled rather than organized into distinct cortex and medulla, and if one looks at the entire series of vertebrate classes an interesting trend in the degree of intermingling is seen (Figure 12-12).

In cyclostomes the interrenal tissue has not been positively identified, but small clusters of cells which are believed to be the interrenal tissue are scattered along the cardinal veins in the vicinity of the pronephros. Chromaffin cells are scattered in small clusters through the same area but are not actually in association with the interrenal cell clusters. In teleosts the interrenal tissue is located mostly within the pronephros either as scattered islets of tissue within the kidney or, more usually, as a band of tissue surrounding the cardinal veins and their branches. The chromaffin cells are to some extent intermixed with the interrenal tissue, especially in the walls of the cardinal veins. In the elasmobranchs the interrenal tissue is organized into morphologically distinct glands along the inner margins of the kidneys, and the chromaffin tissue is completely separate, consisting of segmentally distributed clusters of cells anterior to the kidneys. In amphibians and reptiles the interrenals are embedded within or closely adherent to the ventral surfaces of the kidneys, and the chromaffin tissue is intermingled as strands and islets of cells among the interrenal cells. Lizards are exceptional in that the chromaffin tissue tends to be concentrated in a mass upon one surface of the interrenals. In birds the adrenals are on the anterior surfaces of the kidneys, as in mammals, but the chromaffin tissue is completely intermixed with the interrenal tissue. Finally, although direct intermixing of interrenal and chromaffin cells might appear to have been reduced by the segregation of these cells into separate layers in mammals, vascular interconnection has been perfected in that the medulla receives a large part of its blood supply from the blood sinusoids which drain the cortex.

The significance of the trend toward increasing association of the chromaffin and interrenal tissues is not clear. There is some evidence that adrenal steroids may influence the synthesis and secretion of adrenalin. Adrenalin is formed from noradrenalin by the addition of a methyl group through the catalytic influence of an enzyme known as phenylethanolamine-N-methyl transferase, and certain adrenal steroids increase the activity of this enzyme. In those vertebrates in which the association of the chromaffin and interrenal tissues is slight, the predominant chromaffin-cell hormone is noradrenalin, whereas animals with closer association between the two tissues tend to secrete higher proportions of adrenalin. For example, in elasmobranchs adrenalin constitutes only about 25 percent of the total chromaffin tissue hormones, but in amphibians, reptiles, birds and mammals adrenalin usually amounts to 50 to 75 percent of the total. Is it possible that the association of interrenal tissue with chromaffin tissue provides a means of controlling the amount of adrenalin that can be secreted? It may be significant that both adrenalin and certain adrenal steroids (the glucocorticoids) have an

Figure 12-12. The adrenals, interrenals, and chromaffin tissue of several vertebrates. Chromaffin tissue or adrenal medulla, black; interrenal or adrenal cortex, white.

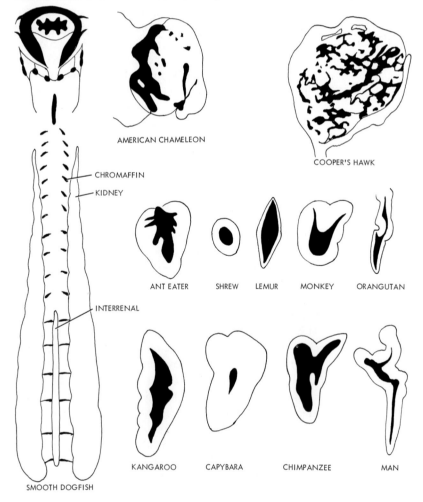

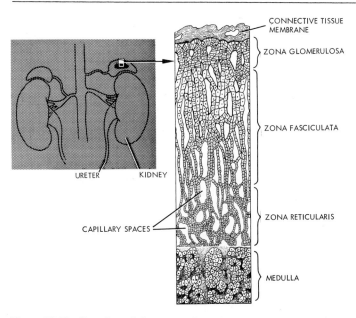

Figure 12-13. Zonation of the mammalian adrenal gland. (From B. Frye, *Hormonal Control in Vertebrates*. New York: Macmillan, 1967.)

important function in stress or emergency reactions. The steroid effect on adrenalin synthesis could be a significant mechanism whereby the functional "tone" of the interrenal could promote a complementary tone in the chromaffin tissue.

The cells of the interrenal tissue are typically arranged in long cords or sheets, interspersed between capillaries or blood sinusoids. In mammals, but not other vertebrates, these cords are regularly oriented radially to the center of the gland and differentiated into three histologically distinct zones. These are an outer *zona glomerulosa,* a central *zona fasciculata,* and an inner *zona reticularis* (Figure 12-13). Formerly it was believed that these zones represented successive stages in the life history of adrenocortical cells, new cells being formed in the glomerulosa, then migrating inward and reaching full functional differentiation in the fasciculata, and finally becoming senile and dying in the reticularis. This view was based upon a somewhat biased interpretation of the appearance of the cells of the respective zones: cell divisions are observed to be more abundant in the glomerulosa than in the inner zones; the cells of the fasciculata are large and filled with lipid droplets containing steroid hormones and cholesterol; and the cells of the reticularis are small, sometimes pigmented, and darkly staining and they were interpreted as moribund in appearance. The cell-migration theory of zonation has now been discredited by labeling cells in the glomerulosa with radioactive isotopes and demonstrating that these labeled cells do not migrate through the gland as formerly supposed. Biochemical analysis of the different zones has now shown that the zonation reflects a functional subdivision of the adrenal cortex, each zone being specialized for the production of particular kinds of steroid hormones. Although the functional meaning of the zonal organization is clear, the evolutionary significance is not. The inter-

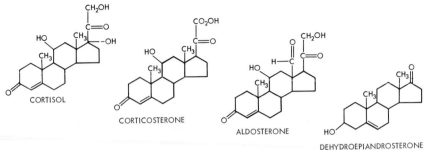

Figure 12-14. Some hormones of the adrenal cortex. Cortisol and corticosterone are the major glucocorticoids. Aldosterone is the major mineralocorticoid. Dehydroepiandrosterone is an example of an adrenal androgen.

renals of other vertebrates lack the zonal organization but secrete much the same steroids as the mammalian adrenal. It would be valuable to know if the individual interrenal cords or sheets of lower vertebrates are functionally differentiated into different zones that are not reflected as morphological zones because of the irregular orientation of the cords.

Extracts of the adrenal cortex or interrenal yield thirty or more steroids, but most of these are intermediates in the process of biosynthesis of the hormones and are not secreted. The principal hormonally active steroids of the adrenal are shown in Figure 12-14. These fall into three major functional classes: steroids affecting primarily the metabolism of sodium and potassium, the *mineralocorticoids;* steroids affecting primarily the metabolism of carbohydrates and proteins and stress responses, the *glucocorticoids;* and *androgens,* having activities similar to the male sex hormone. Because of the great similarity in the structure of the various adrenal steroids there is some overlap in activity, and when a steroid is classified as a mineralocorticoid or glucocorticoid, this indicates its prevalent but not exclusive effects. In the mammalian adrenal, mineralocorticoids—principally aldosterone—are produced in the zona glomerulosa; glucocorticoids—mainly corticosterone and cortisol—originate primarily in the fasciculata; and androgens are secreted in the reticularis.

The functions of the adrenal cortex are best understood in mammals, where, as we have noted, three classes of activities can be distinguished.

Mineral metabolism. Adrenalectomy leads to a rapid loss of sodium chloride from the extracellular fluid into the urine and intracellular fluid. Associated with this loss of solute, water is lost osmotically, leading to a reduction in the extracellular fluid, including blood volume (see Chapter 9). This usually culminates in a precipitous drop in blood pressure, shock, and death. The primary disturbance in salt balance occurs in the kidneys, where the ability to reabsorb sodium from the glomerular filtrate is reduced, and in the tissues at large, where the ability of the cell membrane to regulate the distribution of ions is disturbed. Substitution of saline for drinking water will prevent the collapse caused by adrenalectomy, by compensating for the excessive loss of salt in the urine. Mineralocorticoid steroids, particularly aldosterone, will likewise prevent adrenalectomy collapse by restoring the normal capability for ion regulation. The kidney and adrenal constitute a vital control mechanism for the regulation of salt balance and blood pressure. Low dietary salt intake (or excessive salt loss in sweat or urine) results in a decline in blood volume and pressure.† This is sensed by special cells in the juxtaglomerular apparatus of the kidney, which respond by secreting the enzyme renin. Renin in turn catalyzes the conversion of angiotensinogen, an inactive protein in the blood, into angiotensin. Angiotensin stimulates the secretion of aldosterone by the zona glomerulosa, thus promoting an increase in the rate of sodium reabsorption by the kidney tubules. Excessive sodium intake, conversely, suppresses renin and aldosterone secretion and thereby allows a greater rate of sodium excretion by the kidney. Adrenocorticotropin, which has profound effects upon the function of the inner zones of the adrenal cortex, has relatively little effect upon the zona glomerulosa.

Organic metabolism. Adrenalectomy results in a fall in blood glucose concentrations and liver and muscle glycogen content. All three of these changes are a reflection of the impairment of the ability of the liver to synthesize glucose from noncarbohydrate resources, particularly protein. As might be expected, therefore, this effect of the adrenal is not too apparent when an animal is on a high carbohydrate diet but becomes very important during fasting or when the carbohydrate intake is very low. Under the latter circumstances the liver readily synthesizes the necessary carbohydrate so long as the adrenal cortex is functional. But adrenalectomized animals (given saline to avoid the complications of salt imbalance) do not tolerate fasting and eventually die of hypoglycemic (low blood glucose) convulsions. Hypoglycemia can activate the secretion of glucocorticoids via the hypothalamic-pituitary-neurosecretory circuit, as can other "stressful" stimuli which might be associated with fasting or starvation.

Sex hormone activities. The adrenal androgens are similar in their effects to the principal male sex hormone, testosterone. They tend to be weaker in their masculinizing actions, however, and in normal concentrations they act primarily to promote protein synthesis and growth. This effect is important for the normal growth and muscular development of both males and females. The more powerful anabolic and masculinizing effects of testosterone are in part responsible for the greater size and muscular strength of the males of some species. Occasionally tumors of the zona reticularis occur which secrete excessive amounts of androgen and result in sexual precocity or masculinization of children or women.

The adrenal steroids have other effects which are poorly understood and hard to classify. Glucocorticoids affect the tone of blood vessels, especially the smaller arterioles and capillaries. Even minor injuries to an adrenalectomized animal may cause circulatory "collapse" characterized by pooling of blood in the capillaries and leakage of plasma into the interstitial space. This may lead to shock and death. Muscle work capacity, including that of the

†Sodium is the major solute of the extracellular fluid and therefore through its osmotic effect has a large part to play in regulating the volume of the extracellular fluid, including blood.

heart, is greatly reduced by adrenalectomy. This is probably related to poor circulation as well as to disturbances in salt balance and organic metabolism. Perhaps the least well understood, yet one of the most important, functions of the adrenal cortex is its role in stress tolerance. Two basic facts are clearly established: (1) after adrenalectomy an animal is no longer able to tolerate numerous kinds of stresses, such as injury, burns, infections, fasting, toxic substances, heat, or cold; (2) the adrenals of an intact animal undergo dramatic enlargement and increase in hormone production in stressful situations. These two observations indicate that the adrenal has a vital role in the adjustment of animals to stressful conditions (which must be an almost routine part of life of wild animals), yet this role cannot be satisfactorily explained.

The chromaffin tissue or adrenal medulla is not essential for life, and no important deficiency symptoms have been attributed to its removal. Yet the chromaffin cell hormones have important effects upon a number of physiological processes, particularly those involved in the adaptation of animals to sudden emergencies.

The Parathyroid
Glands

Parathyroid glands are found in all classes of vertebrates above fish. The name parathyroid was invented for the glands in mammals, in which they usually lie near or embedded within the thyroids. Generally, however, the name is a misnomer, for in most vertebrates the parathyroids do not have a particularly close or significant association with the thyroid. Commonly they are located along the jugular veins or in the arches of the carotid and systemic arteries.

The parathyroids develop from the ventral corners of the gill pouches (Figure 12-9). In those species in which two pairs are present, as in the great majority of tetrapods, they usually originate from pouches III and IV. However, all five pairs of gill pouches are capable of giving rise to seemingly homologous tissue, and by this means accessory parathyroids up to five pairs can arise. A single pair of parathyroids is commonly found in lizards, but within this group some species have the usual two pairs, and those which have only one possess a transitory rudiment of the second pair during embryonic development. Most mammals have two pairs, but several species of rodents, including the common laboratory rat, have only a single pair.

Since parathyroids are lacking in fish and do not appear in amphibians until the time of gill regression at metamorphosis, it is interesting to speculate on the possible significance of this seemingly reciprocal relationship between the presence of gills and the presence of parathyroids. Since both the gills and the parathyroids are involved in certain aspects of mineral metabolism, some functional equivalence may exist. One can ask whether, associated with the gill apparatus of fish, there might be scattered glandular cells as yet unidentified that are homologous to the parathyroids of tetrapods. During the course of evolution, when the gills were lost, such hypothetical parathyroid homologous cells might have become consolidated into discrete parathyroid glands. Some support for the hypothesis that fish may have parathyroid-like tissue can be inferred from the fact that some fish have been shown to respond to injections of mammalian parathyroid hormone. These responses are similar to the responses of mammals themselves (elevation of serum calcium, demineralization of bone, and accelera-tion of the rate of calcium turnover). It seems unlikely that a complex hormone response mechanism would evolve without the presence of the hormone molecule required to render the mechanism functionally complete and therefore adaptively significant. Test of this idea by ordinary morpholog-ical criteria is almost impossible, for parathyroid cells are notoriously indis-tinctive by morphological criteria. It is unlikely that individual scattered cells would even be recognized as gland cells. Consequently, a valid test of homology depends upon the demonstration of the secretion by such cells of a protein molecule homologous with the parathyroid hormone of tetrapods.

The function of the parathyroid gland is to regulate blood levels of calcium and phosphate. The blood levels of these minerals are the result of a dynamic equilibrium between the rates of entrance into the blood from the gut and from the dissolution of bone, and the rates of removal from blood by deposition in bone and by excretion. All of these processes go on more or less continuously, and it is the net balance between them that results in calcium and phosphate homeostasis. The role of the parathyroid can be sum-marized as follows. The parathyroid cells monitor the level of calcium in the blood. When this falls below normal, parathyroid hormone secretion is accel-erated and those mechanisms which raise blood calcium are activated. When the calcium level of the blood rises above the normal value, parathyroid hormone secretion slows, and the mechanisms for removal of calcium from blood become dominant. The central role of the parathyroid in this regula-tory process is dramatically illustrated by the rapid fall in plasma calcium concentration which occurs following parathyroidectomy (Figure 12-15).

The consequences of a fall in blood calcium level are drastic. Initially the symptoms are restlessness and hyperexcitability. This is followed by mild involuntary muscle twitches, which build in intensity and become generalized into convulsions. A parathyroidectomized animal may survive the first few attacks, which recur at intervals of a few hours or days, but eventually it

Figure 12-15. Fall in plasma calcium of the laboratory rat after parathyroidectomy. The time of parathyroidectomy is indicated by the arrow. (From B. Frye, *Hormonal Control in Vertebrates.* New York: Macmillan, 1967.)

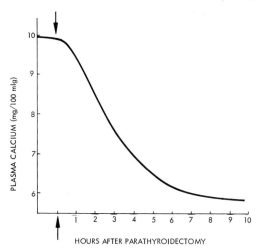

dies in severe muscular spasms and tetany which cause suffocation. The basis for these symptoms seems to be the dependence of both nerve and muscle on normal calcium levels to maintain normal permeability to certain ions, notably sodium and potassium which are essential to their excitable states and functions.

The major target of the parathyroid hormone, so far as precise homeostasis of calcium and phosphate are concerned, is bone. A certain proportion of bone mineral is continuously being dissolved and redeposited. Deposition of calcium and phosphate in bone seems to be a spontaneous crystallization of bone mineral (complex calcium phosphate salts) upon the collagenous framework of bone that has been laid down by osteoblasts. Since the spontaneous equilibrium between bone mineral calcium and plasma calcium is lower than the normal plasma level, this removal of calcium and phosphate from blood goes on continuously at normal blood concentrations of these minerals. But dissolution of bone also goes on continuously, through the activity of bone-degrading cells known as osteoclasts. The effect of parathyroid hormone is to increase the numbers and activity of these cells and thereby to control the rate of dissolution of bone. In addition to the effect on bone, parathyroid hormone has some effect in enhancing the absorption of calcium from the intestine and reducing the excretion of calcium in the kidneys.

The effect of parathyroid hormone upon the phosphate level of blood is the opposite of the effect on calcium: parathyroidectomy results in a rise of blood phosphate levels and reduces the rate of excretion of phosphate. The rise in blood phosphate is the result of the direct effect of parathyroid hormone upon the ability of kidney tubules to excrete the dietary excess of

Figure 12-16. Islet of Langerhans in the pancreas of a tadpole of the frog, *Rana pipiens.* (From B. Frye, *Hormonal Control in Vertebrates.* New York: Macmillan, 1967.)

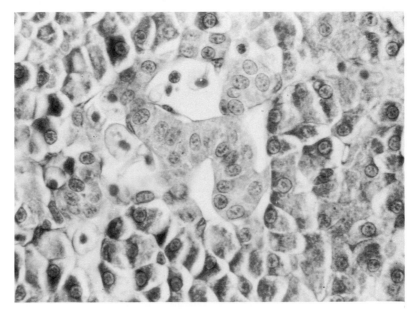

this ion. There is no evidence that the parathyroid gland responds to blood phosphate levels independently of calcium, so in a sense it is calcium that is primarily regulated by the parathyroid and phosphate is secondarily regulated.

Virtually all that is known about parathyroid function is based on work with mammals. A few studies with amphibians and birds suggest that the role of this gland as described for mammals is also applicable to other tetrapods.

The Pancreas   The pancreas lies in the mesenteries near the upper end of the small intestine. Its exact position and form are variable, but it is significant that it always lies in the hepatic portal drainage, between the origin of these vessels in the wall of the duodenum, stomach and spleen, and the liver. This anatomical feature means that a large portion of the absorbed foodstuffs as well as certain gastrointestinal hormones which influence the function of the pancreas pass directly from the gut to the pancreas. It also means that the hormones of the pancreas are delivered directly to the liver, which is a primary target tissue of the pancreatic hormones. Through the hepatic portal blood flow, the upper gut, pancreas, and liver are interwoven into a complex chemical control system concerned with the regulation of the digestion and assimilation of foodstuffs.

The pancreas is, of course, both an exocrine and an endocrine gland. The bulk of the organ consists of the microscopic exocrine acini and only about one percent of the pancreas is endocrine tissue. In most vertebrates this takes the form of microscopic clusters of cells, the islets of Langerhans, which are scattered more or less throughout the gland (Figure 12-16). The size of the individual islets ranges from as little as 20 microns to 500 microns or more in diameter, or from a half dozen to several hundred cells. In mammals, where the only reliable estimates have been made, the total number of islets ranges from several thousands to upward of a million or more, depending on the size and species of the animal. The number and size of the islets, as well as the overall volume of islet tissue, are subject to great variation depending on the overall hormonal balance of the animal and, in particular, on the amount of carbohydrates present in the diet. Any condition that tends to elevate the blood glucose levels above normal for extended periods may stimulate both an enlargement of the existing islets and a proliferation of new islets from the finer branches of the pancreatic duct system.

Certain exceptional features are seen in the organization of the endocrine pancreatic tissue in vertebrates below the amphibians. In teleost fish some species exhibit an aggregation of the bulk of the islet tissue into one or a few principal islets that are nearly or completely separate from the digestive portion of the pancreas. Among the Chondrichthyes, two different conditions are seen. The elasmobranchs have no true islets, but the smaller branches of the ducts of the pancreas are enveloped by a layer of cells which are believed to be homologous to the islet cells. In holocephalans, a condition intermediate between that in the elasmobranchs and typical islets is seen: the smaller branches of the ducts are enveloped by a layer of islet cells, but in places these appear to have "budded off" into large clusters of endocrine cells that retain their connections with the duct system. In this context it is relevant that in all vertebrates the islets originate by proliferation from the walls of the finer ducts. Finally, cyclostomes have no true pancreas at all, but clusters of cells have been described in the wall of the duodenum around the orifice of the bile duct that are believed to be homologous to the islets. A similar situation is seen in Amphioxus.

The islets of Langerhans secrete two hormones, insulin and glucagon. Insulin is present in all vertebrates, and even in the gastrointestinal tracts of certain protochordates and echinoderms. It is obviously a hormone of great antiquity. Glucagon, on the other hand, has been specifically identified only in reptiles, birds, and mammals, and the evidence for its presence in lower vertebrates is indirect, being based mainly upon the presumed homology of certain cells in the pancreas of lower vertebrates with the cells known to secrete glucagon in mammals. Both glucagon and insulin are protein hormones, but of unrelated amino acid sequence.

The functions of insulin are very complex. Its overall role is to regulate the utilization of foodstuffs. Insulin is specifically secreted in response to rising levels of glucose and certain amino acids in the blood. Insulin in turn promotes the removal of glucose and amino acids from the blood, primarily by regulating the storage of glucose as glycogen and fat, and the synthesis of proteins from amino acids. During periods when insulin secretion is low, as during fasting, or even the relatively brief postabsorptive intervals between meals, the ability of insulin target tissues to utilize glucose and amino acids is reduced. Moreover, compensating mechanisms are activated that result in accelerated release of fats, glucose, and amino acids into the blood by storage organs such as liver and adipose tissue. Thus, insulin plays a crucial role in the metabolic homeostasis of foodstuffs by the vertebrate animal.

The major target tissues of insulin are the liver, adipose tissue, and skeletal and cardiac muscle. In the liver insulin promotes the removal of glucose from the blood and its conversion to glycogen. This it accomplishes by activating certain enzymes (glucokinase and glycogen synthetase) which regulate the synthesis of glycogen from glucose. In adipose tissue and striated muscle the primary action of insulin is on the permeability of cell membranes to glucose. In the absence of insulin, permeability, and therefore the ability to utilize glucose from the blood, is reduced. In the presence of insulin glucose permeation of these tissues is accelerated, with the effect that the utilization of glucose in fat synthesis, glycogen synthesis, and oxidative metabolism is accelerated.

Superficially, the main action of insulin is often described as the regulation of blood glucose concentration. One of the more overt symptoms of insulin deficiency is abnormally high levels of blood glucose. However, the effects of insulin on blood glucose are secondary to the basic effects upon glucose metabolism. Hyperglycemia is one of the major symptoms of diabetes mellitus, the disease of insulin insufficiency, but numerous other disturbances in metabolism also occur.

The principal physiological target of glucagon is the liver, where the hormone promotes the activity of phosphorylase, an enzyme that controls the breakdown of glycogen to glucose and thereby stimulates glucose secretion by the liver. Thus, in some ways glucagon is the counterpart of insulin. It acts to maintain blood glucose homeostasis by promoting the release of glucose into the blood. Glucagon is secreted in response to low glucose levels in the portal circulation. The significance of this is that the hormone stimulates the return of stored glucose to the blood where it is available for use by the tissues.

Insulin and glucagon are secreted by separate cell types within the islets of Langerhans. Insulin is secreted by the so-called beta cell. The drug alloxan specifically destroys the beta cells of the pancreas, and this effect is invariably associated with the loss of insulin from the pancreas and the development of diabetes. Glucagon is believed to originate in the alpha cell, a small acidophilic cell usually located on the periphery of the islets, but proof of this is not complete. Glucagon-secreting alpha cells are not positively known to exist in cyclostomes, fish, or amphibians. However, most of these groups do contain cells which resemble the alpha cells of higher vertebrates, and homology together with functional equivalence is likely.

Other Endocrine Glands
The foregoing discussion has considered the major and best understood endocrine glands of vertebrates, except for the gonads which will be discussed in the following chapter. In addition to these a number of other glands and tissues are known or believed to have endocrine functions. For the most part they are either incompletely understood so far as their endocrine function is concerned, or their endocrine functions are secondary or subsidiary to other physiological roles.

Kidney. The kidneys (of mammals, at least) are the source of renin, which catalyzes the conversion of the blood-borne protein, angiotensinogen, into angiotensin. Angiotensin stimulates aldosterone secretion, and also elevates blood pressure by causing constriction of the arterioles in certain tissues, especially the kidney, and thus reduces the peripheral vascular volume. The kidneys may be the source of angiotensinogen, but this is uncertain. Thus, in a glandular as well as an effector role the kidneys are a central part of the endocrine mechanism regulating salt balance and blood pressure.

In addition to the renin-angiotensin system, the kidneys may also be the source of erythropoetin. Erythropoetin is a protein that is extractable from the blood and from the kidney; it stimulates the proliferation and release of erythrocytes into the blood stream. Blood levels of erythropoetin are elevated under conditions such as low atmospheric oxygen pressure or hemorrhage, in which an increase in the production of erythrocytes would be adaptively significant. The fact that the kidneys are important erythropoetic organs during development and in some lower vertebrates, gives some relevance to this otherwise seemingly exotic endocrine function that has been proposed for them.

Corpuscles of Stannius. The corpuscles of Stannius are glandular-looking bodies, several in number, which are embedded in the posterior part of the kidneys of teleosts. Strong evidence for an endocrine function is lacking, but two possibilities are supported to some extent: (1) they may secrete mineralocorticoids and thus may be functionally equivalent to the zona glomerulosa of the mammalian adrenal; (2) they may secrete a vasopressor substance reminiscent of the renin-angiotensin system of mammals.

Pineal. The pineal or epiphysis is an outgrowth of the roof of the diencephalon. Although both photoreceptor and endocrine functions have been proposed for many years on anatomical grounds these functions have only recently been well established. It now seems reasonably certain that a substance, melatonin (N-acetyl-5-methoxytryptamine), with antigonadal activity is secreted by the pineal. Destruction of the pineal in young animals results in precocious puberty; in adults it may advance the sexual cycle or cause constant estrus in females. Pineal extracts, on the other hand, cause suppression or regression of the gonads. The effect is believed to be exerted through suppression of the secretion of the pituitary gonadotropins. Physiologically the secretion of melatonin in adult animals is regulated by the photoperiod; in those species that have been studied, long photoperiods suppress melatonin secretion and promote reproductive development. Melatonin stimulates contraction of melanophores in amphibians, and the name of the hormone was based on this effect. Since the hormonal effects of the pineal are concerned with responses to light, the photoreceptor and glandular functions of the organ may be interrelated. The thick skull of mammals precludes photoreception by the pineal, and in this group the glandular pineal is innervated by branches of the optic nerve.

Thymus. The thymus arises as outgrowths from the branchial pouches, generally III and IV. In the adult it may persist as several pairs of lymphoid bodies in the branchial region (fish, lower tetrapods), or the rudiments may migrate posteriorly and fuse to form a single gland in the anterior thorax (mammals). The thymus is a major lymphatic organ and in addition to the production of lymphocytes it seems to produce a hormone that stimulates the formation of lymphocytes and triggers the capability of such cells to carry out immune responses. Removal of the thymus in young animals before immunological competence has differentiated results in a permanent reduction in the ability of the animals to form antibodies. Removal of the thymus once immunological competence has differentiated does not have this effect.

Digestive tract. The stomach and duodenum produce several hormones that are primarily functional in regulating the digestive process. The pyloric region of the stomach produces *gastrin,* which passes through the circulation to the fundus of the stomach where it stimulates the secretion of gastric juice. The duodenum produces several hormones that regulate the activities of the stomach, pancreas, and gall bladder. Generally speaking these hormones are released in response to the entrance of chyme from the stomach into the duodenum, and not necessarily to a specific component of the chyme. *Secretin* stimulates the release of pancreatic juice, causing a rise in the volume of the juice but has no effect upon the release of pancreatic enzymes. *Pancreozymin,* on the other hand, stimulates the release of pancreatic enzymes without affecting the volume of fluid secreted. *Cholecystokinin* stimulates emptying of the gall bladder. *Enterogastrone* suppresses the muscular activity and hydrochloric acid secretion of the stomach. Finally, the small intestine, including the duodenum, contains and presumably secretes glucagon, but the functional significance of this is not yet clear.

Ultimobranchial glands. The ultimobranchials are glandular masses of tissue that arise from the last pair of pharyngeal pouches. Because the cells are often arranged into thyroid-like follicles, a thyroid-like function was once speculated for this gland. However, attempts to demonstrate such a function using I^{131} have consistently failed. More recently the ultimobranchials have been recognized as the source of calcitonin. In fish and to some extent in tetrapods the ultimobranchials are distinct from other pharyngeal tissues, and extracts of these glands contain calcitonin. In mammals calcitonin is secreted by the thyroid; however, the hormone appears to be produced by so-called parafollicular or "light" cells of the thyroid rather than by the thyroid follicles. The parafollicular cells originate from the ultimobranchials, which fuse with the thyroid rudiment during development, and are thus homologous with the ultimobranchials of lower vertebrates.

The caudal neurosecretory system. This is a neurosecretory organ that is composed of neurosecretory neurons located in the caudal spinal cord of all classes of fish. In its simplest form it is a diffuse aggregation of neurosecretory cells, but in teleosts the glandular area is well defined and is associated with a neurohaemal organ, the *urophysis,* within which the secretory axons terminate. Removal of the gland and injection of extracts of the gland have yielded results suggesting that it functions in either osmoregulation, ion regulation, or blood pressure regulation. Since these functions are intimately interrelated all three could conceivably be affected through some urophysial effect upon any of the three. The anatomical location of the caudal neurosecretory system, draining its supposed hormone into the caudal vein and thence into the renal portal veins to the kidneys, suggests that the kidneys might be a principal target of the hormone. The kidney, of course, plays a key role in osmoregulation, ion regulation, and blood pressure regulation.

References for Chapter 12

Barrington, E. J. W., *An Introduction to General and Comparative Endocrinology.* Fair Lawn, New Jersey: Oxford University Press, 1963. A textbook with comparative emphasis.

——, *Hormones and Evolution.* London: English Universities Press, 1964. A collection of essays on selected topics. Elementary and largely speculative consideration of the origins of and functional role of hormones during evolution.

——, and C. B. Jorgesen (eds.), *Perspectives in Endocrinology.* New York: Academic Press, 1968. The best available book dealing with the comparative and evolutionary aspects of endocrinology. Deals with selected topics, including reproduction, migration, pituitary and hypothalamus, salt and water metabolism, and an excellent first chapter contains a synopsis of the main ideas in comparative evolutionary endocrinology.

Chester Jones, I., *The Adrenal Cortex.* New York: Cambridge University

Press, 1957. This is the only comparative treatment of the adrenal cortex available and, although somewhat dated, it is still excellent. Covers both morphological and functional aspects of the adrenal cortex.

von Euler, U. S., and H. Heller (eds.), *Comparative Endocrinology,* Vols. I and II. New York: Academic Press, 1963. The best relatively brief, advanced presentation of comparative endocrinology covering all major glands. Functional emphasis.

Frye, B. E., *Hormonal Control in Vertebrates.* New York: The Macmillan Co., 1967. An elementary synopsis of vertebrate endocrinology; functional emphasis.

Gorbman, A., and H. A. Bern, *A Textbook of Comparative Endocrinology.* New York: Wiley, 1962. This book has a strong comparative and morphological emphasis, but it is also strong on functional aspects. This is the best source of information on comparative endocrinology at the introductory level.

Harris, G. W., and B. T. Donovan, *The Pituitary Gland,* Vols. I-III. Berkeley: University of California Press, 1966. An advanced review of all three lobes of the pituitary. The comparative and evolutionary aspects are especially well covered. The book includes chapters on neurosecretion and the hypothalamic regulation of the pituitary.

Pincus, G., K. V. Thimann, and E. B. Astwood, *The Hormones,* Vols. I-V. New York: Academic Press, 1948-1964. An exhaustive series of volumes; a sourcebook of information on endocrine physiology. Generally little on morphological and evolutionary aspects.

Pitt Rivers, R., and W. R. Trotter (eds.), *The Thyroid Gland,* Vols. I and II. Washington: Butterworths, 1964. Advanced review of thyroidal endocrinology. Many chapters have a human and medical emphasis, but there are also good chapters with a comparative emphasis.

Scharrer, E., and B. Scharrer, *Neuroendocrinology.* New York: Columbia University Press, 1963. An outstanding introductory presentation. The strong comparative functional emphasis makes this almost an introductory text in comparative endocrinology, and one of the most readable and informative available.

Tepperman, J., *Metabolic and Endocrine Physiology.* Chicago: The Year Book Medical Publishers, 1962. This is a short premedical text. The presentation is almost entirely functional and mammalian, but it is listed here because it is extremely well written.

Turner, C. D., *General Endocrinology,* 4th ed. Philadelphia: W. B. Saunders, 1966. Basic endocrinology with a balanced presentation of function, structure, and comparative endocrinology. An unusual feature of this textbook is that each chapter has extensive references to the original research literature.

13
Reproduction

Introduction   Reproduction by vertebrates is exclusively sexual. Asexual modes of proliferation which are widely found in most phyla of invertebrate animals and in
plants are lacking. Sexual reproduction in vertebrates, as in all organisms,
consists fundamentally of genetic recombination through the cellular
processes of meiosis and fertilization (see Chapter 3). Accessory to these
basic cellular phenomena are a vast array of anatomical, physiological, and
behavioral adaptations that function to bring together the sperm and eggs for
fertilization and to support the development of the young. This spectrum of
adaptations concerned with reproduction is what we normally think of as
constituting the sexuality of organisms and, at the morphological level, as
comprising the reproductive system.

Most vertebrates are sexually dimorphic, individuals of a species being
distinctly differentiated into males and females capable of producing either
sperm or eggs respectively. As obvious as this statement may appear to be,
it is not the rule among living organisms as a whole. There are many more
groups of organisms which are hermaphroditic, that is, in which each individual is capable of producing both eggs and sperm (not necessarily at the same
time and usually not capable of self-insemination). Even in vertebrates some
degree of intersexuality or hermaphroditism is common, especially among
the lower groups.

Anatomy of the   The basic plan of organization of the reproductive tract of vertebrates is
Reproductive   shown in Figure 13-1. It consists of the gonads, or primary sex organs,
Tract   which produce the gametes and sex hormones, and the sex ducts and
accessory sex organs which convey the gametes or offspring to the outside.
Species that practice internal fertilization may have elaborate external
genitalia or copulatory organs, but those in which the eggs are inseminated
outside of the body generally do not.

Testes   The testes of vertebrates have two functions: the production of sperm and
the secretion of steroid hormones. The gametogenic function is obviously
extremely primitive. The phylogeny of the testis in this role must extend
throughout the evolutionary history of the Deuterostome line leading to the
vertebrates. The steroidogenic function, too, is primitive, at least to the
extent that it is found in the testes of all living vertebrates. There is not

497

adequate information whether this function was already in existence in protochordates in advance of the evolution of vertebrates. In all vertebrates the steroid hormones play a crucial supporting role in sexual reproduction by regulating the functional development of the male reproductive tract and other sexual accessories and by regulating sexual behavior.

The location of the testes in the great majority of vertebrates is inside the body cavity, more or less in the primitive embryonic position medial to the opisthonephric kidneys. The testes of mammals, however, typically descend into an extra-abdominal sac, the scrotum. Exceptions to this rule are the monotremes, edentates, cetaceans, and sirenians, which lack a scrotum and retain the testes in the pelvic region of the abdomen. Some species that possess a scrotum may exhibit testicular descent only during the spermatogenic period during and prior to breeding (rodents, stag, horse, elephant), and other species, such as the rat, are able voluntarily or reflexly to withdraw the testes from the scrotum whenever they are threatened by danger.

The scrotum arises as a saccate evagination of the lower abdominal wall and as its structure includes all of the layers of the abdominal wall, including skin, muscle, and peritoneum, the scrotal cavity is thus an extra-abdominal extension of the peritoneal cavity (Figure 13-2). The mechanism of descent

Figure 13-1. Basic plan of the vertebrate reproductive system: (a) male; (b) female. In the male anamniote the Wolffian opisthonephric duct functions as both the urinary duct and the sperm duct. Amniotes differ in that the metanephric kidney possesses a separate duct, the ureter, and the Wolffian duct functions solely as a sperm duct. Note the vestigial oviduct in the male.

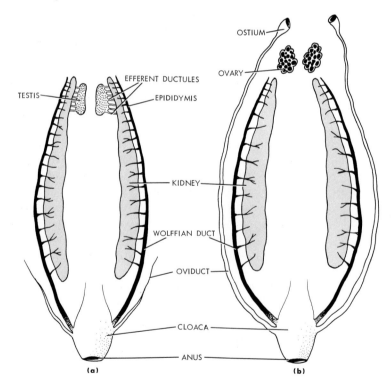

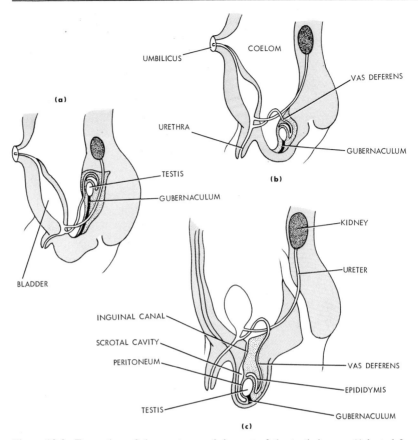

Figure 13-2. Formation of the scrotum and descent of the testis in man (Adapted from L. B. Arey, *Developmental Anatomy*. Philadelphia: Saunders, 1965.)

of the testis is not fully understood. During fetal development the peritoneum posterior to the testis differentiates into a fibrous ligament known as the gubernaculum that is attached at its anterior end to the membranous coats of the testis, and at its posterior end to the abdominal wall at the position where the scrotal evaginations develop. During later development the gubernaculum fails to elongate proportionately to body growth and eventually actually shortens. This would seem to have the effect of pulling the testis into the scrotum (Figure 13-2). However, because cutting the gubernaculum during development does not prevent descent, this rather obvious mechanism cannot be the whole explanation of testicular descent. Androgen injections will stimulate descent, and it is probable that androgen secretion by the embryonic testis during development helps to regulate the normal descent of the glands.

The function of the scrotum is temperature regulation. The internal temperature of the scrotal testis as measured in various species ranges from 1 to 8 degrees Centigrade lower than abdominal temperature. This difference is crucial, for if the testis is retained at the higher temperature of the abdomen the germinal epithelium of the testis degenerates and sterility results. Sporadic retention of one or both testes in the abdomen, a condition known

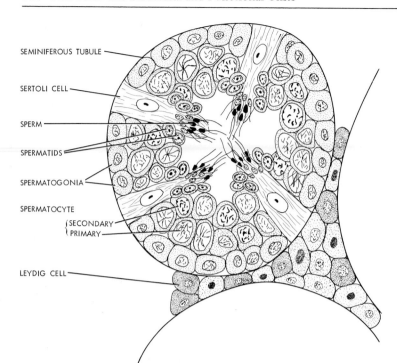

SEMINIFEROUS TUBULE

SERTOLI CELL

SPERM

SPERMATIDS

SPERMATOGONIA

SPERMATOCYTE
{ SECONDARY
{ PRIMARY

LEYDIG CELL

Figure 13-3. Histology of the tubular testis. Diagrammatic cross-section showing semi-niferous tubules and interstitial tissue containing Leydig cells.

as cryptorchidism, may occur in species in which permanent descent is the normal condition, and is always associated with partial or complete sterility. This effect of cryptorchidism can be duplicated by insulating the scrotum or by artifically warming it, substantiating the argument that temperature regulation is the function of the scrotum. The fact that the testes of birds and some species of mammals that lack a scrotum can carry out normal spermatogenesis at body temperatures is completely paradoxical to this conclusion and lacks explanation. The real enigma is that the germinal tissue of most male mammals should be unadapted to function at the deep body temperatures which are optimal for other internal organs.

The thermoregulatory function of the scrotum is achieved in two ways. First, as the arterial and venous supplies of the testes enter and leave the scrotum they intermingle in a convoluted plexus of vessels known as the pampiniform plexus. The convoluted nature of these vessels increases the surface area across which heat is lost. In addition, in the plexus there is cooling of the arterial blood by transfer of heat across the vessel walls into the venous blood which has already been cooled during its sojourn in the scrotum. Secondly, the testes and scrotum are provided with two sets of muscles, the external cremasters which are attached to the peritoneum (tunica vaginalis) surrounding each testis, and the tunica dartos which is adherent to the skin of the scrotum. These muscles contract when cooled and relax when warmed to pull the testes closer to the body or let them drop away, thus warming or cooling the testes.

Corresponding to the two principal functions of the organ, the testis of vertebrates consists of two major tissues: a gametogenic component and a steroidogenic component. In amniotes and anuran amphibians the germinal tissue takes the form of greatly elongated and convoluted seminiferous tubules. Within the walls of these tubules is lodged a permanent population of primordial germ cells, or stem spermatogonia and, depending on the season, cells in various stages of spermatogenesis associated with supportive Sertoli cells. The endocrine component consists of glandular Leydig cells which lie in the interstitial tissue, a cellular connective tissue that fills the spaces between the tubules. The endocrine cells are estimated to constitute between 1 and 5 percent of the total mass of the testis. This familiar pattern of testicular structure is illustrated in Figure 13-3.

In urodeles and most other lower anamniotes a different, though presumably homologous pattern of organization is seen. The spermatogenic portion of the testis consists of lobules or crypts that do not contain a permanent population of primordial germ cells, but are totally evacuated of germ cells at the time of each spawning. After spawning the crypts collapse and cannot be discerned clearly until they become repopulated with spermatogenic cells during the next reproductive cycle. The permanent population of germ cells or stem spermatogonia lies outside of the spermatogenic crypts, sometimes in the interlobular spaces, in a permanent germinal layer around the periphery of the testis, or in a specialized germinal ridge along one margin of the gonad. During a spermatogenic cycle spermatogonia produced by proliferation of these stem cells migrate into the crypts where they divide repeatedly to produce nests of spermatocytes which ultimately differentiate into mature spermatozoa. If the stem cells are located peripherally, successive waves of proliferating spermatogonia push inward from the outside of the lobules producing a pattern in which the oldest spermatogenic nests lie centrally adjacent to the sperm duct, and successively younger stages are arrayed outward toward the periphery of the lobule.

In either type of testis, spermatogenesis begins with the proliferation of the stem spermatogonial cells to produce a population of spermatogonia. In mammals, where the phenomenon has been most studied, during a given spermatogenic wave the stem cell divides twice to produce four spermatogonia; one of these develops no further but remains dormant as part of the residual population of stem cells that will proliferate similarly during subsequent waves. The other three cells divide from one to five times, depending on the species, to produce a nest of six to twenty-four primary spermatocytes, which then divide meiotically and differentiate to produce twenty-four to ninety-six spermatozoa. During their development the spermatocytes become embedded in the cytoplasm of supporting Sertoli cells, and the progeny of an original nest of spermatocytes remain associated with the Sertoli cell until the mature sperm are released into the tubule lumen. The duration of a spermatogenic cycle from the time of initiation of spermatogonial proliferation to the formation of mature sperm is five to ten weeks, depending on the species. The sequence of events in spermatogenesis is illustrated in Figure 13-3. Although the arrangement of cells in the tubule walls appears to the untrained eye to be a chaotic mixture of stages of spermatogenesis, careful study has shown in fact that the various stages appear in particular patterns or "cell associations." This suggests that a given stem cell undergoes repeated waves of proliferation, generating overlapping generations of spermatocytes and maturing germ cells. In man, for example, it has been demonstrated that stem spermatogonia enter a wave of proliferation approximately every sixteen days, whereas the entire duration of spermatogenesis is approximately seventy-four days.

Spermatogenesis in anamniotes differs from the mammalian pattern in two significant respects: (1) the original number of divisions of the spermatogonia during the proliferative phase is greater, resulting in more spermatocytes—up to a hundred or more—in a nest, and a correspondingly greater number of sperm; (2) the nest of cells originating from one stem cell during a wave of proliferation becomes enclosed together in a cyst wherein they develop synchronously into sperm. The cyst appears to be homologous with the Sertoli cell and its nest of spermatogenic cells in the amniote. Both the cyst cells and the Sertoli cells have been regarded as homologous with the follicle cells of the ovary (Figure 13-4).

These two general patterns of spermatogenesis, tubular and cystic, seem to be adaptations to the reproductive habits of amniotes and anamniotes respectively. Anamniotes typically spawn in a brief period during which immense quantities of sperm and eggs are released into the water where external fertilization occurs. The cystic method of spermatogenesis produces the relatively huge numbers of sperm that are required to achieve a reasonable efficiency of fertilization under these hazardous circumstances. Prior to spawning, gametogenesis has been completed and the testes turned into vast receptacles of mature sperm that are totally evacuated from the gland during the brief spawning period. Amniotes, on the other hand, typically indulge in a more prolonged mating season during which repeated acts of insemination may

Figure 13-4. Histology of the mammalian ovary. Successive stages of follicle growth, ovulation, and development of the corpus luteum are shown. This is a composite view; ordinarily all of these stages would not be seen at any one time. (From B. Frye, *Hormonal Control in Vertebrates.* New York: Macmillan, 1967. After C. A. Villee, *Biology,* 4th ed. Philadelphia: Saunders, 1962.)

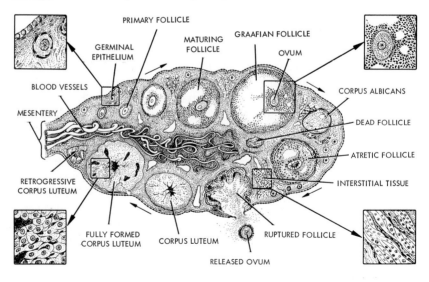

occur, and practice internal fertilization with less waste of gametes. Corresponding to this, relatively fewer sperm are produced and an act of mating does not evacuate the testis of sperm that are being produced continuously during the breeding season.

The fact that the testis is an endocrine organ that secretes male sex hormones or androgens was established long ago by the well-known effects of castration upon the secondary sex characteristics and accessory structures and by the fact that androgens will prevent these changes. More recently, direct biochemical measurements of androgens in testis extracts and testicular venous blood have not only confirmed this role, but have made possible quantitative studies of the rates and biochemical pathways of androgen synthesis and secretion in various reproductive states. Such evidence has directly demonstrated the androgenic role of the testis in all vertebrates except cyclostomes; and even in this group experiments showing that injected androgens cause sexual maturation of the male provide indirect evidence of the androgenic role of the testis. We presume, therefore, that androgenesis is a universal function of the vertebrate testis.

More specific localization of the androgen secreting function in the interstitial cells of Leydig (or tubule boundary cells) is supported by a number of lines of evidence that tend to exclude the seminiferous tubules and favor the Leydig cells as the endocrine tissue:

1. The developmental history of Leydig cells corresponds with patterns of androgen secretion. Thus, Leydig cells are abundant in the testis of the late fetal mammal, disappear shortly after birth, reappear at puberty reaching a peak at the sexual prime, and decline with senescence. The pattern of androgen secretion is similar (Figure 13-5).

2. Leydig cell tumors, which occur occasionally in man, are correlated with excessively high levels of androgen secretion; in young boys such tumors cause sexual precocity.

3. By means of carefully selected doses of X-irradiation the contents of seminiferous tubules can be destroyed without apparent damage to Leydig cells. Under these conditions androgen secretion continues at essentially normal levels.

4. Similarly, in cryptorchidism or certain infections localized in the testes, such as *mumps orchidis,* the seminiferous tubules may be destroyed without much effect on either Leydig cells or androgen secretion.

5. Cytochemical methods that stain steroids or localize certain key enzymes involved in androgen synthesis (such as 3β-hydroxysteroid dehydrogenase) show these factors to be primarily localized in Leydig cells.

6. Steroidogenic tissue can be incubated *in vitro* with precursors such as cholesterol or progesterone and will convert these substrates into steroid hormones. When seminiferous tubules and interstitial tissue are surgically isolated and incubated separately in this fashion, the major steroid synthesizing activity is found in the interstitial tissue fraction.

It should be noted that the cytochemical and *in vitro* evidence, which are the most direct evidence available, point to the interstitial tissue as the principal site of steroid synthesis. However, steroidogenesis also occurs in the tubules, especially in some species at some phases of the reproductive cycle. In many species of vertebrates from fish to mammals the Sertoli or

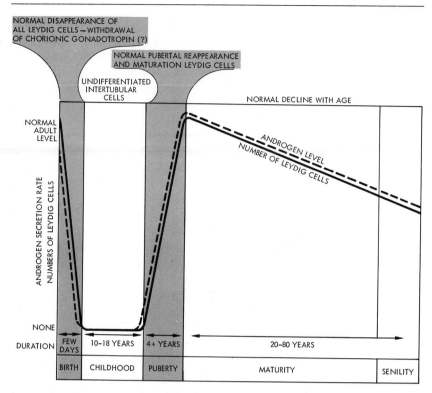

Figure 13-5. The relationship between Leydig cell number and androgen secretion during the life span of man. (Adapted from A. Albert, "The Mammalian Testis," in W. C. Young, *Sex and Internal Secretions,* 3rd ed. Baltimore: Williams and Wilkins, 1961.)

cyst cells differentiate into glandular cells filled with lipids following the release of sperm. Because this differentiation coincides with the appearance of high levels of progesterone in the testes and in the blood it has been inferred that these transformed cells are the site of progesterone synthesis. If this is true, the presumed homology between the Sertoli cells and the granulosa cells of the ovarian follicle is particularly pertinent since this layer forms the primary progesterone-secreting component of the corpus luteum that forms from the empty follicle after ovulation.

The testes also secrete estrogens, but the evidence does not indicate clearly whether these hormones are secreted by the tubules, by Leydig cells, or by both.

Ovaries The ovaries of vertebrates are located in the peritoneal cavity, attached to the body wall on either side of the dorsal mesentery near the kidneys. In cyclostomes and most teleost and elasmobranch fish the ovaries are elongated organs that extend from near the anterior end of the opisthonephros backward through most of the length of the abdomen. In tetrapods the ovaries do not elongate proportionately to body growth and develop into more or less compact, globular, sometimes lobulated bodies. The ovaries of mammals undergo some posteriad migration or "descent" until they lie posterior to the metanephric kidneys. When fully developed the ovaries are dependent from the body wall by a pair of mesenteries, the mesovaria. The blood vessels and nerves of the ovary enter through these mesenteries, the region of the ovary through which they penetrate being known as the hilus.

The ovaries are bilaterally paired in most adult vertebrates whereas the embryonic rudiments are paired in all vertebrates. During development the bilateral condition is lost in a few groups, notably cyclostomes and most birds, but also in scattered instances in other classes. This occurs either by the fusion of the two embryonic ovaries to form a single median gland (cyclostomes) or by the failure of one of the gonads to develop beyond the rudimentary stage (most other cases of asymmetry). While most birds have only a left ovary, the right one remaining rudimentary, some birds, notably hawks, have normally paired ovaries. Viviparous sharks generally have only a right ovary. Among mammals there are a few groups in which only one ovary is present, and this may be variously the right ovary (bats) or the left (monotremes).

Although the asymmetrical development of the ovaries may be accounted for embryologically, the adaptive significance of this condition is not clear. For birds, where the right oviduct is also usually undeveloped, the suggestion has been made that this is a means of reducing the body weight for flight, or alternatively that it is an adaptation to avoid the collision of two synchronously ovulated eggs in the lower part of the reproductive tract. Since there are successful exceptions in birds with bilateral ovaries and oviducts, neither of these explanations is particularly convincing. Among the higher tetrapods where the number of eggs produced is relatively small, one ovary is capable of producing many more gametes than is normally released in a lifetime. Thus, the question might be reversed to ask why two ovaries have persisted in the majority of species of amniotes. The implications raised by such a question are numerous, but one factor to consider is whether the hormone secreting capabilities of one ovary would be adequate for normal reproduction. There is a glimmer of evidence in certain rodents that a single ovary does not produce quite adequate amounts of hormone to maintain gestation if the other ovary is surgically removed.

The basic histological organization of the ovary consists of a supportive bed of cellular connective tissue, called the stroma, within which are embedded the germinal elements or follicles. Each follicle consists of an oöcyte surrounded by one or more layers of nurse cells or follicle cells. Covering the surface of the ovary is a thin cellular membrane known as the germinal epithelium, which is continuous with the peritoneum lining the coelom. The germinal epithelium derives its name from the fact that during embryonic development it is the proliferative layer of cells that gives rise to much of the tissue of the gonadal rudiment. This proliferative function is lost in the adult. The term "germinal" epithelium is misleading for it can suggest that this is the source of primordial germ cells, which is not the case; these cells migrate into the rudimentary gonads from the embryonic endoderm or mesendoderm and establish residence in the outer margin of the stroma, just beneath the germinal epithelium. In mammals, but not other vertebrates, clusters of glandular interstitial cells are scattered through the stroma among the follicles. Following ovulation the follicle cells become transformed into a glandular mass of tissue known as the corpus luteum. Corpora lutea are especially characteristic of the ovaries of mammals, where they play a crucial endocrine function in the sexual cycle and in pregnancy. Although homologous structures are formed in many species of lower vertebrates from elasmobranchs to birds, it is not known whether these play a functionally analogous role to the mammalian corpus luteum.

In cross-section the ovary is roughly divisible into an inner medulla and an outer cortex. The medulla consists of connective tissue and the major trunks of blood vessels and nerves which enter through the hilus and branch out from the medulla into the surrounding cortex. The cortical zone contains the stroma, follicles, corpora lutea, and interstitial tissue. In most lower vertebrates the ovary is hollow, or saccular, the space being formed within the medullary region. The cavity of the ovary of teleosts, however, is formed by invagination of the surface of the ovary, and is thus lined with germinal epithelium. In this group the ovarian tissue often evaginates into this cavity to form a series of ovigerous folds, which greatly increase the mass of germinal tissue.

Following migration of the primordial germ cells into the gonad during embryonic development, the formation of mature ova and follicles occurs in several phases: (1) proliferation of the primordial oögonia into a large population of secondary oögonia and differentiation of these into primary oöcytes; (2) formation of follicles, which is concomitant with (3) growth of the primary oöcytes; (4) ovulation; and (5) completion of the meiotic maturational divisions.

In mammals, birds, and elasmobranchs, as well as some species of teleosts and reptiles, the oögonial divisions are completed during embryonic or juvenile development; the complete store of oöcytes from which will develop all of the eggs produced during the adult life of the individual are already present in the ovary of the immature animal. The adaptive significance of this condition, which is in marked contrast to the repeated proliferation of new generations of germ cells which occurs in the testes throughout life, is not known. The ovaries of amphibians (Figure 13-6), some reptiles, and most teleosts continue to produce new generations of oöcytes after maturity. Some of the evidence in support of the claim that new oöcytes are not formed in the adult ovaries in mammals includes: (1) proliferation of new oöcytes is not observed in histological sections of ovary after late embryonic development; (2) the population of oöcytes present in the young adult declines at a predictable rate until senescence when virtually none are present. This rate of decline can be accelerated by treatments that stimulate the maturation of ova (such as treatment with gonadotropins) or decelerated by treatments that inhibit the maturation of ova (such as hypophysectomy). If the ovary were routinely capable of generating new oöcytes one might expect the germ cell population to be more stable and to be capable of compensatory adjustments for deviations in the rate of loss of ova; (3) carefully selected doses of X-rays can destroy the oöcytes without apparent permanent damage to other ovarian tissues, yet the ovary is never repopulated with new oöcytes; (4) if the oöcytes are labeled by allowing them to incorporate radioactive thymidine into their nucleic acids during the period of oöcyte formation, a high and constant percentage of the eggs subsequently produced in the adult over a prolonged period contain the radioactive label. Were new oöcytes being formed during later life one would expect a

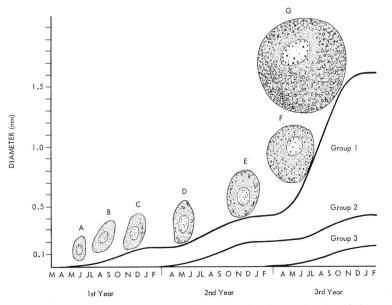

Figure 13-6. Growth of oöcytes in the frog ovary, showing overlapping of three generations of oöcytes. (From P. Grant, "Phosphate Metabolism During Oogenesis in *Rana temporaria" Journal of Experimental Zoology,* **124**: 513-543, 1953.)

gradual decline in the percentage of labeled eggs as a result of the replacement and "dilution" of those formed earlier by new generations of unlabeled oöcytes.

Follicles are formed by the association of a single oöcyte with a nest of cells proliferated from the germinal epithelium. In lower vertebrates this nest of follicle cells, generally known as the stratum granulosum, is usually only one cell layer thick; but in species producing extremely large yolky eggs, including elasmobranchs, birds, and reptiles, the granulosa layer may multiply until it is several layers thick. It is probable in such cases that all cells in the granulosa extend cytoplasmic processes inward to contact the surface of the egg. The follicles of all submammalian vertebrates are solid, that is, the growing ovum completely fills the follicular space. In mammals, however, the ovum remains nearly microscopic in size and a large fluid-filled space, called the antrum, forms within the granulosa layer. The ovum projects into one side of this space where it is enclosed in a hillock of granulosa cells known as the cumulus oöphorus. Growth of the mammalian follicle occurs in three phases. The first or primary follicle is located near the surface of the ovary and is surrounded by a single layer of granulosa cells. The secondary follicle is characterized by some growth of the oöcyte, formation of two to four layers of granulosa cells, and migration of the follicle deep into the cortex. The final stage, or tertiary follicle, is characterized by the formation and rapid growth of the antrum and by the differentiation of additional layers of cells external to the growing granulosa layer. These are the theca interna, which becomes a glandular component rich in lipids, and the theca externa, a connective tissue layer which may also contain some smooth muscle fibers. These stages of follicle formation can be seen in Figure 13-4. The final mature follicle in mammals is known as the Graafian follicle. The functional significance of the formation of the antrum in mammals is not known, although it has been postulated that it is in some way concerned with the ovulation of the minute eggs that mammals produce.

During the growth phase oöcytes may increase in volume 1,000,000 or more times, as a result of which the ovaries enlarge from less than one percent to more than 20 percent of the body weight in many species. Even in mammals in which the eggs are relatively minute and yolkless, the oöcytes increase in diameter ten- to twentyfold. The full growth and maturation of an oöcyte may require two or more seasons in poikilotherms, in which case several generations of developing oöcytes overlap (Figure 13-6). In homeotherms, however, full growth of the oöcytes requires only a few days or weeks. Birds are particularly remarkable in the rate of oöcyte growth: the chicken ovum is said to grow from less than a millimeter in diameter to its full size in only nine days. Growth of the oöcyte occurs mainly by the deposition of yolk. Yolk proteins are formed in the maternal liver and transferred via the blood to the follicle cells and from there into the oöcyte. In support of this function, the follicles of species producing extremely yolky eggs may be highly vascular, as those of birds, and the cell membranes of the oöcyte and the follicle cells are thrown into extremely numerous interdigitating microvilli which greatly increase the area across which the transfer can occur. In mammals, where the ova contain little or no yolk, the stratum granulosum is avascular.

Ovulation is the process of release of the ripe eggs from the ovary. In egg-laying animals ovulation should be distinguished from ovoposition. Ovoposition is the actual release of the eggs from the reproductive tract where they may be retained for several hours or days after ovulation. When the oöcytes are "ripe" the follicles protude from the surface of the ovary and the ovarian tissue over the surface pole of the follicles becomes very thin and avascular. This area is known as the stigma (birds). Immediately prior to ovulation a hole appears in the stigma, through which the egg emerges. Unfortunately it is impossible to describe a mechanism of ovulation that is consistent with all the facts. Some of the theories that have been proposed are (1) a rise in intrafollicular or intra-ovarian pressure owing to an accumulation of fluid or contraction of smooth muscle fibers which forces the egg out through the stigma, and (2) enzymatic digestion of the stigma that creates the opening through which the egg emerges. Whatever the mechanism, it is closely dependent upon environmental circumstances, including photoperiod, temperature, food, a suitable breeding site, and the presence of a mate. These conditions, when suitably combined, trigger the release of a luteinizing hormone which activates the ovulatory mechanism. In most placental mammals ovulation is a spontaneous event that occurs at the time of "heat" or sexual receptivity during the estrous cycle, but some mammals, notably members of the rabbit, cat, and ferret families, require the stimulus of copulation to trigger the secretion of the luteinizing hormone that causes ovulation.

The state of meiotic maturation of the oöcyte varies in different species, but is almost always incomplete until after ovulation or fertilization. Perhaps the most usual condition is one in which the oöcytes enter the first meiotic prophase during embryonic development where they remain arrested until near the time of ovulation when they complete the first division and enter the second meiotic metaphase. At that stage they are again arrested and complete the final division only after activation of the egg by sperm penetration or artificial parthenogenesis. The meiotic divisions of oöcytes are always unequal and yield when complete one large yolky ovum virtually as big as the ripe oöcyte and two or three exceedingly minute polar bodies.† The most obvious adaptive consequence of this is to preserve the accumulated yolk within the definitive egg rather than dividing it among four. Less obvious is the fact that the mature oöcyte has "built into" its surface a great deal of structural specificity concerned with controlling the early development of the embryo that is also preserved by the unequal meiotic divisions.

If for any reason the follicles fail to ovulate, the ripe oöcytes and follicles are gradually reabsorbed, a process known as atresia. In mammals where several hundred thousand oöcytes may be present in the ovary in youth, but only a few hundred are ovulated in the life span of the individual, the vast majority of the oöcytes undergo atresia. Atresia may occur at any phase of the follicle growth cycle, and waves of atresia accompany waves of normal oöcyte maturation at every sexual cycle. The cause of atresia is unknown, but hypotheses that have been proposed to explain this phenomenon include (1) a suppressive effect of hormones produced by adjacent, more advanced follicles, and (2) competition for the limited amount of gonadotropin required for follicle growth. Gonadotropins seem to be involved in some way: hypophysectomy of the immature animal before follicle growth has been stimulated reduces the rate of atresia (and of course prevents follicle development too). On the other hand, hypophysectomy after sexual maturity results in atresia of all growing, developing follicles. It would appear that at the beginning of a sexual cycle more primary follicles are activated to begin development than can subsequently be supported by normal levels of gonadotropin.

The principal hormones secreted by the ovary are estrogens and progestogens, defined as feminizing and pregnancy-supporting hormones respectively. Some androgens are secreted by the ovary, at least in mammals. The actual site of production of these hormones in lower vertebrates is unknown, but is presumed to be the follicles and corpora lutea (when present) since these are the only glandular tissues in the ovary. In mammals the granulosa and the thecal layer of the follicle, the corpus luteum, and the interstitial tissue all appear by cytochemical tests to be steroidogenic at some phase of the sexual cycle (Figure 13-7). The most significant theory of the origin of estrogens and progestogens is based upon a correlation of the morphological cycle of the follicle with the predominant hormones secreted during this cycle. Prior to ovulation, the theca interna is a well-developed glandular layer, actively steroidogenic by cytochemical tests and richly vascularized; the stratum

---

†Whether two or three polar bodies are produced depends on whether the polar body produced in the first meiotic division goes ahead to complete the second division or merely dies. So far as nuclear division is concerned, four haploid products are produced equivalent to the four spermatids produced by the meiosis of one primary spermatocyte.

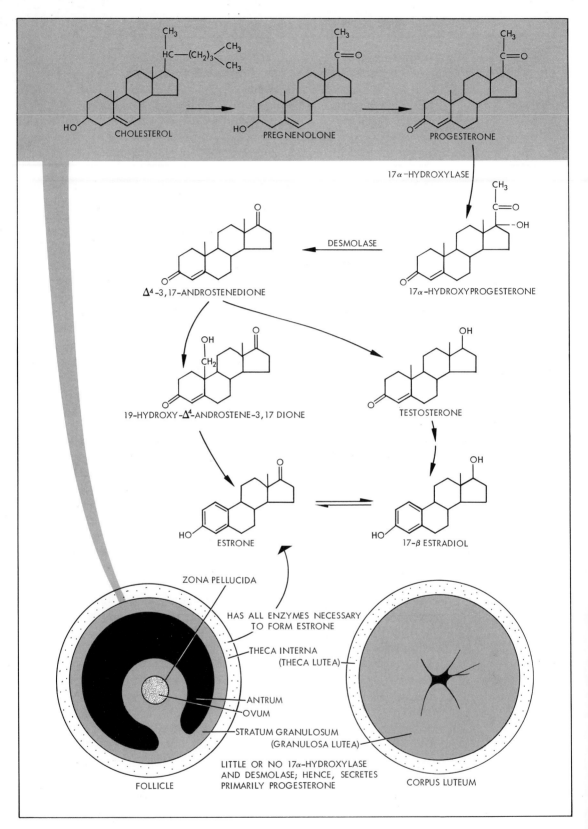

CHOLESTEROL

PREGNENOLONE

PROGESTERONE

17α–HYDROXYLASE

17α–HYDROXYPROGESTERONE

DESMOLASE

Δ⁴-3,17-ANDROSTENEDIONE

19-HYDROXY-Δ⁴-ANDROSTENE-3,17 DIONE

TESTOSTERONE

ESTRONE

17-β ESTRADIOL

ZONA PELLUCIDA

HAS ALL ENZYMES NECESSARY
TO FORM ESTRONE

THECA INTERNA
(THECA LUTEA)

ANTRUM

OVUM

STRATUM GRANULOSUM
(GRANULOSA LUTEA)

LITTLE OR NO 17α–HYDROXYLASE
AND DESMOLASE; HENCE, SECRETES
PRIMARILY PROGESTERONE

FOLLICLE

CORPUS LUTEUM

510

Figure 13-7 (opposite). Synthesis of progesterone and estrogens by the thecal and granulosa layers of the follicle and corpus luteum. The granulosa layer has weak or no 17α-hydroxylase and desmolase activity and consequently cannot convert progesterone into estrogens. (See the text for further explanation.) Note that androgens (androstenedione, testosterone) are synthesized by this pathway, but in the ovary they serve primarily as biosynthetic intermediates and are secreted only in relatively small amounts.

granulosum, by contrast, is avascular and relatively inactive. During this phase estrogens are secreted predominately, and relatively little progesterone is produced compared to the postovulatory phase. After ovulation, the stratum granulosum rapidly becomes vascular and by proliferation and cellular change forms the bulk of the corpus luteum; the thecal layer remains active but constitutes a relatively minor proportion of the corpus luteum. Corresponding to these changes, the secretion of progesterone rises dramatically and estrogen secretion, although it continues, becomes relatively less than progesterone. Thus, the thecal cells appear to have the enzymes necessary for estrogen formation, whereas the granulosa cells lack these enzymes and secrete primarily progesterone (see Figure 13-7). This conclusion is supported by demonstration that the theca and granulosa layers, isolated *in vitro,* have the capabilities to synthesize predominately estrogens and progesterones respectively.

Reproductive
Ducts and
Accessory Structures

Except for the cyclostomes all vertebrates have sets of reproductive ducts that convey the gametes or offspring to the outside of the body. In cyclostomes the gametes are released into the coelom by rupture of the walls of the gonads and escape to the outside by way of abdominal pores that open into the cloaca or posterior end of the urinary ducts (Figure 13-8). Basically, the reproductive ducts of other vertebrates are simple, bilaterally paired mesodermal tubes consisting of an inner epithelial lining and an outer wall of connective tissue and smooth muscle. But in all groups of modern vertebrates there are associated with these ducts a variety of specializations which, for the most part, are concerned with the production of secretions that nurture and protect the gametes, with internal fertilization, and with viviparity.†

1. The male. The male reproductive system of vertebrates has close affinity with the urinary system. The basic condition is one in which the testes drain

†The suggestion has sometimes been made that the reproductive system has undergone more exotic specializations during the course of evolution than any other system in the body. The implication of this claim is that, since this system is not essential for individual survival, the pressures of natural selection on it are such as to allow more variations than for other, more "vital" systems. This can hardly be true. In the first place, "survival" of a trait in the evolutionary sense depends solely upon whether the trait is genetically based and can be transmitted to the next generation. This is obviously just as true of any trait affecting the functional integrity of the reproductive system as it is of a trait affecting the life or functional capability of an individual. More fundamentally, it is doubtful that any morphologist can document the claim that specializations in the reproductive system are any more numerous or exotic than those in any other system of corresponding complexity. Consider, for example, the specializations associated with feeding and digestion (Chapter 7).

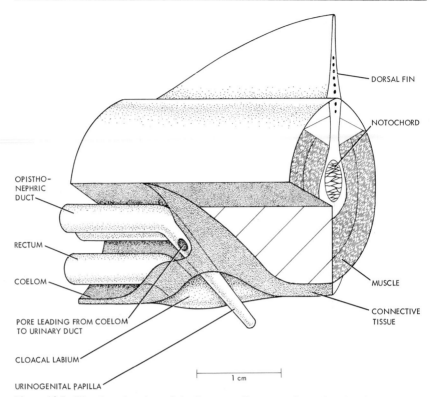

Figure 13-8. The cloacal region of the Lamprey (*Lampetra fluviatilis*) showing the relationship of the abdominal genital pores to the urinary ducts. (From J. M. Dodd, "Gonadal and Gonadotrophic Hormones in Lower Vertebrates," in A. S. Parkes (ed.), Marshall's *Physiology of Reproduction*, Vol. 1, Part 2. London: Longmans Green, 1960.)

via a number of minute ducts, the vasa efferentia, into the anterior opisthonephric tubules, and from there via the archinephric or Wolffian ducts into the cloaca (Figure 13-8). In this condition the archinephric ducts double as both urinary and sperm ducts. These basic units, the opisthonephros, the archinephric ducts, and the cloaca, constitute or form the basic rudiments of the sperm duct system in all vertebrates (Figure 13-9). In all anamniotes except some bony fish this basic condition is retained virtually unaltered except for regional secretory specializations. In actinopterygians there has occurred a trend toward reduction in the number of efferent tubules to one or a few larger ducts, and a "descent" of the point of junction of this duct with the archinephric duct. In teleosts this trend has been carried to the point that a completely separate sperm duct is formed and the archinephric duct is returned to a purely urinary function. In this group the cloaca either disappears entirely, in which case the excretory, reproductive, and digestive

Figure 13-9 (opposite). Reproductive and urinary ducts of various classes of male vertebrates. Kidneys and derivatives, light gray; Wolffian ducts and derivatives, black; testes, darker gray; cloaca and derivatives, stippled; (a) cyclostome, (b) teleost, (c) elasmobranch, (d) amphibian, (e) reptile, (f) bird, (g) mammal.

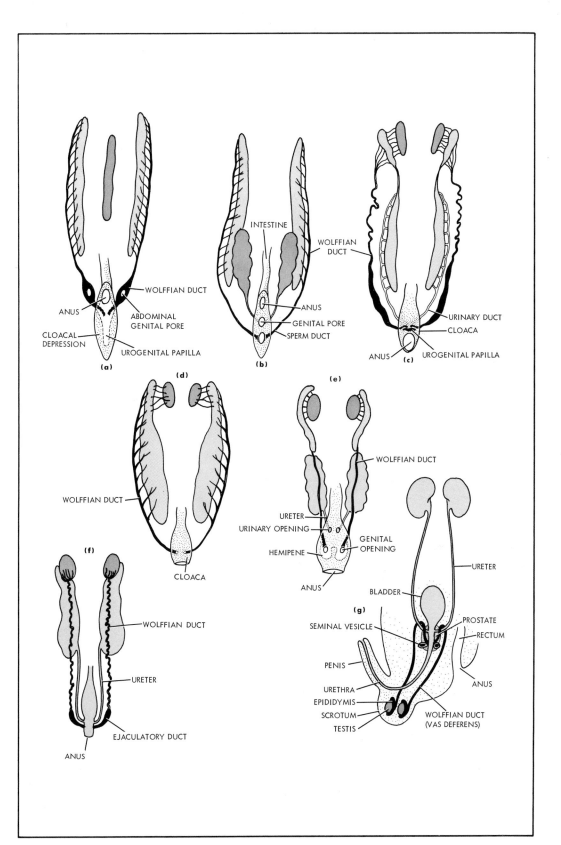

513

canals open separately to the exterior, or is represented only as the urogenital sinus, a common tubular chamber through which the urinary and sperm ducts empty.

In amniotes, with the development of the metanephric kidney, the urinary and reproductive ducts again become separated. A new pair of urinary ducts, the ureters, arise as cloacal outgrowths, and the mesonephric ducts are taken over completely by the reproductive system. The mesonephric kidneys lose all excretory functions and form a pair of glandular, highly tortuous segments of the sperm ducts, the epididymides (singular, epididymis). These receive the efferent ductules on the one hand and drain into the mesonephric ducts, now known as the deferent ducts, on the other. A condition analogous to the formation of the ureter is seen in some amphibians in which some of the more posterior kidney tubules coalesce and grow posteriorly to join the cloaca independently of the Wolffian duct, which becomes mainly a sperm duct. The cloaca persists in birds and reptiles, and even in the most primitive mammals, the monotremes. But in placental mammals it becomes extensively modified by the formation, during embryonic development, of a transverse septum that separates the cloaca into a dorsal digestive

Figure 13-10. Formation of the urogenital sinus as derivatives in mammals: (a) sexually indifferent stage, cloaca undivided; (b) later indifferent stage, division of the cloaca into the rectum and urogenital sinus has occurred; (c) and (d) stages in the development of the male; (e) and (f) stages in the development of the female. (From A. Romer, *The Vertebrate Body*.)

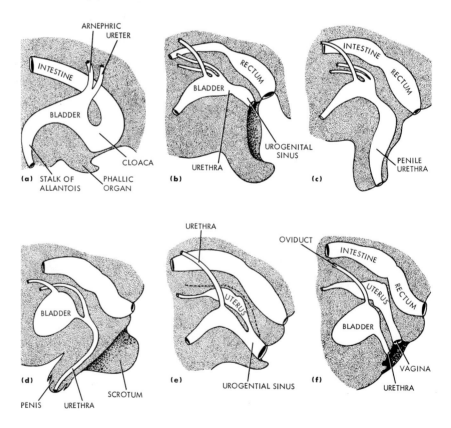

chamber and a ventral urogenital sinus (Figure 13-10). The latter receives both the ureters and the opening of the urinary bladder. In the adult it forms a narrow tube, the urethra, which extends through the penis to the exterior.

Numerous glands and regional specializations are associated with the male reproductive ducts. Except for their general derivation, these structures are not necessarily homologous from group to group. Although extensive discussion of the comparative morphology of these structures cannot be included here, it should be pointed out that there is a great deal of inconstancy even within a group as to the exact battery of glands that a particular species may possess. For example, of the five major glands found in mammals, few species possess all, and some may have only one, the prostate, which is the most consistently present gland of those represented in this class. The general functions of these glands and specialized regions are (1) storage of sperm or (2) secretion of seminal fluids that provide both the vehicle in which the sperm are ejaculated and a suitable medium for maintaining the functional capability of the sperm. Even in mammals, where detailed analyses of the biochemistry of semen have been carried out, hardly more specific statements about the functions of seminal fluid can be made.

Most species that practice internal fertilization possess specialized copulatory structures for deposition of the seminal fluid within the female reproductive tract. In elasmobranchs the copulatory organ is formed by modification of the pelvic fins into a structure known as the clasper. The main element of this structure is, in each fin, a cartilaginous spine that is rolled like a scroll to form a groove, the base of which opens near the cloaca and through which the semen is transferred. The spines are erected by a pair of muscles inserted at their base, and are inserted into the cloaca of the female during copulation. Associated with the base of the claspers are glands or siphons which also open into the groove and pump a secreted fluid or sea water through the claspers, a mechanism which serves to flush the sperm into the female. Somewhat similar copulatory structures are present in some teleosts, in which either the pelvic or the anal fins may be modified for the transfer of spermatozoa. In some teleosts the genital pore opens on a fleshy, penis-like papilla that can be erected and inserted into the cloaca of the female. In at least one species the table has been turned, and the female possesses a genital papilla that is inserted into the genital pore of the male for reception of the sperm. The great majority of teleosts inseminate the eggs externally.

Among the amphibians, virtually all anurans fertilize the eggs externally, whereas fertilization is internal in most urodeles. Copulatory structures are lacking, however; rather, the male deposits a gelatinous capsule of sperm, the spermatophore, which the female picks up and takes internally with the cloacal lips.

In reptiles the penis is a spongy, vascular cone of tissue located on the ventral wall of the cloaca. The penis of turtles is a single median structure, but in snakes and lizards it consists of paired hemipenes. Similar, unpaired, cloacal diverticula form the penis of monotremes and, when present, of birds. Such penes are generally retained inside the cloaca by a retractor penis muscle; erection occurs by relaxation of this muscle and engorgement of the vascular tissue with blood, with the result that the penis is exserted through the cloacal opening. Semen flows from the cloacal openings of the deferent ducts along a groove in the penis into the female cloaca. Most birds, incidentally, lack a penis, and transfer of semen occurs by apposition of the cloacal lips of the male and female during copulation. The mammalian penis arises as a conical outgrowth of skin and mesenchyme outside the ventral margin of the cloaca. During formation of the urogenital sinus the urethral canal extending along the penis as a groove subsequently closes to form the penile segment of the urethra. Two types of penes (with complete intergradation) can be recognized with respect to structure and method of erection. In the first, represented by man, the penis consists of several masses of spongy vascular tissue enclosing the urethra, and erection occurs by engorgement of these masses with blood. In the second type, represented by the bull, the amount of erectile tissue is small, and the penis consists mainly of fibroelastic connective tissue. When not erect the penis is retracted into a fold of skin, the prepuce (equivalent to but much deeper than the foreskin of man), which is attached to the ventral abdominal wall. Retraction is maintained by a pair of retractor penis muscles. Erection occurs by relaxation of these muscles, allowing the penis to protrude from the prepuce. Engorgement of the erectile tissue with blood causes it to become more rigid but does not affect much change in size.

2. The female.   The basic elements of the female reproductive tract in all vertebrates except teleosts are paired Mullerian ducts and the cloaca. The Mullerian ducts extend along the dorsal wall of the body cavity of the embryo lateral to the mesonephric ducts and join the cloaca to form a Y-shaped pattern that persists throughout the vertebrates (Figure 13-11). The Mullerian ducts originate as paired longitudinal folds in the same ridge of coelomic mesoderm that gives rise to the pronephric ducts, in some cases by an actual longitudinal split in the latter. Thus, there is a degree of homology between the male and the female duct systems. The further development of the Mullerian ducts is independent of the opisthonephroi and archinephric ducts, however, and in the female the urinary and reproductive systems remain separate to the level of the cloaca, where they join much as in the male. In the frog, for example, the anterior ends of the Mullerian ducts open into the coelom by a pair of funnel-shaped pores known as ostia (singular, ostium). During ovulation the eggs are released into the coelomic cavity where they are swept by ciliary and muscular activity of the abdominal wall into the ostia, and from there by muscular peristalsis and ciliary action down the oviducts. In cross-section the fully differentiated ducts consist of an inner epithelial or mucosal layer and an outer muscular layer. The mucosal layer contains glands and is often highly folded and richly vascularized. The muscle layer consists of circular and longitudinal layers that may be relatively thin or may be very thick and powerful.

Figure 13-11 (opposite).   Reproductive and urinary ducts of various classes of female vertebrates: (a) cyclostome, (b) teleost, (c) elasmobranch, (d) reptile, (e) bird, (f) mammal (lower end rotated to give lateral view). Kidneys and Wolffian ducts, light gray; Mullerian ducts and derivatives, black; ovaries, darker gray; cloaca and derivatives, stippled.

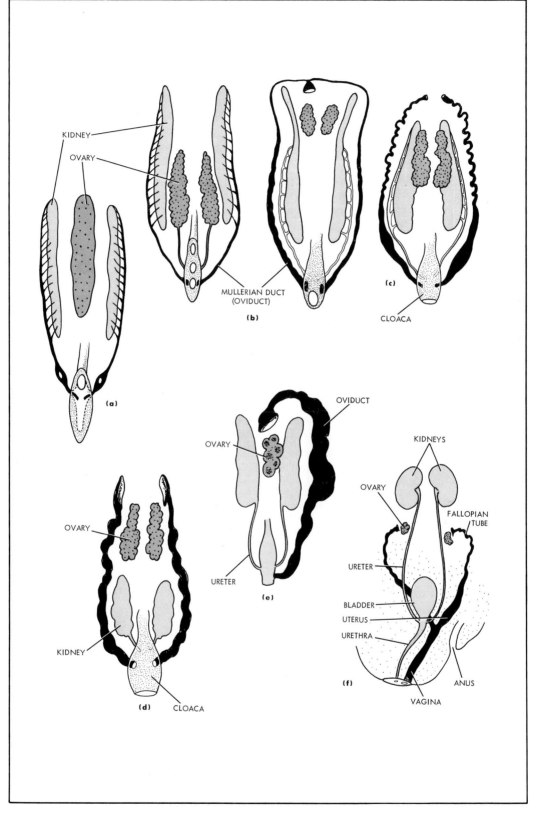

517

Differentiation of the Mullerian ducts into the definitive oviducts involves relatively little change in the basic embryonic pattern, other than longitudinal differentiation into zones specialized among vertebrates for particular functions. These include specialized regions for secretion of gelatinous coats or shells, for egg storage, for gestation, for copulation and, in some cases, for sperm storage.

In elasmobranchs an enlarged glandular region of the upper part of the oviduct, known as the nidamental gland, secretes in sequence albuminous, mucous, and horny layers around the eggs as they move down the duct. The uppermost ends of the two oviducts are united in elasmobranchs and open by a single ostium near the ovary. The posterior parts of the oviducts are expanded into so-called "uteri" or ovisacs. In viviparous species the mucosa in this uterine region is greatly folded and contains extremely numerous minute, finger-like projections called trophonemata. These structures are richly vascular and secretory and presumably function in exchange of materials between the mother and fetus during gestation. The oviducts of amphibians contain several distinct glandular zones whose sequence from anterior to posterior corresponds with the sequence of jelly membranes that are secreted around the egg. The lower end of the oviducts may be expanded into ovisacs in which the eggs accumulate during the interval between ovulation and actual spawning. In birds and reptiles, where very elaborate layers of albumin, shell membranes and membranous or calcareous shells are secreted around the eggs, the zonation of the oviduct may be correspondingly complex. Most birds have but a single oviduct, the left (corresponding to the presence of a single, left ovary), the right Mullerian duct rudiment undergoing degeneration during development of the reproductive tract. The ostium of birds is developed into a muscular funnel that grasps the ripe

Figure 13-12. Degrees of fusion of the uterine horns in mammals. (a) Duplex uterus: two cervixes, no uterine body, horns completely separated. (b) Bipartite uterus; one cervix, uterine bodies small. (c) Bicornuate uterus; one cervix, uterine bodies prominent. (d) Simplex uterus, one cervix, uterine body very prominent, horns absent. (From A. V. Nalbandov, *Reproductive Physiology,* 2nd ed. San Francisco: Freeman, 1964.)

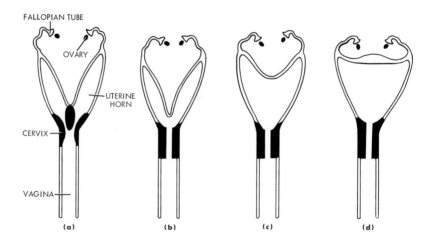

follicle in such a way that upon ovulation the ovum is released directly into the oviduct and does not fall free into the coelom.

In placental mammals the anterior part of the Mullerian duct forms a small convoluted segment called the fallopian tube (also called the oviduct, although equivalent to only the anterior part of the oviducts of lower animals). The ostia are expanded into funnels that cradle the ovaries and sometimes grow completely around them to form ovarian sacs or bursae. The posterior part of the Mullerian duct is enlarged with well-developed mucosal and muscle layers and forms the uterus. In monotremes the condition of the ducts is similar to that seen in reptiles: completely separate oviducts open independently into the cloaca. In higher mammals two major trends are seen in the evolution of the lower regions of the reproductive tract.

The first is formation of the urogenital sinus, eliminating the cloaca, much as described for the male (Figure 13-10). In the female, however, the urogenital sinus is further subdivided into a urethral portion that drains the bladder and a vaginal portion which, together with the posterior ends of the Mullerian ducts, forms the vagina. The urethra and the vagina open separately into a shallow depression, the vestibule, enclosed by fleshy folds of skin, the labia. In some rodents and insectivores the vestibule is absent and the urethra is extended along the clitoris, the female homologue of the penis, to terminate on its tip. In these cases completely separate urinary and genital orifices are formed.

The second trend is for fusion of the lower ends of the Mullerian ducts to form a single median vagina and uterus. In marsupials these ducts remain separate and paired vaginae open into the urogenital sinus. In some marsupials, in addition to the paired lateral vaginal canals, a median vaginal canal forms secondarily. The latter may form a complete connection with the urogenital sinus only during pregnancy and seems to serve as the birth canal, whereas the lateral vaginae function in copulation. Corresponding to this anatomical feature of the female tract, the glans of the penis of male marsupials is bifurcated. In the placental mammals the degree of fusion of the uterine portions of the Mullerian ducts varies from no fusion—in which case completely separate uteri, or uterine horns as they are also called, open into the vagina—to complete fusion to the level of the fallopian tubes (Figure 13-12). This trend toward reduction of the uterus to a single chamber correlates reasonably well with the trend toward reduction in the number of offspring produced in a single pregnancy.

Teleosts are exceptional to the general plan of the female reproductive system in that the oviducts arise not from Mullerian ducts but by posterior extension of the peritoneal folds which create the ovarian cavity. Thus, the cavity of the ovary and oviducts is continuous, and the ova are not released directly into the body cavity as in other forms. This structure has been interpreted as an adaptation to facilitate the rapid release of the large numbers of eggs produced by many teleosts. In fact, however, the oviducts secondarily degenerate in some species with the result that the eggs are ovulated into the body cavity and escape to the exterior through coelomic pores, much as in cyclostomes. Because some species in which this condition is found produce numerous eggs, for example various species of salmon, this interpretation of the relationship between the ovary and oviduct may not be correct.

Intersexuality, Sexual Development, and Sex Reversal

Separate sexes are so overwhelmingly the rule, and sexual dimorphism so pronounced in familiar animals, that we find the concept of intersexuality to be incredible. In fact, intersexuality, in the form of hermaphroditism— defined as the production of both eggs and sperm by a single individual—is a prevailing condition in most organisms. The statement has been made, in fact, "that every organism and every cell is essentially bisexual, and either phenotypically or genotypically influenced, can develop in either the male or female direction." Whether or not the genotype actually allows this amount of plasticity in all organisms can be questioned;† but in vertebrates it is clear that the genotype, while favoring the differentiation of either a male or a female phenotype, is sufficiently indeterminate in its instructions to allow for a complete range of intersexual phenotypes, or even total sex reversal. Intersexuality is rare in vertebrates, but has been observed in all classes. The study of this condition has contributed very significantly to our understanding of normal sexual morphology.

In vertebrates every degree of intersexuality occurs, ranging from complete functional hermaphroditism to mere persistence of vestiges of the sexual rudiments of the opposite sex. This latter condition is a common and normal state and the term intersexuality is usually applied only to more extreme degrees of admixture of male and female traits. In certain families of bony fish functional hermaphroditism is common. Maleness and femaleness may be expressed in sequence as the animal grows older, or they may occur simultaneously. In the first case the gonad functions first as a testis, then as an ovary (or vice versa), whereas in the latter it develops into an ovotestis that produces both eggs and sperm simultaneously. In some cases such hermaphroditic individuals may be self-fertile (fertilization occurring in the gonad), but usually they are not. Complete hermaphroditism is rare in other groups of vertebrates, although true hermaphrodites with ovotestes and complete male and female duct systems have been found in all classes and potentially could occur in any species. Although morphologically bisexual such individuals are very likely sterile as a result of slight imperfections in sexual morphology and behavior. The more common form of intersexuality in vertebrates is one in which the gonadal sex is unambiguous, these organs being distinctly ovaries or testes, but the reproductive ducts and accessory structures of the opposite sex are developed to an anomalous degree. This condition is sometimes called pseudohermaphroditism.

The fact that both male and female structures are differentiated in hermaphrodites suggests that complete sex reversal is possible in vertebrates. In fact, reversal of sex can readily be induced in the laboratory by various experimental treatments, most notably by treatment with sex hormones. Instances of sex reversal are reported from time to time in domesticated

---

†In insects the genotype seems to firmly dictate the sexual phenotype of a given cell. Accidents in cell division during development can lead to abnormal combinations of chromosomes bearing the sex-determining genes. The resulting clones of cells differentiate into patches of tissues whose sex phenotype is determined by their chromosome complements rather than by the overall sex of the organism.

birds and lower animals, but does not occur after embryonic development in mammals (see the following). Occasional publicized instances of sex "reversal" in man are in reality instances of pseudohermaphroditism in which the bisexual anatomy is surgically modified to emphasize the desired traits and eliminate those which are not desired. Sex reversal probably occurs in wild animals but if complete is almost certain to go undetected. Sex reversal is defined as the differentiation of a sexual phenotype which is the opposite of the sex genotype. Hence, proof of reversal, when there is no unusual degree of intersexuality to give a hint of the change, requires identification of the sex genotype. This can be done by breeding experiments as is explained in Figure 13-13, but is much more simply done by cytological examination of the sex chromosomes. The Barr test is such a method and

Figure 13-13. The chromosomal basis of sex determination. (a) In the normal male, two classes of sperm, X and Y, are produced. The sex of the offspring is determined by the kind of sperm which fertilizes the egg. (b) In the sex reversed female, the genetic sex is not altered. Consequently, only one class of sperm, X-bearing, is produced, and the offspring are all female. A refers to the autosomes. In this example the male is heterogamic, i.e., produces two classes of gametes, but in many species the female may be the heterogamic sex. In that condition the female is designated WZAA and the male WWAA.

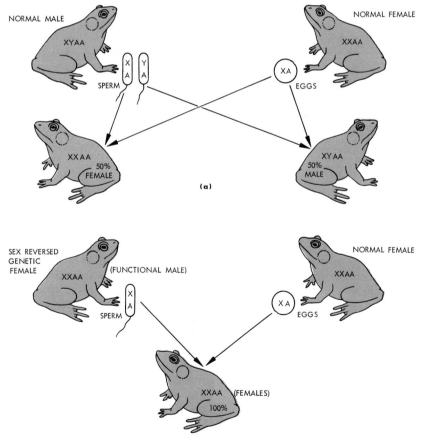

makes use of the fact that the sex chromatin of certain kinds of cells has a distinctive position and staining properties in the female.

Sexual Differentiation

The possibility for intersexuality and sex reversal rests basically in the fact that up to a certain point in development every embryo is morphologically bisexual regardless of its genetic sex. That is, a complete set of both male and female sexual rudiments is formed in the early embryo. These include (1) the gonadal rudiments, (2) the Wolffian and Mullerian ducts and associated mesonephric structures, (3) the cloaca or urogenital sinus, and (4) the phallus or genital tubercle. Normal sexual development involves the growth and differentiation of one set of these rudiments while the other fails to develop beyond the rudimentary condition or undergoes gradual involu-

Figure 13-14. Differentiation of the sexual rudiments of the mammalian embryo. Compare the fate of the genital tubercle, urogenital sinus, Mullerian ducts, Wolffian ducts, and gonads on differentiation in either the male or the female direction. (From B. Frye, *Hormonal Control in Vertebrates.* New York: Macmillan, 1967.)

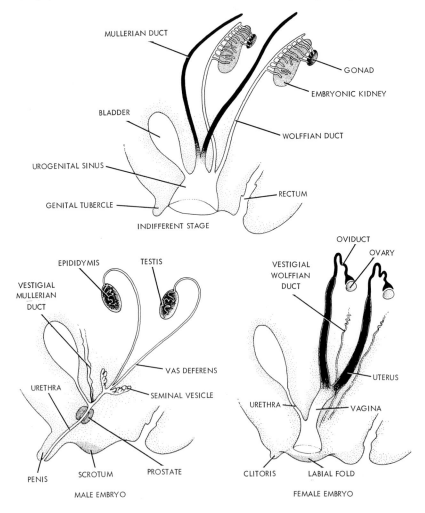

tion (Figure 13-14). With respect to the nature of the bisexual potential, these rudiments fall into two categories: (1) those which are truly sexually indifferent, being capable of developing in either the male or the female direction; (2) those which are destined to differentiate in only one sex or the other. In the first category are the gonads, cloaca or urogenital sinus, and genital tubercle; in the latter are the Mullerian and mesonephric ducts and their derivatives.

Generally the gonads undergo definitive sexual differentiation relatively early, especially in higher vertebrates. In cyclostomes and many teleosts, however, they may undergo definitive differentiation into ovaries or testes at sexual maturation. As has already been noted, several families of teleosts retain the hermaphroditic condition as adults and have a functional ovotestis. Cyclostomes, however, do not remain hermaphroditic but form definitive ovaries or testes at maturity. Occasional cases of persistence of rudimentary gonadal bisexuality occur in higher vertebrates. Male toads possess, at the anterior end of the testes, a vestige of the rudimentary gonad which is capable of differentiating into ovarian tissue but in the normal male is repressed from doing so. If the testes are removed this structure, known as Bidder's organ, can develop into a fertile ovary, and such individuals have become functional females and produced fertile eggs. This degree of functional sex reversal depends upon the fact that in the toad, as in most male amphibians, the Mullerian ducts persist throughout life and can undergo functional development in the presence of female sex hormones. In birds the right gonadal rudiment has little or no capability to form an ovary. Consequently, in the female only the left ovary ordinarily develops. But if the ovary is removed or destroyed by disease, the rudimentary right gonad may then undergo development to form a testis. Although it has often been claimed that such reversed hens function as fathers, this is not well authenticated and is doubtful because the male duct system is absent or imperfectly developed; however, they may develop cock feathering, the ability to crow, and male behavior.

The rudimentary ducts and accessory structures usually persist in the bisexual condition much later in development than the gonads. Sometimes they persist indefinitely, as the Mullerian ducts of male amphibians, but generally they regress to a vestigial condition before sexual maturity. Intersexuality results when both sets of rudiments persist and develop to an unusual degree. Reversal of sex occurs when the set which undergoes definitive development is the opposite of the genotype. Complete reversal can occur only at a stage when regression of the alternate set of rudiments and differentiation of the indifferent rudiments has not proceeded to an irreversible point.

Consideration of the nature of the bisexual organization of the embryonic gonad has special relevance to our understanding of the organization of the reproductive system of the adult with respect both to the relationships between the ovaries and testes and to their relationship to the sex ducts. In its initial stage the gonad rudiment consists of a slight thickening of the peritoneal epithelium overlying the medial border of each mesonephric rudiment. Shortly, a thickening of mesonephric mesenchyme forms underneath the peritoneal rudiment, the resulting bulge constituting the genital ridge. Into this ridge migrate the primordial germ cells. Subsequent further thickening of these two layers results in the formation of a double-layered gonad rudiment consisting of an inner medulla derived from the mesonephric mesenchyme and an outer cortex derived from the peritoneal epithelium. Put simply, these two layers constitute the rudiments of the testis and ovary respectively. In a normal male (or sex-reversed female) the medulla differentiates into a testis and the cortex regresses. In a normal female (or sex-reversed male) the cortex develops into the ovary and the medulla regresses (Figure 13-15).

This description explains the bisexual potential of the rudimentary gonad but it does not fully explain the significance of the association between the original peritoneal and mesenchymal thickenings. A broader view of the role of each of these two components is as follows: the peritoneal thickening constitutes the progenitor of the germinal elements of the gonads. In it are lodged the primordial germ cells which, together with the surrounding epithelial cells, form the primary follicles of the ovary, and the equivalent units—the Sertoli cells plus spermatogonia—of the testis. Most workers agree that these structural units are homologous in all groups of vertebrates. This role of the peritoneal epithelium, which we may now call the germinal epithelium, is very clear in amniotes where it goes through two separate phases of proliferation. In the first, groups of cells from the germinal epithelium and associated germ cells grow into the underlying mesenchyme and form the so-called primary sex cords. If the embryo is to become a male no further proliferation of the germinal epithelium occurs and the primary sex cords differentiate into the seminiferous tubules. In a female this first wave of sex cords begins to regress, together with the mesenchymal blastema, and a new wave of proliferation occurs that results in the formation of a thick outer cortical layer surrounding the inner regressing testicular

Figure 13-15. Diagrammatic representation of the development of the gonad. The broken arrows indicate the mutually antagonistic interactions between the cortex and medulla. (From R. K. Burns, "Role of Hormones in the Differentiation of Sex," in W. C. Young, ed., *Sex and Internal Secretions*, Vol. I, 3rd ed. Baltimore: Williams and Wilkins, 1961.)

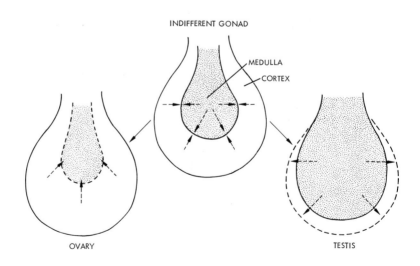

INDIFFERENT GONAD

MEDULLA
CORTEX

OVARY   TESTIS

rudiment. These phases of gonadal development are illustrated in Figure 13-16.

In the development of the testis the medullary or mesenchymal component contributes the rete tubules and, together with the contiguous mesonephric mesenchyme, the efferent tubules. These ultimately connect the seminiferous tubules with the mesonephric tubules and thus establish the path of sperm exit from the testis into the urinary ducts. In addition it forms a supporting framework of mesenchymal tissue that gives rise to the interstitial tissue of the testis and, in some species, apparently forms the basic framework of the tubules within which the germinal elements become lodged. In addition to its structural contributions we may suppose that the mesenchymal blastema in some way induces or supports the ingrowth of the primary sex cords and their differentiation into the seminiferous tubules. If this is true, and it is not proven, then the mesonephric mesenchyme of the genital ridge plays a key role in determining whether the gonadal rudiment will develop as an ovary or a testis. In the genetic male, differentiation of the primary sex cords into testicular tubules is supported, and the cortex or germinal epithelium regresses; in the genetic female this support does not persist long; the medullary testicular rudiment degenerates and the germinal epithelium undergoes a second wave of proliferation to form the cortical or ovarian rudiment. If this relationship is true, then the connection between the urinary and reproductive systems in the male is not so much a matter of "invasion" of the mesonephros by the testis, as is sometimes said, as it is a "seduction" of the testis by the mesonephros. Whatever the mechanism, the morphological relationships point quite strongly to some regulative interaction between the peritoneal and mesonephric components of the urogenital ridge in determining the ultimate direction of sexual differentiation.

The Physiology of Reproduction†

Reproduction in vertebrates requires close coordination between the functional development of the gonads and accessory reproductive organs and sexual behavior. Generally speaking, the morphological and behavioral changes that accompany sexual maturity are geared to environmental conditions in such a way that reproductive capability and activity occur in cycles coordinated with the seasons. Primary control over reproductive functions is vested in the endocrine system. Hormonal effects range from control over the gametogenic and endocrine functions of the gonads and control of the growth and development of the reproductive tract and accessory structures to control over male and female patterns of reproductive behavior. Gestation and parental care of the offspring, when they occur, are also strongly dependent upon hormonal regulation. Integration of reproductive functions with environmental conditions is achieved through the hypothalamic-pituitary-neurosecretory system described in Chapter 12.

Hormones of Reproduction

The principal hormones involved in reproduction are the sex steroids and the gonadotropins, The steroids constitute three functional categories, androgens, estrogens, and progestogens, which are respectively masculinizing, feminizing,

†This section is taken, in part, from Chapter 6 of the author's *Hormonal Control in Vertebrates* (New York: The Macmillan Co., 1967).

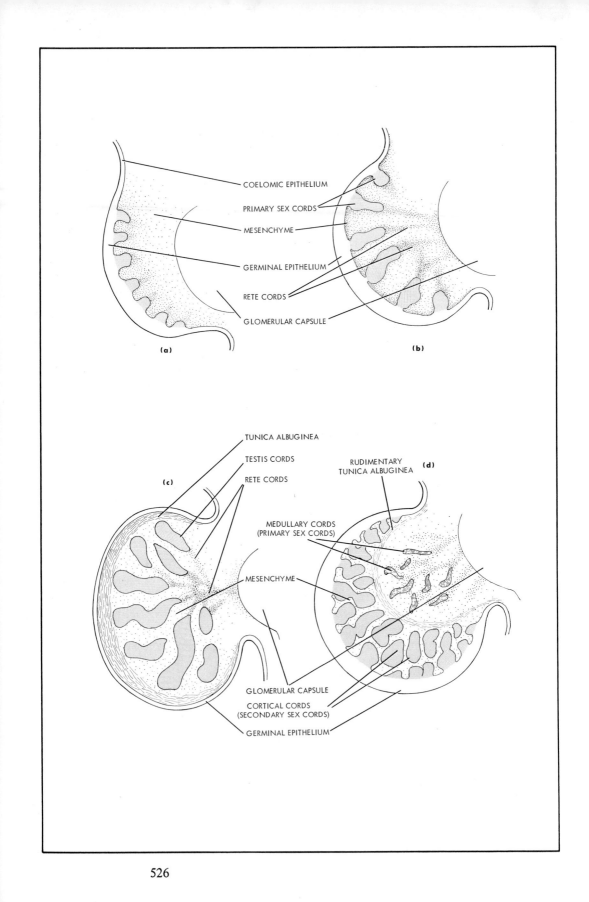

COELOMIC EPITHELIUM

PRIMARY SEX CORDS

MESENCHYME

GERMINAL EPITHELIUM

RETE CORDS

GLOMERULAR CAPSULE

(a)

(b)

TUNICA ALBUGINEA

TESTIS CORDS

RETE CORDS

(c)

RUDIMENTARY
TUNICA ALBUGINEA

(d)

MEDULLARY CORDS
(PRIMARY SEX CORDS)

MESENCHYME

GLOMERULAR CAPSULE

CORTICAL CORDS
(SECONDARY SEX CORDS)

GERMINAL EPITHELIUM

and gestational in their activities. The gonadotropins control the endocrine and gametogenic functions of the gonads. The principal gonadal steroids and the metabolic pathways by which they are synthesized are shown in Figure 13-17. *A synopsis of* their principal effects follows.

Androgens have profound effects upon the male reproductive tract, including the testes themselves, and the accessory structures. Androgens support spermatogenesis in the seminiferous tubules. Because hypophysectomy abolishes spermatogenesis, pituitary gonadotropins are usually regarded as exerting primary control over this function. However, since androgen injections will prevent this effect of hypophysectomy under some circumstances, the gametogenic action of gonadotropins may in part be secondary to their stimulatory effect upon androgen secretion. The sperm ducts and accessory sex glands are almost totally dependent upon androgens. This is dramatically illustrated by the effects of castration and androgen injections upon these organs (Figure 13-18). Injection of androgens into a castrate or immature animal induces rapid development of these organs to mature size and function. Numerous biochemical properties of the accessory sex glands and their secretions are dependent on androgens. For example, the active accessory glands of mammals have a high content of fructose, citric acid, and certain enzymes, notably phosphatases. The content of these substances falls drastically after castration and is elevated to normal or above by androgen treatment.

Androgens also determine the secondary sexual characteristics of vertebrates. In man, there are obvious hormonally determined sexual differences in hair pattern, pitch of the voice, muscle development, skeletal size, fat distribution, skin pigmentation and texture, and many other features. In other animals many additional sexual characters of an ornamental or defensive function are androgen dependent. These include not only morphological traits, but many aspects of male behavior such as aggressiveness, sex drive, and complex patterns of courtship and mating. Treatment of females with androgens often leads to masculine sexual behavior. In mammals, experience is a very important factor in the sexual drive. Castration of mature, experienced animals may have little or no effect upon sexual activity, even though androgens are essential for the development of sex drive and behavior patterns in the immature, inexperienced animal.

Although androgens are characteristically male hormones, they are also produced in the female in considerable amounts by the ovaries and the adrenal cortex. The androgens produced by these glands are relatively weakly

Figure 13-16 (opposite). Formation of the primary and secondary sex cords from the germinal epithelium, and differentiation of testis or ovary: (a) origin of the primary sex cords; (b) the indifferent gonad stage, with well-developed primary sex cords and thick germinal epithelium; (c) differentiation of the testis, with further development of the primary sex cords and reduction of the germinal epithelium to a thin peritoneal covering overlying a connective tissue layer, the tunica albuginea; (d) differentiation of the ovary, with regression of the primary sex cords, and proliferation from the germinal epithelium of the secondary sex cords which form the cortex of the rudimentary gonad, and differentiate into the ovary. (From R. K. Burns, "Role of Hormones in the Differentiation of Sex," in W. C. Young, ed., *Sex and Internal Secretions,* Vol. I, 3rd ed. Baltimore: Williams and Wilkins, 1961.)

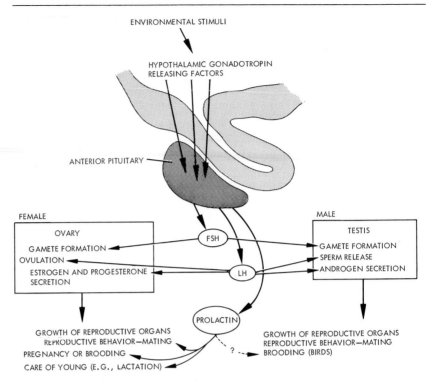

Figure 13-17. Neuroendocrine control of reproduction. (From B. Frye, *Hormonal Control in Vertebrates*. New York: Macmillan, 1967.)

masculinizing, compared to testosterone, but are probably significant in promoting growth and protein synthesis in the female.

Estrogens affect the female in ways that parallel the effects of androgens in the male. They promote the proliferation of the germinal epithelium of the ovary and formation of primary follicles. The later growth phases of the follicles and oöcytes depend upon gonadotropins, however, and complete oögenesis cannot be supported by estrogens. In fact, there is evidence that estrogens in high concentrations will cause atresia of growing follicles. This is probably a consequence of negative feedback inhibition of gonadotropin secretion. Ovariectomy results in regression of the mature female reproductive tract, but development of the Mullerian ducts during the embryonic phase may occur in the absence of the ovaries. Injected estrogens cause growth and development of the female ducts of immature or castrated animals. Estrogens are required for the development of many of the secondary sexual characteristics of the female, but not uncommonly female traits seem to depend as much upon the absence of masculinizing levels of androgens as upon the presence of estrogens. The smaller size of the female as compared to the male in many species of birds and mammals is caused by a growth-inhibiting effect of estrogens upon the skeleton, combined with a strong growth-promoting effect of testicular androgens upon muscle and certain visceral organs. Many of the reproductive structures and functions of the female mammal require synergistic or sequential action of estrogens and progesterone, in the sequence seen in the normal sexual cycle (see 'Progestogens"). These include normal cycles of uterine growth, mammary gland growth and secretion, and sexual behavior.

The testes produce estrogens too, but their function in the male is not well understood. The most probable role of estrogens in the male is regulation of gonadotropin secretion through negative feedback inhibition, an effect which may secondarily help regulate the process of spermatogenesis and male sexual cycles.

Progestogens characteristically function to support pregnancy and lactation in mammals. Their effects often depend upon a previous period of estrogen "priming" during which the target tissues reach a stage of development in which they are sensitive to progestogens. Indeed, when given to a castrated or immature animal, progestogens have little effect unless estrogens are administered prior to or synchronously with the progestogens. Thus, progesterone promotes the differentiation of the estrogen-primed uterus to a progestational state in which it will respond to the embryo by implantation and, combined with estrogen, supports the growth of the uterus and retention of the placenta and fetus during pregnancy. Progesterone is necessary for full development of the mammary glands to a presecretory

Figure 13-18. Effects of castration and testosterone replacement on the seminal vesicles of the rat. (a) Drawings of glands from (1) normal, (2) castrates of three weeks, and (3) castrates of three weeks given 1 milligram of testosterone per day during the last week. (b) Assay of testosterone activity by seminal vesicle weight. The rats were castrated for three weeks and given the indicated doses of testosterone daily for the last week. (From B. Frye, *Hormonal Control in Vertebrates.* New York: Macmillan, 1967.)

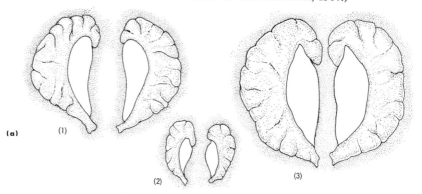

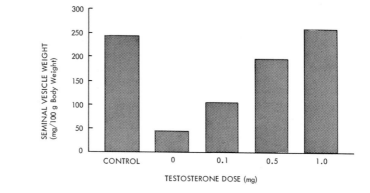

state. Although progesterone is secreted by both the ovaries and the testes in many lower vertebrates, its function in most groups is very unclear. In female birds, progesterone stimulates albumin secretion by the oviduct, and there is some evidence that it has a similar effect upon jelly secretion by the amphibian oviduct.

Progesterone stimulates ovulation. This effect, which has been most studied in birds and mammals, depends very much on the time of the sexual cycle at which the hormone is administered, and at certain times the opposite, inhibitory, effect is obtained. The ovulation-inducing effect of progestogens probably occurs through an effect upon the hypothalamus, causing secretion of luteinizing hormone, which causes ovulation. During pre- or postovulatory phases of the sexual cycle, progesterone inhibits secretion of gonadotropins, particularly follicle-stimulating hormone. The effect of this is to block the development of follicles during pregnancy, a period when progesterone levels are particularly high. These effects of progestogens upon gonadotropin secretion in birds and mammals suggest the possibility that an important physiological role of progesterone in lower vertebrates of both sexes might be the regulation of gonadotropin secretion and sexual cycles.

This synopsis of the effects of steroid hormones supports the general view that the action of male hormones is specific to male traits and the action of

Figure 13-19. Effects of sex hormones upon the differentiation of the external reproductive organs of the opossum: (a) normal male and female; (b) male and female treated with androgen; (c) male and female treated with estrogen. Note that although the phallus undergoes dramatic enlargement and reversal in response to hormone treatment, the scrotum and pouch remain unchanged. (From R. K. Burns, "Role of Hormones in the Differentiation of Sex," in W. C. Young, ed., *Sex and Internal Secretions*, Vol. I, 3rd ed. Baltimore: Williams and Wilkins, 1961.)

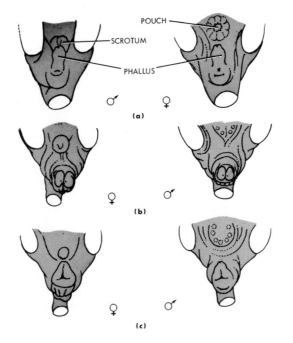

female hormones is specific to female traits. Although basically correct this view must be qualified in certain respects:

1. Some traits are hormone independent and are determined directly by the sexual genotype of the organism. For example, the scrotum of the male opossum and its homologue, the pouch in the female, develop according to the genetic sex of the individual even when total sex reversal of the gonads and reproductive tract has been caused by treatment of the newborn opossum with sex hormones (Figure 13-19).

2. Sexual structures that are identical or homologous in both sexes may be dependent upon the same hormones. For example, many female rodents possess well-developed prostate glands that are maintained by androgens secreted by the ovaries and adrenals. The clitoris, homologue of the penis, is sensitive to androgens; high doses of androgens during development cause it to enlarge to a size equivalent to the penis. Muscle growth in both sexes is sensitive to androgens, and differences in the degree of muscle development in males and females is due to differences in the amount and degree of androgenicity of the androgens produced rather than to basic differences in the response.

3. Sexually dimorphic characters may depend upon hormones in one sex only, the contrasting sexual character developing as a consequence of the absence of a hormone rather than the presence of the alternate hormone. The male plumage pattern in some birds is an example. Castration of the male does not affect plumage but castration of the female results in the development of cock plumage.

4. Sex specific traits may be hormone dependent but may respond nonspecifically to either androgens or estrogens. For example, the orifice of the vagina of female rodents is closed until puberty when it opens under the influence of estrogens. Injections of androgens will also cause opening of the vagina. Such nonspecific or paradoxical effects are most frequently seen when large doses of hormones are injected. For example, treatment of embryos with androgens not only accelerates growth of the male organs but can also cause hypertrophy of the Mullerian ducts. Growth of the Mullerian ducts is ordinarily sensitive to estrogens. Paradoxical effects of hormones can theoretically be explained either by metabolic interconversion of steroids in the tissues (e.g., estrogens from androgens), or by a true lack of absolute specificity of the target tissue for either estrogens or androgens.

5. Some sexual traits may depend upon hormones other than sex steroids. For example, the brilliant beak and plumage color of the male weaver finch is evoked by luteinizing hormone. Estrogen inhibits this effect of luteinizing hormone in the female.

Gonadotropins are a basic part of the team of reproductive hormones because of their effects upon the gametogenic and hormone-secreting functions of the gonads. Hypophysectomy causes involution of the seminiferous tubules or ampullae and interstitial tissue. So far as steroid dependent secondary sexual characteristics are concerned, hypophysectomy causes changes equivalent to castration. Injection of extracts of the anterior pituitary reverses these effects of hypophysectomy or causes sexual precocity in immature animals. Purification of pituitary extracts of mammals has led to the identification of two distinct gonadotropins, follicle-stimulating hormone and luteinizing hormone (FSH and LH). FSH stimulates growth of the follicles in the ovary and formation of sperm in the testes. Luteinizing hormone stimulates androgen secretion by the testis and has several effects in the ovary, including induction of ovulation, formation of the corpus luteum from the ovulated follicle, and stimulation of estrogen and progesterone secretion by the follicle and corpus luteum. The pituitaries of lower vertebrates have similar activities but as yet these activities have not been associated with distinctly different molecules. Some endocrinologists believe that the two classes of gonadotropic activity are properties of one hormone, or at least of two closely related molecules that exhibit some overlap in activity. Some of the effects of gonadotropins are illustrated in Figure 13-20.

Prolactin, or lactogenic hormone, is also sometimes classified as a gonadotropin because in some mammals it stimulates the corpus luteum to secrete progesterone and estrogen. However, this effect seems to be restricted to a few species, notably laboratory rodents, and the more usual reproductive functions of prolactin are not gonadotropic. Among the reproductive effects of prolactin are stimulation of milk secretion by the mammary glands, formation of crop milk by pigeons and related birds, formation of the brood patch in birds, nesting, brooding, and parental-care behavior in a variety of species, and migratory activity related to reproduction.

Hormonal Control of Sexual Differentiation

Sex determination is basically genetic, males and females differing in one pair of chromosomes, the so-called sex chromosomes. In some animals, notably insects, the genotype rigidly influences the phenotypic sex of the offspring. In vertebrates, however, the genetic sex predisposes the development of an embryo in either the male or the female direction, but the actual differentiation of phenotypic sex is under hormonal control. This was first discovered through studies of a spontaneous sexual abnormality in cattle known as the freemartin. A freemartin is a sexually abnormal female calf, born as a twin to a normal male calf. Although sterile, a freemartin is essentially a true hermaphrodite, having more or less well-developed components of both the male and the female duct systems and gonads with both ovarian and testicular regions. In 1916, F. R. Lillie noted that the placental circulation of the male and female twins is always fused in the case of freemartins, and suggested that the sexual modification of the female occurs as a result of transfusion of androgens across the placental union from the male to the female. As a general theory of sex differentiation, Lillie proposed that the rudimentary gonad secretes male or female sex hormones according to its presumptive or genetic sex. These hormones act upon the sexual rudiments to support differentiation in either the male or the female direction. Thus, the embryonic gonad of the genetic female secretes predominantly estrogens, supporting female development, and the embryonic gonad of the genetic male secretes predominately androgens, supporting male development. Spontaneous or experimentally induced intersexuality occurs whenever this normal pattern is reversed, or when mixtures of estrogens and androgens act simultaneously. In the case of the freemartin, the male twin begins sexual differentiation slightly earlier than the female and thus initiates modifications in her sexual differentiation before the normal genetic tendencies are strongly expressed.

The hormone theory has been amply confirmed by a variety of methods, including treatment of embryos with pure sex steroids. By this means complete, functional sex reversals have been induced in all classes of vertebrates, indicating the susceptibility of the sexual rudiments to hormonal influence. Estrogens stimulate development of the Mullerian ducts and their derivatives and cause development of the cortical or ovarian component of the rudimentary gonad and regression of the medullary or testicular component. Androgens stimulate development of the Wolffian ducts and their derivatives and induce regression of the gonadal cortex and development of the testis. In addition, in many species androgens cause regression of the Mullerian ducts. Estrogens, on the other hand, have little effect upon the Wolffian ducts. Castration of embryos at the indifferent stage has shown that the Wolffian ducts not only are stimulated to undergo accelerated development by androgens, but regress in the absence of the testes. The Mullerian ducts, on the other hand, persist after castration. Hence, although stimulated by estrogens, they are not hormone dependent for differentiation through the embryonic phases.

In some respects the response of the embryonic reproductive system in mammals is exceptional to the hormone theory of sex differentiation. The Mullerian and Wolffian ducts and their derivatives, as well as the urogenital sinus and external genitalia, respond in the expected way and complete reversals of these structures can be induced by steroid hormones. The

Figure 13-20. Actions of pituitary gonadotropins on the ovary and testis. This effect of prolactin on the ovary (marked by the asterisk) occurs in some rodents, but not in other vertebrates. An effect of prolactin upon the testis has not been demonstrated. (From B. Frye, *Hormonal Control in Vertebrates*. New York: Macmillan, 1967.)

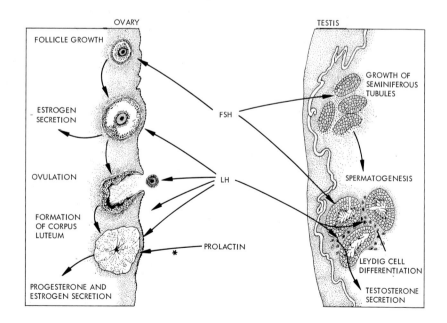

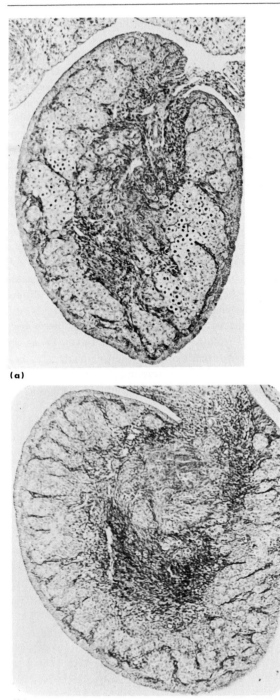

(a)

(b)

Figure 13-21. Reversal of gonad development in the opossum: (a) normal ovary; (b) testis which has been reversed by estrogen treatment. The reversed gonad has a fully formed cortex, complete with primordial germ cells, and cannot be distinguished from a normal ovary at the equivalent stage of development. Genetic sex was confirmed by the presence of the scrotum (see Figure 13-19). (Photographs courtesy of R. K. Burns.)

gonads, however, respond only to a limited degree in most species, and complete reversal has been achieved in only one species, the American opossum (Figure 13-21). In other mammals, androgens may cause slight hypertrophy of the rudimentary medulla of the female, or estrogens may cause unusual persistence of the germinal epithelium in the male. But ultimately such gonads develop into ovaries or testes according to the genetic sex of the individual, irrespective of hormonal treatment. The placenta is not a hormonally neutral environment, and steroids from the mother readily enter the fetal circulation. Hence the gonadal sex-determining mechanism may have evolved toward a more stable genetic control not susceptible to the influence of maternal hormones that would be expected to inhibit normal male development. With respect to this point, it may be significant that in the opossum, which is susceptible to hormonal influence, the young are born at a sexually indifferent stage of development and hence do not come under the influence of maternal hormones during the period of sex differentiation. The classic case of hormone-induced sex reversal in mammals, the freemartin, is thus exceptional among the eutherians, but even in this case the male gonad has not been shown to be susceptible to hormone effects.

Following embryonic sexual differentiation the reproductive system remains in an essentially infantile condition until the age of sexual maturation or puberty. Sexual maturation is caused by the secretion of gonadotropins, which stimulate the processes of gametogenesis and hormone secretion by the gonads. Experiments involving transplantation of immature gonads and pituitaries to adult animals indicate that these organs are capable of mature function during the infantile or juvenile period. Control over sexual maturation apparently resides in the hypothalamic centers that regulate the secretion of gonadotropins. Both inhibitory and stimulatory centers exist: damage to the former causes precocious puberty; damage to the latter delays or permanently prevents the occurrence of puberty. The factors that influence the differentiation of these centers and thus control the age of onset of sexual maturation are almost completely unknown. However, there is some evidence that the pineal is involved since its removal results in precocious puberty in some animals.

Sexual Cycles

In most animals reproduction is seasonal. Periods of reproduction alternate with periods of sexual inactivity. During the sexually inactive period the reproductive tract regresses to a juvenile condition and the animal is anatomically, physiologically, and behaviorally incapable of reproduction. With the onset of the reproductive season the gonads grow rapidly to their mature size and functional state and the reproductive tract develops to a state of readiness for breeding. In most cold-blooded vertebrates the reproductive cycle culminates in a period of courtship, mating, and spawning, after which the offspring are abandoned and the parents return to a sexually nonfunctional condition. This is by no means universal, however, and there are many species of elasmobranchs, teleosts, and reptiles that gestate or otherwise care for the offspring for an interval after fertilization. In virtually all birds and mammals mating is followed by incubation or gestation of the fertilized eggs and, after hatching or birth, by a period of parental care of the offspring. In these animals the complexity and duration of the reproductive cycle is considerably increased.

Seasonal sexual cycles are controlled by cycles of secretion of the reproductive hormones. During the nonreproductive part of the year, gonadotropins are secreted in very small amounts or not at all. With the approach of the breeding season the pituitary gland is activated and begins to secrete gonadotropins in gradually increasing amounts. These hormones induce gonadal recrudescence and sex hormone secretion, which in turn brings about the changes in anatomy, physiology, and behavior, characteristic of the breeding animal. Timing of the basic endocrine events (gonadotropin secretion) and therefore of the cycle itself is determined by environmental signals or cues. Many seasonal changes in the environment, including light, temperature, rainfall, abundance of food, and even moon phases, serve as cues for different species. The most common cue that governs patterns of reproductive activity among temperate zone animals is seasonal changes in the daily photoperiod, either the decreasing daylength of autumn or the increasing daylength of spring. Within the general seasonal pattern, numerous more specific cues may be involved in directing the sequence of events through the final stages of gonadal recrudescence and gamete production, mating, and rearing of the offspring. For example, among temperate zone birds in which the reproductive cycle is basically regulated by the photoperiod, completion of successful reproduction depends upon the interaction, often in proper sequence, of many factors, including an acceptable temperature range, a suitable food and water supply, an acceptable nesting site and nesting materials, the presence of a mate, courtship, the presence of eggs in the nest, and so on.†

Environmental influences on sexual cycles are mediated through stimulation or suppression of the gonadotropic functions of the pituitary gland, as already suggested (Figure 13-17). External stimuli that influence the pituitary are relayed through the central nervous system to the hypothalamus. There the environmental information is translated by the hypothalamic neurosecretory centers into hormonal output in the form of releasor substances that activate the secretion of gonadotropins. Although the influence of the hypothalamus over gonadotropin release is primarily stimulatory (except prolactin, the secretion of which is inhibited by the hypothalamus), there is also evidence for a restraining influence. In some animals it has been shown that lesions in some parts of the hypothalamus result in premature onset of reproductive activity.

Intrinsic factors are also important in the regulation of seasonal cyclicity, although the nature of these factors is poorly understood. Some animals continue to show normal or vestigial cycles for a year or more after reversal of the environmental cycle or after blinding, suggesting that some sort of physiological "clock" with a period of about a year exists. Many temperate zone birds, and possibly other animals as well, exhibit a so-called refractory period following the normal reproductive season. During this period stimuli

†This involves more than the obvious need for "two to tango." In some species gonadal development to the point of formation of mature gametes will not occur in the absence of a mate; hence there is some basic effect upon gonadotropin secretion.

that would cause development of the breeding condition in the spring at the beginning of the normal period of recrudescence are ineffective and the animals go into the period of sexual regression and inactivity that continues through the fall and winter. Sometime during this interval refractoriness ends and the animals are again able to respond to photoperiod changes or to other stimulatory cues in the spring. The nature of this refractoriness is not known, but it must involve some change in the sensitivity of the neuro-endocrine control mechanism to environmental stimuli. The apparent biological significance of refractoriness is that it prevents the production of offspring too late in the summer for their full growth and maturation before fall and winter, even though the summer environmental conditions might themselves be adequate to stimulate the reproductive processes.

During the annual reproductive season, female mammals go through one or more shorter sexual cycles known as estrous cycles. The most overt charac-teristic of the estrous cycle is a relatively brief period of estrus, or heat, during which the female is sexually receptive to the male. In fact, however, the estrous cycle is a complex combination of several interdependent cycles involving the pituitary gland, the ovary, and the reproductive tract. The basic function of the estrous cycle is to bring the reproductive tract of the female into a condition favorable for gestation and to synchronize this progestation-al state with sexual receptivity, ovulation, fertilization, and movement of the fertilized eggs into the uterus which is in a progestational state. Some species of nonmammalian vertebrates, especially among the birds and teleosts, exhibit repeating periods of reproductive activity during the breeding season and are capable of producing several broods of offspring per year. Although functionally similar, these cycles probably are not homolo-gous to the estrous cycles of mammals. Male animals usually do not show these lesser cycles of sexual activity and are continuously capable of repro-duction throughout the breeding season.

On the basis of events in the ovary, two distinct functional phases of the estrous cycle can be distinguished, a follicular phase and a luteal phase. During the follicular phase the young follicles grow under the influence of FSH and reach a stage of maturity ready for ovulation. LH stimulates an increasing level of secretion of ovarian hormones by the growing follicles. The predominant hormones secreted by the follicles prior to ovulation are estrogens, which promote the growth of the reproductive tract, particularly the uterine endometrium. This effect is augmented by the small amounts of progesterone secreted during the follicular phase.

Ovulation occurs under the influence of an abrupt rise in LH secretion that occurs during the last few hours of the follicular phase. This rise in LH, sometimes called the ovulatory surge of LH, is controlled by a special group of cells in the hypothalamus, which we may call the ovulation center. In most mammals the feedback of estrogen and progesterone upon the hypo-thalamus seems to trigger the release of the ovulatory surge of LH and ovulation occurs "spontaneously." There are some (notably members of the cat, ferret, and rabbit families), however, in which the stimulus of copulation is necessary to induce the release of the ovulatory surge of LH. Such animals are known as induced or reflex ovulators. The estrous cycle of reflex ovulators is normally arrested at the end of the follicular phase and the animals remain more or less in constant estrus until copulation occurs or the follicles degenerate.

Ovulation marks the beginning of the luteal phase of the estrous cycle. The empty follicle is transformed into the corpus luteum, which secretes large amounts of progesterone in addition to some estrogen. Progesterone acts upon the uterus to bring it into a progestational state. This includes (1) extensive growth of the endometrial glands and secretion by them of a fluid known as uterine milk; (2) inhibition of the contraction of the smooth muscle of the myometrial layer of the uterus and thus prevention of peristaltic movements of the uterus that would expel the embryo and prevent implantation; (3) susceptibility of the endometrium to the decidual reaction, a phenomenon basic to implantation. Briefly described, the decidual reaction is as follows: when a small object, normally the mature blastocyst, contacts the uterine wall the endometrial cells around it grow rapidly and soon encompass and overgrow it. At the same time the uterine tissue directly underneath the blastocyst is eroded, allowing it to sink into the surface of the endometrium. In this way, the blastocyst comes to be implanted in the uterine wall in close proximity to the uterine blood vessels. This reaction occurs only when the uterus is strongly stimulated by progesterone, and therefore normally occurs only during the luteal phase of the estrous cycle.

Progesterone also blocks the secretion of pituitary gonadotropins. As a consequence, further growth and ovulation of follicles is prevented. A new cycle of ovarian follicle growth cannot begin until the corpus luteum ceases to function. Regression of the corpus luteum in the infertile cycle appears to involve either a fall in LH secretion or the production of a "luteolytic" substance by the nonpregnant uterus, or both. As a result of the withdrawal of progesterone and estrogen support, the thickened endometrium is eroded and sloughed off. By the beginning of the next cycle it will have returned to its original size. In menstruation, which occurs only in higher primates, the erosion of the endometrium at the end of the cycle is more abrupt than in other mammals and is accompanied by bleeding. Endocrinologically, the menstrual cycle of primates is equivalent to the estrous cycle of other mammals, but generally there is no pronounced period of heat.

Gestation and Lactation
The primitive mode of reproduction in vertebrates involves release of the eggs and sperm into an aqueous environment where external fertilization occurs and the young are abandoned to develop without parental care. By this method a great wastage of gametes results from inefficient fertilization and the offspring have a low survival rate. Two general kinds of compensation for this wastage have arisen. The first is the production of extremely large numbers of gametes, with the result that the low percentage of fertilization and survival can be afforded. This condition is prevalent among the aquatic-breeding lower vertebrate classes. The second is the occurrence of some form of parental protection of the gametes and embryos, with the result that the efficiency of reproduction is increased and smaller numbers of gametes are required. In this latter category of adaptation are included internal fertilization, nest building and incubation or brooding of the eggs and young, and viviparity or gestation of the embryos within the reproductive tract of the female. Such adaptations, which are universal among terres-

trial vertebrates and make possible reproduction in the absence of environmental water, are also relatively common in some groups of aquatic animals,
especially elasmobranchs and some families of teleosts.

Viviparity, or the bearing of live young, is universal in mammals (except
the egg-laying monotremes) and also occurs in some representatives of
all other vertebrate classes except birds. Three stages in the evolution
of viviparity may be recognized: (1) oviparity, in which eggs are laid
and the young develop outside the body of the mother; (2) ovovivi-
parity, in which the eggs are retained in the reproductive tract
of the female where they develop to the point of hatching, but
in which the essential nutrients required by the developing embryo are
contained in the yolky egg, and little or no exchange occurs between the
embryo and the mother; (3) true viviparity, in which the embryos are not
only protected within the reproductive tract of the mother but also carry
out extensive physiological exchange of nutrients, respiratory gases, and
wastes with the mother. There is no absolute distinction between ovovivipar-
ity and viviparity. Generally ovoviviparous species produce large yolky eggs
and do not form intimate connection between the fetus and the mother,
whereas viviparous species produce relatively less yolky eggs, epitomized by
the minute alecithal eggs of mammals, and form an elaborate placenta for
physiological exchange between the fetus and the mother.

Placentation always involves some sort of intimate apposition or fusion of
fetal to maternal tissues. Gestation usually takes place in the oviduct (elasmobranchs) or uterus (mammals). In teleosts, however, gestation occurs
either in the follicle itself, or in the ovarian cavity. In ovoviviparous amphibians the eggs may be retained in the oviduct or they may develop in a
temporary pouch or pit in the skin of the back of the female.† Whatever
the site of gestation, the maternal tissue around the embryo becomes highly
vascular and thin, and is often thrown into folds or villi that increase the
area of contact with the embryo. The fetal portion of the mammalian
placenta is most commonly formed from the extra-embryonic membranes,
yolk sac, chorion, and allantois (Chapter 3), but among teleosts and amphibians other specializations are found. Thus, in cyprinodontid teleosts the pericardial cavity or the hindgut may develop into an expanded vascular sac that
is closely applied to the wall of the follicle, or villous folds of the ovarian
wall may grow into the mouth and gill chamber of the embryo and temporarily function in the role of placenta. In amphibians the tail is expanded
into a vascular membrane which acts as a placenta.

In mammals, the placenta is always formed from the extra-embryonic
membranes (see Chapter 3). Depending on which of these membranes are
primarily involved, several kinds of placentae may be recognized in various
groups or at progressive stages of fetal development. These include (1) the
yolk sac or choriovitelline placenta, (2) the chorionic placenta, and (3) the
chorioallantoic placenta.

In its simplest form the yolk-sac placenta consists of the apposed
membranes of the endodermal yolk sac and the ectodermal trophoblast.

---

†True viviparity is not found in amphibians, and only a few ovoviviparous species are
known.

Sometime the trophoblast is secondarily eroded away in some areas, exposing the yolk sac directly to the uterus. This type of placenta is not vascularized, and apparently absorbs secretions ("uterine milk") from the uterine lumen and transfers it from cell to cell to the embryonic vascular area or gut. When mesoderm invades between the trophoblast and yolk sac, the membrane becomes vascularized from the vitelline vessels and is known as a choriovitelline placenta. Yolk-sac placentae are found in viviparous elasmobranchs, reptiles, and marsupials, and form transiently during the early development of eutherian mammals. In some ungulates and rodents the yolk sac may persist as an important part of the placenta until relatively late in pregnancy, or even until term.

The chorioallantoic placenta is formed by the apposition of the splanchnopleure of the allantois,† which expands into the extra-embryonic coelom, against the overlying somatopleure of the chorion. Vascularization is via the allantoic or umbilical vessels. The surface of the placenta is thrown into a series of small folds or projections, the chorionic villi, each of which contains a vascular core derived from the allantoic mesoderm. These villi may occur over the entire surface of the chorioallantoic membrane, forming a so-called *placenta diffusa*. Often, however, they have a more restricted distribution, as in a disk on one side of the chorionic sac (*placenta discoidalis*), a band around the middle of the sac (*placenta zonaria*), or scattered patches (*placenta cotyledonaria*). Basically there are six cellular or tissue layers interposed between the maternal and fetal blood streams. These are (1) the endothelium of the uterine capillaries, (2) the endometrial connective tissue, and (3) the uterine epithelium on the maternal side of the placenta, and (4) the trophoblastic ectoderm, (5) the chorioallantoic connective tissue, and (6) the endothelium of the fetal capillaries on the fetal side. Although collectively quite thin, these layers constitute a selective barrier to the rapid exchange of substances between the mother and the fetus; but as an adaptation to facilitate more rapid exchange they become secondarily reduced or lost in various species.

In mammals, at least, pregnancy is under hormonal control and the placenta itself is a major source of the hormones involved in the maintenance and termination of pregnancy. A simplified view of the endocrinology of pregnancy is that it is a prolongation and intensification of the luteal phase of the estrous cycle. Under the influence of LH, and chorionic gonadotropin, a placental hormone with actions similar to LH, the corpus luteum persists and continues to secrete progesterone and estrogen. These hormones are essential for the progestational development of the uterus and for implantation, as described before, and for the continued growth of the uterus during gestation. Under the predominant influence of progesterone the myometrium is kept in a relaxed state and thus premature labor is prevented. The corpus luteum is the primary source of progesterone and estrogen during early pregnancy, and in some animals it is the major source of these hormones throughout pregnancy. In many species, however, the placenta also secretes progesterone and estrogen and ultimately becomes the predominant

---

†The endodermal layer of the allantois usually undergoes only very limited outgrowth, and the allantoic contribution to the placenta is mainly mesodermal.

source of these hormones. Similarly, the placental production of gonadotropin at first supplements, then eventually replaces, the gonadotropic functions of the pituitary as pregnancy proceeds. The secretion of gonadotropins and sex steroids by the placenta seems to be an adaptation for maintaining sufficient amounts of these hormones to meet the requirements for a prolonged pregnancy. In addition, since the levels and balance of these hormones are important in the initiation of labor, this aspect of placental function is vital in regulating the normal duration of gestation. Nothing is known about the control of placental endocrine function, however.

Labor is a series of rhythmic muscular contractions of the uterus that lead to the expulsion of the fetus and placenta. The hormonal control of labor includes (1) reversal of progesterone/estrogen domination of the myometrium: progesterone suppresses contraction, estrogen facilitates contractions. At the end of pregnancy progesterone secretion falls earlier than estrogen, with the result that contractions are favored; (2) induction and/or augmentation of labor by oxytocin. Oxytocin is secreted by the posterior pituitary during labor, presumably in response to stimuli emanating from the gravid uterus. Oxytocin greatly augments the contraction of smooth muscle in the estrogen-dominated uterus. Experimentally, oxytocin injections will induce labor to begin, but whether secretion of oxytocin is the event that normally initiates labor is unknown.

The endocrinology of gestation and labor in lower vertebrates is almost completely unknown. As has been mentioned before, corpora lutea are formed in the ovaries of most groups of lower vertebrates. Because in some viviparous and ovoviviparous species these structures are larger and persist longer than in related oviparous species, they may play some role in pregnancy. This has not been demonstrated, however.

All birds and mammals as well as a few species of lower vertebrates provide the young with a period of protection and/or nutrition after birth or hatching. Feeding of the young by means of milk produced by mammary glands is an exclusive mammalian characteristic.† The number of glands ranges from one to eleven pairs, located along the ventral abdomen from the thoracic to the inguinal region.

Lactation includes three phases, all of which are hormone dependent.

1. Development of the ducts and secretory cells of the mammary glands. Estrogen promotes the early stages of duct growth. Progesterone is synergistic with estrogen. Together they cause full growth and branching of the ducts and the formation of the secretory alveoli at the ends of the ducts. This state of development is reached in the sexually mature, prelactating female, but maximum morphological development occurs during pregnancy under the influence of the high levels of estrogen and progesterone.

2. Milk secretion. Secretion refers to the synthesis and accumulation of milk in the mammary alveoli. Prolactin is the major hormone involved in stimulating secretion by the fully formed gland, but insulin and somatotropin also play an important role in this process. Continuation of milk

---

†Analogous structures are occasionally found in other groups, however. Passerine birds have crop glands that produce a secretion which is regurgitated and fed to the young. The discus fish possesses a glandular patch on the abdomen that produces a secretion which is sloughed off and eaten by the young.

secretion requires continued suckling. If the young are weaned, the mammary glands rapidly involute to a nonsecretory state. Apparently, suckling provides a stimulus that, acting through the hypothalamus, causes a continuation of prolactin secretion. Progesterone, although promoting the morphological development of the mammary gland, actually inhibits milk secretion. Hence, lactation during pregnancy is prevented until progesterone levels fall near term.

3. Milk let-down. Most of the milk produced by the lactating mammary gland is retained in the secretory alveoli until suckling, at which time the milk is ejected from the alveoli by the contraction of a "basket" of smooth muscle fibrils around the alveoli. This active ejection of milk following stimulation of the nipples, or other stimuli such as sight or sound of the hungry infant, is the result of a neuroendocrine reflex that causes secretion of oxytocin from the posterior pituitary. Oxytocin causes contraction of the muscle fibrils around the alveoli much as it promotes contractions of uterine muscle.

References for Chapter 13

Barr, W. A., "Patterns of Ovarian Activity" in *Perspectives in Endocrinology,* E. J. W. Barrington (ed.), New York: Academic Press, 1968. A brief, comparative treatment of the ovary, including development, structure, oögenesis and ovulation, regulation, and endocrinology.

Bullough, W. S., *Vertebrate Reproductive Cycles.* New York: Wiley, 1961. A very concise, elementary book on sexual cycles of vertebrates.

Burns, R. K., Jr., "Urogenital System" in *Analysis of Development,* B. H. Willier, P. A. Weiss, and V. Hamburger (eds.), Philadelphia: W. B. Saunders. This is recommended for its excellent presentation of the development of the reproductive system and its relationship to the urinary system. Thoroughly treats the experimental work, including hormonal control of sex differentiation.

Chester Jones, I. (ed.), "Hormones in Fish." *Symposia of the Zoological Society of London,* No. 1, Four of the eight chapters deal with reproduction.

Lofts, B., "Patterns of Testicular Activity" in *Perspectives in Endocrinology,* E. J. W. Barrington (ed.), New York: Academic Press, 1968. An excellent treatment of testicular morphology and function with comparative emphasis.

Nalbandov, A. V., *Reproductive Physiology,* 2nd ed. San Francisco: Freeman, 1964. An introductory text, very readable. Emphasis is on domesticated mammals and birds.

Parkes, A. S. (ed.), *Marshall's Physiology of Reproduction,* Vols. I-III. London: Longmans Green, 1952-1966. This is a sourcebook of information concerning all aspects of the biology of reproduction. Covers structure, function, and comparative aspects. Most chapters are exhaustively detailed.

van Tienhoven, Ari, *Reproductive Physiology of Vertebrates.* Philadelphia: W. B. Saunders, 1968. An introductory, comparative text. Although function is emphasized, there is a balanced treatment of morphology as well.

Velardo, J. T. (ed.), *Endocrinology of Reproduction.* Fair Lawn, New Jersey:

Oxford University Press, 1958. This is an introductory text, strongly human in orientation.

Young, W. C. (ed.), *Sex and Internal Secretions,* Vols. I and II. Baltimore: Williams and Wilkins, 1961. An advanced treatise by many authors, covering all aspects of reproduction from sex determination and development to psychology and sociology. Not good for morphology, except development.

Zuckerman, S. (ed.), *The Ovary,* Vols. I and II. New York: Academic Press, 1962. An advanced comparative treatise of ovarian biology, all aspects.

Part three: the integrated organism

14

A model for the further study of chordate structure and function

In the preface to this book it was stated that the summary chapter would present briefly the quantitative phylogenetic method of synthesis described in Chapter 1, with actual data on chordate structure and function derived from other portions of the present text. To realize this goal we have accepted as OTUs the eight classes of the Vertebrata delimited in Chapter 2: Agnatha, Placodermi, Chondrichthyes, Osteichthyes, Amphibia, Reptilia, Aves, and Mammalia. The data used to describe these OTUs are taken entirely from Chapter 6, "The Musculoskeletal System: An Evolutionary Perspective." Sixty-two characters are employed, and they are coded in the binary form of present or absent (see Table 14-1). Other characters from this chapter were also considered, but in the final tabulation they were eliminated because they seemed to be logically redundant, at least in some large part, to others already used. Although the binary coding has forced some rather coarse interpretations of the data, it has been used for convenience of discussion, and also because the problems of character standardization and differential character weighting are largely bypassed. Decisions on which character state to score for a particular OTU were based on the following criterion: If a state is believed to be present in the more primitive (as inferred from other evidence) members of an OTU, but not in derived forms (although the latter may occur in more taxa), it was scored as present. For example, in the OTU Reptilia, the sternum is considered present; this acknowledges the fact that the more primitive reptiles possessed a sternum, and it ignores the absence of the structure in snakes and some other reptile lineages that are believed to be derived. Table 14-2 lists the sixty-two characters in their numerically described form (either 0 or 1).

In the reconstruction of the most parsimonious phylogenetic tree shown in Figure 14-1, those character states possessed by the Agnatha were considered primitive. Although lengthy and cogent arguments can be generated for the primitiveness of 50 percent of the agnathan states,† the remainder of the characters are either questionable or appear to directly contradict the thesis that the Agnatha is the most primitive OTU. Most of the characters that are difficult to interpret relate directly to the evolution of jaws, paired appendages, girdles and derived conditions, and associated functional features. If the

†Characters 1, 2, 3, 4, 7, 9, 11, 12, 15, 16, 19, 20, 28, 29, 30, 32, 40, 42, 43, 44, 45, 46, 47, 48, 49, 50, 54, 55, 60, and 62.

Table 14-1. Sixty-two binary characters taken from Chapter 6.

Characters	Agnatha	Placodermi	Chondrichthyes	Osteichthyes	Amphibia	Reptilia	Aves	Mammalia
1. Intrinsic integumentary muscles present							+	+
2. The extrinsic integumentary muscle, panniculus carnosus, present								+
3. The extrinsic integumentary muscle, platysma, present								+
4. Axial locomotion present	+	+	+	+	+	+		
5. Appendicular locomotion present					+	+	+	+
6. Trunk musculature divided into epaxial and hypaxial masses		+	+	+	+	+	+	+
7. Distinct myomeric segmentation present	+	+	+	+	+			
8. Sternum absent	+	+	+	+				
9. Sternum bony							+	+
10. Dorsal ribs present		+	+	+	+	+	+	+
11. Ventral ribs present (functioning as ribs)		+	+	+				
12. Dorsal ribs bicipital				+	+	+		
13. Neural arches present		+	+	+	+	+	+	+
14. Haemal arches present		+	+	+	+	+	+	+
15. Intercalary plates present			+					
16. Intercentrum present				+	+			
17. Pleurocentrum present				+	+	+	+	
18. Sclerotomic-centrum resegmentation				+	+	+	+	
19. Sclerocoel present in middle of sclerotome						+	+	+
20. Fin-fold type of appendages	+	+						
21. Biserial fin type of appendage (or its tetrapod derivative)			+	+	+	+	+	
22. Coracoid present		+	+	+	+	+	+	+
23. Scapula present		+	+	+	+	+	+	+
24. Suprascapula present		+	+	+	+	+	+	+
25. Glenoid fossa located on scapula only					+	+	+	+
26. Clavicle present		+		+	+	+	+	+
27. Cleithrum present		+		+	+	+		
28. Supracleithrum present		+		+				
29. Posttemporal present		+		+				
30. Posttemporal firmly articulates with dermocranium		+		+				
31. Interclavicle present					+	+	+	+
32. Procoracoid present								+
33. Pelvic girdle develops from three centers of ossification					+	+	+	+
34. Pelvic girdle in contact with vertebral column					+	+	+	+
35. Gills function as a major respiratory surface	+	+	+	+				
36. Costal suction type of respiratory pumping mechanism						+	+	+
37. Gill arches jointed		+	+	+	+	+	+	+

Table 14-1 (continued)

Characters	Agnatha	Placodermi	Chondrichthyes	Osteichthyes	Amphibia	Reptilia	Aves	Mammalia
38. Branchiomeric musculature internal of gill arches	+							
39. First visceral arch forms jaws		+	+	+	+	+	+	+
40. Jaws exclusively, or nearly so, cartilaginous		+	+					
41. Second visceral arch forms (in part) hyoid apparatus					+	+	+	+
42. Third visceral arch forms (in part) hyoid apparatus					+	+	+	
43. Fourth visceral arch forms (in part) hyoid apparatus					+			
44. Fifth visceral arch forms (in part) hyoid apparatus					+			
45. Sixth visceral arch forms (in part) hyoid apparatus					+			
46. Muscularized diaphragm present								+
47. Paleostyly type of jaw suspension present		+						
48. Hyostyly type of jaw suspension present			+	+				
49. Autodiastyly type of jaw suspension present					+	+	+	
50. Craniostyly type of jaw suspension present								+
51. Columella (hyomandibular) present					+	+	+	+
52. Articular bone, or its derivative, forms as separate center of ossification				+	+	+	+	+
53. Quadrate bone, or its derivative, forms as separate center of ossification				+	+	+	+	+
54. Malleus (articular) present								+
55. Incus (quadrate) present								+
56. Superficial layer of enamel present in dermal armor (dermal scales included)	+	+	+	+				
57. Dentine-like layer of material present in dermal armor (dermal scales included)	+	+	+	+				
58. Vascular or spongy bone layer present in dermal armor (dermal scales included)	+	+		+				
59. Lamellar or compact layer of bone present in dermal armor (dermal scales included)	+	+		+	+			
60. Cosmine layer present in dermal armor (dermal scales included)				+				
61. Dermocranium present		+		+	+	+	+	+
62. Opercular series of dermal cranial elements present		+		+				

working hypotheses that ancestral vertebrates were jawless and without paired appendages and girdles are assumed, then the agnathan states of these sets of characters may be considered primitive also. Both the paleontological record of vertebrates and the supposed derivative relationship of the vertebrata from the cephalochordate-tunicate stocks support this assumption unequivocally. Similar reasoning and evidence exist to support the view that the states exhibited by the Agnatha in the characters of the vertebrae, gill arches, and dermal armor composition and related dermocranium should be considered primitive. In summary, the assumption that all agnathan states are primitive can be reasonably well documented; errors of interpretation are

Table 14-2

Characters	Classes of vertebrates and hypothetical intermediates	Agnatha	Placodermi	Chondrichthyes	Osteichthyes	Amphibia	Reptilia	Aves	Mammalia	Intermediate 1	Intermediate 2	Intermediate 3	Intermediate 4
1.		0	0	0	0	0	0	1	1	0	0	0	0
2.		0	0	0	0	0	0	0	1	0	0	0	0
3.		0	0	0	0	0	0	0	1	0	0	0	0
4.		1	1	1	1	1	1	0	0	1	1	1	1
5.		0	0	0	0	1	1	1	1	0	0	0	1
6.		0	1	1	1	1	1	1	1	1	1	1	1
7.		1	1	1	1	1	0	0	0	1	1	1	1
8.		1	1	1	1	0	0	0	0	1	1	1	0
9.		0	0	0	0	0	0	1	1	0	0	0	0
10.		0	1	1	1	1	1	1	1	1	1	1	1
11.		0	1	1	1	0	0	0	0	1	1	1	0
12.		0	0	0	0	1	1	1	0	0	0	0	1
13.		0	1	1	1	1	1	1	1	1	1	1	1
14.		0	1	1	1	1	1	1	1	1	1	1	1
15.		0	0	1	0	0	0	0	0	0	0	0	0
16.		0	0	0	0	1	1	0	0	0	0	0	1
17.		0	0	0	0	1	1	1	1	0	0	0	1
18.		0	0	0	0	1	1	1	1	0	0	0	1
19.		0	0	0	0	0	1	1	1	0	0	0	0
20.		0	1	1	0	0	0	0	0	1	1	0	0
21.		0	0	0	1	1	1	1	1	0	0	1	1
22.		0	1	1	1	1	1	1	1	1	1	1	1
23.		0	1	1	1	1	1	1	1	1	1	1	1
24.		0	1	1	1	1	1	1	1	1	1	1	1
25.		0	0	0	0	1	1	1	1	0	0	0	1
26.		0	1	0	1	1	1	1	1	0	1	1	1
27.		0	1	0	1	1	1	0	0	0	1	1	1
28.		0	1	0	1	0	0	0	0	0	1	1	0
29.		0	1	0	1	0	0	0	0	0	1	1	0
30.		0	1	0	1	0	0	0	0	0	1	1	0

almost certain to be few and therefore will have very little effect on the reconstructed phylogeny.

The character states of the four hypothetical intermediates required to generate the most parsimonious tree (Figure 14-1) are listed in Table 14-2. Figure 14-2 is an exact translation of the reconstructed most parsimonious tree. The translation was employed as the final graphic product of the reconstruction because it reflects all the seven extant taxa onto the same horizontal plane in time that is equivalent to the Recent period. Moreover, the translated tree approximates more closely in a graphic sense those classically formed and therefore makes comparisons easier between the two.

Table 14-2 (continued)

Characters	Classes of vertebrates and hypothetical intermediates	Agnatha	Placodermi	Chondrichthyes	Osteichthyes	Amphibia	Reptilia	Aves	Mammalia	Intermediate 1	Intermediate 2	Intermediate 3	Intermediate 4
31.		0	0	0	0	1	1	1	1	0	0	0	1
32.		0	0	0	0	0	0	0	1	0	0	0	0
33.		0	0	0	0	1	1	1	1	0	0	0	1
34.		0	0	0	0	1	1	1	1	0	0	0	1
35.		1	1	1	1	0	0	0	0	1	1	1	0
36.		0	0	0	0	0	1	1	1	0	0	0	1
37.		0	1	1	1	1	1	1	1	1	1	1	1
38.		1	0	0	0	0	0	0	0	0	0	0	0
39.		0	1	1	1	1	1	1	1	1	1	1	1
40.		0	1	1	0	0	0	0	0	1	1	0	0
41.		0	0	0	0	1	1	1	1	0	0	0	1
42.		0	0	0	0	1	1	1	0	0	0	0	1
43.		0	0	0	0	1	0	0	0	0	0	0	0
44.		0	0	0	0	1	0	0	0	0	0	0	0
45.		0	0	0	0	1	0	0	0	0	0	0	0
46.		0	0	0	0	0	0	0	1	0	0	0	0
47.		0	1	0	0	0	0	0	0	0	0	0	0
48.		0	0	1	1	0	0	0	0	0	0	0	0
49.		0	0	0	0	1	1	1	0	0	0	0	1
50.		0	0	0	0	0	0	0	1	0	0	0	0
51.		0	0	0	0	1	1	1	1	0	0	0	1
52.		0	0	0	1	1	1	1	1	0	0	1	1
53.		0	0	0	1	1	1	1	1	0	0	1	1
54.		0	0	0	0	0	0	0	1	0	0	0	0
55.		0	0	0	0	0	0	0	1	0	0	0	0
56.		1	1	1	1	0	0	0	0	1	1	1	0
57.		1	1	1	1	0	0	0	0	1	1	1	0
58.		1	1	0	1	0	0	0	0	1	1	1	0
59.		1	1	0	1	1	0	0	0	1	1	1	1
60.		0	0	0	1	0	0	0	0	0	0	0	0
61.		0	1	0	1	1	1	1	1	1	1	1	1
62.		0	1	0	1	0	0	0	0	1	1	1	0

From the point of view of the robustness of the untranslated and translated versions (Figures 14-1 and 14-2 respectively), that is, how much perturbation the two can withstand without being affected significantly, the more classically formed one is the best. For example, the translated tree shows Aves and Mammalia derived from a common stock, whereas the untranslated form shows Aves giving rise to Mammalia. The latter condition is simply a product of the fact that Aves is identical to a hypothetical intermediate OTU which is the ancestor of both Aves and Mammalia. In the translated version the derivation of Aves and Mammalia from an ancestral OTU which is different from either is consistent with the fact that the two OTUs are different. It is due only to an artifact of our restricted data set that we have not been able to express that difference.

If we assume that phylogenies constructed previously by other workers are working hypotheses, intuitively formed or not, then Figure 14-2 can be compared with them for degree of fit. This approach permits us to ascertain points of similarity that therefore may be taken as tentatively confirmed. But more important from a heuristic point of view, the points of poor fit are to be considered as areas that demand further independent testing with data other than those employed in the reconstruction of the trees. It is true that we will want to recheck all the observations and test independently all the assumptions that have gone into the formation of the trees being compared, but it is the areas of poor fit that demand immediate attention. A

Figure 14-1. The maximum parsimony phyletic tree based on the eight classes of Vertebrata and the sixty-two binary characters described and tabulated in Tables 14-1 and 14-2. Except for the Prevertebrate-Agnatha lineage, the relative lengths of the lines between the branching points are proportionate to the sum of the character state differences that distinguish the OTUs connected to them.

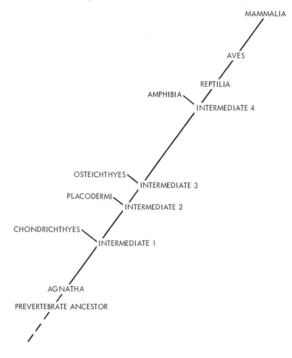

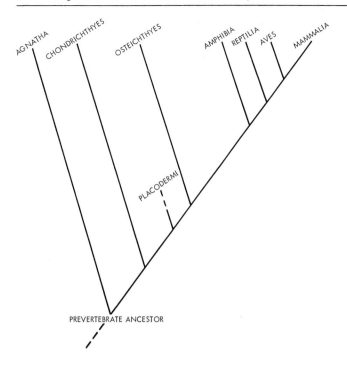

Figure 14-2. The maximum parsimony phylogeny of vertebrate classes (from Figure 14-1) translated into the more classically formed dendrogram. The relative lengths of the lines between the branching points are proportionate to the sum of the character state differences that distinguish the two OTUs. All of the phyletic lines are extended to the same horizontal level in time owing to their contemporaneity in the present, except the Placodermi, which became extinct in the Mississippian.

comparison of Figure 14-2 with Figure 2-1, which is an intuitively formed summary of a large number of other works, immediately focuses attention on two areas of dissimilarity: the relationship between chondrichthyians, placoderms, and osteichthyians, and that between reptiles, birds, and mammals.

The discrepancy between the two phylogenies, in terms of reptiles, birds, and mammals, may in fact be more a function of graphics than a biological reality. That the taxonomic boundary of the OTU Reptilia includes the inter-mediate that gave rise to both Aves and the Mammalia is almost certain to be true. Therefore, the present characterization of the lineage termed Reptilia may be based on characters that describe a primitive stock that gave rise to some reptiles, but do not describe the primitive stock from which evolved the bird and mammal lines. A recent re-interpretation of the relationships between the Archosauria, which includes the ancestors of birds, and the Lepidosauria and the Synapsida supports this point of view (see Figure 14-3).

The relationship of the chondrichthyians to the placoderms that is expressed in the parsimony phylogeny (Figure 14-2) differs considerably from the current, generally accepted point of view. As intuitively summar-ized in Figure 2-1, the chondrichthyians (at least in part) are always shown to be derived directly from a placoderm ancestor, whereas the parsimony phylogeny depicts them as derived from a preplacoderm ancestor. Given this difference of opinion we are forced to ask the question: What are the data that have led to the generally accepted, contradictory point of view (Figure 2-1)? In answer, a brief review of the literature strongly suggests that in fact the scant existing data are either circumstantial or conjectural or both. For example, Romer [4] has commented recently: "Of the living cartilaginous jawed fishes, it is quite possible that the elasmobranchs are of placoderm origin, but there is no positive evidence." He went on to elaborate further that the evidence for deriving the other major group of chondrichthyians, the Holocephali (chimeras), from placoderms is of a more positive nature, but even here there are radically different opinions on just which placoderm lineage it was. Actually, the current opinion may be based on a very old

Figure 14-3. An intuitively constructed dendrogram of the relationships and origins of archosaurian and lepidosaurian reptiles. (Not to scale; redrawn from Reig, 1967.)

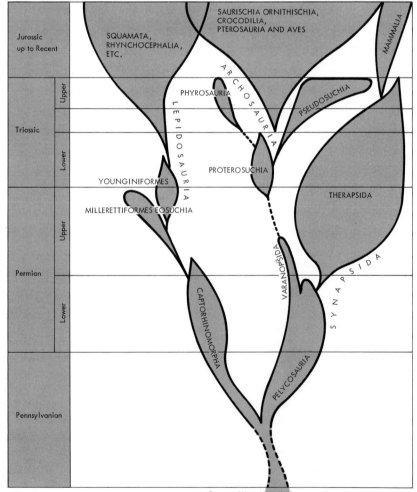

Common Mississippian Anthracosaur Ancestors

error, at least in large part. Early students of phylogeny assumed that the absence of a bony skeleton in chondrichthyians was unequivocal evidence of their primitiveness (e.g., cartilage precedes cartilaginous bone in vertebrate ontogeny), and accordingly they were placed very near the ancestral stock of vertebrates. Today it is generally assumed that the chondrichthyians are skeletally degenerate and therefore the absence of a bony skeleton is really a derived condition. The data supporting this current belief appear to be rather circumstantial, and indeed the associated reasoning does not seem very sound. The circumstantial nature of the data derives from the fact that the first chondrichthyians do not appear in the fossil record until the middle Devonian, and then only as isolated teeth, whereas the placoderms had already undergone considerable radiation by that time.

The defense of the current majority view on chondrichthyian relationships is very often concluded with the question: "Why don't we find them earlier if the group is so primitive, since their teeth are found in abundance later in the fossil record?" In countering this rhetorical question we would point out that it seems very unrealistic to use this kind of indirect evidence to infer phyletic relationships for a group that is supposed to be skeletally degenerate. Also, it is very important to note that Silurian vertebrates have been found at very few sites, and that these sites have not yet been thoroughly studied. In the parsimony phylogeny the position of the chondrichthyians is greatly influenced by their "skeletal degeneracy"† which for obvious reasons relates them more closely to agnathans than to placoderms. From this brief review it should be clear even to the beginning student that the problem of the origin of the chondrichthyians has not yet been solved, nor can we offer any unequivocal opinion on the matter in this short chapter. However, the objective nature of the data recorded here and the objective procedure used to reconstruct the phyletic relationships should give future researchers a much firmer foundation on which to build and to criticise.

Ultimately, in a study of this kind one should check the predictive power of his quantitatively constructed tree. One way of assessing the predictiveness is to restudy separately those characters which the tree indicates have homoplasious states. In a sense, the reality of the tree can be assessed directly from a knowledge of its ability to generate accurate predictions. In the present most parsimonious tree, characters 11, 12, 16, 20, 40, 42, 48, 49, 58, 59, and 62 all exhibit evolutionary reversals. It is hoped that the reader will undertake their restudy and thereby ascertain the predictive reliability of the tree. Most of the restudy of these suggested reversals will necessarily impinge on other methodologies that will in turn produce additional data. These restudies will almost certainly emphasize the functional aspects, as stressed in the previous chapters.

As you read this book and pursue related courses, you will find it very profitable to recheck all the characters that have been recorded from the chapter on muscles and the skeletal system (Tables 14-1 and 14-2). Similarly, you should go through all other chapters and from them build a much larger data set. If this data set is carefully compiled, it should be robust in terms of the quantitatively formed phyletic conclusions which can be derived from

†Characters 26, 27, 28, 29, 30, 47, 61, and 62.

it. In addition, it would be very instructive to develop laboratory exercises or independent studies around the discovery of new characters and the restudy of old ones. More advanced students will very likely wish to study specific problem areas, for example the relationship between placoderms, chondrichthyians, and osteichthyians, the evolution of tetrapodism, and the relationship between reptiles, birds, and mammals. Although most of these studies will require a review in depth of the literature, particularly that on the fossil forms, and embryological studies as well, much can be learned by simply dissecting representatives of extant taxa from each problem area. This will be particularly true if one selects species for dissection that have as yet received little study. Moreover, in most of these studies the investigator will be able to consider as OTUs taxa much below the hierarchic level of the classes used herein. In these cases there will be proportionately fewer artificial cases of polyphyly, and the results should be considered more in keeping with the details of our present knowledge.

References for Chapter 14

[1]   Ørvig, Tor (ed.), "Current Problems of Lower Vertebrate Phylogeny" in *Proceedings of the Fourth Nobel Symposium* held in June, 1967, at the Swedish Museum of Natural History (Naturhistoriska Riksmuseet) in Stockholm. New York: Interscience, 1968. Twenty-eight separate papers are included in this volume, most of which are devoted to studies in depth or reviews of specific taxa or problems. Most of the papers are excellent and relevant to this textbook.

[2]   Reig, Osvaldo A., "Archosaurian Reptiles: A New Hypothesis on Their Origins." *Sci.*, **157**, No. 3788 (1967), 565-568. The author has re-interpreted the characteristics of the first archosaurs and concludes that they could not have had a common ancestry with lepidosaurs.

[3]   Romer, Alfred S., *Notes and Comments on Vertebrate Paleontology.* Chicago: The University of Chicago Press, 1968. This book is devoted to a discussion of the more controversial problems of the evolutionary history of vertebrates. The book forms a companion volume to Romer's *Vertebrate Paleontology.*

[4]   ——, Review of Tor Ørvig (ed.), "Current Problems of Lower Vertebrate Phylogeny" (the first item above). *Sci.*, **164** (1969), 1510-1511. The review clearly points out the numerous different points of view on vertebrate relationships. The differences between the American and Swedish schools of paleontology are particularly obvious.

Index/glossary

Italic numbers refer to illustrations or tables.

A

Abiotic evolution, *46*

Ablate: *To remove surgically,* 460

Acanthodians, *73*

Accomodation: *Automatic focal adjustment by the eye for various distances,* 398, 401

Accretion: *Increase by external addition,* 144

Acetabular fossa: *Cup-shaped depression on the hip bone into which the head of the femur fits, 199*

Acetylcholine: *Chemical mediator (neurosecretion) at many synapses in the nervous system,* 425, 431, 434

Acinus: *Smallest lobule of a compound gland (salivary gland, pancreas), or a sac-like dilation,* 251, *252*

Acoustic: *Pertaining to the sense of hearing,* 414, *415*

Acromegaly, 474

Acrosome: *Cap-like structure investing the anterior half of the spermatozoan head, 93, 93,* 94

ACTH, 473

Actinopterygians, *73*

Acousticolateralis system, 409

Adaptation: *Hereditary adjustment to the environment by means of natural selection; adjustment by the eye,* 7, 398

Adaption, 7

Adipose tissue: *Fatty tissue,* 146, 148

Advanced character state: *One derived from another; a relative term, involving a comparison of two states,* 16

Afferent systems: *Conveying inward, from the periphery to the center,* 388, *389, 428,* 451, 454

Agnatha, 66, 499

Agnathia: *Jawless, as in the most primitive vertebrates (Ostracoderms),* 43

Agonistic behavior: *Behavior in attack and defense, during "fight or flight,"* 436

Air bladder (*see* Swim bladder)

Air breathing, phylogeny, 299

Air sacs, 312, 314

Allantois: *Tubular diverticulum of the posterior part of the hindgut of an amniote embryo,* 81, *124,* 126

Allele: *One or two or more contrasting genes, situated at the same locus in homologous chromosomes, that determine alternative characteristics in inheritance.*

Allocortex: *Older cerebral cortex comprised of the archicortex and the paleocortex,* 438

Allophenic mouse, 104, *106,* 107

Alveolar sacs, 302

Alveolus, lung, 302

Amacrine: *Neuron in the retina with dendrites but no axon,* 404

Amblystoma (Ambystoma) *jeffersonianum, 430*

Ameloblast: *Cell that gives rise to tooth enamel,* 268

Amia, 75, 153, *232, 238,* 301

Ammocoetes, 253, *254,* 478

Amnion: *Cellular membrane of embryonic origin enclosing the amniote embryo,* 81, *124,* 126

Amniotes: *Vertebrates whose embryo is enclosed by the amnionic membrane.*
aves, 84
mammalia, 85
reptilia, 80

C

D

E

Ear
to Fins

F

G

Gonads [*cont.*]
  rudimentary, 523
  steroids of, 527
Graafian follicles, *103, 127,* 505
Granulocyte: *Mature granular leukocyte (white blood cell).*
Guanophore, *Cell containing guanine crystals which produce interference in the light and thus give the cell a silvery appearance,* 149

Gupherus agassizii, 173
Gustatory (gustation): *Pertaining to the sense of taste,* 393
Gut (*see* Digestive tract)
Gymnarchus niloticus, 240
Gyrencephalic brain: *Mammalian brain with a cerebral cortex marked by convolutions (gyri and sulci),* 438
Gyrus: *Convoluted ridge between sulci on the surface of the cerebrum,* 438

**Graafian
to Integumental**

H

Haemal (hemal) organ, 466
Hagfish, 67, 255
  archinephros, 366
  digestive system, 255
  evolution, 69
  gill, 297, *298*
  pronephros, 366
Hair, 164, *165*
  color, 166
  follicle of, 166
  lanuago, 165
Head of sperm, *93,* 94
Hearing, *416,* 418
Heart, 317, *332*
  amphibian, *341*
  bird, 353
  electrical conduction mechanism, 317,
    319
  fish, action of, 330, *332, 335*
  mammal, 353
  pace maker, 319
  reptile, *347, 348, 349, 351*
  valves, 317, *318*
Heat, sense of, 392
Hemachromatosis (hemochromatosis): *Disorder of iron metabolism, showing excess deposition of iron in tissues, pigmentation of the skin, hepatic cirrhosis, and decreased carbohydrate tolerance,* 169
Hematoxylin: *Stain that colors the nuclei of cells, an ether extract of logwood, 136*
Hemichordata, 47, *51, 52, 53*
Hemipenes, 515
Hepatic portal system, 252, *338*
Heptanchus, 293
Hermaphroditism, 57, 520
Hesperornis, 261
Heterogamic, 521
Heterostraci, 176
Heterozygosity: *Condition where an or-*

ganism receives from its parents alleles that are different, 9
Hippocampus, 153
Histamine: *An amine occurring in animal tissues, dilator of capillaries and stimulator of gastric secretion,* 392
Histology: *The science of microscopic anatomy; that branch of anatomy dealing with the minute structure and function of tissues and organs.*
Holoblastic cleavage: *Total cleavage; the entire egg becomes divided into cells,* 101, 102, *102,* 103
Holocephali, 554
Holonephros: *Type of kidney developing from the entire mass of the nephrotome (mesodermal mass giving rise to kidney tissue), and thus extending essentially from end to end of the body cavity (larval cyclostomes, hagfish).* 363, *365* (*see also* Opisthonephros)
Holostei, 75, *75*
Homeostasis: *Stable nature of the internal environment or fluid, matrix of the body,* 182, 183, *183,* 184, 464, 490
Homogenous: *Having structures in common because of descent from a common ancestor.*
Homoiotherm: *So-called warm-blooded animal; animals possessing mechanisms for controlling body temperature,* 159, 171
Homology: *Structural similarity in different organisms owing to the inheritance from a common ancestry. The commonness of embryonic origin, viz., from the same anlage, of two or more structures is very often used as explicit evidence of homology.* 4, 5, 11, 12, 188
Homonomous series: *Refers to a sequence of structures, all of which have the same general form, e.g., ribs, somites in the embryo; homologous serial parts,* 13

I

Intermedin to Mammals

JK

L

M

Mutation: *Spontaneous change in the elements responsible for heridity; a change in a gene that breeds true,* 6

Myelencephalon: *The afterbrain; includes the pons, medulla oblongata and lower part of the fourth ventricle,* 438

Myelin sheath: *Fat-like substance forming a sheath around medullated (myelimated) nerve axons, white substance of Schwann,* 425

Myomeres, 204, *205*

Myotome, 200

Myxine, 255

Myxinoidei, 66, *66*

N

Nails, 163, *163*

Natality: *Defined as either maximum natality, which is the maximum possible births under ideal environmental conditions, or realized natality, which is the amount of successful reproduction that actually occurs over a period of time.*

Natural selection: *Essentially the differential reproduction of different genotypes; differential survival of certain genotypes in a population through successive generations,* 6, 9

Necturus, 153, 244, *245,* 247, 253

Neoceratodus, gills, 296

lung, 308, *309*

Neocerebellum: *Phylogenetically the newest portion of the cerebellum; integrated functionally with the neocortex of the cerebrum,* 460

Neocortex: *Newest phylogenetically acquired portion of the cerebral cortex, nonolfactory (neopallium),* 454, 460

Neontology: *Study of living organisms,* 10

Neornithes, 85

Nephridium, *64*

Nephron: *Tubular secretory unit of the vertebrate kidney; typically composed of a plasma filtration system (renal corpuscle) leading to a tubule in which secretion and reabsorption of specific chemical components occurs. In some vertebrates the renal corpuscle may be absent or much reduced, and great variation exists in the structure and function of the tubule.* 368, *369,* 375, *375, 378 (see also* Kidneys: tubules)

Nephrostome: *A ciliated funnel-shaped structure giving access for passage of fluid from the body cavity (coelom) into pronephric or opisthonephric tubules; in some amphibians into renal veins,* 368

Nephrotome (nephrogenic tissue), 115, *365*

Nerve cells, 424, *426*

Nerve endings, *390, 391*

Nerves

abducens, (VI), 445

auditory or vestibulo-acoustic, (VIII), 392, 445

branchiomeric, 447, *448*

coccygeal, 427

comparative anatomy of, 427, *428,* 448

cranial, *393,* 444, *446, 447, 448*

function, 446

facial, (VII), 392, 443

free endings, 291

glossopharyngeal, (IX), 392, 445

hypoglossal, (XII), 446

lateral-line, 408, *411,* 412, *413*

oculomotor, (III), 445

olfactory, (I), 392, 445

optic, (II), 392, 445

plexuses, 428

spinal, 426, *428, 429,* 431, 448

spinal accessory, (XI), 495

terminal, (0), 392, 445

trigeminal, (V), 445

trochlear, (IV), 445

vagus, (X), 392, 445

Nervous system: *One of the two coordinating systems of the body, the endocrine system being the other, comprised of the central (brain and spinal cord), peripheral (nerves and ganglia), and autonomic nervous systems,* 388, 422, 449

afferent, 454

associated cells, 425

autonomic, 434, *435, 436,* 448

central, 426, 438

comparative function of, 454

efferent, 455

origin of, 449

parasympathetic, 434

pathways, 451, *452, 453,* 455, *456,* 457

primary divisions, 422

sensory pathways, 455

sympathetic, 436

Neural crest cord: *Cord arising during neu-*

Opossum
to Phonoreceptors

PQ

R

U

V

WXYZ